THE DAWN OF
MODERN GEOGRAPHY.

THE DAWN OF
MODERN GEOGRAPHY

VOL. I

A HISTORY OF
EXPLORATION AND GEOGRAPHICAL SCIENCE FROM
THE CONVERSION OF THE ROMAN EMPIRE TO
A.D. 900, WITH AN ACCOUNT OF THE
ACHIEVEMENTS AND WRITINGS OF THE
CHRISTIAN, ARAB, AND CHINESE
TRAVELLERS AND STUDENTS

By C. RAYMOND BEAZLEY, M.A., F.R.G.S.

FELLOW OF MERTON COLLEGE, OXFORD

WITH REPRODUCTIONS OF THE PRINCIPAL MAPS OF THE TIME

NEW YORK
PETER SMITH
1949

This volume was originally published by Mr. John Murray in 1897.

Reprinted 1949
By Permission Of
The Clarendon Press
Oxford, England

PREFACE.

THIS volume aims at presenting an account of geographical movements in Christendom, and especially in Latin or Western Christendom, during the early Middle Ages (from about A.D. 300 to about A.D. 900) ;—to which has been added a summary account of non-Christian movements, especially in the Arab and Chinese dominions and races, during the same period. Every geographical enterprise or speculation of importance in these centuries should thus come within the scope of this attempt. But, here, I wish to make two disclaimers.

First, narrow and poor (comparatively) as is the geographical literature of Christendom in these ages, I cannot hope, even with the aid of the collections furnished by the *Société de l'Orient Latin,* to have noted every passage of importance, or in fact to have done so vast a subject more than imperfect justice. In non-Christian geography again, this survey is professedly selective; and the Arab and Chinese movements are treated as an appendix to those of the Christian West.[1]

Secondly, I must plead for a liberal interpretation of the words used above, "every passage of importance." Any one who is at all acquainted with the literature in question, must surely admit that the true method of dealing with the same is hard to find and harder to follow. For while it is

[1] See pp. 46, 392, 393.

best to aim at what may be called a typical or representative account, which seeks to avoid an intolerable repetition of petty detail, it must not be forgotten that in that very dull and servile repetition of the same axioms, the same fancies, the same astonishing blunders, is seen a true reflection of the European decadence in science throughout this time. And, above all, it is important to remember, for such a subject as this, that a true view of history will not ignore the weakness, or the degradation, or even the lifelessness of the past ; for almost as much light may sometimes be thrown on the progress of mankind by the attentive examination of those centuries when the tide of life seemed ebbing, as by the prospect of those other and brighter times, which, taken at the flood, led on to fortune.

In the Introductory Chapter more has been said about these and other general aspects of the question, and, at the beginning of each section of the detailed narrative that follows, some attempt has been made to connect this geographical thread of mediæval history with others of more general interest.

After the introduction, the next five chapters (ii.–vi.) are concerned (1) with the practical exploration and (2) with the geographical study, of Christendom, down to the time when the Norsemen began to change the face of Europe, circa A.D. 300–900. Of these five chapters, the first four (pp. 53–242) are taken up with the travels of pilgrims, merchants, and missionaries ; while chapter vi. (pp. 243–391) describes the geographical science or pseudo-science of the " Lower Empire " and the " Dark Ages." Chapter vii. is occupied with the Moslem and Chinese geography of this time, which forms (down to about A.D. 950) so surprising a contrast to the contemporary ruins of classical enterprise and culture in the West.

In all this, we shall have especially to notice many ideas and circumstances somewhat strange to us of the present day. On the one hand there is the overwhelming importance of religious conceptions both in practical and theoretical geography; the wonderful diffusion of Christianity through missionary travel (especially of the Nestorians); the part taken by pilgrimage in exploration: the curious survival of so much of the ancient cosmical myth, along with the comparative and temporary disappearance of the real classical science; and the ambitious attempt of Cosmas and others to construct a theological Universe from texts of Scripture. On the other hand, we have the rapid, perhaps too rapid, development of the Arab mind; the activity of the Buddhist propaganda, and the remarkable inter-connection (at least of commerce) between all parts of Asia at such an era as the eighth and ninth centuries A.D. All these features, in their different ways, are full of suggestion, when viewed by the light of the past and future position of Europe.

In these pages we have to do with the time when the Oriental reaction, which was in various ways evidenced by the triumphs both of Christianity and of Islam, by the revived Persian Empire of the Sassanidæ, and by the decay of Greek and Latin science, was at its height, naturally affecting human history along the path of geography as along every other road. The subject as a whole, of course, points on to the crusading time, the later Middle Ages, and the Renaissance period (marked by the great maritime discoveries), when Europe gradually retrieved the position it had lost, and entered upon its modern life by the commercial and colonial expansion of the fifteenth, sixteenth, and seventeenth centuries. But that brilliant epoch is parted from the subject of this volume by a gulf whose depth and width grow steadily upon any student of mediæval life and thought; and over some parts of our present period there hangs an intellectual gloom like that which enveloped Caprera and its hermits in the eyes of the fierce old pagan poet—" Squalet lucifugis insula plena viris." [1]

The illustrations we have to offer are principally of the maps of this time. Crude and curious as they may be, they are not the less instructive. For they are the only examples of map-science that have survived to us from their age. To these a few more or less plausible attempts at the reconstruction of lost map-schemes have been added; as well as a few illustrations of places or objects which have some connection with the more extensive or remarkable travels of the time.

Two notes have also been added, (1) on the Manuscripts, and (2) on the Editions, of the principal texts for the literature of the subject; but it has not been possible to give (as was hoped) a more detailed account of either in this volume. Here it may be said that, with certain exceptions, few texts of Western literature can have been less thoroughly examined. The manuscripts of several, e.g. of the pilgrim, narratives have been very inadequately collated. Cosmas has not been edited (independently) since 1765, or Raban Maur since 1626-7; till 1885 the Acta Sanctorum, like Gregory of Tours or Vincent of Beauvais, had never been thoroughly sifted for their geographical material, and even now this has only been done for the *earlier* Christian centuries by Molinier and Kohler; and the allusions, not infrequently found in works of professed scholarship, to authors so important as Arculf, Dicuil, Massoudy, or Hiouen-Thsang, to say nothing of Cosmas,

[1] Rutilius Namatianus.

often betray the extreme dimness of the general conceptions of mediæval geography. This is well borne out by the fact that no attempt whatever has yet been made to deal with this subject as a whole, except in such brief summaries and allusions as may be found in Peschel's *Erdkunde* or Vivien de St. Martin's *Histoire de la Géographie.* Works such as Santarem's great *Essai sur la Cosmographie* or Lelewel's *Géographie du Moyen Age* (like Konrad Miller's new *Mappæmundi*) are almost exclusively concerned with mediæval maps.

I have to acknowledge with many thanks the kindness of Mr. J. W. McCrindle, of Edinburgh, who has courteously allowed me to see his forthcoming edition of Cosmas in manuscript, after this volume first went to press. Wherever I have made use of this I have noted the source by the initial [McC.].

I have also to thank Lord Ashburnham for permission to photograph the Beatus map, once in the possession of Libri, from MS. No. 15 at Ashburnham Place; and the authorities at the University Library in Leipsic, at the Laurentian Library in Florence, and at the Coin Department in the British Museum, for the same privilege in respect of the Sallust map, the Cosmas sketches, and the Merovingian coins herein reproduced.

As to the spelling of Arabic and Chinese names, it may be well to mention that, for the former, M. Reinaud has been usually followed (and especially the orthography of his Abulféda), and, for the latter, M. Stanislas Julien.

C. R. B.

CONTENTS.

———◆◇◆———

CHAPTER I.

INTRODUCTORY.

CHAPTER II.

THE PRIMITIVE PILGRIMS OF LATIN CHRISTENDOM DOWN TO JUSTINIAN (CIRC. A.D. 300–530) IN DETAIL.

CHAPTER III.

THE PILGRIMS IN DETAIL, CONTINUED, FROM JUSTINIAN TO MOHAMMED.

CONTENTS.

CHAPTER IV.

THE PILGRIMS IN DETAIL, CONTINUED, DURING THE LATTER CENTURIES OF OUR PERIOD, CIRC. A.D. 680–870 (900).

CHAPTER V.

COMMERCIAL AND MISSIONARY TRAVEL.

CHAPTER VI.

GEOGRAPHICAL THEORY.

CHAPTER VII.

NON-CHRISTIAN GEOGRAPHY OF THE EARLY MIDDLE AGES.

LIST OF ILLUSTRATIONS.

———◆◇———

* Old Syrian [Nestorian] Churches in South India, commemorating Nestorian missions in Far South of Asia, and all probably containing work of eighth and ninth centuries.

GEOGRAPHY OF THE MIDDLE AGES.

CHAPTER I.

INTRODUCTORY.

THE expansion of Europe in the way of geographical progress is commonly spoken of as if it affected only that modern world which the fifteenth century saw gradually evolved out of the mediæval, and which received so immense an enlargement from the discovery of America, of the Cape route to India, and of the ocean way round the globe.[1] Classical geography has also received a good share of attention, but few have troubled to inquire how those forces that displayed themselves with such effect in the lifetime of Columbus were stored and matured in the long " Middle Age " of preparation, or how the great successes were led up to by the futile ventures or partial triumphs of the thirty generations that lay between the two periods of European ascendency.

The geographical progress of the Middle Ages and of modern times is, from our point of view, essentially connected with the extension of Europe and Christendom into its present dominion over the best and largest part of the earth ; and the history of this progress falls naturally into two parts—the mediæval time of dejection and recovery,

[1] In 1492, 1486–98, and 1520.

and the modern age of consequent success. These periods obviously pass into one another in the great forty years of discovery between the rounding of the Cape of Good Hope by Bartholomew Diaz in 1486, and Magellan's circumnavigation of the globe (1520–22). In the mediæval period, which we may consider as lasting down to the aforesaid voyage of Diaz, we have again (from the European outlook) two main divisions—divisions which may be conveniently termed the Dark Ages, and the Crusading Time, to which last the movement of Norse or Viking enterprise forms an introduction. The former of these we have tried to deal with in the present volume, and its sub-divisions are indicated in their place; but, after all, these are unimportant, and, speaking roughly, we may assume that the whole of this earlier period of the Christian Middle Ages is marked by the same leading features; and among these, religious conceptions, both in travel and in science, are the most prominent.

There is in general during this time a lack of geographical enterprise or study for the sake of knowledge, of political dominion, or even of commercial gain. The chief journeys of these centuries (c. A.D. 300–900) are undertaken, and the chief cosmographies or geographies are written for religious interests, and in a religious spirit; but the result of this, as will be seen, is not altogether to the advancement of man's "earth-knowledge."

The first of our mediæval periods, it is true, offers comparatively little variety, but the second has at least three clearly marked and distinctive epochs. First there is that of the Northmen; who begin their career as discoverers on the fringe of the known world, and as the awakeners of Europe to a new and more vigorous life in the latter years of the ninth century, but whose more decisive achievements are reserved for the tenth and eleventh.

Secondly, there is the age of the Crusades proper, from 1096 to 1270, or, in a juster view, from the accession of Hildebrand as pope in 1073, to the close of the thirteenth century. This period thus includes the travels of Marco Polo, and is especially marked by overland journeys.

Thirdly, we have the time of transition (from about 1300 to 1486), in which Prince Henry the Navigator, of Portugal, is the principal figure, and maritime exploration the main interest.

In each of these developments, something is accomplished towards the enlargement and the quickening of European life. Pilgrimage and missionary travel, trading enterprise and political conquest,—above all, the fierce, restless, and inquisitive love of wandering and of adventure, were responsible for the successive steps of advance. In the Dark Age time, religious and proselytising fervour is the cause of many remarkable and extensive journeys, but the religious spirit did not chronicle these in a scientific manner, and religious divisions were a great obstacle to the transmission of new knowledge. How little did Catholic Christendom know or value the discoveries of Nestorian missions or Arab travellers in the Far East, till its own interest had long been awakened and its emissaries had laboured for generations in the same parts of the world. How little effect did Moslem science produce in Christian geography till the latter had undergone an intellectual revival from within.

A more permanent gain for our European world was realised by the emigration and expansion of the Scandinavian peoples. This was not merely because their pioneers penetrated to Greenland and North America; nor because, on the other side of Christendom (towards Asia), they rounded the North Cape, explored the recesses of the White Sea, and opened up many districts of North-Eastern Europe;

nor even because they were the true founders of the Russian
Kingdom as an organized State,—but because they spread
their arms, their settlements, and their race into every
Christian country. By so doing they effected an essential
revival of the European blood and spirit; they imparted to
well-nigh every one of the peoples of Christendom something
of their own fire; and thus began that forward movement
which the West seemed to have abandoned in the decline
of the Roman Empire, but which was now again as it were
caught up by mediæval Europe, persisted in against all
discouragements, and carried through to complete success in
the fifteenth century and in modern times.

Such we may conceive to have been the mission of the
Vikings. The two later stages of European advance, up to
the era of the Great Discoveries, had the task of carrying
out into action some part of what the Norse energy had done
so much to render possible, and of preparing for the accomplishment of the rest. In the crusading age, the barriers
which Islam had erected against the political, and so against
the geographical, the commercial, and the scientific expansion of Europe, were pierced through on the eastern side;
and a fuller revelation was gained of the treasures of India
and of Cathay than the Christian federation had ever
possessed before. And as this knowledge was bound up
with material wealth; as the Polos and their companions had
discovered afresh those great prizes of Further Asia, which
old Rome had coveted so ardently, but had never been able
to seize; it was a knowledge not easily forgotten.

From the end of the thirteenth century to the success of
the Portuguese on another road, at the end of the fifteenth,
Europeans were steadily engaged in pressing forward upon
the old land routes, and getting an ever larger share of their
profits.

And however great the political exhaustion left by the crusading wars, this could not turn aside the stubborn perseverance of the new commercial, military, and colonizing ambitions of Europe, or put out the light of its reawakened science. And so came the final touch. One thing was lacking for the commercial victory of the West over its Eastern rivals; for an effective military diversion against the heavy odds of Asiatic numbers; for a healthy extension of the European race and its political organizations.

A flank movement round Africa, if successful, might bring all this to pass. By such a now sea route, Europe would gain a private way, as it were, to the very source of Eastern wealth, a way on which no competition was to be feared; it would also take its old enemies on their most vulnerable side; and it would throw open new lands, possibly of enormous extent, for Western settlement or colonization.

It was precisely this attempt, gradually carried through, which was the special and decisive achievement of the later Middle Ages. Even before the Portuguese mariners had arrived at the solution of their task, their progress and prospects on the Southern Ocean track inspired the thought of a similar attempt upon the most hidden riches of Asia by the West. The old and true doctrine of the roundness of the earth,—known as a respectable tradition to learned men, and recognised as certain by keen students of nature in the fifteenth as in the first century after Christ,—combined with the success of African coasting to bring about the venture of Columbus. This was of course intended, not as a quest after an unknown continent, but as an attempt to reach Cathay and India by the most direct sea route; and it largely resulted from the discoveries of Henry of Portugal and his lieutenants and successors between the Canaries and the Cape of Good Hope.

In 1486 Diaz reached the Cape of Tempests; in 1492 Columbus sailed for "the Indies." He never got there, for he found America lying across his path. The New World thus disclosed left no interest at the time for the further prosecution of his original idea; and it was not till 1520–22 that Magellan, in proving the round world that Columbus had assumed, appeared (as his great predecessor had always meant to do) upon the shores of the Furthest East from the extremity of the West. Meantime Da Gama's voyage from Lisbon to Malabar (1497–99) realised the hopes and the prophecies of the Portuguese, Southern, or African school of maritime explorers; and it was from the victory of the new European enterprise in these various directions that the Christian nations were at last raised into a position of predominance throughout the world. Like men besieging a stubbornly-defended citadel, they had out-manœuvred their antagonists by hidden, winding, and far-fetched mines, and breached the defences with sudden and terrible effect. Like men, again, attacking one point of vantage, they had, while making their approaches, found others not less worth holding; for in pursuing their trade rivalry with Asia, they had lighted upon a new continent, and discovered unexpected recesses of an old one, in which they might develop their energies without a competitor, and thus call in the unknown countries to "redress the balance" of the known.

These were perhaps the chief stages, objects, and results of the geographical movements of the Middle Ages in Europe and Christendom. By the side of these we attempt to give a sketch of the non-Christian movements of the same time, and especially of those which sprang from the Arab or Moslem civilisation. The history of this Eastern part of our subject is in sharp contrast with the Western. While the thirteenth century saw, in the land of the Franks, an exploring energy develop itself beyond that of earlier times, and apply itself to new discoveries and to safer, if longer, ways to the goal of its ambition,—in Asia it witnessed convulsions from which the science, trade, and expansive activity of the Levant have never recovered.   All the best work of Mohammedan travellers and students was done before the days of Marco Polo; and even in survivors like Aboulfeda and Ibn Batouta we cannot prolong the life of the higher Mussulman geography beyond the middle of the fourteenth century. In this volume we have briefly described the history of that geography down to about 950, when the Caliphate had fairly lost its political power; and it will be easily seen that these ages (630–950), of peculiar darkness for us, were light indeed to our chief rivals.   The succession of Moslem explorers and inquirers does not cease with the weakness and division of their Empire; in some ways their work shows an advance : but on the whole it may be called stationary, from the beginning of the Second Christian Millennium.   As it was in the political struggle with Crusading Europe, so it was in exploration, and, with some exceptions, in science also.   It held its own, but it had lost its aggressive mood ; and as man cannot stand still (at least outside China), but must fall back if he does not advance, so the Mohammedan peoples waited on events and subsisted on their traditions until they had allowed their Christian foes to get the start of them, to circumvent them, and at last to win from them many of their choice possessions ; thus forcing them into a secondary place, and completing the ruin of their higher life or civilisation.

The historical changes which affect other races and countries produce in China a more and more perfect indifference to the movements, the discoveries, and the interests of the rest of the world.   In the period covered by this

volume, the Land of Silk tries the experiment of comparatively free intercourse with "remote barbarians;" but it
gives up the uncongenial part as far as possible, after the
civil troubles of 878 and following years; and, until the
Mongol Conquest of the thirteenth century, it does not
repeat, as a nation, the hazardous venture.

The great rulers of the House of Ghenghiz and of Kublai
do indeed bring China for a time into the main stream of
the world's history; but even they fail to break up permanently the proud exclusiveness which had only deepened
since the time of Pliny;[1] which, gradually severing itself
from the Tartar over-lordship, held Europeans stubbornly
at bay when at last they reached its ports by the Cape route
from the West; and which still offers a singular contrast with
that earlier time in which the Celestials had not yet outlived
their interest in so many of the activities of human life.

When any one tries to gain a hearing for a subject which
is obscure, apparently uninteresting, and possibly despised,
he is bound to show cause for his intrusion. And the
reason why the travels and geographical science of the later
Empire and the darker Middle Ages are important to history
cannot easily be found in the evidence we actually possess
of those travels and that science. Practical and theoretical
geography were at a low ebb between the conversion of
Pagan Rome and the Crusades; but they had in themselves
great possibilities. The time of sowing must not disappoint
us if it fail to give a crop: in the age of the making of
the modern nations we cannot expect the discovering
instinct to show much activity. But to gain anything
like a complete view of the development of European
Christendom upon the surface of the earth, it is necessary

---

[1] Cf. Pliny's description (H. N. vi. 20).

to begin with the origins. And these we find, as far as are required for our purpose, in the pilgrim-travellers and convent-maps and religious science of the centuries between Constantine and our own English Alfred.

For the sake of clearness, it is perhaps well not to go further back. From the conversion of the Empire to the sixteenth century the story of Christendom is unbroken; the later Roman Dominion is the Church-state of a Christian Prince, as much as the France of St. Louis, the England of Henry VII., the Spain of Ferdinand and Isabella. Mediæval Europe delighted to think of itself as the old world-state under religion; the two main elements in our civilisation were the same in the days of Constantine and of Columbus—the classical tradition and the Christian Church. And so, throughout this time, the expansion of European life, in discovery, exploration, and geographical knowledge, has a continuous history. But before the time of Constantine one of the main conditions of mediæval and modern life is unfulfilled, and it is open to question whether this alone does not constitute a real difference between ancient and modern history. In exploration the mediæval Christian world certainly did not carry on the work of the ancient without a break; much of that work had been partially forgotten or obscured in the century of pagan decline before Diocletian; and in the break-up of the fifth and seventh centuries the whole matter was altered, the problem was recast, and the greater part of what was known to Augustus or to Trajan had to be learnt over again. The ancient and often mistaken theories of premature science, of reflection which had outrun observation, were lost sight of in the general confusion, along with much of the ground really won. We do not find Europeans of the earlier Middle Ages following in the steps of Ptolemy—correcting his miscalculations, or dominated by his theories. Their geography is turned off upon a different path, and occupied with very different problems; and it is not the lineal descendant of Greek thought in the same way as Arabic metaphysic is the lineal descendant of Aristotle. The great names of ancient science have a vague, but not a very exact or penetrating, influence upon Christian geography and exploration before the fourteenth century.

In any account, therefore, of mediæval travel, at least before the Crusades, it may be safe to treat the higher classical geography as a deposit rarely used, a legacy generally forgotten, though realised by some. From the modern point of view, it belongs rather to the literature than to the life of exploration in its slow development between the collapse of the old pagan society and the emergence of the Christendom which replaced that society into a universal energy.

It was with the conversion of Constantine that Christian travel, in pilgrimage, really began. And this activity was largely unlike anything to be found in the pagan world of Greece and Rome, and different in many important respects from all similar movements in the pre-Christian Oriental religions, and in all those other forms of faith which have moved in a different orbit from the Roman Empire. Only in the greatest of the imitations or adaptations of Christianity, in Mohammedanism, does Christian pilgrimage find a real parallel. The journeys of pious Greeks to their oracles are on quite a different platform— they went to get advice, rather than to worship relics of a divine visit to their world or to awaken a fuller appreciation of their faith, a fuller insight into the meaning of their sacred writings. The Jewish habit of going up to Jerusalem was undoubtedly one of the precursors of the Christian sentiment, and is in some ways a parallel to the Christian custom as settled in the fourth century. For the Hebrew idea of visiting the capital of a religious empire is also clearly seen in the travels of Western Catholics to Rome, in which relic worship was combined with more practical reasons. But the Palestine and other Levantine pilgrimages (like the Gallician to Compostella) were mainly sentimental, and accordingly more liable to decay. As the practical interests encroached upon the ideal, the Eastern pilgrimages became of less and less importance; they were performed by a humbler and more ignorant and superstitious class · in the fifteenth century the "Information for Pilgrims" and similar works cater for the lowest of the people; and in the sixteenth century the habit was comparatively rare. Columbus is rather a late case of a great man who makes the thought of pilgrimage practically important in his life. Yet the pilgrimages of pure sentiment lasted in considerable vigour for nearly twelve hundred years. They served as a powerful motive force, a very persuasive surface reason for the Crusades, whose real causes lay deep down in the life of the nations of the West. And during six centuries, as we have always to remember, these religious travels represented the most active enterprise of Latin Christendom; they were performed, sometimes at least, by men with comparatively enlarged experience and knowledge; they were evidences of energy rather than of superstition or folly; and their literature forms an eminently suggestive chapter in that great mass of writing which is, after all, the expression in speech, however incoherent, of the coming races of the world, during a long period of their development.

Christian pilgrimage, like Christian preaching, was to a great extent a new thing; and in it we must recognize, as we so often have to do in other developments, both earlier

and later, that the secret of its strength was also the secret
of its weakness. It was, above all things, due to a devotional impulse; but the religious feeling, which drove men
from such great distances, closed their senses to much of
human life, to most things that lay not exactly in the
path of their devotion, when they got so far. Thus what
they tell us, of interest to our subject, is incidental and,
so to say, unintentional. The first pilgrims serve us as
a sufficient type of all, and in their ranks are to be
found the most enterprising of their class. The amount
of secular information contained in their records is usually
small: they had great opportunities for observation and
material discovery, but they let them slip by mostly
unheeded; they were interested in a different kind of learning, and they did not relate what did not offer food for
their theological meditation. For the same reason, pilgrim-
travel is not progressive; the ninth century finds us and
leaves us worse off for extensive and systematic religious
journeyings than we were in the sixth or in the fourth; and
the value of these enterprises is really comparative, and
rests upon their being the principal geographical records of
their time. Once, therefore, that the old aggressive in-
stincts, of commerce, of conquest, or of colonisation, are
awakened afresh, and begin to send out their shoots, the
religious travels lose all except a theological interest.

So confined, indeed, is the outlook of many of our pilgrims,
and of nearly all our professed geographers of the pilgrimage, that some may find an interest even in the extent, the
variety, and the daring of their absurdities. For these have
a special place as illustrating the mental habits of the time.
They help to show us how difficult material progress must
have been when such were the thoughts and words of the
travelled and learned Christian; they throw a good deal

of light on the growth of that geographical mythology which offered so obstinate and tangled a hindrance to scientific discovery ; and they point to the underlying truth in the story of the world's exploration. And that seems to be, that for material progress—of this kind, as of others— material and not sentimental ambitions are needed. It is the love and the hope of material gain, partly political or imperial, partly scientific, but above all commercial, which has been the motive power of our geographical, as of our industrial, revolution. The secrets of the present world have been disclosed to those who lived in the present; they have naturally been hidden from those who did not value the actual world around them. For the religious emotions, in their essence, however valuable to civilisation in certain other fields, such as art, were not of a kind to promote the exploration of the physical universe, either upon the surface of our earth, or beneath it, or in the world of space outside its atmosphere. And so the religious age of Christian travel was of neces- sity unprogressive and unproductive. Devotional travel was as little in sympathy with exploration for the sake of knowledge, as the theological doctrines of a scriptural geography (as we have them in Cosmas or in some of the more elaborate mediæval maps) were in sympathy with the formation of a scientific theory of the world's shape, as expressed in modern atlases and treatises.

At the end of this long and difficult chapter of history— the early Middle Ages—we come face to face with a new people and a new energy. The Northmen supply the spirit to the body, the fire to the powder. It is the impulse given by them, as we have already suggested, which is seen in the upheaval of the Crusades, when all Christendom rises to that new and ever-increasing activity which has continued to produce fresh results till now. From the crusading

movement (we may repeat) spring the overland and
commercial explorations, the maritime ventures, and the
scientific discoveries of the later Middle Age, of the now
re-civilised West; from these, again, result the plans, the
theories, the attempts which, in their success, reveal the
prime secrets of the unknown. The age of our victory over
nature, or rather of our initiation into nature, beginning
with the unveiling of the earth-surface, is thus connected
with the first groping of our Western world after a wider
room and a broader life. Dim at first is the light, staggering
and uncertain are the steps; false and deceitful ambitions,
disappointing hopes, superstitious fears are ever checking
the onward course: but from the time that pilgrimage first
led to conquest (in the eleventh century), that course has
been steadily onward and outward. Yet not always as it
had been planned. The Franks came to smite the Moslem
unbelievers, but they stayed to trade with them and to learn
of them. The incidental gain proved to be even greater
than the first object.[1] The Mohammedan world had more
to give to Christendom by commerce and friendship than
was to be won by stamping out the worshippers of the God
of the Koran. By the religious wars was gradually recovered
that secret which the pre-Christian world had found out
and abused, which for centuries remained inarticulate, felt
but unexpressed—the secret that the religious feeling by
itself was inadequate for material prosperity, that the present
was an unmistakable and fundamental fact, and that progress could not be made in this life by renouncing it.

But this revelation was not yet. In the time with which
we have here to deal, religion, sometimes fanatical and

---

[1] So in Columbus's discovery, the
incidental success—the finding of
America *en route*—proved to be
even more important than his original aim, the reaching of India from
the West, by the West.

ignorant religion, governs the men who are representative
of literature and of science. So exclusively theological is
their outlook, that we are often in danger of forgetting that
the modern world, with all its splendour and its variety, can
be traced back on one side to their work. Christianity, of
a type very unlike the present, has indeed been one of the
factors of our civilisation. And in our particular subject
we have especially to take this into account. In ages when
the only kind of exploring and geographical interest was
theological, we must beware of ignoring this phase, or of
treating it as a symptom of decay or weakness. We cannot
pass by the fact that the theological interest, in the hands
of the Church organisation, mastered that Empire, or Political
Society, which possessed the intellectual heritage of Aristotle
and Plato, of Ptolemy and Strabo, of Lucretius and Tacitus,
of Cicero and the Roman jurists. Neither can we deny that
the barbarians from beyond the Rhine and Danube gradually
subdued and settled themselves upon that same empire,
which seemed so final. Least of all can it be disputed that
those conquering barbarians, without doubt the strongest
physical force in the Western world, bowed to the faith
and the religious system of the Empire, and moulded their
states, and directed their progress from barbarism to civilisation, by its teaching. The Church, therefore, in its various
expressions, must be treated with respect by any one who
respects the facts of life. It had triumphed over civilised
refinement and uncivilised, or semi-civilised, strength. It
had taken possession of the best minds of the European races.

So much may be allowed, and yet it may be said that
a certain element of weakness and lowered strength was
responsible for its victory. The Roman Empire, in which
the Church saw all things put under its feet, certainly had
not the strength of the first Cæsars. They could have

repelled the Teutonic invasions, just as they came near to the conquest of all Germany, and left that conquest unfinished rather from choice than from necessity. Almost as certainly, they could have stood the shock of the Saracen invasions, which, indeed, were rendered possible by the theological phase that had passed over the Roman world. Christianity and Judaism inspired Islam to be their own rival, and its place in men's hearts was prepared for by their work. The whole appeal of Mohammed would have fallen flat upon the Agnostic world of Augustus.

Yet, if the new era of world-religions, controlling the political and social life of nations, was associated with a certain decline of intellectual and physical vigour among the more advanced peoples, it certainly went along with a great increase of mental activity and social progress among the more rude and brutal nations. For both Christendom and Islam raised the average of the society they respectively conquered, taken as a whole. The check inflicted on the seventh-century prosperity of Syria and Egypt by the Arab invaders, or the repression exercised by Catholicism on the philosophy of Porphyry or the poetry of Claudian, was not to be weighed against the impulse towards better things which the one communicated to the Berbers and the Arabs themselves, or which the other inspired in Germans, English, and Russians.

Up to a certain point. For here comes the difficulty. In the face of the natural philosophy, or the classical revival, of the twelfth century, and still more of the fourteenth,[1] fifteenth, and sixteenth, the religious spirit in

---

[1] In the thirteenth century the Catholic theologians attempted, with some success, to absorb as much of the new and revived learning as appeared in any way compatible with their inherited dogmas. When this broke down, the Church had only the choice of war with science, or an alliance with it.

Christendom, as in Islam, declared itself, to a large extent, obscurantist. And when this attitude seemed to be passing away in the papacy and the curia, the cause of non-reasoning faith was revived in the Protestant Reformation and the Catholic reaction; the science which this double movement could not suppress was forced back into its old attitude of hostility; and religion became terrible to many as the principal opponent of advancement and knowledge.

In the case of Islam, on the other hand, the great "Unitarian" religion, as a less dogmatic, intricate, and systematised faith, without priesthood, or sacraments, or mystic ritual, except of a simple kind, seemed for a time more fortunate. It found the conflict with science much less searching, and more easily evaded or postponed; but in the end the same struggle loomed before the future of the civilised Caliphate, when further danger was averted by the ruin of theologians and scientists alike in a common doom. On the one side, in the Levant, the utter and irredeemable barbarism of the Turks covered all. Incapable of any form of science or of art, except the war-like,[1] they spread like a blight over the fairest portions of that field where the first intellectual harvest of the Middle Ages had been reaped. On the other side, in the West, the Moslems of Spain fell a prey to anarchy within, and as the crusading spirit rose higher and higher in Christendom, the Emirate of Cordova perished altogether. But at first, after the old culture and the old government of Rome had been submerged, there was no question whether the science of the time was to be friend or foe of religion. The theological forces were then wholly on the side of order, of peace, and

---

[1] And except to a certain extent in architecture, as may be seen from the Mameluke buildings in Cairo. But it is only in a very qualified sense that the Mameluke rulers of Egypt can be called "Turkish."

of learning; they were among the most powerful allies of
the good, and among the most influential enemies of the
bad, tendencies in society. So it was largely due to Churchmen that certain parts of ancient civilisation were preserved,
and that the old political unity was replaced by the spiritual
community of a religious federation which was constantly
struggling to express itself in political forms.[1]

And in our particular inquiry, it was through the
writings and the travels of Churchmen that geographical
conceptions were kept before the world of Bede, of Charles
the Great, or of Gerbert. Even Cosmas, though sinning
against light and apparently taking a more superstitious
and unnatural view of the world than the "sceptical"
Christians whom he denounces, still preserved a good
number of scientific needles in the midst of the intolerable
deal of hay which he called his "Topography." In other
and more barbarous places and times, writings such as those
of Dicuil, of the Ravennese geographer, or of Guido—maps
such as those of Beatus or of Albi,—are valuable for their
monopoly of the subject, if for nothing else. They are the
only teachers of geography in their age and among their
people. And in the light of what their countrymen afterwards became — masters of the world — these teachings,
however grotesque, are suggestive. The absurdities of Dark
Age map-making are the precursors of the first accurate
charts and of modern atlases; the creeping ventures of the
pilgrims are the first movements of an ultimately invincible
race-expansion.

Now, many of the monuments of early Christian travel
have scarcely been treated yet in their proper relation to
progress in general, or to the special kind of progress they

---

[1] E.g. the Empire of Charles the
Great, or of the Ottos, the Crusades,
or the temporal suzerainty of the
popes over Christian kingdoms.

illustrate, which is geographical.   They have had, perhaps,
a fair amount of attention from the theologians and the
philologists ; they have certainly been neglected by the
historians.   They have shared in the effects of the vicious
tendency which puts religion and all its works on one side,
and tries to isolate them from ordinary life ; they have been
relegated to the theological shelves of the library.   But just
as the main importance of the writings of the Christian
apostles and fathers is in relation to the general life of their
time, and the general progress, or retrogression, of the race,
so the essential value of these Christian travel-documents is
in their bearing upon the history of civilisation, then and
afterwards.   There are certain ages of the world which are
quite unintelligible except through the proper understanding of their theological literature.   Even so late as the
Tudor period in England, not a little of our political philosophy has its origin in works of divinity ; in the age of
Justinian the chief geographers and travellers seem to have
been priests and monks of the Church.   An endeavour to
connect and interrelate the sacred and the secular in the
story of exploration could hardly fail to throw an additional,
even if sometimes a flickering, light on certain parts of
history.

It has often been pointed out that human progress is far
from being always continuous, and that its course is more
like the confused movements of a crowd, whose advance is
only to be clearly seen after many swayings and stoppages,
than the orderly forward motion of an army along a military
road.   Early Christian geography is a good illustration of
this.   For centuries the new religious interest seems to
exercise little or no effect in the advancement of science—
rather the reverse—yet, under the Christian civilisation, was
at last awakened an interest both in practical and theoretical

geography greatly transcending that of the pagan world. We must therefore look behind the literature for the vitalising facts, for the progress which certainly was now being made possible. The early Christian period was, after all, a time, not of harvest, but of planting. European life and manhood were regenerated, but the European mind seemed almost to lie fallow for a time.

The growth of the geographical.myth during this period points to the same conclusion as the poverty of results from religious travel. In the course of these centuries were elaborated or popularised most of those travellers' tales which we think so pleasant in Solinus or in Mandeville, and wonder at on the maps of St. Sever or of Hereford, but which were a real and formidable hindrance to enterprise. The terror and ignorance of nature that they reflected was the prime cause of the isolation, poverty, and barbarism of the earlier Middle Ages. The imagination of folly and of pseudo-science peopled the world with monsters, curtained the seas with impenetrable darkness, and travestied every known fact of geography by an attendant fiction which tended to supplant the original.

Again, in examining the reasons for the prolonged backwardness and even occasional retrogression of Christendom, our attention is recalled to some particular influences of a general anti-Christian and anti-European movement, to which we have already alluded. First, the Spanish Caliphate cut off all access to the Western sea beyond the Bay of Biscay, from the eighth to the twelfth centuries; similarly the communication of Christendom with the far East and South — with Abyssinia, or India, or China—was fatally interrupted by the intrusion of the new rulers of the Levant and of North Africa. The geographical outlook of Christian Europe was thus materially contracted. And as Moslem traders and pirates shut up or abstracted Western commerce, so Moslem schools stole away some of the ablest of Western thinkers, till in the ninth and tenth centuries the triumph of the Prophet's followers in every art of life, in every comfort, in every science, over their older rivals seemed complete.

The materials for the subject in hand may be divided under three heads: first, the writings of travellers, almost without exception pilgrim-travellers; secondly, the scattered notices of missionary or commercial enterprise; lastly, the writings of geographical theorists, of untravelled students, who are equally, as a rule, theologians; with these may also be reckoned the maps of draughtsmen who tried to illustrate Scripture or Divinity of some kind by a picture of the world, and a few compilations of marvels from the late pagan period which were fortunate enough to gain an enthusiastic acceptance from the Christian world. The pilgrim-travellers last for our purpose up to the time of the extinction of the Frankish Empire on the continent, and the reign of Alfred in Wessex. In other words, it is only during the first nine centuries of the Christian era, or, more exactly, from the opening of the fourth to the close of the ninth, that the work of exploration, such as it is, falls to their share. And in this time, we may find, if we look a little more closely, that the more important of our pilgrim-records fall into certain groups, and are associated with certain prominent persons and events. Thus we have the travellers of the first period grouped, as it were, round the work of the Emperor Constantine and his mother Helena in Palestine; those of the second age, around Jerome in Bethlehem or in Rome; those of the third, round the Imperial and Catholic Majesty of Justinian, whose buildings in Jerusalem, like those of Constantine, mark an epoch

in the topography of the Holy City. Lastly, the leading
pilgrims of the fourth age, as we may call it, though more
scattered, are nearly all associated with the conversion of
the Franks or the English, and with the joint movement
of the two great races for the further conversion of heathen
Germany.

Again, in the history of pilgrim-travel, we have to
deal with two main classes of records, those made by the
travellers themselves, and those contained in the writings
of others, such as Gregory of Tours, who allude to or
describe in some detail the journeys of pilgrims who have
or have not left any account of themselves. With a very
few exceptions, the former class holds all that is important
for us. As to the merely allusive notices, even the more
valuable of these are generally so vague, as in Gregory's
accounts of travellers to India from the West, that little
can be gathered from them.

The case of Cosmas, "the man who sailed to India,"
presents an especial difficulty. He is more known as a
theorist who set himself to disprove the roundness of the
earth, but he is also a practical explorer, of an unusually
ambitious type. He journeyed to Malabar and Ceylon, it
would appear, from the head of the Red Sea, and returned
to Egypt, probably visiting Palestine as well, before he
left his old profession of a trader, settled down in his
monastery, and wrote his "Topography." Preposterous as a
philosopher, he was no contemptible observer ; and his book
has a place of its own, standing as it does by the side of
contemporary works such as those of Procopius and Gregory
of Tours, and partaking both of the reason of the one and of
the credulity of the other. And the case of Cosmas is an
exception which justifies a rule. It may be said, speaking
broadly, that the only travel which need be attended to, in

those centuries which coincide with the first six hundred years of the Byzantine Empire, is Latin, is from the lands west of the Adriatic, from the Christendom which is conveniently called Roman. The Byzantine provinces, it is true, carry on a not inconsiderable trade with the further East, though this is of ever-decreasing importance and extent from the time of Justinian ; but they show no discovering spirit, except what we may find better represented in Britain, Gaul, Italy or Spain. The Byzantine influence on Western or Latin Europe was surprisingly slight, from the days of Heraclius to the Crusades, and as its power waned within its more immediate surroundings it was not natural that it should exercise a very stimulating effect in distant lands that had practically renounced its authority long before they formally did so. The importance of the Eastern Empire, in checking the progress of the Saracens[1] at their most dangerous period, cannot easily be overrated. It saved Europe from the Asiatic deluge at a time when resistance to such a double attack as was then in progress (through the Taurus as well as through the Pyrenees) could hardly have been successful ; but, after all, the place of the Byzantine civilisation in history was rather passive than active, and its travel enterprise has but little to do with the rest of Christendom.

What slight proof do our Latin travellers give us of any overshadowing influence of the Byzantine world on the West they came from. Though Arculf and Willibald, for example, both have a good deal to tell us about the Constantinople of their day, and allude to it as the greatest city, and the " metropolis " of the whole Roman Empire, they seem little touched by its spirit. The whole literature of our Latin geography in the Dark Ages is inconsistent with any deep knowledge of the Greek Christendom whose very language

---

[1] As well as of barbarians, like the Avars.

was becoming forgotten in the West. When the Roman
Church carries out the religious exploration of central
Europe in the eighth and ninth centuries, it is allowed to
push its conquests within the limits of the original Eastern
Empire and even to dispute with St. Sophia for the allegiance
of Bulgaria, which, if once given, in spirituals, to the Lateran,
would not be easily rendered, in temporals, to the palace on
the Bosphorus. The Greek missionaries,[1] whose travels into
Moravia are of some interest to our subject, went in the
service of the Old Rome and not of the New; in the same
way Hungary and all the North Danube tracts became
adherents to the faith of the more distant power, which by
the winning of Scandinavia completed its religious exploration of unknown Europe. Only in the case of Russia did
Byzantine orthodoxy show any expansive force, and this,
a success of the eleventh century, was rather due to dynastic
ambitions and Norse adaptability than to Greek missionary
zeal.[2] As time went on, the superior energy of Latin
Catholicism was seen in its conquests, though temporary, of
Syria and of Constantinople itself, as well as of so many
islands and outlying points of the Levant. East and West
were really severed long before the dogmatic schism of the
Churches, and it is not, after all, of great moment whether or
no Byzantine merchants at certain times travelled to India
or to the Wall of China or penetrated into Abyssinia, unless
they handed on their work to successors or influenced a more
persistent and virile race than their own. As a rule—Cosmas
is a partial exception—they did not do this; their labours
were so far from permanent that they were on the contrary
continually receding, and we must not overrate the importance of such an unfruitful and disappointing " expansion."

[1] Especially Cyril and Methodius.

[2] This happens well within our next period—the Viking Age.

I. Before the conversion of Constantine, Christian pilgrimage is just existent, and that is all; before the close of the Diocletian persecution, the number of credible journeys of this sort, from the West to the Levant, may be counted on the fingers of one hand—the two Placentian travellers of A.D. 303–4—John and Antonine the Elder—are perhaps the chief of these; and their travels include Sinai as well as Jerusalem.

But the example set by the empress-mother, Helena, and the buildings erected by the bounty of Constantine and her own piety, in the holiest sites of Palestine, coupled with her discovery of the true cross, was the beginning of a new age. Her pilgrimage seems to have been independent of any expectation of such discovery. She sought out Jerusalem, Rufinus tells us, and inquired the spot—not where the cross was to be found,—but only "where the body of Christ was fixed to the tree." The search, it is admitted, was difficult; and this proves that to earlier pilgrims there could not have been available that exact cult of particular sites which became established from the time of Helena's "inventions." From A.D. 136, when the last revolt of the Jews under Bar-Cochab was suppressed, Jerusalem had been forbidden ground to the Hebrew race, and the city of the famous Semitic priests and kings had become the Roman garrison town of Ælia Capitolina. A statue of Venus, too, in one tradition, had been erected over the site of the Crucifixion by the persecutors of the Church.

What Helena really discovered it is impossible now to determine; all that concerns us here is that with her visit Christian pilgrim-travel really begins. Yet we may notice how greatly the original story is amplified by later writers. To the simple statement that she discovered the sign of the cross at Jerusalem, Rufinus adds the healing of the sick

by the new-found relics; in Gregory of Tours, the nails
have the power of quieting storms; fragments of the wood
could save a city besieged. And so on, and better still,
in infinite progression; for there is scarcely a book, a tract,
or a sermon of the mediæval time, in any way referring to
the treasures of the Holy Land, which does not mention
Helena's pilgrimage and its results.

The effect of this journey on the Latin West is seen at
once[1] in the "Itinerary from Bordeaux to Jerusalem," the
earliest work of Christian travel, — a witness alike of the
recent triumph of the Church, the restored peace and order
of the Empire, and the resettlement of politics and society
with fresh religious interests.

Our itinerary follows the main roads of Southern Gaul
and North Italy, to Aquileia; thence it goes through
Sirmium and Belgrade to Constantinople, and across Asia
Minor by the military highway to Antioch and Palestine,
returning along a more southerly route from the Bosphorus
to Albania and Otranto. Composed in the year 333, or at
any rate giving the journal of certain pilgrims in that
summer, this tract, which roughly and inaccurately adapted
for the use of Christian travellers a portion of the old
imperial surveys, remained for a long time the principal
handbook of the class whose needs it met. Its course is
usually followed; and its relics form the staple of every
account. Yet it has little claim to originality. It simply
reproduces—in all except its more detailed notes on the
sacred sites themselves—the road-books of the Cæsars: to
its tables of pagan place-names it adds a Christian tour in
Judæa and the Syrian coast; but it has been doubted by
some, from the state of the St. Gall and Paris manuscripts,
whether this last is not a later insertion.   While this

[1] Within ten years (325–333).

difficulty may be dismissed, on the strength of the oldest text at Verona, we still have to consider the curious fact that the objects of devotion herein mentioned, as in the case of the crypt of Solomon for the torture of the devils, are in most cases of a rather extravagant kind, and argue a high development of superstition and credulity at an age fondly supposed by many to be too early for such corruptions. Those who imagine an ideal Church, before its establishment by the State, and derive all its abuses from this source, would perhaps find it hard to explain how it is that in a tract dated within ten years after the "establishment" of Constantine, so large a number of highly apocryphal relics occur among the few which are mentioned at all.

The Bordeaux itinerary throws an interesting side-light upon the question whether the primitive Christian intelligence was or was not more enlightened than that of later ages; but here we cannot notice this point, except as illustrated by our subject. And as a record of travel or exploration, this pilgrimage certainly holds an obscure place. It never leaves the well-known roads, except for a few *détours* in Palestine. It tells us of only one site beyond Jordan, and of none of the famous spots in Galilee; the more distant fields of Egypt, Sinai, and Mesopotamia are entirely beyond its ken. In all these respects, it contrasts curiously with the journey of Silvia, our next important record. After the Bordeaux pilgrim, we get no other memorial of Christian travel so nearly related to, and so suggestive of, the classical and official geography; but we get many more important and extensive journeys from Western Christendom. In the next generation, the fashion of pilgrimage spread apace; it was recognised by the Church of Rome as an act of advanced piety, meriting considerable indulgence or a heavy cheque upon the treasury of merits; and the leading men

of the Catholic world found their way to Palestine in
ever-increasing numbers. Julian's attempt to re-establish
paganism and restore the Jews to their old home (361–363)
seems to have checked the new movement for a time—as a
certain peace and prosperity was necessary for the development of such an external activity ; but after the reaction
had collapsed, it is seen again in full swing.

Constantine and Helena closed one age of this movement
and began another. They ended the period of a simply
historical pilgrimage, unaided or nearly unaided by relics,
shrines, privileges, and visible memorials of the Bible story.
The Bordeaux guide-book, again, ends the unrecorded and
begins the self-recording age of the same. Jerome's visit to
Palestine in 372, still more his second coming for a residence
of five and thirty years in 385, is a third landmark, commencing the most fashionable age of pilgrim-travel. In the
interval, seemingly, between his two journeys (and without
any immediate summons from him, or influence exerted by
him), occurred the visit of the traveller whose narrative,
recently discovered,[1] goes by the name of Silvia of Aquitaine.
The questions of authorship, and of the writer's country,
date, sex, and station, will be discussed elsewhere ; but it
will be safe to assume here that this work was written by a
Roman lady of rank, a Christian of Southern Gaul, belonging
to some sisterhood, to whom the narrative is addressed, and
that she journeyed in the Levant between 378–9 and 384–5.
What is of more importance to us is the extent of her
wanderings, and the interest of her occasional remarks. She
not only travels through Syria : she visits Lower Egypt,
and Stony or Sinaitic Arabia, and even Edessa in Northern
Mesopotamia and on the very borders of hostile and heathen
Persia. The torrent of the Euphrates she compares to the

[1] In 1883.

Rhone, the greater to the less, a foreign to a native example ; and, on the way home by the military high-road between Tarsus and the Bosphorus, likens, with unconscious historical irony, the brigand habits of the Isaurian mountaineers, who endangered this part of her route, with the similar failings of the Arabian Saracens, who were one day to be driven back by those very Isaurians from the city of Constantine. The future subverters and saviours of Christendom were then alike outcasts from civilisation.

In this letter we have described for us the most far-reaching and enlightened pilgrimage of the first five centuries. Its entire omission of Jerome's name, and various incidental notices in the course of its story, can leave but little doubt that it is of a date earlier than 385. It also gives us evidence, parallel to that supplied by Jerome, of the growing importance and fashionableness of pilgrimage; for the author, whoever it be, is clearly a person of importance, and it is difficult to picture such a one undertaking the toil and danger of so distant a journey in earlier times. Lastly, while from this example it is clear that the monastic organization of Syria and Egypt was now a powerful attraction to Western devotees, and allowing for a natural preference for objects of religious interest, Silvia's casual remarks, historical, geographical, or social, are of quite unusual breadth and value, and suggest by contrast the probability that most of our pilgrim records have been composed by persons of no very high education or employment.

After St. Silvia, our memoirs for some time are of a strictly devotional character, such as the notices of Paula or Eustochium, or the two Melanias; and though Jerome boasts that men came to see him from India and Ethiopia, our Latin travel-documents of this age have scarcely any bearing on geography.

Between the death of Jerome and the accession of Justinian we have, indeed, occasional notices of the journeys of Westerns to the holy places, not only of Syria and Egypt, but of Malabar; but it is nearly impossible to make much out of them, as will be seen from the details to be given in the next few chapters. They serve, however, to emphasise the fact, confirmed by so many different witnesses, that Christianity reached its most complete and deep-rooted extension in the Old World before the rise of Islam. It is true that the Churches of the far East have little or no connection with Europe; and that their prosperity is now only to be seen, by us who look back over so many centuries, through a haze as tantalising as the mist that conceals their decline and fall;—but the vision, though dim, is not a mirage.

Between Constantine and Heraclius, between the fourth and the seventh centuries, the gospel, though for the most part in heretical forms, came to dominate not only the world of the Roman Empire, but vast districts of Africa and of Asia, beyond the limits of the Cæsars' power. Even in Europe it won Ireland and the Caledonia of Northern Britain, which the legions had never quite subdued; south of Egypt it conquered Nubia and Abyssinia; across the Red Sea it won Yemen to itself; in the Erythrean Ocean it made the Island of Socotra a centre of its activity; as early as the Bordeaux pilgrim its missionaries planted a bishopric at Merv in Khorasan; in the time of Justinian, Nestorians preached the faith among the mountains of Herat and in the Garden of Samarcand; in the lifetime of Mohammed the name of Jesus was first proclaimed in China; and at the same time Ceylon, Persia, and the Deccan contained an "infinite number of Christians, both priests, monks, solitaries, women vowed to the religious life, and laymen." Yet

almost none of these offshoots were Catholic. With strange
perversity, the sun appeared to shine upon the followers of
Patrick, who used the tonsure of Simon Magus, and upon
the communion of the " Wolfish " Nestorius, who denied the
claims of the Mother of God, even more than upon those
who preferred soundness of belief to that heretical restless-
ness which travelled so far and compassed sea and land to
make one proselyte.[1]

The most important of our travel-documents in this
intermediate time—the tract of Bishop Eucherius of Lyons
(c. 440), " On Certain of the Holy Places," and the " Descriptio Parrochiæ Hierusalem " (c. 460)—are, as Ptolemy
would have said, topographical [2] rather than geographical;
and the notices of such adventurers as David of Wales are
clouded with miracle, and only the bare fact of a journey
to Syria can be recovered from the ideal world which has
coloured all the details.

During the reign of Justinian, Cosmas Indicopleustes
journeyed and wrote. In the same reign the first Christian
description of the Holy City, in any detail, was composed
under the name of " The Breviary of Jerusalem ; " and the
two curious pilgrims, Theodosius and Antoninus of Placentia,
recorded their impressions " concerning the situation of the
Holy Land." These remarkably credulous, careless, and
imaginative writers add a good deal of myth to the already
unreal pilgrim-geography, and present the Palestine legends
in a thoroughly formed and hardened state. They preserve,
however, some notices of a more extended kind. Theodosius,
indeed, only indulges in a few flights of fancy beyond his

[1] Before Gregory the Great, indeed, the Catholic Church seemed content with dominion for the most part inside the Empire, and left outside enterprise to the heretics.

[2] The same is true of the entries in the " Notitia Antiochiæ ac Iero-solymæ Patriarchatuum " of the sixth century.

proper ground of Palestine, as when he refers to countries
"where no one can live for the serpents and hippo-centaurs;"
but for the rest his knowledge is not extensive or peculiar,
and his narrative, unlike the Bordeaux pilgrim's, has neither
the appearance of a journal or time-table nor of a guide-book.
Antoninus, on the other hand, is an even more travelled
pilgrim than Silvia; he goes beyond her into Upper Egypt,
and traverses all the usual ground of Sinai and Palestine,
penetrating into Mesopotamia and visiting Edessa. In his
narrative he appears as a sort of older Mandeville, who
mixes truth and fiction in pretty equal proportions, but with
a resolute partiality to favourite legends. Along with his
marvels, such as the yearly stoppage of the Jordan at the
Epiphany, the devils to be seen by night on Mount Gilboa,
or the salt pillar of Lot's wife, lessened, as had been falsely
reported, by the licking of animals—with all this he gives
us every now and then glimpses of a larger world, rarely
noticed at all by our pilgrim-travellers. He tells us of the
effects of the recent earthquakes (of 526 and 551) along the
coast of Phœnicia; he notices the splendour and civilisation
of Tyre, Gaza, and Alexandria; he describes the hospice of
Justinian in Jerusalem, and the Ethiopians whom he met in
the Holy City. In the Sinai desert he speaks of Saracen
beggars and idolaters; in the Red Sea ports he thrice
records the appearance of ships from India laden with
aromatics. He travels up the Nile to the cataracts, and
describes the Nilometer of Assouan and the crocodiles in
the river; lower down, the Pyramids become for him the
twelve barns of Joseph—a number which later pilgrims
altered to fit the text of the seven years of plenty.

But far more wonderful than the practical jumble of
Antoninus is the systematic nonsense of Cosmas, whose
" Christian Topography" we must not enter upon here, for

its place is among the works of early Christian theory or science—with Dicuil and others of that class. Yet, as a traveller, his journey is deserving of especial attention. Unfortunately the references to it in his writings are only incidental, as his main purpose was to set forth a system of the universe. But his travels to Western India, to Abyssinia, to the coasts of the Red Sea, to the Ajan shore-lands beyond Guardafui, and probably to Ceylon and Palestine compose a very exceptional record; and, naturally enough, it is as a trader that he makes these extensive wanderings.

And whatever the absurdities of Cosmas and his dogmas "evolved out of holy Scripture," he is of interest to us as the last of the old Christian geographers, and in a sense, too, the first of the mediæval. He closes one age of civilisation which had slowly declined from the self-satisfied completeness of the classical world, and he prepares us to enter another that, in comparison, is literally dark. From the rise of Islam the geographical knowledge of Christendom is on a par with its practical contraction and apparent decline. Even more than actual exploration, theoretical knowledge seemed on its death-bed for the next five hundred years.

From the time, indeed, that Islam began to form itself into an organized civilization till the twelfth century, Christendom seemed content to accept it as the principal heir of the older Eastern culture, and took its geography, its ideas of the world in general, mainly from the Arabs, who in their turn depended upon the pre-Christian Greeks.

Yet our last group of pilgrim-travellers between Cosmas and the Viking Age, between the creation of the Empire of Mohammed and the fall of the Empire of Charles the Great, however limited and unprogressive, has a special interest to us through its association with the conversion of England

and the beginnings of English science and letters in the age of Bede.

Arculf, Willibald, and Fidelis—the first a Frank, the second an Englishman, the third probably Irish—all fall within the century (660–770) in which England definitely joined the communion of Rome, and allied itself with the Frankish kings and the Italian popes in the work of Christianising Central Europe. Arculf, the first of Latin travellers in the Levant since the Mohammedan conquest, on his return from Syria (c. 680) was hospitably entertained by Adamnan, abbot of Iona and successor of St. Columba, to whom he told his story. Bede abstracted and paraphrased this account, and in his version it became perhaps more widely known than any other of these older pilgrim-records.

Like Willibald, who made his journey in the next generation, and who is especially noticeable as the earliest English pilgrim (721–731), Arculf is full of confusions, omissions, and repetitions. The narratives of both belong to the infancy of thought and of expression; but they are at least records of a devout persistence and of a physical endurance, whose simple pathos and dignity never quite allow us to forget that we are now dealing with the actions of the men of a great race, though still only half developed.

Again, the impression given by our two principal guide-books of this "Frankish" Age is confirmed by the monk Fidelis, whose journey (of about 750) is narrated by the Irish philosopher, Dicuil,[1] and by Bernard the Wise of Mont St. Michel, who went over all the pilgrim-ground a century later (c. 870). Fidelis, indeed, who describes for us the Pyramids in a curious passage, and who sailed from the Nile into the Red Sea by the fresh-water canal of Necho and

[1] In his tract on the "Measurement of the Earth."

Hadrian, is probably one of a separate group of travellers, the Irish devotees, who, between the sixth and the ninth centuries, went out into all lands; but Bernard is a genuine Frankish pilgrim, and the last of any importance. His account shows us the Moslem oppression of Christian visitors at a more acute stage than any earlier narrative, although he bears witness to the good government and order of the Caliphate. He went on his travels at one of the worst and weakest times in the history of Christendom. He pictures the people of South Italy being swept off as slaves to Moslem countries; the Campagna of Rome overrun with brigands; Christian travellers fearing to move within their own lands, save in strong armed companies. The new rulers of the Levant have now changed the main lines of traffic between the east and west of the Mediterranean world, and forced the Syrian route from " Frankland " to go, as Bernard has to travel, through Egypt; for the Arab dominion is now in the height of its power, controlling all the lands between the Pyrenees and the Sahara, between the Sea of Aral and the Indian Ocean, between the Atlantic and the Indus. More than that—while Christian commerce, like Christian travel, barely arrests the attention of the casual observer by any sign of life, Moslem enterprise is opening up a vigorous trade with China, with Further India, with Malabar, and with Ceylon, exploring and colonising the eastern coast of Africa to the equator, and even approaching the harbours of Korea and Japan, where in the tenth century they began a certain trade. Never before or after did Islam appear more nearly in the light of a universal system; never before or after did it work more nobly for enlightenment and for progress. Arabic science was in its earlier prime; Arabic astronomy and geography were shaping themselves after Greek models; the sword of

Aristotle had passed into the keeping of the schools of Cordova, of Cairoan, and of Bagdad,—for a time.

It is difficult to imagine that the Europe of Bernard's day was destined ever to witness such a turn of the tide as that Christian armies would carry war into the heart of the Caliphate; still more difficult to conceive of the same Europe as once again controlling, as in the days of the Cæsars, the best parts of the world; most difficult of all to think of the fellow-countrymen of our pilgrims as the discoverers, settlers, and conquerors of the then unknown three-quarters of the earth which lay shrouded in mist beyond the limits of the known or half-known world. The new time needed new forces, a fresh inspiration of virility and daring. But here, with the Empire of Charles and his Franks all in ruins, and but little promise of revival, with heathen Northmen and Moslem Saracens seemingly allied for the destruction of Christendom, this section of our story must be left,—where the secret of the future seems most impenetrable, and the dark hours have deepened into that intenser blackness that comes before the dawn.

At the same time, or a little earlier than the Breton traveller, another Latin had written a short tract (c. 808?), "On the Houses of God in Jerusalem," which, with Bernard's note-book and the Story of the Penitential Pilgrimage of Frotmund (c. 870), is our last record of religious journeyings before the "coming of the Northmen." The new time, indeed, had come already, and men knew it not; in the Viking pirates—pagan, cruel, fearless, the destroyers of monasteries and fortresses, of books and men, of art and armies alike—it was not easy to recognise the future strength of Christendom, the men who were to call Europe out of sleep, and to awaken the new nations to the fact of their growth into life.

II. The Levantine pilgrimages are the principal, but not the only examples of early Christian travel. There was a good deal of Roman missionary exploration in Northern and Central Europe, as in the journeys of Augustine of Canterbury, of Cyril, of Methodius, and of Ansgar, from the sixth century. In the same time, and to a large extent in the same countries, the Irish monks, such as Gall or Columban, were busy with their work, pursuing it even to such outlying parts of the world as Iceland,[1] whose first discovery is due to them. The Byzantine conversion of Russia afterwards (in the eleventh century) extended this work of religious enterprise to a field but slightly known to the older Empire; and Byzantine trade in distant quarters of Asia and Africa, though declining, continued to struggle along the old caravan routes.

But here, in the further East and South, the Moslem ousted the Christian merchant more and more till the Crusades; while in the North-east, as late as the close of the ninth century, and long after the appearance of the Northmen upon the theatre of the world, the limits of Christendom and of civilisation might be said to follow the courses of the Elbe and the Danube. In some places Slav and Teutonic heathendom had crossed these boundaries; but in other districts, as in Moravia and Bohemia, it had been driven back far beyond them. Charles the Great's scheme for a separate Church province beyond the Elbe, under a metropolitan of its own, was not realised in his own lifetime: but his son Lewis the Pious made a good beginning when he sent Ansgar to be bishop in Hamburg (A.D. 831); for this resolute and saintly missionary, who had already travelled to Sweden to preach the gospel, journeyed, during an episcopate of four and thirty years, in all the South Baltic lands,

[1] *E.g.* in 795.

and introduced the first, though temporary, Christianity
into Denmark, Sweden, and Nordalbingia. Similarly, the
Frankish conversion—in somewhat forcible manner—of the
Saxons, of the King of the Moravians, of some of the
Bohemians, and of scattered tribes beyond the Elbe, opened
the way for the extension of Christendom by the missionary
travels of Cyril and Methodius, who, between 863 and 885,
added Moravia to the Western world and the Western faith;
the conversion and consequent exploration of the Frisian
country between the Rhine, the Ems, and the Weser had
been already accomplished by English and other preachers
during the seventh and eighth centuries. Bavarians and
Thuringians were first touched by the new religion in the
time of the Merwings, but with widely different results.
Under the succeeding dynasty of the Karlings, Thuringia is
a definite part of the Latin Church and the Frankish State:
Bavaria, on the contrary, was just as definitely outside the
political federation, and only to a very limited extent incorporated in the religious communion, of the West. In all
these directions there was some advance of geographical
knowledge through religious effort, beyond the limits of the
old Empire,—before the conversion of the Northmen, or
the age of their exploring and conquering activity.

The Irish missions, meantime, recovered Northern and
Central England for Christendom, added Ireland itself to
the Catholic world, and combated barbarism with no small
courage and success in France, in Switzerland, in North
Italy, and in still more distant fields. With their religious
work they helped forward the progress of social order, knowledge, and art. In other words, they did real and manful
service to civilisation, in arresting a further decline, and in
commencing a revival of culture; parallel with their crusade
against heathendom went their struggle with anarchy.

Their geography, or study of the world, will be seen most completely in the tract of Dicuil, who is, for his age, a scientist of unusual merit ; and their exploration, though as narrowly devotional as that of the Latin pilgrims, is worthy of a certain place in the story of Western expansion.   We shall have to notice more fully in another place their most important journeys, already mentioned, such as that of Fidelis and his companions to the East, or of the eighth-century hermits to the Northern islands.

Byzantine trade and travel in Central and Southern Asia and " Erythrea " will also claim a more detailed study in the body of this volume—so far, at least, as it relates to extension of geographical knowledge, or a maintenance of anything like a far-reaching geographical outlook.   Here it will be enough to repeat that the record is a poor one for our purposes, and that its main interest is connected with those Nestorian missions which fought their way so stubbornly in China during the seventh and eighth centuries, and founded Churches in Hyrcania, Bactria, and various regions of Tartary down to the middle of the eleventh.

III. Geographical theory or science in Christendom, between the age of Mohammed and that of the Vikings, is in a state scarcely less rudimentary than travel.

Much of the advance made by the pagan world is now abandoned ; part of the knowledge once gained has been forgotten, part seems to lie in a sort of limbo on this side of Lethe, not altogether out of sight, but, as it were, out of touch of the new time, uncared for, unattended to.   The word seems reversed—" Let us *not* now remember our fathers, and the actions of famous men."   As Bacon said in another connection, everything of value seemed to sink, and only the light and worthless rubbish came floating on down the stream of time.   Ptolemy and Strabo, Herodotus and

Hipparchus, passed almost wholly away from Christian
memory, and the only works of the pagan period which held
much attention were compilations of marvels such as those of
Solinus, or the lists of place-names which Orosius, Guido, or the
anonymous geographer of Ravenna put under contribution.

The compilation of Solinus, probably made in the third
century, by a pagan analyst of the classic Mirabilia, and
especially of Pliny, became so fashionable in the Christian
Middle Ages, and exercised so powerful an influence on their
geographical imagination, that it cannot be passed over. It
is simply a collection of marvels, chiefly of natural history
—beasts, birds, fishes, reptiles, minerals and precious stones—
brought together apparently on the principle " Credo," or at
least, "Lego, quia impossibile." Never perhaps do we penetrate more deeply into the enchanted world of " geosophists "
than when we turn over the pages and study the conceptions
of Solinus or of Cosmas. In the former, geography is only
taken into account as a framework on which the web of the
story-teller is woven into the garments of romance in which
the naked repulsiveness of fact is becomingly draped. In
the latter, geography in its abstract and general relations is
restated in terms of theology.

Cosmas, as the first scientific geographer of Christendom,
if not popular or influential, is at least remarkable, and holds
a distinct place. His Topography, which alone has survived
to us, is, above all, a work of theological interest. It is both
destructive and constructive. It denies the roundness of the
earth, as asserted by the leading Greek geographers and
astronomers ; it denies especially the existence of antipodes,
or land inhabited by human beings beneath our feet ; and it
attacks the belief that the world can be suspended in mid-
air, or in any sort of motion. On the other hand, it alleges
and tries to prove a positive system of its own, which has

become proverbial among the curiosities of literature and of thought. According to this, the universe was a flat parallelogram, its length exactly double of its breadth. In the centre of the universe lay our world, surrounded by the ocean. Beyond the ocean was another earth, where men lived before the flood, and from which Noah came in the Ark. To the north of our world was a great hill (an Indian conception) round which sun and moon revolved, thus causing day and night. The sky consisted of four walls, meeting in the dome of heaven, on the floor of which we live; and those walls were glued to the edges of the outer world of the patriarchs. Heaven, moreover, was cut in two by the firmament, lying between our atmosphere and the Paradise of God; below this firmament lived the angels, and above it were waters—the waters that be above the firmament.

But besides these and other cosmological points, a great deal of attention is devoted to purely theological questions, such as the precise state, history, and future prospects of the angels; and to questions where theology and science "falsely so-called" mingle in a daring confusion, as in the handling of those two fundamental truths, " Of the independent being of heaven and earth," and " Of Moses' tabernacle, the true model of the universe."

The reasoning throughout is like that to be found in St. Isidore and St. Augustine, on the effects of man's fall upon the stars and the vegetable world, or the atmospheric changes due to angels. But far more valuable than Cosmas' arguments, are his digressions into matters of fact.[1] Of these we have to make mention elsewhere, and it will be seen that their importance is considerable; but to the author they were merely incidental, and occupy scarce a tenth of the

---

[1] As in the case of the Adule inscription or the Roman intercourse with Ceylon.

space given to Scriptural quotations alone in this enormous treatise.[1]

Passing by the geographical summaries of encyclopædists such as Isidore, the next among our men of science are the tabulists Guido of Ravenna[2] (c. 800–850) and the Anonymous Geographer of the same city (c. 650). They are fairly called Tabulists because, though professing to give us a general account of the world, or a summary of geography, they are really occupied in drawing up a list of place-names, derived, by their own confession, from the works of previous "philosophers." Thus their writings, like most of early Christian cosmographies, are connected with the pre-Christian civilisation. As the Bordeaux itinerary points back to the Antonine survey, as Solinus refers us back to Pliny, so these Ravennese catalogues are almost certainly based upon the Peutinger table, that great ribbon-map of the Roman roads, which in all likelihood reaches back, ultimately, to the Augustan Age. Thus, like the still more wretched compilations of Julius Honorius and Julius Æthicus, both the "Anonymous" and his disciple Guido belong rather to the expiring age of classical geography than to the mediæval spirit. A few incidental expressions are the only hints we get of the Christian period in which these catalogues were put together.

Dicuil's treatise on the measurement of the earth (A.D. 825), like that of the Anonymous Ravennese, gives us a kind of view or description of the world mainly taken from older compilations. But in this are embedded two valuable accounts of original travel, the voyage of Fidelis to the

[1] The "Christian Topography" is further illustrated by a map of the world, with the rivers of Paradise, the ocean, and the outer or patriarchal earth, which, if original, is perhaps the earliest of Christian *mappe-mondes*.

[2] Or of Pisa, according to some recent conjectures.

Levant, and the journeys of Irish monks in the Northern islands, both of the eighth century. Compared with most of his sources and co-workers—in the systematic exposition of geography—Dicuil is not at all contemptible ; and his work is perhaps the chief memorial of the distinctive Irish tradition, as it is the latest. In his own lifetime began the Viking attacks upon the British Isles—a few years after he wrote upon the measurement of the earth, the Ostman kingdoms were founded in Leinster. Barbarism, though the barbarism of a supremely creative and progressive race, overwhelmed in the ninth century that civilisation of Christian Ireland which is so interesting in itself, and so irritating in its poetic obscurity and uncertainty to us of the modern world. The art, the literature, and the missions of Patrick's Church perished under the first heathen onslaught, and its scientific, in particular its geographical, study naturally sank with other treasures in the storm.

In addition to our four chief examples of geographical theory in this time—Solinus, Cosmas, the Ravennese geographer, and Dicuil—we have also tried to select from every side of the Christian literature of the earlier Middle Age, examples of geographical theory, so far as these had anything distinctive or remarkable about them, either for wisdom or for folly ; and we have attempted to touch upon every one of the minor geographical writings of this time, in Latin Christendom, that seemed for any reason worthy of notice. The result of this is such as we might expect, from the fierce opposition between the extremist element in the early Church and the spirit of pagan science,—an opposition which the later Middle Ages grew less and less disposed to accentuate, till, in the time of the Renaissance, churchmen seemed ready to do what St. Jerome so feared for himself, and to become half Ciceronian and half Christian. But

before the tenth century there was little danger of that.
The wisdom of this world was reckoned by most of the
Patristics as mere folly in the sight of God, and both the
physical and metaphysical study of the Greeks was freely
dismissed as "windy babble" by the more fanatical school
of Christian writers. On the other hand, an extraordinary
proportion of ancient myth was eagerly adopted into the
service of the new system; questions of pure science were
settled by Biblical texts after the manner of a remote and
oracle-guided antiquity; and fresh questions of almost
incredible pettiness or absurdity were mooted and discussed.
What must have been the state of physical science in
general, and of geography in particular, when one of the most
learned and least superstitious of the Fathers, St. Isidore
of Seville, could spend his time in debating whether the
stars had souls, and, if so, what they would do at the day
of Resurrection; when so great a scholar as Theodore of
Mopsuestia could substitute the personal agency of angels
for the natural laws of celestial movements, thus employing
them, as John Philoponus complains, like porters to hold up
and push about the heavenly bodies; or when Alcuin, in
trying to give some true ideas of nature to the court of
Charles the Great, was obliged, in language suitable for
little children, to speak of the year as a waggon with four
horses, Night and Day, Warmth and Cold; driven by two
coachmen, Sun and Moon; passing by the twelve stations of
the months; and escorted by the twelve watchmen of the
Signs of the Zodiac? [1]

The belief in a round or spherical world professed by the
Venerable Bede with tolerable clearness,[2] and by some others

[1] See Alcuin's "Disputatio Re-
galis;" Isidore, "De Natura Rerum,"
27; John Philoponus, "De Creatione
Mundi," throughout.

[2] As in "De Natura Rerum.

with varying degrees of confidence, was robbed of all
practical value, in the few cases where it gained a hearing,
by the dogma that only one race of human beings could be
supposed—all derived from Adam, and included in the
nations to whom the gospel had been already preached.   In
the almost universal belief moreover, the torrid zone could
not be crossed for the heat; and so the notion of the " lower
parts" of the globe (apart from the difficulties of a topsy-
turvy world) was generally condemned, as both unscriptural
and ridiculous.

Lastly, the maps of this time, as far as they have survived to us, barely show even the commencement of
mediæval cartography.   True, we have the scheme, if
genuine, of Cosmas himself;   the *mappe-monde* of Albi
seems to have been executed about 730; and the original
plan of the Spanish theologian Beatus was probably composed in 776; but of the last named we only possess the
later derivatives of " St. Sever " (c. 1028–1072), " Turin " (c.
1080), " London " (1109), and " Ashburnham " (tenth century), with six others of the eleventh, the twelfth, and the
thirteenth centuries.

The position and work of Beatus will be examined in
another place; but it may be well to note here, how his
map, like the tenth-century almanack of Bishop Harib of
Cordova, was drawn in the time of complete Moslem
domination over the peninsula.   Beatus himself, seemingly
a priest and monk of the Asturias, was possibly deprived by
this very fact of many opportunities of wider knowledge ; and
so, although his map is free from the elaborate absurdities
and deceptions of some later examples, it is, as a world-
sketch, among the crudest,—for in it the rudimentary truths
of the earth's surface, and of the distribution of its seas and
lands, are nearly lost.   Its interest, of course, is mainly

theological: it is an attempt to illustrate the Bible world, in a commentary on the Apocalypse; and it is the work of the chief orthodox opponent of the Adoptionist heretics, Felix of Urgel and Claudius of Turin, whose contempt for pilgrimage is also noticeable.

The Albi map, though only a little sketch by comparison, has a rather closer relation to facts: its place-names are apparently derived from the geographical section of Orosius' "Universal History" and from Julius Honorius, whose text it is especially drawn to illustrate. Some have conjectured that the draughtsman had seen Cosmas' map of the Mediterranean world and its outliers; but this does not seem to be proved by a close comparison of the two plans.

By the side of Christian enterprise it may be useful to place a brief summary of non-Christian parallels in the same period. Without attempting to treat these in anything like an exhaustive manner, we shall find material enough to show how inadequate the knowledge of Christendom then was, if judged only by contrast. The subject of this inquiry, as we have already pointed out, is mainly the geographical movements of Western or Latin Christendom; but both in this and subsequent parts some attention will be given both to exploration and geographical literature among Greek or Eastern Christians and among non-Christian races, such as the Arabs, the Chinese, or the early Norsemen. Our inner circle will be therefore strictly a part of European history; but outside this we shall try to deal with the progress of discovery and "earth-knowledge" in non-European lands, though only in the way of selection.

Now, many of the more important monuments of Arab and Chinese travel and science belong to a time earlier than the epoch when, at the close of the ninth and beginning of the tenth century, both Islam and China underwent their

most important mediæval revolution; and it is not a little
singular that at the very same period when the expansive
energy of Western Europe, even in pilgrimage, seemed to
have become practically exhausted, or at least unfruitful,
both the Caliphate and the Celestial Empire should have
suffered so severely from social and governmental disorder
The whole world seemed to receive about this epoch a
certain lowering of its tide of life.

On the one hand, the Bagdad Caliphate lost all its
political force—the last caliph who could be termed both
pope and emperor of the Saracens died in 940; and with
this political degradation ended the first great school of
Moslem geographers and travellers, in the person of Massoudy
—a school which had had a continuous and active existence
for a century and a half, or even more.[1]

On the other hand, the domestic revolution of 878, and
the consequent depression of foreign trade, inaugurated a
new era in China. In the course of the next two generations
the whole spirit of the government and of the people seemed
to have altered; the age of comparative enterprise and open-
ness was definitely closed; and the age of comparative
exclusiveness as definitely begun.

Modern China, the most suspicious, self-contained, and
anti-foreign of countries, now had its starting-point. The
stream of Buddhist pilgrims from the Celestial Land to India
and the "countries of the West" markedly decreased in the
ninth and tenth centuries; in the same age the Christianity
which Nestorian missionaries had imported into the Silk
Land became practically extinct; at the same time Chinese
merchants ceased to frequent the ports of Southern and
South-Western Asia, and nearly all Chinese harbours were
closed against import traffic.

[1] Circ. 780–950.

Spain was almost the only country of the civilised or semi-civilised world where, during the tenth century, a high standard of political efficiency, of mental culture, and of social progress was kept up : and even this was a deceptive splendour ; for the next forty years (A.D. 1000–1040) witnessed an utter collapse of the Kingdom of Cordova; and a great weakening of its intellectual energy accompanied the political and social breakdown. Just as the Persian and Arabian Empires normally stopped short, in their Indian dominion, at the great Rajpoot deserts beyond the Indus, so the history of most mediæval kingdoms, from the Atlantic to the Yellow Sea, seems to pause, as it were, on the edge of an unproductive, unprogressive, and often reactionary or half-anarchic interval, as it nears the end of the first Christian millennium.

1. Beginning in the age of the Caliph Al Mansor, the immediate predecessor of Haroun Al Raschid, the early Arabic geography was brought to maturity under Haroun's successor, Al Mamoun (813–833), in the age of Charlemagne and Louis the Pious. In his reign many of the chief works of Greek geography were translated ; observatories were built ; the positions of places were ascertained by astronomical calculation ; original or quasi-original works were composed on the basis of the Hellenic models now so eagerly studied ; and Arab explorers traversed nearly every country of Southern and Central Asia, of Northern Africa, and of Mediterranean Europe.

Rising out of a host of lesser figures, we have in this age, the early ninth century, three pre-eminent Moslem geographers — Mohammed Alkharizmy, Alfergany, and Soleyman the Merchant. The first two occupied themselves with theory and science, the last with practical travel; the one wrote upon the astrolabe, upon the climates, upon

Greek and Indian observations; the other gave the first
Arab account of China and of many of the coast-lands of the
Indian Ocean. His voyages seem to have been made about
A.D. 850 ; but at least ten years earlier the Caliphs had
begun the systematic exploration of the countries of Turkestan
and of what is now called European Russia, lying beyond
the northern frontiers of Islam. Sallam the Interpreter,
sent from Bagdad on this mission (in 840), traversed the
regions to west, north, and east of the Caspian; and his
discoveries, disfigured as they were by the legendary and
superstitious spirit of their narrator, were carried forward
with far sounder results by Ibn Fozlan in his Russian
travels of A.D. 921.

From voyages such as Soleyman's gradually arose the
series of narratives which we know by the name of Sindbad
the Sailor—a real account, with a little more of mystery and
exaggeration than usual, of the experiences of early Arabic
mariners in the Southern Ocean, " selected and arranged for
popular use." A very different class of geographical work is
represented by Ibn Khordadbeh's description of trade routes,
lands, and taxes (A.D. 890), where statistical tables are oddly
interspersed with legendary narratives, and where there is a
marked absence of first-hand experience; but where we find
a digest of many facts as to places, distances, and commercial
highways useful for the Caliph's government. Lastly, surprising precision was given to Moslem science at the close
of our period by men like Albaïeny; extensive overland
travels were accomplished, and interesting observations were
made by Ibn Haukal; the borders of the civilised world
were pushed southwards along the East African coast by
Arab traders and warriors, such as those of the Emosaid
family; and encyclopædic work began, both in practical
travel and literary geography, with Massoudy. To the

last named certainly belongs the leading place among all those men who, in the interests of Geography, either journeyed or wrote within the limits of the early Middle Ages. As an explorer, he touched the Atlantic on one side, and the China Sea on the other; towards the South, he seems to have crossed the equator and reached the Zanzibar Islands, if he did not visit Madagascar; only on the northern side was he content with the limits of Islam and the excursions of the less ambitious of his predecessors. As a writer, Massoudy has almost the quiet confidence of Lord Bacon, that he has taken all knowledge for his province; and few indeed are those in ancient or modern times who have collected a geographical anthology of equal variety and bulk.

2. Never did China display a less exclusive spirit than during this same period. In trade, it kept up a pretty constant intercourse, from the fifth century, with the southern coast of Asia as far as Ceylon; and at times this intercourse was extended to the Persian Gulf, and even to the mouth of the Euphrates. Foreign merchants crowded its ports in the time of the earlier caliphs and under the emperors of the Thang dynasty; foreign embassies and visitors were received at court; and diplomatic missions were despatched, though more rarely, to outside lands. In religious travel, a series of pilgrims journeyed to India between the beginning of the fourth and the end of the seventh centuries; the names of more than sixty are preserved; and among them at least two enjoyed great renown.[1] Fa-Hien and Hiouen-Thsang may rank among the foremost of the purely religious travellers. The latter especially was a man of profound learning and trained intelligence, and had no small share of scientific interest, as any one may see by the descriptions of foreign countries in his "Life" and "Records."

[1] The first journeying from 399 to 414; the second from 618 to 636.

It is strange enough to find two other achievements of great moment claimed by the Chinese of this age—the discovery of America, and the invention of the compass. We shall see, later on, what is the chief evidence under each of these counts; here we may perhaps express a belief in the possibility of Buddhist missionaries and others creeping, as alleged, or rather suggested, round the northern angle of the Pacific from Corea to Alaska and the fiords of British Columbia, in the fifth and sixth centuries. On the other question, it seems clear that the Celestials were acquainted with the indicating power of magnetised iron before the Christian era, and that various improvements in the use of the same were made by the Emperors of the Thang in the seventh and eighth centuries. But the water or pivot compass, as we know it, was not employed till about A.D. 1110.

As we look back upon the course of a movement which through so many centuries of European life appears often stationary or even retrograde, in the midst of our disappointment and weariness we may find some comfort in the comparative value even of such devotional enterprise. And as comparison is the only test of any age or of any man therein, the very blunders and limitations of the past have a constant as well as an historical value to us. For they remind us not only how we have come to our present mastery over the world, but also how imperfect the work even of our time must be in the light of the ultimately possible.

So, if our pilgrim-travellers and Bible scientists have interests the very reverse of ours, thoughts which to us seem unthinkable, or fancies that repel us as rather absurd than poetic, it will not be for us to utterly despise men who, in a true sense, were making their times ready for better things.

And especially we must remember this [1] in our mournful and threatening close. A half-barbarised world had entered upon the inheritance of a splendid past, but it took centuries before that inheritance was realised by the so altered present. In this time of change, we have men writing in the language of Cæsar and Virgil, of Alexander and Sophocles, who had been themselves, or whose fathers had been, mere "whelps from the kennel of barbarism" to Greeks and Romans of the Old Empire.

We have been passing through the time of the reconstruction of society, the only apparent reaction which our Western world has known, and that only apparent, when savage and strong men who had conquered were set down beside the overworked and outworn masters of France, and Italy, and Spain, and Britain to learn from them, and to make of them a more enduring race.

[1] Particularly, of course, in relation to Christendom.

CHAPTER II.

THE PRIMITIVE PILGRIMS OF LATIN CHRISTENDOM.[1]

I. BEFORE JEROME—A.D. 370.

THE earliest traditions of Christian pilgrimage to the Holy Land from Western Europe are those of the very doubtful Gallic matron who was said to have returned to her own country with a shell full of the blood of John the Baptist, then newly murdered by Herod Antipas (A.D. 31);[2] and of Quilius, King of the Brito-Saxons, as he is absurdly called, who, in or about the year 40, was supposed to have visited Jerusalem and brought back relics. But all the stories of this kind, from the first, second, and third centuries, are vague and shadowy, as far as they relate to Latin or Western enterprise. It is in Greek pilgrimage that the oldest authentic memorials are to be found;[3] and the mass of these memorials is rather Asiatic than European. In any case they do not concern us here, in an attempt to trace the earlier story of Christian explorers. To all men

---

[1] *The Primary authority for almost all the texts in chs. ii., iii., and iv., is Tobler and Molinier's Collection, vols. i., i. 2, and ii.:* "Itinera Hierosolymitana et Descriptiones Terræ Sanctæ Bellis Sacris Anteriora et Latina Lingua exarata Sumptibus Societatis illustrandis Orientis Latini Monumentis ediderunt Titus Tobler et Augustus Molinier." Genevæ, Typis J. G. Fick, 1877 and 1885. [Vol. ii., ed. by Molinier and Kohler.]

[2] Greg. of Tours, De Gloria Martyrum, c. 12.

[3] Guibertus de Novigento, De Vita Sua, ii. 1. Cf. also Paulus Orosius, Hist. vii. 6; Josephus, Antiq. Jud. xx. chs. 2–4, etc.; Euseb. ii. 12.

of the Greek-speaking provinces the way to Syria presented no more difficulty than the antiquarian researches of such a student as Pausanias encountered in Greece itself.

But of more distant journeys, and more real exploration, from the West, we have a great increase from the fourth century. And the pioneers of this new fashion seem to have been obscure men, such as Antoninus the Martyr, John the Presbyter, and Alexander the Bishop, who went to the Holy Land "for prayer and to obtain knowledge of the sacred places by inquiry." Both Antonine and John came from Placentia, or Piacenza, in North Italy, and they made the Syrian pilgrimage about A.D. 303, some twenty years before Helena, the empress-mother, discovered the relics in Jerusalem which gave new life to an old custom and made a ruling fashion out of the habit of a few devotees. Antoninus visited Jerusalem and Sinai, where he saw a statue of pure white marble defiled and blackened by idolatrous sacrifices,[1] but which became as white as ever when these abominations had ceased. John the Presbyter died in Capernaum, and was buried there, without any special or exciting experience to record.[2]

Next comes the journey of St. Helena, mother of

---

[1] "Tetra ut pix efficiebatur." Cf. John, Archd. of Placentia, Tract on finding of S. Antonine's body, lects. vii. and viii.; AA. SS., July ii. p. 18; and the (MS.) *Passionarium* at Milan (Ambros E. 22). Cf. It. Hi. (303–304 A.D.), ii. 33, 34.

[2] The Alexander who is sometimes alluded to as the earliest Christian pilgrim is probably Alexander Flavianus (c. 212, A.D.), "Bishop of Cappadocia," whose pilgrimage Jerome records in De Viris Illustribus, c. 62 (Migne, P. L. xxiii. 674).

Though a bishop in Greek-speaking lands, he must have been of Western or Latin family: cf. Gesta Epp. Hieros.; Delpit, Essai sur les Pèlerinages à Jérusalem, p. 19; Eusebius, H. E. vi. 11, 20. The pilgrimage of the great Origen of Alexandria was shortly after Alexander's. We may notice that the latter became Bishop of Jerusalem on accomplishing his journey. See the references in the collection of the Société de l'Orient Latin, Série Géographique (Itinera Hierosolymitana, ii. 21, 22).

Constantine the Great, and the "Invention" of those relics
of the Passion which made Jerusalem the great pilgrim-
museum of later time.   The references to her visit are, of
course, innumerable, but they are all repetitions or ampli-
fications of St. Jerome's statement in his Chronicle,[1] under
the year 321, that the "mother of Constantine, warned by
heavenly visions, found the most blessed sign of the cross
at Jerusalem"—an event which is now fixed by the
chronologists to the date 326.

Before her visit, we are expressly assured by Rufinus, the
exact spot of the Crucifixion had been "almost entirely con-
signed to oblivion."   But now the site was discovered, and,
finding Pilate's title "in Hebrew and Greek and Latin on
one cross" (out of the three that had been dug up), Helena
was disposed to think this was the Redeemer's, when the
actual proof was given by a miracle—the "saving wood"
restored a dying woman to life and strength.   On this, the
Empress at once built a splendid church over the spot; and
carried the nails and a part of the cross itself to the
Emperor: the rest was kept in silver chests in the Memorial
she had erected.

From another source[2] we hear how the discovery was
first made.   The three original pilgrim-churches of the
Passion (or Holy Sepulchre), Resurrection, and Ascension of
Christ, were only built by Helena, after she had found the

[1] Chronicon, A.D. 321; cf. Migne,
P. L. xxvii. 671. Ruf. Hist. Ecc. i.
7–8.

[2] Bede, Hom. Subdit. xciii.; Sul-
picius Severus, Hist. Sacra, ii. 33,
34: and cf. also S. Paulinus of
Nola, Epist. xxxi. cc. 4, 5 (Migne,
lxi. c. 327); Cassiodorus, Tripartite
Hist. ii. 18; Ambrose, De Obitu
Theodosii Oratio; Greg. Tours, Hist.
Franc. i. 34; De Glor. MM. i. 5–6;
Altmannus Altivillarensis, Vita S.
Hel. ii. 26–28; Ansellus, Epistola ad
Eccl. Paris., a. 1108 (Migne, P. L.
clxii. c. 731); Berengosus (De Laude
et Inv. S. C. ii. 5–7 (Migne, P. L. clx.
956–958); Alcuin, Carmina, c. 147,
ii. 219 (Froben); Eusebius, De V.
Const. iii. 42–44, and other refs. as
in Soc. de L'O. L., S. G. (It. Hi. ii.
pp. 51, 52, ed. Molinier and Kohler).

true position of the Gospel sites by threatening the Jews with death for their conspiracy of silence. "By the God who made me," the Empress was made to say, in Christian homilies, "unless you tell me, I will kill you every one."[1] A later story confidently declared that Helena would have burnt alive those enemies of the Cross, if they had not confessed.[2] A man named Judas, renamed as Quiracus on his baptism, was specified as the actual discoverer of the site, by the help of an old story in his family that had been handed down from his great-grandfather. The woman whose miraculous recovery showed which of the three trees was the Saviour's cross, was named Libania, and in the tradition she appears as the widow of Issachar the Jew. The reliance of the story upon Jewish aid is remarkable, and surely goes to discredit the whole. For what Jewish family would preserve a local tradition about a victim of Jewish persecution between Hadrian, who expelled all Hebrews from Ælia, and Constantine, nearly two centuries later?

One Eustathius,[3] a priest of Constantinople, is named as the builder of the new church of the Holy Sepulchre, the capital, for the future, of the whole pilgrim-world of Christendom; and from this time the number of notable pilgrims whose names are preserved increases rapidly.

[1] Cf. Bede, Hom. xciii.

[2] The difficulty of the preservation of the wood for three centuries was surmounted by Paulinus of Nola, with the argument that it had been anointed with the blood of Christ, and was therefore indestructible. Gregory of Tours (De Gloria Martyrum, i. cc. 5–6) adds the story we have noticed in the introductory chapter, of one of the nails of the cross quieting a terrible storm in the Adriatic merely by being dropped into the water; and both he and Cassiodorus agree that another was fixed in the imperial statue which crowned the Porphyry Column at Constantinople. Several early accounts, and especially Altmann's "Life of St. Helena," speak, as we have noticed before (introd. ch.), of a temple of Venus erected over the spot by Hadrian when he destroyed Jerusalem, at the instigation of the high-priest of the Jews.

[3] Jerome's Chron. It. Hi. ii. p. 52 (Migne, P. L. xxvii. c. 679).

For instance, under the year 330,[1] Potentinus, Felicius, and Simplicius, "Eremites from the diocese of Cologne" and a group of devotees from Western Europe—not to mention Eutropia, the Emperor's mother-in-law, who must be reckoned rather with Greek than with Latin pilgrims,—made the journey to Jerusalem "for the sake of the holy relics."

Again, in 333, the Bordeaux pilgrim compiled the first of Christian guide-books, the "Itinerary from Bordeaux to Jerusalem," which symbolises the beginning of a new and extraordinary kind of literary activity. Like Origen, he came "to search after the footsteps of Jesus and His disciples and the prophets;" like Queen Helena, "to seek knowledge of a land so worthy of veneration," and to "render thanksgivings with prayers,"—to put, as the letter of Paula to Marcella urges, "the finishing stroke on virtue by adoring Christ in the very places where the gospel first shone forth from the Cross." But he did more than any devotee before him—he recorded what he saw, for the help of others. And of this, the earliest of our travel-documents,[2] some detailed notice should be taken. It coincides pretty closely with the start of the Christian Empire of Rome, under Constantine, and with the impulse given by the pilgrimage of his mother, and is one of the many witnesses to the reconstruction of society, and to the new movements which stirred it at that time. It immediately follows the proclamation of the new faith of the Court, the foundation of the new capital of Constantine's creation, and the gathering of the first general assembly[3] of the new

[1] Acta SS. (Boll.), Iune iii. p. 576; Act. SS. 7 Sept. iii. p. 56.

[2] "Itinerarium a Burdigala Hierusalem usque:" best text in S. de

L'O. L. S. G. It. Hi. i. 1. 1–25 (Tobler).

[3] In the Council of Nicæa, A.D. 325.

spiritual state, of that Catholic Church which now claimed a partnership with the Empire. Thus it is an evidence of a new kind of activity created by the new and victorious religion, or, rather, a fresh variety of an ever-active interest —the interest of travel and of sentiment, the wish to see new things, and the wish to see memorable places. "Adorabimus in loco ubi steterunt pedes ejus."[1]

But the record of the Bordeaux pilgrim is not only the earliest narrative of a Christian pilgrimage, it is also the most detailed and exact among the fragments of the Roman itineraries that have come down to us, of which the Peutinger table gives us the expression in map form, and which were made by imperial warrant. Its exact measurements point to a direct copyist of the old surveys as the author—a copyist whose name is unrecorded, but who was certainly a Christian, and probably a native of Guienne. But, apart from the knowledge it shows of the great highways (derived from works like the Antonine itinerary), its notes are of too short and business-like a nature for us to infer much about Christian knowledge of the world in the fourth century. Its geography, unlike its superstition, is of the slightest. Yet, after all, only a few of the later host of apocryphal relics are noticed,[2] such as the house of Hezekiah, or the "true monolith" which was the tomb of Isaiah. On the other hand, scarcely anything is said about the places through which the pilgrim-route on the way to, and from, Palestine itself must pass. The names of town after town,

---

[1] Cf. remarks of A. Stewart in his preface and notes to the translation of the Bordeaux pilgrim, in the Palestine Pilgrims' Text Soc. (1887).

[2] For instance, there is no mention of the "holy lance," or the crown of thorns, the reed, the sponge, the cup of the Last Supper, the stone rolled away from the sepulchre, or the "charger" in which John Baptist's head was carried. Most of the legendary sites in our pilgrim are connected with Jewish history and the Temple, rather than with the life of Christ and the Holy Sepulchre. Cf. Walckenaer's essay on the B. P.; Delpit, pp. 54-62.

mountain after mountain, sea after sea, are just recorded, with the distances between the places named, and with summaries, every now and again, of the total mileage along some great section of the road.[1]

But, besides these figures and names, there are a few things in the itinerary of more general interest. Thus, for example, the date is fixed by the statement of the original traveller or travellers who went over the route, and laid down the plan,—"And so we journeyed from Chalcedon on the 30th of May, in the year of the consulship of Dalmatius and Zenophilus,[2] and returned to Constantinople on the 25th of December in the same year" (A.D. 333). Again, at a certain number of places, especially in the Holy Land itself, something is said about the surroundings, the history, or the objects of interest. Thus, at Bordeaux, the starting-point " is the river Garonne, through which the Ocean Sea ebbs and flows for one hundred leagues, more or less,"—a reckoning which is only kept up as far as the city of Toulouse (Tolosa), when all distances begin to be stated in miles. From Bordeaux to Arles, by way of Carcassonne, Narbonne, and Nimes,—this is the first main

---

[1] *E.g.* from Bordeaux to Arles, "372 miles, 30 changes, 11 stations"— "millia ccclxxii., mutationes xxx., mansiones xi." The numbers, however, as Tobler remarks (pref. xiii.), are in hopeless confusion: thus the manuscripts have muddled up *leagues* and *miles* in reckoning the total distance from Bordeaux to Arles " 372 miles," composed of 106–108 leagues, and 211–214 miles, and really making, even in jumble, only 317–322. As the Gallic league, however, equalled 1½ miles (Roman), the difference is much less than at first appears. Cf. A. Stewart in P.P.T. ed., p. 1. But it is quite outside our task to discuss the intricate and lengthy topographical questions which rise out of the itinerary, and which belong, on one side, to Roman historians, and, on another, to Palestine antiquaries. We have more excuse for noticing the glowing language of Ausonius on the Bordeaux of this day ; our pilgrim came from one of the most rising cities of the West, already famous for its scholars—men such as the later Paulinus (afterwards Bishop of Nola).

[2] Flavius Valerius Dalmatius, brother of Constantine, and M. Aurelius Zenophilus (Xenophilus).

section of the journey; from Arles the pilgrim goes on to Milan,[1] through Orange (Arausio), where Rome had once received so shrewd a knock from the Gauls, over Mount Gaurus and the Cottian Alps. Continuing across North Italy to Aquileia, we are taken through Bergamo and Verona. From Aquileia to Sirmium (Mitrowitza), the next stage crosses the Julian Alps, passes the boundary between the Diocletian division of Eastern and Western Empires, and traverses Pannonia.[2] From Sirmium to Singidunum (Belgrade), from Singidunum to Serdica (Sophia), from Serdica to Constantinople, the traveller moves on through the European provinces of what was even then in process of becoming the Byzantine Empire.

Leaving the new Christian Rome on the Bosphorus, "you cross the Pontus, come to Chalcedon, walk through Bithynia." At Libyssa (Gezybeh), two stations before Nicomedia, the pilgrim (who has already been reminded of recent history at Viminacium in Europe, "where Diocletian killed Carinus,") is told of something more ancient—"Annibalianus is laid there,[3] who was once king of the Africans." Still pressing on and crossing Asia Minor by the great military road from Constantinople to Syria, we pass through "Ancyra (Angora) of Galatia;" through Andavilis (Andaval), "where is the villa of Pampatus,[4] whence came the curule horses;" through "Tyana,[5] the home of Apollonius the Mage;"

---

[1] From Milan to Constantinople the itinerary agrees with the route laid down in the Antonine survey, except for the section between Burdista and Virgoli. The importance of Milan at this time (as of Aquileia) was at its height—"Mediolani mira omnia," as Ausonius said.

[2] From Petovio (Pettau), where the pilgrim enters Pannonia, he follows the northern banks of the Drave, along the southern boundary of modern Hungary. Cf. Zozimus, ii. 18.

[3] I.e. on his suicide at the Court of Prusias, king of Bithynia, B.C. 183.

[4] Probably a famous stable of that day, conjectures Walckenaer, 17.

[5] Kiz Hissar.

through the Cilician gates,[1] "where are the borders of Cappadocia and Cilicia," and through "Tarsus, where Paul the Apostle was." From Tarsus the pilgrim proceeds to Antioch and the "palace of Daphne," then in process of rebuilding at the hands of Constantine, crossing the frontier of Syria on the way; and entering Phœnicia, our route now ceases to copy the imperial itineraries, or to follow the beaten paths, after taking the ordinary course along the coast to "Cæsarea Palestina," by way of Antaradus,[2]—"a city in the sea, two miles from the shore,"—Tripolis (Tarabulus), Beyrout (Berytus), Sidon (Saide), Tyre (Sur), and Sarepta, "where Elias went up to the widow and asked food for himself."

Finally, passing beneath Mount Carmel, "where Elias made his sacrifice," the pilgrim comes to the borders of "Syria, Phœnicia, and Palestine," and finds himself at Cæsarea in Judæa (Kaisarieh).

"Here is the bath of Cornelius the Centurion," proceeds our guide-book, now beginning to be more detailed, and enlarging itself, so to say, from a Bradshaw into a Baedeker.[3] The last piece of the journey to Jerusalem is not made along the direct route, but by a circuitous way, through Jezreel, Bethshan (Scythopolis), and Shechem (Nablous), possibly to complete the list of places connected with the history of Elijah. In this *détour* we pass very close to Nazareth and the Sea of Galilee, but without finding any mention of either in our itinerary.

---

[1] Ghulek Boghaz.

[2] In Ruad island, where still exist walls of huge stones, near to the *Tortosa* of the Crusades. Similarly the pilgrim's (1) Pagrius, on the Borders of Syria and Cilicia, is the crusading *Bagras*, a fort proverbial for strength; and so (2) his Ladica is *Laodicea* (of Phœnicia); (3) his

Alexandroschene is William of Tyre's *Scandaleon*, "Champs de Lion"; (4) his Porphyrion is *Haifa*.

[3] This part is wanting in the St. Gall and Paris manuscripts, which present the itinerary simply as what Tobler calls "arida quædam viarum descriptio" (pref. xii.).

First of all, on leaving Cæsarea, the pilgrim reaches Mount Syna, " where is a spring, in which, if a woman wash, she becomes pregnant." [1]   Next he comes to the town of Stradela, or Jezreel, " where King Ahab sat and Elias prophesied," and near it " the field where David slew Goliath." [2] Then through Bethshan, or Scythopolis, by way of Aser, " where was Job's country-house," to Neapolis, or Nablous, " where is Mount Gerizim," and where the Samaritans declared Abraham used to sacrifice, " ascending to the top of the mountain by three hundred steps." [3]   Following Eusebius in the distinction he makes between Neapolis, Sichem, and Sichar, our guide points out in Sichem, " at the foot of the mount (Gerizim), a tomb where Joseph lies, in the parcel of ground [4] that Jacob gave him."   Going on towards Jerusalem, we come to the " village " [4] of Bethar, or Bethel, where " Jacob slept, when he was going into Mesopotamia, and the angel wrestled with him."   And here, too, was " King Jeroboam, when the prophet came to him," who was " slain by a lion on the way as he returned."   From this point it is only twelve miles to Jerusalem ; and here the pilgrim is to notice the " two great pools " that Solomon made on the right and left sides of the temple, " with five porches, which are called ' Bethsaida ' " (Bethesda) : also the crypt where the aforesaid Solomon tortured the demons ; [5] the lofty tower, where the Lord was tempted—" If thou be the Son of God, cast Thyself down "—the corner stone of which it was said,

---

[1] Cf. the crusading historian, Albert of Aix, vi. 41.

[2] Probably from a confused remembrance of the mention of a battle fought here between Israelites and Philistines.

[3] They must have been patriarchal steps, or only up a part of the mount, for it is 1174 feet high.

[4] Villa.

[5] Only in the Bordeaux Itinerary, which is also alone in its mention of, e.g., (1) Mt. Syna and its procreative fountain ; (2) the field, near Jezreel (Stradela), where David slew Goliath ; (3) the chamber where Solomon described Wisdom ; (4) the perforated stone at the Jew's wailing-place.

"The stone which the builders rejected is become the head of the corner;" the palace of Solomon, "where he sat and described Wisdom;" the great vaults and pools underneath the temple area.   More than all this, the very hob-nails of the soldiers' boots left their marks "throughout the whole enclosure of the temple," so plain "that you would think them impressed on wax;" and the men who left these marks were the very same who slew Zacharias between the temple and the altar.   Needless to say, the traces of his blood were also clear enough upon the stone.   Two statues of Hadrian must also be seen, commemorating the final expulsion of the Jews; "and not far from the statues, a perforated stone, to which the Jews come every year, and anoint it, bewail themselves with groaning, and rend their garments, and so depart."[1]   Both Hadrian and Antoninus Pius, we may remember, placed their "images" in the temple of Jupiter Capitolinus, which Hadrian built on the site of the Holy of Holies; and St. Jerome speaks of these as still existing in his day, at the end of the fourth century. In the time of the Bordeaux Pilgrim, the profanation of

[1] This must have been very recent, as Hadrian's prohibition of Jews setting foot in the city (A.D. 136) remained in force till the days of Constantine—at least, till his accession as sole emperor, in 324.   During his refoundation of the non-pagan city, from the year of Helena's pilgrimage (326) down to the dedication of his Martyrion, or Church of the Passion, in 336, the Jews seem slowly and gradually to have begun their return.   But perhaps the law had long been evaded, as in the similar exclusion of Jews from England between Edward I. and Cromwell. A relic of Roman Ælia, such as is here referred to by the Bordeaux Pilgrim, was used in the substructures of the Mosque El Aksa, on the site of Justinian's Church; it bears the inscription: TITO ÆL. HADRIANO. ANTONINO. AUG. PIO. P.P. PONTIF. AUG. D.D.   See Vogué, "Eglises de la Terre Sainte," p. 267; and Jerome, "Commentary on Wisdom," iii.   On the Zacharias story see Jerome's "Commentary on Matthew," which welcomes even an erroneous tradition springing from a righteous hatred of the Jews.   The "perforated stone" of the text was probably the Sacred Rock of the Temple Area, the Es-Sakhrah of the Moslems, the Altar-stone of the old Hebrew temple.   See Delpit, pp. 59, 60.

Mount Moriah, as of a place sacred only to the unbelieving Jews, was complete. Not until the reign of Justinian did any church arise upon the spot; and even then no attempt was made to hallow the spot on which the Temple had once stood.

In describing Jerusalem, our guide, in thoroughly methodical manner, commences with the north end of the Eastern Hill, and then proceeds southwards; crosses the valley above Siloam to the Western Hill; returns towards the north, and leaves the city by the east, on the way to the Mount of Olives and Bethany. He almost certainly saw Constantine's buildings, on the site now occupied by the Church of the Holy Sepulchre; and the Jerusalem of his day must have preserved all the main lines of Hadrian's Ælia.

In the neighbourhood of Jerusalem, as one goes round the city, the pilgrim first notices the pool of Siloam, which stops dead on the Sabbath, "running neither by day nor night for that space;" the house of Caiaphas, where is the pillar of Christ's scourging; the place of the palace of David; the walls of the house of Pilate; the "little hill of Golgotha;" and the crypt where the Lord's body was laid, a stone's-throw only from the hill of suffering. "And there, by order of the Emperor Constantine, a church of wondrous beauty has been built."[1]   But of the seven synagogues that once were to be found in Sion, "one alone remains; the rest are ploughed over and sown upon, as said Isaiah the prophet" (a confusion of Micah iii. 12 with Isaiah i. 8).

On the eastern side of the city, going out towards the Mount of Olives, the pilgrim crosses the valley of Jehosha-phat, and sees the "stone at the place where Judas Iscariot betrayed Christ;" the "tree from which they took branches and strewed them in the way;" and the two "notable tombs" of Isaiah and Hezekiah, king of the Jews. Upon Olivet is

[1] Cf. Euseb. Life of Const. iii. 31.

to be found another of Constantine's basilicas, apparently built to commemorate the Ascension, "over the cave where Christ is said to have taught his disciples ; " close by is the "little hill" of the Transfiguration, conveniently brought from the north of Palestine to the south ; a mile and a half to the east is Bethany, with the crypt of Lazarus.

Next, taking the way to Jericho, we see the sycamore of Zacchæus ; the fountain of Elisha, which once made women barren, but now fruitful ; and the house of Rahab the harlot. Here once stood the city of the Canaanites ; but nothing was now to be seen of it, except the place where rested the Ark of the Covenant and the twelve stones which the children of Israel brought out of Jordan,[1] together with the spot at which " Jesus, the son of Nave (Joshua, the son of Nun), circumcised the children of Israel, and buried their foreskins "—a first outline of the later pilgrim legend of the " hill of the prepuces." [2]

Nine miles from Jericho, continues our guide, is the Dead Sea, of a water most bitter, without ship, without fish, which *turns over* any man who tries to swim in it. Thence to the Jordan, "where the Lord was baptized by John," is a distance of five miles ; and a rock upon the left or further bank of the same marks the spot " whence Elias was taken up to heaven."

On the south, going from Jerusalem to Bethlehem, a journey of six miles, we pass the tomb of Rachel ; and in Bethlehem visit the new church, " built by the orders of Constantine," and enjoy a perfect round of sacred sights, with the tombs of Ezekiel, Asaph, Job, Jesse, David, and Solomon ; while only fourteen miles further on is the " fountain where Philip baptized the Eunuch," at Bethasora

[1] But which were really set up, not at Jericho, but at Gilgal (compare Josh. iv. 20).

[2] " Acervus preputiorum."

(Bethzur, Beit Sûr). Thence to Terebinthus, or Mamre, two miles from Hebron, where the pilgrim can sit under the shadow of the same oak that sheltered Abraham, when he "spoke with angels, and ate food with them," a spot now marked by a "wondrously fair church" of Constantine's. Lastly, in Hebron itself is the great monument [1] in which lie the three first Hebrew patriarchs and their wives— Abraham, Isaac, Jacob, Sarah, Rebekah, and Leah.

Here ends abruptly, without any notice of the sites of Galilee, and with but few allusions, comparatively speaking, to New Testament history, our guide's account of the Holy Land, and what the religious traveller is to visit in the same. The Bordeaux pilgrim now begins again to copy the Antonine itinerary, and giving us a summary of the whole distance from Constantinople to Jerusalem (1164 miles), relapses into his first condition, that of a mere time-table, or mile-record, briefly noting the chief stages of the return journey, which, unlike the way out, is not all by land. And of these notes, the only ones of general interest are the mention of Heraclea in Thrace, where the traveller diverges from his former route to follow the *Via Egnatia* due west through Macedonia to the Adriatic near Durazzo ; of Philippi, or Filibeh, "where Paul and Silas were thrown into prison ;" of Euripidis (Vrasta), "where lies Euripides the poet ;" of Pella (Yenikeui), "whence came Alexander the Great of Macedon ;" and of Aulon in Epirus (Aulona), at the end of the Egnatian Way, where we are to take ship for Italy. A voyage of one hundred miles will land the returning traveller at Hydruntum or Otranto, and from this point his course is easy, by way of Brindisi, Benevento, Capua, and Appii Forum, to Rome. The rest of the way home is only described as far as Milan, and this in the

---

[1] Memoria.

briefest and most cursory manner, without a note of interest upon any place. For the guide-book is business-like to the last. Its object was to indicate the way to and from Jerusalem for Western, and especially for Aquitanian, pilgrims, and to give a short account of the great things that the pilgrim was to see when he had gone so far.

And the notes of the Bordeaux guide-book, as we have pointed out, are not only the first faint signs of Christian interest in geographical movement; they are also the groundwork of most of the narratives of religious travel from Latin Christendom to Palestine during the next three centuries. Nearly all the men who followed upon the path of our Gallic traveller between Constantine and Heraclius must have found his record useful; and very few added much to its solid information. Its mistakes and confusions belong to its character; we can only be thankful there are so few, by comparison with those of later devotees: for the aims of the mediæval pilgrim were simply devotional, and the form or size of the buildings, the exact appearance of the country, which enshrined the objects of his faith, mattered little. He lived in two worlds—the religious and the real,—and the transition was easy from one to the other; sometimes the result was a curious blending of the two.

The fresh impulse given to pilgrimage by Helena and the Bordeaux traveller is seen in the traditional decree of Pope Sylvester I. (335), which announced indulgences for all pilgrims to the sanctuaries of Constantine in the Holy Land, and, above all, to the Martyrium, or Church of the Passion, in Jerusalem,[1] just visited by another person of importance—Athanasius of Alexandria.[2]

[1] Cf. Bulla Pii IV., 9 April, 1561. Cf. Lavigerie, Ste. Anne de Jer. p. 10; Algiers, 1879. (But as yet the original is indiscoverable, as Molinier notes, ii. p. 55.)

[2] Cf. Theophanes, Chron. 5827 (ann. mund.); Eutychius, Annals (Pococke, i. 165).

The Roman legates, Elpidius, Philoxenus, and Gabianus, who in 342 carried the letters of Pope Julius to Palestine;[1] the poor who flocked to Jerusalem from all parts, as Eusebius declares; the other Eusebius of Vercelli, who journeyed to the Holy Land, though under the gentle pressure of an Arian persecution, between 355 and 358;[2] Gaudentius the priest, Syrus the deacon, and Victorianus the exorcist, who accompanied him: and Ursicinus, another Gallic bishop, who followed in 360[3]—all witness to the great advance of intercourse between various parts of the Catholic world, and particularly between the Levant and Western Europe, at this time.

Unfortunately this intercourse, with rare exceptions, did not point to anything beyond itself; knowledge of the world was a very different thing from knowledge of the holy sites: and the close of the seventh century found a greater ignorance of the surface, shape, and divisions of the globe in such great centres of our Western civilisation as Rome, Milan, Ravenna, Narbonne, Bordeaux, or Toledo than had prevailed at any time since the old pagan Empire of the Eternal City took shape in the first century before Christ.

The outlook of the early Church upon geography is more or less clearly indicated by a certain constant and very suggestive habit of the Bordeaux pilgrim. Almost every site of the Holy Land suggests to him some verse of the Scriptures, and often he dwells upon the thought of prophecy fulfilled. Isaiah's word is realised in the synagogues of Sion ploughed over and sown upon; the great stone (seemingly of the south-east angle) of the temple wall

---

[1] Julius, Ep. 342; Mansi, Conc. ii. 1211.

[2] Cf. St. Ambrose, Serm. lvi., Ep. c.; Jerome, De Viris Illustrib. c. 96; and the Anonymous Life of St. Eusebius.

[3] Gallia Christiana, xii. 5; and Eusebius, Ep. ad Presbyteros et plebem Italiæ (Migne, P. L. xii. 947).

has now, indeed, become the head of the corner, he notices
with triumph; the fountain at Jericho now performs what
Elisha had commanded, and aids conception.   Everywhere
the traveller is haunted by his prejudices.   Before he reaches
Syria he knows what he wishes to see, and he sees it without
fail.   In this there is no true exploring spirit : the sentimental interest of the past has quite overlaid the practical
interest of the present.   To this habit of mind certain parts
of the world assume an altogether fictitious importance, and
dwarf everything else.   Directly such a view, implicit in
the pilgrim-journals, finds expression in maps or formal
treatises, we naturally have such distortions as we find in
the " Psalter," " Hereford," and other wheel maps, where the
world centres round Palestine ; where Jerusalem—as large as
Sicily—forms the hub, and the ocean the hoop, of the earth ;
and where the places and countries of the globe are not
delineated according to actual relations, but according to
ideal importance.

II. From Jerome to Justinian—A.D. 370–527.

The pilgrim-travellers of our next group belong to what
may be called the Age of Jerome—to the time when this
great Father exercised so powerful an influence in drawing
devotees to the Holy Land, and especially to his own cell at
Bethlehem.   He is the centre of all the religious exploration
of Western Christians in the Bible-countries during the
last years of the fourth, and the early years of the fifth,
century.   But he was not only the leader, he was also the
candid friend of the pilgrimage now so fashionable.   His
vehement exhortations to friends to retire from the world, in
Bethlehem or some other secluded and peaceful hermitage,
are a commonplace; and we shall have to notice some of

them presently; but it is often forgotten how vehemently, too, he insisted on the danger of sacred sight-seeing. "There is no matter of praise," he writes Paulinus, "in having been at Jerusalem, but only in having lived religiously at Jerusalem.[1] But as for those who say, 'The temple of the Lord, the temple of the Lord,' let them hear the apostle's words, 'Ye are the temple of the Lord, and the Holy Spirit dwelleth in you.' For the kingdom of heaven may be reached from Britain even as from Jerusalem." Gregory of Nyssa[2] went beyond Jerome—he wrote a tract against indiscriminate pilgrimage; and St. Hilarion, during fifty years' life in Palestine, boasted of having only once visited the sacred places. But these examples of moderation were rare. Pilgrims flocked to Syria from every country of the West; and, not content with water from the Jordan, earth from the Sepulchre, or splinters from the Cross, some were said to have gone on into Arabia to see the dunghill[3] on which Job endured his sufferings and disputed with his friends.

Nearly all these travellers go on their journey by the same road, and stop at very much the same point. Only a

---

[1] Jerome, Ep. lviii. 2, 3; imitated from Cicero, Pro Muræna, 12. "Non Asiam nunquam vidisse, sed in Asia continenter vixisse laudandum est."

[2] "De iis qui adeunt Hierosolyma," Works, ii. 1084–1087; cf. Fabric. ix. 120; and Robertson, Ch. Hist. ii. 64, 65. Gregory declared the sight of the holy places added nothing to his faith, while the desperate wickedness of their inhabitants showed him there was no peculiar grace given to those who dwelt there (contrast Jer. Epp. xlvi., xlvii.).

In the same way Claudius of Turin, the famous "protestant" bishop of the ninth century, wrote against the pilgrimages of his time (Migne, P. L. civ.); not, however, absolutely condemning them, as their effects were different with different persons. To the same effect speaks St. Augustine. Do not meditate lengthy journeys; it is in loving, not in journeying that one travels to Him who is everywhere: [for the Lord has not said, Go to the East for justice, or fly to the West for pity]. See Augustine, Epp. clv., lxxviii.; Serm. I. De Verb. Apost. Petri; and Serm. III. De martyr. verb [disputed].

[3] Chrysostom, Ad. pop. Antioch. Hom. v. 1 (t. ii.).

few have left us any record of their own journey; but a
large number of names are quoted—for instance, in Jerome's
letters—to prove the now triumphant attractions of religious
devotion.   And among these pilgrims of the " second age,"
the first of any importance is Jerome himself (372), quickly
followed by Melania the elder,[1] who went to Jerusalem in
373, and, as Jerome asserts, gained the surname of Thecla
" from her virtues and miraculous humility."   A later
tradition adds the story of her founding, with the help of
her friend Rufinus of Aquileia, a monastery near Jerusalem,
in which she lived herself, with fifty others, for seven and
twenty years.[2]

One noticeable feature in the pilgrim movement of
Jerome's age is the prominence of women in the same.
The fiery controversialist, whose friendships with his fellow-
men were so strictly dependent on the agreement of their
opinions with his own, was perhaps never more at ease than
with the submissive admiration of that innermost group of
his Roman friends, which largely consisted of certain noble
ladies.   Submissive we may fairly call it, for Marcella's
playful trick of disputing with the Father about the meaning of various texts was hardly more serious than the
theological dissent of Catherine Parr from the infallibility of
Henry VIII.   As time went on, several members of this
circle (which included Paula and her daughter Eustochium,
the two Melanias, Rufinus the Church historian, and Fabiola
a descendant of Quintus Maximus, all Pilgrims in their time)
left Rome, and, not content with visiting the Holy Sites of
Palestine, stayed there for good, in cells and convents, often
constructed by their own labour and at their own expense.

---

[1] Jerome, Epp. iv., xxxix., xlv. ;
Chron. A.D. 377; Paul. Nola. Epp.
xxxi., xxxii., xxviii., xxix., xlv.

[2] Vincent of Beauvais, Spec. Hist.
lib. xvii. c. 89 ; xviii. 99 ; xix. 35.

Thus Paula undertook the erection of the great monastery at Bethlehem for Jerome himself; Melania the elder devoted herself to the service of some exiled[1] monks at Sepphoris; Melania the younger lived for fourteen years in a cell on the Mount of Olives: all died in Syria. And some of these devotees were disposed to regard the fate of Marcella as almost a retribution. Devout Christian as she was, she had hung back from the pilgrimage which would have perfected her virtues; the time went by, and she perished in the sack of Rome by Alaric. Nor is it wonderful that women such as Paula, even apart from her imitation of Jerome, should have found a home, for a season at least, in the Levant. At one time or another she had helped to entertain many of the most prominent men of the Eastern Churches. Epiphanius of Cyprus, Paulinus of Antioch, Isidore of Pelusium, Theophilus of Alexandria, were all guest-friends of hers, and all seem to have been visited by her in the course of her pilgrim journey. Family affliction was often an important, sometimes a determining element in the pilgrimages of these Roman ladies. Just as Constantine's execution of his son Crispus, and his wife Fausta, was probably an immediate cause of the journey of St. Helena, so friends urged upon Paula the deaths of husband and daughter, and upon Marcella the loss of her mother, as decisive reasons for seeking the consolation of pilgrimage.

The journey of Silvia of Aquitaine was in all likelihood connected with something of the same kind; and the enthusiastic devotion of these women in the century that elapsed between Helena and Eudoxia did much to spread the custom of pilgrimage,[2] and to combat the old prejudice

---

[1] Exiled from Nitria in Egypt during the persecution of Valens.

[2] This prejudice, however, continued to be felt against the specially Jewish site of Mount Moriah till Justinian's day, and even he did not venture to build on the site of the Temple; but raised his church at the south-east angle of the Noble Sanctuary.

against Deicidal Palestine, against the country that had rejected and killed the Divine Saviour of mankind.

But we must now look at the memoirs of Jerome's friends and disciples in more detail.

Another pilgrim of the same time is Philastrius, bishop of Brescia,[1] whose visit is usually put under the year 375; but Julius Honorius, writing in 376 a description of Palestine, is not to be counted, any more than Julius Æthicus or the other and probably later Æthicus Istricus, in the roll of Christian travellers, and what he says is only, and very slightly, interesting to geographical *science*.

In 380,[2] Caprasius of Lerins, Honoratus, afterwards Archbishop of Arles, and his brother, Venantius, who died on the way, may be added to the list of Gallic pilgrims; and about the same time occurred the important journey of Silvia of Aquitaine, or whoever else is the author of the "Peregrination" that bears her name.[3] Among all the devotees whose memoirs form our best commentary on the Bordeaux guide-book, this one is the most enterprising and instructive. Nearly half a century after the first Christian traveller from Southern Gaul had described the overland route to Syria and the wonders of the Holy Land for his fellow-pilgrims, another, starting from the same part [4]

---

[1] Acta SS., July iv. p. 387.

[2] Acta SS., 1 June, i. p. 78; 16 Jan., ii. p. 18; May, vii. p. 241.

[3] Text first given by Gamurrini, 1883–7; first in English, by Bernard, in ed. of Pal. Pilg. Text Soc., 1891.

[4] For though the name is conjectural, we may be sure that the author of the "Peregrination" was a "Roman" from Southern Gaul. Cf. (1) the comparison of the Euphrates with the Rhone (p. 48); (2) the words of the Bishop of Edessa—"De extremis terris venires ad hæc loca" (pp. 48, 49); (3) the explanations of Greek phrases in Latin, *e.g.* pp. 45, 46, 56; (4) the use of peculiar words and constructions of South-west Gallic dialect of Latin, agreeing, *e.g.*, with Prosper of Aquitaine, as *quod* in sense of *quando; eo quod* for *acc. with infin.* after verbs of narration, and expressions *perdicere, peraccedere, consuetudinarius.* Cf. Wölfflin and Geyer, Archiv für Lateinische Lexikographie, pp. 259, 611; and Mommsen in Sitzungsberichte der Berliner Akademie der Wissensch., 1887.

of the world, reaches Palestine by way of Egypt and Arabia, after a series of journeys now lost to us. It seems probable that Silvia went by sea from Gaul to Egypt, and in the same way from Alexandria to Constantinople; and that she then made her way by land from the Bosphorus through Asia Minor. What we have left of her journey discovers her at " Sinai, the mount of God," from whose summit the pilgrim saw " Egypt and Palestine, and the Red Sea and the Parthenian Sea, which leads to Alexandria, and the boundless territories of the Saracens; " from this point she journeyed slowly through the deserts of Stony Arabia to Suez and the land of Goshen, to Rameses and the " city of Arabia," [1] on the Red Sea. So far she had been escorted by a guard of Roman soldiers; but now, dismissing these as needless on the great military road from Pelusium to Syria, she pressed on to Jerusalem "through the several stations in Egypt, by which we had formerly taken our course, . . . and which I had seen when I was before at Alexandria and in the Thebaid." [2]

Having spent some time in the Holy City, Silvia set out for Mount Nebo, in Moab, to the east of the Dead Sea.

---

[1] Page 39 of original manuscript. " Arabia " is the Thuku of the Hieroglyphics, Thou of the Romans; where the road to Clysma (Suez), in the Antonine itinerary, left the main track from Memphis to Pelusium; cf. Herod. ii. 158 (. . . τὴν Ἀραβίην πόλιν). In Rameses, Silvia sees two colossi, which she thinks are statues of Moses and Aaron, and a sycamore tree, planted by the patriarchs, and called the " Tree of Truth," which cured any one who plucked off a twig of it.

[2] The places in Arabia and Egypt mentioned by Silvia are (pp. 31–40) *Sinai* and *Horeb, The Bush, Taberah,* " where the children of Israel lusted for food," *Faran, Clesma* or *Suez* (*Goshen Land*), *Epauleum* or *Pihahiroth, Migdol, Belesfon* or *Baal-Zephon, Oton* or *Etham, Succoth, Pithom, Heroöpolis,* " where Joseph met Jacob, his father," the city of *Arabia, Rameses, Taphnis* (*Tanis* or *Zoan,* or possibly *Tahpanhes* (?)), and *Pelusium.* It may be noticed that the pilgrim's references to the Old Testament all follow the Septuagint pretty closely, and that she shows no knowledge of the Vulgate.

Starting from Jerusalem, "and journeying with holy men," she "arrived at that place of the Jordan where the children of Israel had crossed." A little higher up the river was the spot "where the children of Reuben and Gad and the half-tribe of Manasseh had made an altar, where Jericho is," and crossing the stream, the pilgrim came to the "city called Livias,"[1] in the "plain where the children of Israel encamped, under the mountains of Arabia above Jordan." The "foundations of that camp and of the dwellings of the people" were duly seen, and then the travellers went aside about six miles to see the water flowing out of the rock "which Moses gave to the children of Israel," before they made the ascent of Nebo. The greater part of the mountain could be accomplished, they found, "sitting on an ass," but there was one piece that had to be performed "laboriously on foot." At the summit they were, of course, shown the tomb of Moses, —a comfort to weak brethren who might have fancied, as Scripture said, that "no one knew where he lay;" and in the prospect from the topmost peak, Silvia saw the "most part of the Land of Promise," and the "whole Jordan territory and all the land of the Sodomites and Segor (Zoar)." Also "the place where was the inscription about Lot's wife was shown to us: but believe me," continues the pilgrim with an outburst of candour, "the pillar itself was not visible, only the place is shown. The pillar itself is said to be covered in the Dead Sea. We saw the place, but no pillar; I cannot deceive you about this matter." The bishop of the place, however, said that it was only a few years since the pillar was visible, and later pilgrims did not agree to this quiet renunciation of a venerable site; two hundred years after Silvia, travellers not only saw and touched the pillar, but knew all about its past.[2]

---

[1] The *Liviada* or *Salamaida* of Antoninus Martyr, ch. x.

[2] Heshbon (Esebon) of the Amorites and Sasdra (Edrei) the city of Og,

After the grave of Moses, Silvia naturally wished to see the grave of Job, in the region of Ausitis (Uz). So she took her way from Jerusalem to Carneas,[1] the city of the patriarch, on the borders of "Idumæa and Arabia." On the outward journey she passed the "city of Melchisedek" at Salem, above the bank of Jordan. Here were to be seen "ancient and vast foundations;" hard by was the "Garden of John" (Baptist), and the valley of the Cherith, where the ravens fed Elijah; while just beyond, the "parts of Phœnicia" suddenly came into view, with a "lofty mountain (Hermon?) which extended a great distance." In Carneas itself, all doubt about the grave of Job had been lately put to silence by the discovery of a stone, found after a little digging, with the name of the patriarch neatly carved upon it.[2]

Returning again to Jerusalem, and having now seen all the holy places, Silvia had a mind to visit her own country once more. But first of all she wished, God willing, to go to Mesopotamia, for the holy monks were said to be numerous there, and of such blameless life as baffled description. Besides this, she longed to pray at the tomb of St. Thomas at Edessa. There is no Christian, proceeds Silvia—whose religion at least gave her the resolution to travel where few women, at any time, would have cared to venture—there is no pilgrim who has journeyed as far as Jerusalem, and does not also wend his way thither (to Edessa).[3] "And since from

king of Bashan, were also pointed out from the Mount of Promise, as well as the Hill of Balak and Balaam, and the delighted but unsatisfied wanderers now returned for a short breathing space, to Jerusalem (pp. 41-43).

[1] "Formerly called Dennaba," the Dinhabah of Gen. xxxvi. 32, and really in Bashan; apparently Ashtaroth-Carnaim, near the "home of Job" at Sheikh Saad. It was the traditional belief of the early Christians that Uz lay at this site, where Job's stone is still shown, and not in Edom or in Arabia proper where the O.T. "Land of Uz" must be looked for. (Cf. Wilson, appendix to edition of Silvia in P.P.T.S., p. 146.)

[2] Cp. pp. 44-47.

[3] Cf. Cureton, "Early Syriac Documents relating to Christianity in Edessa."

Antioch it is nearer to Mesopotamia, it was convenient for me, as I was returning to Constantinople, and my way was through Antioch, that I should go from thence." [1]

So she set out, and travelled through the stations of Cœlesyria and Augusta Eufratensis, to Hierapolis. Fifteen miles further she reached the " great river Euphrates, rushing down in a torrent like the Rhone, but greater ; " and passing this, and entering Mesopotamia, came to Bathanis, or Bathnæ in Osrhoëne, a " place swarming with inhabitants ; " and finally to Edessa, the city of Thomas the Apostle, and of Abgarus, the correspondent of Jesus Christ.

The "memorial" of Thomas, Silvia found, had been *lately rebuilt* (viz. under Valens, in A.D. 372); and in the palace of King Abgar she saw a statue of the prince in marble, " which shone as it were of pearl," and the letters that had been sent " by the Lord to him, and by him to our Lord." Already the story was full grown, of the immunity of the city from all hostile attack by the virtue of these relics : the letter of Christ had cast darkness upon the eyes of the Persians when they came to besiege it ; and the same power had caused fountains of water to burst forth in the town and supply the besieged in their need. All this was explained by the bishop to Silvia, who had known something of it before, " but indeed the account I received here is more full." Copies of the sacred letters she already had in her country, but now she had gained a whole commentary upon their meaning. For " blessed is the stronghold wherein thou abidest, Edessa, mother of wise men, which by the living mouth of the Son was blessed ; this blessing shall abide in her till the holy one be revealed." [2]

After three days in Edessa, Silvia, " still advancing,"

---

[1] Cp. pp. 47, 48.
[2] Ephraem Syrus, Testament | (Assemani's ed. ii. 399). Cureton Syriac Docs. 152.

went on to Abraham's Charræ, or Haran, a city where, except clergy and monks, " all were heathen." [1]   Still it was not deficient in relics—the " house of Abram ; " the wells of Rebekah and Eliezer, of Rachel and Jacob ; and the " farm " of Laban the Syrian. These only whetted the pilgrim's appetite for more : and she asked for " that part of the Chaldees where Terah dwelt first with his family."   But here, at last, her energy was checked ; the place was only ten stations off, by way of Nisibis, but there was " no access for Romans," for " Persians held all the country " since Julian's fatal attack in the summer of 363.[2]   To atone for this disappointment, Silvia feasted her eyes on the great stone that Jacob rolled away from Rachel's well, on the home of Laban in Fadana (Padan-Aram), on the place where Rachel stole her father's idols, and, above all, on the " unheard of piety " of the monks and solitaries, living all around.

Here Silvia had gone more than 2000 miles from her home, reaching the extreme limits of the Roman Empire, and in one or two places actually passing them, both in Arabia and Mesopotamia.   She had now spent quite four years in travel, and yet had no intention of giving up her quest.   Her religious enthusiasm is unbounded : everywhere she seeks out clergy and monks, whose condescension amazes her—they deign with willing mind to receive her insignificant self, to guide her from one point to another, to admit her to salutation, all undeserved, to show her the holy relics and the famous sites.   Yet she must have been a

---

[1] Page 51.   A very unusual notice with Silvia, who always consorts with the Christian clergy, and has no dealings with the natives, never alluding, for instance, to the lay population of Syria, Egypt, Palestine, and Asia Minor, except in the case of a few garrison towns and forts and some titles of provincial governors.

[2] The words of her guide, "Modo ibi accessus Romanorum non est," by themselves imply that this part of the country had only been lost very recently, pp. 52, 53.

person of consideration [1]—her Roman escort in Arabia, the
frequent kindnesses of governors, the attentions of bishops,
all seem to prove this: as she herself confesses, the way
was made smooth to her; "everywhere she saw what she
purposed." In rank she is probably a parallel case to the
noble Roman matron, Paula, the friend of Jerome: but in
travel for religion's sake, as we have said before, she scarcely
has an equal among these early Christian pilgrims.[2] Scarcely
any other takes us to so many different parts of the East
"for love of the Faith and of the monks;" scarcely any other
conforms so little to the accepted types, which most pilgrims
reproduced with only an addition of legendary wonders.

Through the mist of marvel and miracle in which Silvia,
like other devotees, continually moved we are generally
able to perceive some solid ground of fact, some actual piece
of travel accomplished. Even her credulity is more restrained
than the ordinary traveller's. Her distortions of fact are less
violent: the wilder legends, as in the case of the pillar of Lot's
wife, she either omits or expressly denies. Had all our records
of religious travel been written by persons of her own class,
who had enjoyed some of the profane learning and worldly
enlightenment lacking in many of the pilgrims, we should
have a very different light upon the path we are following.

[1] On these grounds, Gamurrini
has suggested that our author was
St. Silvia, of Aquitaine, a sister of
Rufinus, Prefect of the East under
Theodosius I., whose journey from
Jerusalem to Egypt is recorded in
the "Historia Lausiaca" of Palladius.
But that ascetic, who boasts (Hist.
Laus. p. 143) of not having washed
for sixty years, except the finger tips
for communion, and never travelled
in a litter, presents some inconsistencies with the writer of this peregrination, who would have gone up

Mount Sinai in a chair if she could
(p. 32), and rode up the last part of
Mount Nebo on an ass (p. 42).

[2] "From the portion which alone is
left to us, it seems probable that the
peregrination as a whole furnished
a more clear, intelligent, extensive, and independent account of
the Christian holy lands than any
other writing of this class and
time." See Geyer, Kritische Bemerkungen, 1890; Comptes rendues Ac.
Inscr. et B. L., 1885.

But to return.   Haran was Silvia's furthest : from this point she made her way back to Antioch, and so by the great military road [1] through Tarsus, Isauria, Cappadocia, Galatia, and Bithynia—"provinces I had passed through on my outward journey."   At times she was in some danger from the brigand Isaurians, as she had been before from the Bedouin Saracens, both being " very mischievous and given to robbery ; " but she escaped with persistent good fortune, although, to visit a famous shrine, she was always ready to run risks that most pilgrims would have shunned.   Finally, when safely housed in Constantinople, she registers a vow, after worshipping in the churches of the imperial city, to " go to Asia " (and especially to Ephesus), for a further pilgrimage ; and if, after this, she were still in the body and able to acquaint herself " with any more of the (holy) places," she promises to keep a full record of the same for the benefit of the sisterhood in Gaul, whom she had left to come to the East, and for whose benefit she writes.

The rest of her home letter is entirely taken up with an account of the services and ritual of the Church of Jerusalem, especially during holy week, and in the course of this we find one of the earliest references to the festival of " Palm " Sunday and to the Christian use of incense.   In all this we cannot follow St. Silvia—although this latter part of her book is of as much value to students of liturgies and ceremonial as the earlier part is to students of geography,—except to notice that the pillar of scourging, the holy wood of the Cross, Solomon's ring, the horn of anointing, and the various churches of Constantine's building are mentioned among the sights of most importance to the worshipper in the Holy City.[2]

[1] The route of the Bordeaux pilgrim.   Cf. Silvia, 54, 55.

[2] The " great accuracy " of Silvia's account of Sinai has led Sir C. W.

Silvia's journey may be fixed, as we have said, to the years between 379 and 385.[1] At this latter date, Jerome was in Palestine for the second time, and settled at Bethlehem,[2] where he became the leader, guide, and friend of all Western pilgrims, their chief correspondent, their principal attraction. His fiery appeals gave a new impulse to religious travel, and the presence of such a figure, " glorious throughout the world," [3] and directing, to a great extent, the fortunes of the whole Church from a cell in Judæa, could not possibly have been ignored by any visitor to the Holy Land in the next thirty years (385–415).

Sabinian the Deacon, from Italy (about 390), though an unsatisfactory sort of Christian, according to Jerome ; Paula and Eustochium from Rome (386), invited by the saint of

Wilson, perhaps, to attach overmuch topographical importance to her travels in Egypt (on the other side is Naville; cf. his Goshen, pp. 19, 20), but all her descriptions unquestionably bear the mark of personal experience. She saw all the places she writes about, and very probably " compiled her account from notes written on the ground."

[1] Several reasons for this may be pointed out ; as, *e.g.*—

1. The allusion to Persians holding all the country about Nisibis (pp. 52, 53) seems to point, as already noticed, to a date later than 363, when this territory was ceded to the Persians by Jovian ; and the wording of the passage, " Modo ibi accessus Romanorum non est," makes, as we have seen, for a recent transfer of possession.

2. The church of St. Thomas of Edessa, described as " newly rebuilt " (nova dispositione), was finished under Valens, A.D. 372.

3. Edessa and all the rest of the East was quiet when she visited it. This would make it probable she was there *after* Valens's persecution of the Catholics, ended by his death in 378.

4. The Bishop of Edessa, mentioned as a *confessor* (p. 48), was probably Eulogius, who died in 387–8, and had been put out of his see by Valens. Cyrus, his successor, suffered no persecution whereby he could gain this title. He translated the tomb of St. Thomas to the great church in 394 ; whereas Silvia seems to make the " martyrium " quite distinct, as would be the case of a visitor arriving *before* 394.

5. There is no mention of Jerome, who settled permanently in Palestine in 385, and was the main object of interest to all pilgrims from that time.

[2] Cf. Jerome's Epp. xiv., lxxiv., cxvii., lxvi., lxxxi., lxxxii.

[3] Prosper of Aquitaine, Chron. pt. ii. ; cf. Migne, P. L. li. c. 586.

Bethlehem in his usual fervent style—for whether in love
or hate, Jerome left nothing to be desired in the cordial
vehemence of his language;—and Gaudentius, bishop of
Brescia, who visited Jerusalem about 390, were all representative of this new "Hieronymic" class of pilgrims.[1]

And of these journeys, that of Paula and Eustochium
(386) is especially commemorated in the "Letter to Marcella about the holy places." The chief point of this is a
rhetorical justification of pilgrimage. What man could
learn Greek or Latin properly without a stay in Athens or
in Rome? What Christian could be reckoned a master in
religion without a visit to the Holy Land? This was felt
by every one. "Whoever may be a leading man in Gaul,
hastens thither [to Palestine]. Even the Briton, separated
as he is from our world, seeks the place known to him
by general report as well as by the word of the Scriptures.
And why should we speak of Armenians, of Persians, of the
peoples of India and Ethiopia, of Egypt, fertile in monks,
of Pontus and Cappadocia, of Syria and Mesopotamia, who
come by one accord to these sacred places, according to the
Saviour's word, 'Wheresoever the body is, there shall the
eagles be gathered together.' "[2]

The language, indeed, of this pilgrim host is different,
but the religion is one. Holier, indeed, is this place,
continues the letter, speaking more narrowly of Bethlehem,
than the Tarpeian Rock at Rome, so often struck by
lightning—an evidence of the wrath of God. The virtue
of Palestine must atone for the wickedness of Italy. Pagan
Rome was the Babylon of the Apocalypse; and though the
Church of the Eternal City had the trophies of apostles and

---

[1] Cf. Jer., Epp. xlv., lxxxvi., cxlvii.,
etc.; Gaudentius, Sermon xvii., in
Migne, P.L. xx. 964; Acta Sanctorum,
July iv. 383.
[2] cc. 1, 2.   (Jer., Ep. xcvi.)

martyrs, the true confession of Christ, and the faith preached
by his messenger, yet the size, and stir, and distractions of
so great a place were enemies to the life and peace of a monk.
But here, in Bethlehem, in Christ's village, was "nothing
but quiet country life, a quiet unbroken except by psalms."
A Puritan might have envied the picture that is drawn
to attract Marcella. It is like a realised kingdom of the
saints. "Wheresoever you turn, the ploughman, holding his
plough, sings loudly his 'Alleluia.' The sweating reaper
diverts himself with psalms, and the vine-dresser, as he lops
the vine with his sickle, chants something of King David's.[1]
These are our love-songs here, these are our pastorals, our
weapons in our war of husbandry." Cannot such a prospect
draw Marcella from the throng of Rome? Would it not be
glorious to visit the Lord's tomb together, to weep with
sister and mother, to ascend with the risen Christ from
Mount Olivet, to pray in the tomb of David and of Abraham,
to set eyes upon the Jordan, to adore the ashes of John
Baptist and of Elisha, to kiss the wood of the Cross?[2]

What the Bordeaux pilgrim had left unnoticed, Paula
invites Marcella to do—to go to Nazareth and "see the
flower of Galilee," to Tabor and "visit the tabernacles
not[3] of Peter," to set eyes upon the Sea of Gennesareth
and the town of Nain, the hill of Hermonim and the torrent
of Kishon; above all, upon Capernaum, the favoured spot
of the Lord's miracles.[4]

Paula and Eustochium have seen all this, and their tract
on the holy places is simply an "open letter" to Latin
Christendom, addressed to one intimate friend by name,

---

[1] Elsewhere Jerome gives an account of a storm at Bethlehem, which
draws a different picture of the
state of the city.

[2] cc. 3-7.
[3] A "non" expunged by later pilgrims.
[4] C. 8.   See Delpit, pp. 116-129.

but looking beyond this to a general migration of Catholic Christians to the old home of their religion.

Nearly twenty years after the writing of this appeal, Paula's own journey to the holy places, upon which the same appeal was based, is separately and lengthily described by Jerome himself.[1] The saint's friendship with this enthusiastic and high-born lady, like Hildebrand's with Countess Matilda, was famous throughout the Christian world of that day, and seemed to satisfy the monastic ideal of a spiritual marriage, a higher state than the physical union of the sinful children of this world.

Paula had given up " houses, lands, and children," for " the gospel's sake," and in spite of the appeals of " brother, friends, and son," embarked at Rome for Palestine, with a " piety not to be conquered by entreaties."　With Eustochium, her only companion, she passed the island of Pontia, celebrated as the prison of " that noblest of women, Flavia Domitilla," under the Domitian persecution, and sailing by Rhodes and Cyprus, touched the Syrian coast at Seleucia, the port of Antioch.　From this point she followed the route of the Bordeaux guide-book along the coast, " admiring the ruins of Dor, a city once most powerful," and visiting Joppa, famous, " from the fables of the poets," for the rock of Andromeda.　Thence, going up the country to Jerusalem, the Roman pilgrim passed Bethoron, Ajalon, and Gibeon, " where Joshua fought with five kings, and gave orders to the sun and moon ; " and was welcomed in the Holy City, as a lady of noble rank, by the governor, " who knew her family right well."　She visited the Sepulchre, the relics of the Cross, the column of scourging ;[2] and, going

---

[1] Ep. lxxxvi. [= 108 in Migne], written in 404 ; referring apparently to journeys of 385–6.

[2] At this very time Prudentius was celebrating in his verses (Dittocheum, 121–124) the " corner-stone of the first temple, which survived the ruin of the second."

on to Bethlehem, declared, in Jerome's hearing, that she
"saw with the eyes of faith" the Divine child in the
manger, the magi, the shepherds, the star, and all the
wonders of the gospel of the childhood, as if actually before
her sight.   From Bethlehem, Paula moved on to Hebron,
and stood by Abraham's oak, "beneath which he saw the
day of Christ and was glad;" then, by Engedi and Mount
Olivet, to Jericho and the "hill of circumcision."   After
this, in Central Palestine, the "peregrination" began to
take something of a more marvellous character.   While in
Samaria, Jerome's friend, in her own words, saw "devils
writhing and yelling in different kinds of torture; and men,
before the tombs of the saints, howling like wolves, barking
like dogs, roaring like lions, hissing like serpents, bellowing
like bulls.   Here women also had hung themselves up by
the feet." [1]   She prayed for these unfortunates, and went on
into Galilee, where, says Jerome, "daylight would fail me
sooner than words, if I were to go over all the sites that
venerable Paula now came to with a devotion beyond
belief."   So he brings her, with a stroke of the pen, to
Egypt, Alexandria, and Nitria, the "home of monks," on
which last name the saint puns a little: "Nitria, in whose
pure *nitre* of heavenly virtues the stains of many are daily
washed away."

Here Paula was in her element, and she revelled in
monastic humilities.   "Whose cell did she not enter?   At
whose feet did she not cast herself?"   Here, "forgetful of her
sex and weakness," she would have stayed, had not the longing for the soil of Palestine drawn her back to Bethlehem.

Yet we may remember that while so large a proportion of
the Christian world was devoting itself to religious ecstacies,

[1] Cf. cc. 15, 16; Delpit, "Essai sur les Anciens Pèlerinages," pp. 96–116.

the Empire was breaking up. Six years after Jerome's first visit to Palestine, the Goths overthrew Valens at Adrianople (378); less than ten years before Jerome's death, Alaric sacked Rome (411). The saint of Bethlehem himself admits that the inroads of the Barbarians had largely increased the number of the religious travellers, and especially of those ladies from Rome, who now "filled all the cities" of the Levant. The pilgrim movement that he championed may have been towards a heavenly country; but it hardly strengthened the defence of his earthly fatherland. To his pagan enemies, it seemed as if the " worship of the cross had eaten out patriotism." [1]

After Paula's journey, news from the far West came to Palestine again with Eusebius of Cremona, who seems to have visited Jerome about the year 394, and with the letters he brought from Amandus, presbyter of Bordeaux; [2] while, in his next budget of letters (under the year 395–6), the hermit of Bethlehem notices [3] the arrival of Fabiola and Oceanus from Rome, of Vigilantius from Gaul, and of Paulus and Sysinnius from North Africa (397 ?). In 398 Zenon the shipmaster brought Jerome letters from Italy, but hardly seems to have made a pilgrimage. As a letter-carrier, the saint complains, he had been grossly remiss.

Next year some copyists [4] came over from Spain (399) to help Jerome in his work: in 400 Theodorus, returning from Alexandria to Rome, visits the great doctor of the Roman

---

[1] Nor was Jerome the only famous counsellor of pilgrims and pilgrimages in this age. In the same spirit, and about the same time, St. John Chrysostom, while at Antioch, indulged in vigorous pulpit exhortation to intending or reluctant visitants, and in warm commendation of those who had performed the duty. Cf. Migne, P. G., lvii. 74; lv. 221, 242, 274; and xlix. 191.

[2] Jer. Epp. lvii., liv., lv.

[3] Epp. lxxvii., lviii., lxi., cii., cv., lxxii.

[4] Jer. Ep. lxxv. (Migne, P. L. xxii. c. 688).

Church at Bethlehem, and Vincentius, the priest of that same Church, who had accompanied Jerome[1] on his second pilgrimage in 385, is again heard of in Palestine. About the same time, Alexius of Rome,[2] according to a doubtful story, travels to Edessa, adores the miraculous napkin, and is found by his own children sitting among the beggars of the town—found, but not recognised. An extraordinary amount of interest was roused by the journey of Alexius : later authorities brought him to Jerusalem ; poems in Latin German, and French, of various metres, celebrated his humility ; and a whole group of English " Alexius legends " took shape in the fourteenth and fifteenth centuries, in material interesting to philologists.

The journey of Postumianus,[3] in or about the same year 400, which saw so great a concourse of pilgrims wending their way to Syria—from Narbonne to Carthage, from Carthage to Alexandria, from Alexandria to Bethlehem and Jerusalem,—is one more witness to the importance of Jerome's stay in the Holy Land as a *point d'appui* for pilgrims ; and the same is proved by his complaints of the constant flow of letters to him from the West, and the demands for his full and immediate answer to one and all.[4]

The early years of the fifth century, like the closing years of the fourth, show St. Jerome's influence at its height.[5] Frequent notices are preserved of the intercourse between Rome, Hippo Regius, Alexandria and Bethlehem

---

[1] Jer. Ep. lxxxviii.

[2] Acta SS., Jul. iv. pp. 238–270, esp. p. 252; and Vita S. Alex. (Anonymous), It. Hi. ii. 97–106.

[3] Migne, P. L. xx. 183, etc.

[4] " Uno ad Occidentem navigandi tempore tantæ a me simul epistolæ flagitantur, ut si cuncta ad singulos velim rescribere, occurrere nequeam "

(Jer. Epp lxxxv.).

[5] Avienus' (c. 401–450) description of the Holy Land, in the course of his Descriptio Orbis terræ, has no concern with pilgrim-travel. But see the note of Marcus Diaconus, in his Vita S. Porphyrii, on " Ægyptii *Mercatores* " (c. viii. § 58; Acta SS. Feb. iii. 655).

during these years,[1] and in one letter [2] the saint alludes to
monks from India, Persia, and Ethiopia arriving daily in
the Holy City and its neighbourhood in such numbers as to
cause some confusion.   Thus, in 403, one Firmus,[3] a priest,
brings a letter from the women of the nation of the Getæ,
outside or barely on the borders of the Roman world.[4]

About this time (405) occurs, moreover, an apparently
independent pilgrimage from the extreme north-west of
Spain.   Turribius, a bishop of Astures in Galicia,[5] near
Cape Finisterre, went to Jerusalem, was entrusted by the
patriarch with the charge of some relics, and, learning in a
dream that the Holy City would fall into the hands of
unbelievers, carried them off—with or without the consent
of the patriarch, does not appear—and housed them in a
shrine at the Monte Sacro of his own native district (S. Maria
de Monte Sacro).[6]

In 406 three visitors from distant parts are noticed in
Jerome's letters : Sisinnius, a Spaniard, sent by Exuperius,
bishop of Toledo ; [7] Ausonius a Dalmatian ; and Apodemius
a Gaul, "from the furthest parts thereof," who came to
Bethlehem by way of Rome.   In 409 a second visit of
Melania is recorded,[8] and another attempt, not fully accomplished, of Rufinus of Aquileia ; an impassioned exhortation
to pilgrimage, dating from the same year, is to be found in
the letters of Paulinus of Nola.[9]

Next comes a journey of Avitus [10] the Spaniard (of Braga),

---

[1] *E.g.* Jer., Epp. xcix., cxiv., cxii., cvii.

[2] Ep. cvii.

[3] Jer. Ep. cvi.

[4] The same Firmus seems to have been employed later (in 405) in the correspondence between Jerome and Augustine ; Jer. Epp. cxv., cxxxiv. ; Aug. Ep. lxxxii.

[5] Brev. Ast. Vetus (Acta SS. 16 Apr. ii. 422).

[6] The fame of this exploit was especially preserved at Palentia ; L. M. Siculus, lib. v. De rebus Hispanicis.

[7] Præfatio in Zach. ; Jer. Epp. cxix., cxviii., cxx.

[8] Paul. Nol. Epp. xxix., xxxi.

[9] P. N. Ep. xlix.

[10] Migne, P. L. xxxi. 1214, li. 913, lviii. 1085.

reported by Orosius in 409 or 410; in 411 occurred an attack of the Saracens[1] upon Palestine, which now seems ominous in the light of later history; in 412 came the famous visit of Pelagius, the British heresiarch, famous, however, mainly in the story of theological controversy.[2]

In 414 a company of noble women from Gaul was compelled by "fierce storms of enemies" to go "through Africa" to the Holy Land;[3] and, in 415, Paulus Orosius, the historian, the friend of Augustine, the "religiosus Juvenis" of his Epistles, who had been in Palestine already during the time of Pelagius' visit, passed to and fro with letters between Jerome aud Augustine.[4] He was a Spaniard, and was credited with a great service to the Latin Church. For he was the first who transported the relics of St. Stephen to the West, after their rediscovery about this time in Palestine; and he brought the account of this new "invention," as translated by Avitus from the original Greek of Lucian the discoverer, to Rome, and Carthage, and Hippo.[5]

The year 417 was marked by some important pilgrimages, about which a good deal has been written, especially those of Paula and Melania the younger. The latter of these, in the anonymous life of St. Melania, recently printed[6] from a manuscript in the Paris library, is the most considerable and detailed of all the minor pilgrim-notices of the first six centuries.

Starting from Rome, and sailing by Sicily, the travellers were caught by storms and driven on to a hostile coast, made prisoners and in danger of worse, when they were

---

[1] Jer Ep. cxxvi.

[2] But interesting as a very early journey from so distant a corner of the Roman world as Britain; Migne, P. L. xxxiii. 762, xxxii. 649, xliv. 359, etc., li. 271, etc., xxii. 1165.

[3] Jer. Ep. cxxx.

[4] Aug. Ep. clxvi.; Jer. Ep. cxxxiv.

[5] Bede De VI. Ætatibus Mundi. (And see Migne, P. L. cvi. c. 1243.)

[6] Anonymus Coævus, Vita S. Melaniæ; Bib. Nat. n. acq. lat. 2178.

rescued by the local bishop, who had heard of the fame of their journey. Thence they escaped to the shore of Africa, near Carthage, and coasted along to Alexandria, where they were received by St. Cyril. From Egypt they went on to Jerusalem, being encouraged to persevere by the words of Nestor of Alexandria, "a man full of the spirit of prophecy." "The end of toil," he told them, "completes your joy. The sufferings of this time are not worthy to be compared to the glory that shall be revealed in us."

In Jerusalem they were alarmed at hearing that the barbarians had broken into Spain, where Melania's brother seems to have had possessions; and she proposed to him that they should return to Egypt, and pray for God's mercy from the monks—"My lord, let us go and see our lords, the holy servants of God, that they may succour us by vision and prayer." After this visit of devotion they are again found in Jerusalem,[1] where Melania's mother died, and then in Northern Syria, at Tripolis, seemingly on the way to Constantinople,—where the narrative breaks off abruptly, giving no account of the rest of the journey, or of the death of Melania, both which are believed to have been in the original record.[2]

Jerome died in 420, and in the same year, St. Petronius, bishop of Bologna, erected in his own city, on his return, an imitation of the Church of the Holy Sepulchre, after measurements and notes which he had made on the spot. While in Jerusalem he had erected a sumptuous monastery on the top of Olivet; he travelled over Egypt, and won the favour of the Emperor Theodosius II.; his Italian

[1] For a stay of fourteen years.

[2] Her story of a pious but unsuccessful fraud, by which she tried to bestow a few coins upon one of the solitaries who prayed for her family, leaving them in a corner of his cell while his attention was distracted, reminds one in different ways both of Silvia and Willibald.

buildings stood till they were burnt in an invasion of the Hungarians.[1]

About the same time (420–430), the relics of St. Jerome themselves became an object of veneration;[2] in 431 a certain Germanus, a presbyter from Arabia, is heard of at Jerusalem in the course of a very long journey to Gallicia in Spain; and a little later, another imperial pilgrimage attracted some attention. This was undertaken by Eudoxia,[3] the wife of Theodosius the younger, the spiritual daughter of Melania, in 438 (or '9): and the complete story of this, as we have it in Vincent of Beauvais, finds here the origin of the festival of St. Peter ad Vincula, in Rome.[4] For Eudoxia, it was said, had the good fortune to unearth the relics of the apostle's chains, of which the filings became in time so favourite a papal present to devout monarchs.

An extraordinary story of an attempted pilgrimage,[5] at this epoch, comes from Isidore of Seville. The devil appeared under the form of Moses to the Jews of Crete, and offered to lead them to Palestine through the sea, upon dry land—thus destroying many. This legend pleased the taste of later times: Godfrey of Viterbo has a poem upon it, and allusions to the story are frequent in mediæval hagiology.

To the same period[6] belongs the tract of Bishop Eucherius of Lyons (434–450), "On Some of the Holy Places " (" De Aliquibus Locis Sanctis "), written as a letter to the priest Faustinus.[7]   But this appears not to be a record

---

[1] Acta SS. Oct. ii. 459, 464.

[2] Migne, P. L. xxii. 302, 304; li. c. 880.

[3] Migne, P. L. li. c. 926; Evagrius, H. E. I. 21.

[4] Spec. Hist. lib. xx. c. 37.

[5] Circ. A.D. 439, Isodore, Chron. c. 109; Migne, P. L. lxxxiii. 1052.

[6] Circ. A.D. 440. In 441 he attended

the First Council of Orange as Bishop of Lyons.

[7] A priest of the monastery of Insula Barba. The importance of this letter to Palestine topographers is that it disproves the theory that the " Dome of the Rock " was erected by Constantine over the tomb of Christ.

of an actual journey, so much as an epitome of what the author had "heard or read about Judæa, and the site of Jerusalem." It is only upon " *certain* of the holy places," after all; and slight as is the exploring interest in most of these Christian travellers, by the side of the devotional, it is more than Eucherius gives us.   There is nothing in his pamphlet but an enumeration of the wonders of Jerusalem itself, with a mention of Hebron, Joppa, Dan, Panias, Bethlehem, Jericho, the Dead Sea, and the Jordan—whose upper course above the Sea of Tiberias he seems to know nothing about, giving us instead thereof the information— so often repeated in these pilgrim-travels,—" The Jordan is so-called, because two fountains join to give rise to it, and of these one is called *Jor*, and the other *Dan*."   On the other hand, Eucherius shows a little more caution than some devotees, in his notice of the " Church on Olivet where Christ is *said* to have preached," and the place " from which tradition tells us He ascended."   It is interesting, moreover, to compare the almost total absence of relics in this account of Jerusalem with their only too abundant presence in the " Breviary " of a century later (c. 530).

From Vincent of Beauvais [1] we now have the doubtful story (referred to the middle of the fifth century) of James of Britain, who following in the track of S. Ursula and the Eleven [Thousand] Virgins, is ultimately made Archbishop of Antioch ; and to the same time is referred the curious tale of merchants carrying letters between Simeon Stylites,[2] who now replaces Jerome as the great attraction for Palestine pilgrims, and various friends and correspondents of his in Spain, Gaul, Italy, and Britain.

The remaining notices of Christian travel in the fifth century are of very slight interest, and of these the

[1] Spec. Hist. xx. 42.   [2] Acta SS. Jan. i. pp. 140, 263.

" Descriptio Parrochiæ Hierusalem " (c. 460) is perhaps the most important. Yet this is a mere enumeration of place-names, giving us a list of the Churches subject to the four metropolitan sees of Cæsarea, Scythopolis, Petra, and Bostra, which together composed the patriarchate of Jerusalem; and it has been plausibly supposed,[1] therefore, to com-memorate the recent erection of Jerusalem into a patri-archate by the Council of Chalcedon (451).

Beside this, there is little indeed to record during the last sixty years of the fifth century. The " legacies " of the great popes of the time to Eastern bishops, councils, and synods do not bear on our subject, except in the most incidental way; and the only individual case of Western pilgrimage which is worth mentioning, is that of a Gallic bishop, Licinius, reported by Gregory of Tours [2] as if in or near the year 490.

A certain number of allusions occur to the visits of devout Romans, chiefly ladies, as in that of the year 500, reported in Ethiopic tradition. A journey of the Emperor Zeno is mentioned, on doubtful authority, as occurring in the Annus Mirabilis,[3] which saw the extinction of the Western Empire of Theodosius and his sons; but such a journey, even if authentic, has but slight interest. It does not represent any particular movement, and it breaks no new ground. The same sterility is observable in the notices of the early sixth century, before the Age of Justinian, the next great period of pilgrim-travel; but in 514 or 515 is placed the legendary pilgrimage of Arthur of Britain. The earlier Latin story of this in Nennius,[4] brings the King

---

[1] It. Hi. pref. *ad loc.*
[2] G. T. Hist. Fr. ii. 39, x. 31.
Licinius was eighth in succession
after St. Martin (It. Hi. ii. 177).

[3] 476 A.D.
[4] Nennius De Sex Ætat. Mundi;
cf. Coll. de Chroniques Belges, ii.
214; It. Hi. ii. 190, 191.

merely to Palestine; the later, and ever more and more imaginative, accounts (in Old French) take him to Saxony, Africa, Antioch, and Hungary besides: but the whole thing, both in earlier and later versions, hardly comes into serious history at all.

A little more like fact sounds the tradition of the pilgrimage of the patron saint of Wales,[1] David, archbishop of Menevia (c. A.D. 518), though it is attributed to direct angelical instigation, and David is said to have been endowed, like the "apostolic band," with divers languages, that he should not have to employ the earthly and degrading offices of an interpreter. The story is also connected with a curious tale of reviving Jewish activity in Palestine,[2] reaching such a pitch that the Welsh strangers were appointed by the Patriarch of Jerusalem to preach against Judaism; but the whole matter is of uncertain authenticity, and we can do no more than note the tradition of the visit, and point out, that, if true, it is a pilgrimage of an unusually ambitious character.

Somewhere between 518 and 523, St. Avitus, bishop of Vienne, sends to Jerusalem to beg for relics;[3] and about 520 one Peter goes from the Latin Church of North Africa; but nearly all the pilgrim-notices of this time are Greek, Arabic, Armenian, and Levantine, for of Western travel to the Holy Land there are very few traces just now.[4]

---

[1] It. Hi. 192–200; Acta SS. March, i. p. 44.

[2] Cf. Giraldus Cambrensis, V. S. Dav. lect. vii.; Anglia Sacra, ii. 637.

[3] It. Hi. ii. 201 (Av. Ep. xviii.); Migne, P. L. lix. cc. 236, 239.

[4] A certain Cerycus, general of the Roman army, who appears as a pilgrim of the year 527, seems to have been regularly employed in Eastern service, as in the war against the Persians; but the tradition of his Latin origin is doubtful (It. Hi. II. 206).

CHAPTER III.

THE PILGRIMS, FROM JUSTINIAN TO MOHAMMED—

CIRC. A.D. 527–600.

BETWEEN the time of Jerome and the time of Justinian, as we have seen, our travel-documents are of a very slight nature. But with that reconstruction of the Christian Empire which is the central fact of the sixth century, these records assume a far greater length and importance. Except for St. Silvia's journey, none of the earlier memoirs of religious wandering have given us much more than devotional appeals or bald itineraries. With the same exception, too, our pilgrims have practically confined their interest to a few places in Palestine west of the Jordan, telling us scarcely anything about the east beyond the sacred horizon of Syria, or the Jordan valley. And, again, the mythological tendency has been in want of one or two daring inventors, of men of genius like Antonine the Martyr, whose peregrination we have now before us. To understand how the Dark Age system of sacred geography reached the perfection we find in some Western maps of later time, we need something more systematically deceptive than the rhetoric of Jerome or the slow accumulation of the mistakes and confusions of practical travellers. In the period of Justinian we may see an important advance towards the shaping of that religious conception of the visible world which we have noticed as fully developed in theorists like Cosmas the monk, and in the artificial symmetry of mediæval maps. This Bible-geography, as we have said, gave to Palestine a quite fictitious size and position as the central country of the inhabited earth; and it developed purely traditional sites, like Eden, or the resting-place of the Ark, or the tree of the Virgin Mary in Egypt, into important landmarks, that were to determine the position of more prosaic regions, like France, or Italy, or Greece. Thus legend, as it grew more powerful, assumed authority over science; fiction over fact. The Age of Justinian also witnessed a great extension of commerce between the Roman Empire and the further East. In his reign and under his auspices, silk-worms were brought from China to the West, by Persian monks in the service of their co-religionists, against the interests of their fellow-countrymen, who had long enjoyed the monopoly of this trade. Intercourse also with the Ethiopian Christians of Abyssinia was largely developed; "Roman" merchants penetrated almost to the equator in their company,[1] in search of gold, emeralds, and spices; and, through the Christian missions of India, a footing was gained in Malabar and in Ceylon, where a pioneer of Western enterprise, in Cosmas' day, challenged his Persian rivals to a comparison of the coins and claims of their respective sovereigns. The renewed intercourse between the eastern and western parts of the Empire under Justinian, and the restoration of the "Roman" rule in Africa, Italy, and Southern Spain, may be our apology for a somewhat detailed examination of a commerce and a geography which are really Greek in language and Byzantine in character. For, in attempting to describe the system of a Cosmas and the trade-developments of his time, in subsequent chapters, we shall be taken away from Latin records, and shall be occupied more with writings of the eastern

[1] Cosmas Ind. ii. pp. 137, 138, 140–143; xi. 337–339 (Montfaucon).

Mediterranean than with those of the western; but the inter-connection of religion, the place of Cosmas as a defender of Augustine against the heresies of the Greeks, and the temporary reunion of so much of the Western Church and State under a sovereign reigning at Constantinople, are reasons enough for this digression. In other words, we must take account of the peculiarly Roman character of the Byzantine Empire under Justinian, who completed the codification of Roman law; as well as of the undoubted influence of Byzantine commerce and geographical science on the Latin world of this age.

For since the time of Jerome the Roman Empire had utterly collapsed in the lands west of the Adriatic, never to be restored except as a dependency of the New Rome on the Bosphorus, or as a Germano-Italian kingdom, half-Frankish, half-ecclesiastical and papal. With the triumph of Islam in the seventh century, Latin and Greek are again separated, more decisively than ever; and in the eighth and ninth centuries the schism of the Churches completes that estrangement of the kingdoms which lasts to the Crusades: but, in the period we have reached, the undivided Church and the restored Empire give a unity to all the enterprises of trade, of religious proselytism, or of science, undertaken in the names of Christ and of Rome.

But to return to pilgrimage. We may dismiss as purely legendary the wild Ethiopian story of Justinian [1] meeting with the King of Abyssinia and the patriarchs of Constantinople and Alexandria in Jerusalem, at some unfixed date between 528–565; and we may pass over the notices of the emperor's buildings in Palestine and of St. Saba's great foundation [2] in the Kedron gorge ("Mar Saba,") as belonging

[1] It. Hi. ii. 207.
[2] It. Hi. ii. 207, 209, and Procopius on Justinian's Buildings. P.P.T.Soc.

has published a translation of part of this.

to topography rather than to exploration or travel of any sort. In this way we shall come at once to the *Breviarius de Hierosolyma*, or "Short Account of Jerusalem," written apparently somewhere in the years 527–530, which gives us a brief outline of notable things in the style of Bishop Eucherius, but with a far greater admixture of legend. Short as is the account, it is packed full of news for the relic-seeker. He is told of the "holy lance, made of the wood of the Cross, which shines at night like the sun in the glory of the day;" of the "horn with which David and Solomon were anointed;" of the "ring of amber, with which Solomon sealed his books;" of the "earth of which Adam was formed;" of the "reed and sponge, and the cup of the Last Supper;" of "*the* stone with which Stephen was stoned;" of the crown of thorns, the identical "lamp" of the upper chamber, and the "rod of scourging, enclosed within a silver column." But apart from this catalogue of marvels in a distant part of the world, the "Breviary" has very little to do with Christian travel, though perhaps it throws some light on certain developments of Christian doctrine.

Under the year 530,[1] another doubtful Welsh pilgrimage is reported. Like King Arthur, one Saint Cadocus (son of the King Gundleus), who had become bishop of Beneventum, went, according to his own statement, thrice to Jerusalem; to say nothing of seven journeys to Rome, and one, at least in intention, to St. Andrew in "Scotia" Like St. David, he was relieved of the trouble of learning the different tongues of the countries he traversed; the Lord giving him the knowledge he required. For when did a Welsh traveller ever come behind the very chiefest of the elect?

[1] It. Hi. ii. 211, Acta SS. Jan. ii. p. 604; Capgrave Nov. Leg. Angl. (1516), f. liii. b.

About the same time was written the book of Theodosius, "On the Position of the Holy Land," with which has been coupled a quite distinct tract, "On the Way of the Children of Israel."[1] The former is essentially in the nature of an itinerary, and the historical and other notes are incidental; but, such as they are, they offer a good deal of suggestive material. We know little enough about the author, who is described as archdeacon in one manuscript, and deacon in another, but without any further detail; and it cannot be said that Gildemeister's conjecture (from § 56), that he came from Northern Africa, because he alludes to Vandal and Roman monasteries in Memphis, throws much light on the subject. The date of the work, however, may be fixed as Tobler has assigned it, viz. to about A.D. 530, for various reasons. It seems to have been used by Gregory of Tours, who probably refers, in his tract, "On the Glory of the Martyrs,"[2] to our pilgrim's descriptions of the tombs of St. James, Zacharias, and Simeon, on Olivet (in § 50); and to his account of the meeting of the streams under the town of Baneas (in § 13); of the warm springs of Livias (in § 65); and of the miracle at the place of St. Clement's martyrdom, where the sea every year retired in reverence from the spot (in § 54). Again, while Theodosius is acquainted with the buildings of Anastasius at Jerusalem, he does not notice those of Justinian.

He begins by describing the gates of Jerusalem; then, passing to Jericho and Gilgal, speaks of the field where our Lord ploughed one furrow with His own hand, and of the twelve stones lifted out of Jordan by the children of Israel. Thence by Scythopolis, "where St. Basil suffered martyrdom," to Magdala, where the Virgin was born; to the seven

---

[1] De Situ Terræ Sanctæ et de Via Filiorum Israel. The refs. here are to | Gildemeister's edit. of Theod. (1882).
[2] De Glor. MM. i. 17, 18, 27, 35.

fountains, where Christ "baptised the apostles;" and to
Baneas, where the Jor and Dan met under the city to
form the Jordan,—whence also came the woman healed of
the issue of blood, named Marosa,[1] who made, afterwards, an
amber statue [2] of the Lord.

In Joppa the pilgrim may see where the whale threw
up Jonah; sixteen miles from Jerusalem is the place where
Philip baptized the Eunuch; one mile only from Olivet is
the village where Abdimelech, the disciple of Jeremiah,
"slept under the fig-tree for six and forty years." [3]   It was
at the place of Calvary,[4] or, rather, at the bottom of the
mountain that Abraham offered up his son, close to where
the Lord was crucified, and buried, and rose again, and
where His cross was found.   Barely two hundred paces
from Golgotha is the Church of Sion, which Christ founded
with His apostles; it was formerly the house of Mark the
Evangelist.   The pillar at which the Lord was scourged is
now in Sion; [5] it was once in the house of Caiaphas, but, at
Christ's bidding, it followed Him, and upon it are imprinted
the countenance, chin, nose, and eyes, the arms, hands, and
fingers of the Sufferer as He clung to it.   In the pool of
the Sheep-market is still to be seen the bed [6] of the palsied
man; and here Theodosius introduces the story of James,[7]
"whom the Lord ordained bishop with His own hand,"
being thrown down from a pinnacle of the temple, and
"in no wise harmed," till a fuller killed him with a blow
from a pole.   James, Zacharias, and Simeon, he adds, all

---

[1] Possibly a corruption of αἱμαρ-
ῥοουσα (Luke viii. 43).

[2] The fame of this marvel in after
days spread to "France," and
Gregory of Tours preserves a mention
of it; cf. Theod. cc. 1, 2, 7–14; and
G. T. De Glor. MM. i. 21.

[3] Caps. 24, 30, 39; Jerem. xxxviii.

7, xxxix. 15, 16.

[4] It may be noticed, in ch. 42,
Theodosius makes a distinction between Calvary and Golgotha.

[5] Caps. 40–43, 45.

[6] C. 48.

[7] C. 50.

lie together in one monument, constructed by James himself.

Here the pilgrim's rough jottings quit Palestine abruptly, and he tells us of the memorial of St. Clement at Cherson,[1] on the Black Sea. Here the saint had been drowned, with an anchor round his neck; but once a year, on his birthday, the sea now retired for a space of six miles, to allow the faithful to celebrate the anniversary, and any one who touched the martyr's anchor was freed from demons immediately, however much vexed by them before. At Sinope, again (mentioned as if near Cherson), the traveller must note the spot where Andrew delivered Matthew from prison, and hence, adds the itinerary, we come to Armenia.[2]

Next, we are taken to Egypt, to Memphis, the city of Pharaoh and Joseph, where we are told of two monasteries, of Vandals and Romans,[3] under the invocation of St. Jeremiah and St. Apollonius the hermit. Thence to Cappadocia, to Cæsarea, and Sebaste; to Galatia, to the cities of Gangra, Euchaita, and Anquira,[4] all famous for monuments of martyrs; and to the "mountain of Armenia," whence flow Tigris and Euphrates. "And of these, the former waters Assyria and the latter Mesopotamia," while, of the other streams of Paradise, Phison irrigates Ethiopia, and flows through to Egypt, while Geon waters Evilath (or Havilah), and passes near to Jerusalem[5]—a confusion of the pool of Gihon with the rivers of Eden.

In his next section, Theodosius returns to Palestine and the "Lord's field" in Galgala, watered by the fountain of Elisha, and bearing every year about six bushels, more or

---

[1] On the west side of the quarantine harbour of Sebastopol: cf. Bernard's note; and Gildemeister, pp. 21, 22.
[2] Caps. 54, 55.

[3] = Arian and Catholic (?), c. 56.
[4] Ancyra or Angora. Gangra is Changra; Euchaita, Chorum.
[5] Caps. 57–62.

less. For minute accuracy is, perhaps, not to be had in such details; but our traveller will come as near the truth as he can. A "vine, that the Lord planted" close by, provided wine for the Communion at Pentecost quite regularly, and some of this was sent to Constantinople at the proper season. Across the Jordan, twelve miles from Jericho, is Liviada,[1] where Moses struck the rock, and departed from this life. Here, too, are warm springs, where Moses bathed, which heal lepers even to this day. At the place of Christ's baptism, Theodosius speaks of a church, built by Anastasius, the emperor; and on the other side of the Jordan he tells us of the little mount of Hermon,[2] where Elijah was taken up to heaven. Five miles from this point we come to the Dead Sea, the plain of Sodom, and the salt-pillar of Lot's wife, which waxes and wanes with the increase and decrease of the moon—a refinement which is at least ingenious. But there is more than ingenuity in all this: there is precision enough to satisfy the most doubtful.

Upon a certain stone of Mount Olivet the imprint of Christ's shoulders is plainly to be seen, as upon soft wax. Theodosius is very properly dissatisfied with only one marvel of this kind, in the case of the column of scourging.[3] Still more remarkable are the little hills found along the lower course of Jordan, which, when the Lord descended to baptism, " walked exultingly before him," as David said; " the mountains skipped like rams and the little hills like young sheep." And even to this day, adds the observer, they look as if in the act of jumping.

From the extreme south of Palestine we now go to the

---

[1] Caps. 64, 65. The Livias of Silvia, now Tell-er-Ramah. Cf. Sir C. W. Wilson's note in P.P.T. ed.

[2] Caps. 66, 67, 70.

[3] Caps. 71, 72.

extreme north, to Sarepta of Phœnicia, and to Sidon, near Mount Carmel. Thence we pass as suddenly to Arabia, where Theodosius tells us of the thirteen cities[1] destroyed by Joshua, and following on this we get an order of countries according to geography—first Canaan, "where is Jerusalem," then Galilee, then Syria, then Mesopotamia, and (on the left of these) Armenia "first and second," and Persarmenia, "all which[2] are subject to the emperors." In the Province of Asia,[3] Theodosius next remarks, apropos of nothing, is Ephesus: "where are the seven sleepers," and, still leaping from province to province, we have to follow our guide to Mount Sinai;[4] to Infra, "where Moses fought with Amalek;" to Elusa, three stations from Jerusalem; to Glutiarinalia, "built by Alexander the Great of Macedon;" and to the stone of the Virgin,[5] three miles outside the Holy City, on which St. Mary sat, and which the wicked Urbicius tried to carry off. For Urbicius, major-domo of the imperial palace,[6] once ordered the sacred block to be transported to Constantinople. But at St. Stephen's Gate, in Jerusalem, it could be moved no further, and so men made it into an altar for the Holy Sepulchre. Nor did this avert the doom of sacrilege. When Urbicius was buried, the earth would not hold his corpse, but three times did the grave cast him forth.

From this, Theodosius flies off to Mesopotamia, and tells us about the city of Dara, built by Anastasius to guard the

---

[1] Vincta, Volunta, Medeba, Musica, Philadelphia, Gerasa, Genara, Bostra, Damascus, Gadara, Abila, Capitolias, Astra.

[2] Text is ambiguous: "que Armenie sub imperatore sunt."

[3] Caps. 73-76.

[4] Infra is Phara (Feiran); Elusa =Khalasah: cf. Ant. M. 35 and 40: see note in P.P.T. ed.

[5] Caps. 77, 78, 80.

[6] This is what text comes to: "There was a governor of the Empire called Urbicius, etc." "Urbicius dicebatur præpositus imperii, qui ad vii. imperatores præpositus fuit, et coronas ipsis imperatoribus in capite imponebat, et ipse eas de capitibus eorum deponebat, . . . et ipse eos castigabat."

frontier against the Persians; thence he moves on to Persarmenia, to Persia, and to Babylon, where monsters quite excluded man, according to the report of Eudoxius the deacon.[1] The tract concludes with notes on the province of Cilicia and the notable cities therein,[2] and a series of distances on a sort of journey from Tarsus to Antioch, and from Antioch to Edessa, Dara, and Amida.

In all this it is rather difficult to believe that we have the record of any actual journey, and not rather a collection of statements from the writings or the talk of other men. For there is no sign of personal knowledge in these scraps; the distances given are constantly and recklessly inaccurate. The account, in particular, of the Gihon seems entirely from a misreading of authorities; and the story of the Pillar of Salt counts against any real visit to the Dead Sea. In view of the geographical mythology that became so developed later, it is interesting to find Theodosius alluding to Jerusalem as "the navel[3] of all the region (of Judæa)," an earlier form of Arculf's Navel of the World and of the wheel map-schemes which put the Holy City in the centre of the earth-circle. But no one of our travel-documents is more difficult to deal with than this. The account of Palestine in the earlier part is fairly orderly, though fragmentary and rather like a bad attempt at book-keeping by double entry : but later, with the mention of St. Clement's memorial at Cherson, the tract becomes hopelessly confused, and seems to have no method of dealing with the various places it mentions, the transitions being as startling as in a modern examination-paper for school geography.

[1] Caps. 81–83.

[2] Particularly the city of Ægaea, "where for forty days traffic is carried on, and no demand is made, but if after the forty days a man is found transacting business, he pays the fiscal dues."

[3] Pref. (not in Gildemeister's Recension).

With the book of Theodosius is associated the wholly
different treatise, " On the Route of the Children of Israel," [1]
which, however, may be assigned to about the same date, and
which is chiefly occupied with historical and theological
controversy about the passage of the Red Sea. And this is
not so called, proceeds the author, because the water is red,
but because all the land round about is of that colour, and
so is everything that can be eaten swimming in the waves
thereof. There, too, men find red jewels. And of the two
parts of the Red Sea, we are told, the eastern is called the
Persian Gulf, because the Persians live on the shore of it;
the other is the Arabian Gulf, because it looks towards Arabia.

For the passage of the Israelites, moreover, through the
Red Sea, the writer is not content with one division of
the waters, but makes twelve, one for each tribe,[2] " as the
vehement blast of wind brought it about; " for the rest,
he merely transcribes the list of stopping-places between
Egypt and Palestine from the Pentateuch, with a few
elucidations of his own—as where he tells us that when the
Israelites reached the Land of Promise, the sons of Lot
destroyed the giants, the sons of Esau the Horites, and the
Cappadocians part of the Hivites.

A steady flow of Italian pilgrims to Syria is reported,
upon unusually good evidence, as happening in or about this
same year 530,[3] when St. Isaac, abbot of Spoleto, and St.
Herculanus, afterwards bishop of Perugia, were the leaders,
it is said, of a company of more than three hundred pilgrim-
travellers.[4]

---

[1] Circ. A.D. 530.

[2] Though he mentions the Hebrew
tradition that the Israelites did not
cross at all, but merely went along
the shore.

[3] Cf. It. Hi. ii. 211.   Pope Gregory

I.'s Dialogues, iii. 14; Fabricius,
Bibl. Gr. xi. 114; Acta SS. April ii.
pp. 28, etc.

[4] But great uncertainty hangs
about most of the names recorded,
except the two mentioned above, and

Some time before A.D. 533, one St. Berthaldus of Chaumont, a reputed son of Thealdus "king of Scotia," and a certain Amandus,[1] a hermit from the diocese of Rheims, and (either then or a little later) Cosmas Indicopleustes himself, are said to have visited Jerusalem. The latter's mention[2] of the pilgrimage of certain Æthiopian merchants to Palestine is curiously confirmed by a later allusion in Antoninus of Placentia; and his exceptional place in the history of geographical theory and of pseudo-science makes his (probable) journey unusually suggestive. Unfortunately it is only a probability. The journeys of the legates[3] of Pope Agapetus in 536, and of "Pelagius, deacon and apocrisiarius" of the Roman see, to Antioch and Jerusalem in 540 are concerned with matters of ecclesiastical politics; and with these exceptions we get hardly anything during these years of Western travel to the Levant; for the notices collected by the laborious editors of the "Itinera Hierosolymitana" are almost wholly of journeys from the Greek-speaking lands of the nearer East, from Constantinople or from Egypt, and these pretty well destitute of geographical interest.

In 550 we come again upon one of the ever-doubtful British[4] records. One Petroc, an abbot from Cornwall, is reported to have set out, in that year, upon a long-promised pilgrimage to Rome, after Divine admonitions of stormy weather for his delay; from Italy he went on, like the legates of Æfred in 883, to Jerusalem, and proceeded still further towards India.[5]

---

it is doubtful whether many of these devotees suffered in the third century under Diocletian, or travelled in the sixth under Justinian.

[1] Acta SS. Jun. iii. pp. 98, 99.

[2] Cosmas, xi.; Migne, P. G. lxxxviii.

c. 53, 499; Ant. Mart. c. 35.

[3] It. Hi. ii. 216–218.

[4] Acta SS. Jun. i. p. 401; Capgrave, Nov. Leg Ang. (1516), f. 266b.

[5] It is a little off our track, but it is curious that in the same year as

About the same time, men "of many nations" are vaguely said to have flocked to Syria to visit the wonder of the age, the younger Simeon Stylites, glory and crown of the pillar saints.[1] Among these "nations" various Westerns must, of course, be included.

The terrible earthquakes (from July 9, 551, to August 15, 553) which shook the whole of the Phœnician coast and upland are noticed in Antoninus Martyr, and may have roused a fresh interest in pilgrimage, touched with terror, among Latin Christians; but there is no evidence of their immediately increasing the stream of religious travellers —rather the reverse. Till 560 we get no more notices of Western pilgrimage, and then it is only of the journey of a Spanish Saint Martin, archbishop of Braga.[2] His epitaph, composed by himself, speaks of him as a humble imitator of Martin of Tours,[3] and locates him in Pannonia and Gallicia,

" Pannoniis genitus, trancendens æquora vasta
Galliciæ in gremium divinis nutibus actus,"—

while Gregory of Tours makes him take ship at Oporto, on an earlier pilgrimage to the relics of his great namesake and patron in Gaul. The same authority brings him to the holy places of the East, makes him one of the most learned men of his time, and settles him finally as a bishop in Gallicia.[4]

occurs this story of *British* pilgrimage (550) Elesbaan, king of Ethiopia, is said to have sent envoys to the Holy Sepulchre from the other extremity of Christendom, to lay his crown at the feet of Christ (It. Hi. ii. 226; Acta SS. Oct. x. p. 758). Were these, by any chance, the Æthiopians whom Antoninus met?

[1] It. Hi. ii. 226; Acta SS. May v. 343-394, etc.

[2] It. Hi. ii. 229; Acta SS. March iii. p. 89; Greg. Tours, De Virt. [or, Mirac.] S. Martini, i. c. 11.

[3] Who died c. 290.

[4] Greg. Tour. Hist. Franc. v. 38. "Martinus," says pseudo-Isidore, in Migne, P. L. lxxxiii. c. 1100, " *Dumiensis* monasterii sanctissimus pontifex, ex *Orientis* partibus navigans, in *Galliciam* venit."

One other trace[1] of Western pilgrimage is supposed to be discoverable in the same year 560 or 561, but this is a very shadowy "Anonymus Gentilis ex Occidente," who cannot be further traced.

We must not here notice at any length the work of Procopius "On the Buildings of Justinian," in Jerusalem and elsewhere,[2]—its relation to the immediate subject of this chapter is too distant; but we are now nearing the time of Gregory of Tours, and the latter years of the sixth century accordingly give us an unusual amount of material partly gathered from his pages.

First of the allusions in question comes that to St. Tygris (or Thecla, A.D. 562–593)—a woman of Maurienna,[3] in Savoy, whose journey is associated with that of some monks from the same city. Prostrate in prayer, she passed most part of three years at the Holy Sepulchre, seeking, as a sign from God, for some part of the body of the Great Forerunner. At last, in despair, she lay for seven days and nights without rising from the pavement—meaning not to stir till she had obtained her request. While on the point of perishing of hunger and exhaustion, the miracle was vouchsafed,[4] and a thumb of the saint appeared to her.[5] At the beginning of her travels she was encouraged to undertake the journey by the visit of some Irish monks, who passed through Maurienna on their way back from Jerusalem to "Scotia,"

---

[1] It. Hi. ii. 231.

[2] It. Hi. ii. 231; Procop. De Ædificiis. Like the similar work of Eusebius, "On the Buildings of Constantine," it is useful for Palestine topography; and it gives details about the frontier fortresses of the Empire which show a good geographical knowledge of the Roman world, as it was in about A.D. 550.

[3] Maurienna = St. Jean de Maurienne, near Grenoble ("inter Alpes," as It. Hi. ii. 236).

[4] Greg. T. De Gloria MM. i. c. xiv.: "Apparuit super altare pollex miri candoris ac lucis effulgens."

[5] This happened in the days of King Gontram, adds the office of St. Tygris. It. Hi. ii. 232–234.

and who told her where the relics might be found. Her journey lay through Rome and the "threshold of the apostles;" and after her return such wonders were wrought in Maurienna by the newly recovered relics, that three bishops from neighbouring towns, notably Turin, came to see them and the saint who had brought them.

Another and later account brings Tygris and her relics into "Normannia,"[1] still another to Mauritania; but to explain how the Church of S. Jean de Maurienne gained possession of a certain bone that purported to come from Syria is the main point of the story, which, after all, is of a very doubtful authority and date.

Hardly less doubtful is the account, not found in Gregory of Tours, of the journey of St. Germanus,[2] bishop and prefect of the city of Paris, to Jerusalem and Constantinople, where he obtained a collection of relics from Justinian, instead of gold and silver, "which he spurned."

Rather more certainty attaches to the next of our pilgrimages.

In 569 the historian of the Franks[3] reports the journey of Reovaldus or Reovalis, and others, sent out by Queen Radegund through the whole of the Levant to collect relics, of which a great number, especially from Jerusalem, were afterwards to be seen in Poictiers.

And now we come again to an important traveller, to Antoninus of Placentia, whose journey, in or about the year 570, shares with Silvia's peregrination the credit of being the most extensive, curious, and suggestive of all the pilgrim-records before the rise of Islam. His "Perambulation" is also the last of pre-Mohammedan journeys

---

[1] It. Hi. ii. 236, 237.
[2] Acta SS. May vi. 778; April iii. p. 111.
[3] Greg. T. De Gl. MM., i. 5; It. Hi. ii. 239.

of any note, and in it we find the superstition and muddle-headedness of its class developed more fully than in any previous example : it may be a question, too, whether its inventive faculty is not as strongly marked as its ignorance ; and whether Antonine may not take rank as a man of genius, who contributed somewhat towards the mythology of geography. The title of "Martyr," attached to the author, is probably from a confusion with an earlier pilgrim whom we have noticed already ; it is pretty certain that our present traveller has no right to the name. But we know nothing definite about him, though there seems little reason to question that he really made his journey, as he records it, at the end of the Age of Justinian, and that he came from " Placentia on the Padus," the starting-point of so many earlier pilgrims. Moreover, it may be granted, as probable, that he was a priest, or professed "religious" of some sort, secular or regular. The friends he mentions— John, husband of Thecla, his companion and fellow-towns-man, and the Lord Paterius his fellow-countryman—seem to be only known from his notice of them.

Among the extraordinary blunders which have given support to the doubt whether Antonine really went to the East at all, are the identifications of Neapolis with Samaria (c. 6) ; of Gadara with "Galaad," or "Gabaon" (c. 7) ; of Azotus with Lydda, or Diospolis ; and of Cæsarea Philippi with Cæsarea on the coast (cc. 25, 46) : the placing of Scythopolis, or Bethshan, "on a mountain," though actually in a plain (c. 8) : and the daring assertions that nothing will float in the Dead Sea (c. 10), and that the Kedron runs into the Jordan (c. 24).[1] Over and above

[1] Cf. Sir C. W. Wilson, pref. in P.P.T.S. edit. ; also F. Tuch's study, "Antoninus, seine zeit und seine Pil-gerfahrt," Leipzig, 1864 ; Geyer's essay, "Kritische und Sprachliche Erläuterungen zu Anton ..." 1892 ; and Gildermeister's edition of the text of Antoninus (1889) ; the most valuable of recent contributions.

these pleasantries, the towns he mentions in his visit to Egypt are named in the wrong order (c. 43), and the same applies to his notices of the cities of Syria (c. 46). A corrupt text, with the bad memory and exceptional carelessness of the original writer, who (in c. 22) confesses that he had quite forgotten the relics shown him in the Church of Sion, and (in ch. 32) attributes Isaac's wells at Beersheba to Jacob, may be explanation sufficient of a good many of these mistakes; but in the case of some we can hardly doubt that Antoninus shaped his tale to please and astonish his readers, who were only too glad to believe where they could not trace.

On the other hand, the passages where the pilgrim records, for instance, his conversation with the Bishop of Berytus upon the recent earthquakes (c. 1), his bathing in the fountain of Chana (c. 4), the death of his companion at Gadara (c. 7), the bringing home of certain dates for Paterius (c. 14), the passage of the desert (c. 36), and the visit to the city of Phara (c. 40) are all fairly good evidence for the reality of his journey.[1]

Antonine's style and language are of the simplest; he is entirely without literary and rhetorical form, and his choice of words is meagre; the same expressions are constantly repeated; and the whole narrative is written in the late "vulgar" or colloquial Latin, in which most of our pilgrim-records are cast, and to which even Silvia is only a partial exception.

With all its shortcomings, however, this perambulation, as we have pointed out already, gives us glimpses of a broader world, and of a more active, if not a more intelligent

---

[1] Points that occur only in Antoninus are, *e.g.*, (1) the Spring of Chana, c. 4; (2) Bahurim, c. 16; (3) the Steps to Siloam, c. 24; (4) Majumas of Ascalon, c. 33.

secular interest than any other of the pilgrim-journeys of
the sixth century, and these merits may be set off against
its obvious defects—a rather grovelling literalism, a very inaccurate recollection, and a strong belief in magic, witchcraft, and diabolical possession.[1]

From Italy Antoninus went to Constantinople, at a time
(c. 560–570) when the overland route must have been
extremely dangerous from the raids of Lombards, Avars, and
Gepids. From the imperial city, again, the traveller came
by sea to Cyprus and Syria, landing at the "Island of
Antaradus,"[2] and thence proceeding to Tripolis, destroyed
by an earthquake in the time of Justinian—probably in
May, 526, or in July, 551. In the first of these disasters
Antioch was overthrown, as Cosmas tells us;[3] in the latter,
Beyrout was shaken; but in which Tripolis suffered is
uncertain. Visiting Byblus, Trieris (Tridis?), and the
"most magnificent" city of Beyrout, the pilgrim everywhere discovered traces of the recent catastrophe, which
had ruined the "School," or "University," of the aforesaid
Beyrout, and destroyed thirty thousand people.

Next, in Sidon, clinging to the slopes of Lebanon, and
still partly in ruins, Antonine found the "vilest of mankind." Sarepta appeared to him "small, but very Christian,"
with all the relics of Elias: Tyre, on the contrary, seven
miles from Sarepta, as Sarepta from Sidon, was very wicked,
with such luxury as passed description; silk and various
kinds of woven stuffs were worn there, as was fitting in a
town dedicated to the worship of Venus. Ptolemais, or
Acre, again, was a "chaste town," with "good monasteries;"

---

[1] Cf. cc. 25, 31, 42.

[2] Ruad Island, cf. the Bordeaux
pilgrim. Sir C. W. Wilson suggests
that Antoninus went by land only
from Antaradus to Berytus, and then
by sea from Berytus to Ptolemais
(pref. to P.P.T. edit. p. v.).

[3] Cosmas, Top. Christ. i.; Agathias ii.

and Antoninus took advantage of his stay here to visit Mount Carmel, seeing both the "hamlets of the Samaritans" under the hill, and the "monastery of Elisha" upon the ridge.   And on Mount Carmel, he continues, is a small, round stone, solid and ringing when struck, which has such virtue that, if it be hung on to any woman or animal, they will never miscarry.

Reverently prepared for further wonders, the pilgrim followed the coast to Diocæsarea, the Sepphoris of Josephus, on the borders of Galilee, where he "adored the pail and basket of blessed Mary."   Three miles beyond this was Cana of Galilee, where he rested on the "very same couch" as did the Lord, at the famous wedding feast, "and here I, unworthy that I am, did inscribe the names of my parents." Two water-pots (relics of the miracle?) Antoninus found there, and one of these he filled with wine, and dedicated at the altar of the church; and in the fountain of the town he bathed "for a blessing"—by this account fixing the site of his Cana at Kefr Kenna, as there is no spring at the rival site (Khurbet Kana).[1]

In Nazareth our traveller was shown many excellent things: as, for instance, the book from which Christ learnt His ABC; and the bench upon which He sat at school with the other children, and which could now be only moved by Christians.   Many cures, too, were wrought by the garments of the Virgin, that were still to be found in her house; and such was the virtue of the place, that the hatred which most

---

[1] Tobler reads "filled with water and brought forth wine,"—apparently an (almost blasphemous) gloss.   See Gildemeister's note, and C. W. Wilson, pref. to P.P.T. edit., pp. v., vi. This incident can hardly be thought a conclusive proof of Antonine's status as a priest, as Delpit takes it ("Anciens Pèlerinages," 180).   On the name-scribbling, see Letronne's collection of similar instances from Bethlehem and Jerusalem, especially the Holy Sepulchre, in *Journal des Savants*, 1844.

Jews felt for Christians was here exchanged for love, while the beauty of the Hebrew women of Nazareth was "all excelling," due, as it was, to St. Mary, whom they claimed as their parent.[1]

Thence up Mount Tabor, six miles in circuit, three miles in ascent, and with a "plain of one mile" at the top,[2] and down again to the city "once called Samaria,[3] and now Neapolis," where Antonine noticed the well at which Christ talked with the woman, and which we may suppose the pilgrim visited by a short turn from his straight road. Here a church had been built over the well,[4] and in it a water-pot was preserved from which the Lord was said to have drunk —now, of course, working many miraculous cures.[5]

From Neapolis Antoninus came to the city of Tiberias, to Capernaum, and (travelling up the course of Jordan) to the fountains of Jor and Dan ; then, turning south again, he crossed the river to "Gadara, which is Galaad," [6] with its warm springs, like those of Tiberias, at which visions of healing were of regular occurrence. The cure, at any rate, was ineffective for Antonine's companion, John of Placentia, who died here ; [7] and our author, resuming his journey, passed on to "Scythopolis, the metropolis of Galilee, standing on a hill,"—an account unfortunately at issue with the

---

[1] C. 5.

[2] *I.e.* probably one mile in circuit. Here, of course, were the three churches, "at the spot where it was said, Let us make here three tabernacles."

[3] An apparent confusion between Sichem (Shechem) and Samaria.

[4] Possibly a confusion between the Church of St. John at Samaria, and that "of the Well," at Shechem. Cf. Jerome, Per. S. Paulæ, c. 16, who mentions the church ; Arculf, ii. 19,

who describes the church as cruciform, with a diagram ; and Willibald, c. 27, who mentions church and well, as near Sebaste. Cf. P.P.T. edit., which proposes to dislocate this section, and put it in c. 8, after mention of Scythopolis: a very fragmentary reform, where the whole text is Koranic in its confusion.

[5] C. 6.

[6] Gabaon in inferior manuscripts.

[7] Caps. 7, 8.

facts, but amply covered by the more important record, that
" here St. John performed many miracles."   At Sebaste, his
next station, the pilgrim found himself a mark for scorn and
spitting.[1]   "Through the open country, the cities and the
villages of the Samaritans, the Jews followed us, burning our
footsteps with straw.   And such is their hatred for Christ,
that they will scarcely give an answer to Christians.   Money
even they will not take from your hand, but first throw the
coins into water.   And beware of spitting yourself in this
country, if you would not give offence."

Next coming to the scenes of the miracle of the Five
Loaves, of the passage of the Jordan by the Israelites, of
Christ's baptism, and of the translation of Elias, on the left
or eastern bank of Jordan, Antoninus saw the fountain
where John baptized, the valley where the ravens fed Elias,
and the little hill of Hermon, "from which ascends the
cloud that distils upon Jerusalem, as is said in the psalm,
' The dew of Hermon that fell upon the Mount of Sion.' "
" And near here is the city called Liviada,[2] where the two
tribes and a half of Israel tarried before they crossed over
Jordan ; and here are the hot springs of Moses, where lepers
are cleansed ; " while only a little further is the " Salt Sea,
into which the Jordan flows below Sodom and Gomorrah," in
which " no stick or straw can float, and no man can swim ;
but whatever is thrown into it is swallowed up and sinks
to the bottom,"—as exact a falsehood as was ever told by
traveller.

By the side of Jordan[3] Antoninus celebrated the
Epiphany, and here he recounts the yearly miracle at the

---

[1] Possibly, however, this section
is interpolated, though given by
Tobler.

[2] Or, Salamaida, caps. 9, 10.   Cf.
Silvia's account of Livias and Theo-

dosius, c. xix., who probably refers
to the modern Tell-er-Ramah and
Tell-er-Hamma.

[3] C. 11.

baptism of catechumens. "At the hour when the water is blessed, the Jordan, with a roar, returns upon itself, and the upper water stands still until the baptism is finished; but the lower runs off into the sea, as says the psalmist, 'The sea saw that and fled: Jordan was driven back.'"[1] Many Egyptian Christians now come to this solemnity, adds our pilgrim, transferring to the Jordan the old "homage of the Nile."

The quaint and venerable stories that had long been told of Jericho, the Cities of the Plain, and the Lower Jordan valley do not lose any of their piquancy in the hands of the Placentian traveller. Thus, at Jericho, the Lord's holy field was sown by him with just three measures of wheat; and from the dates growing in the sacred plain Antoninus brought home some, and gave one to the "Lord Paterius, the patrician," who may be supposed to have represented the Roman government in some part of North Italy. Again, the tree of Zacchæus appeared still withered to the devout observer; clouds and a sulphurous stench hung for ever over the ashes of Sodom and Gomorrah;[2] as to Lot's wife, and her salt pillar, the report was false "that she is diminished in size by the licking of animals." On the contrary, the statue was just the same as it had always been.

From the vale of Sodom,[3] Antoninus toiled up the hills to Jerusalem, passing through Bahurim, and crossing the brow of the Mount of Olives. He entered the Holy City[4]

---

[1] Omitted in some manuscripts.

[2] Which Antoninus places at the north-west end of the Dead Sea.

[3] Caps. 13–15. It is in relation to this district — the "desert beyond Jordan," the "land of Segor, near the Salt Sea"—that Antoninus tells, in c. 34, the story of the fifteen or eighteen consecrated maidens who had tamed a lion, and kept it close to their cell (". . . Leonem pitulum mansuetum, qui dum appropinquassemus cellulæ ante rugitum illius omnes *animales*, quos habuimus, *minxerunt*," etc.)

[4] Caps. 16, 17. Cf. Arculf, i. 1. As Wilson conjectures, by a postern adjoining the present Golden Gate, now walled up.

by "many steps from Gethsemane," through a gate adjoining what was once the Beautiful Gate of the temple, and, "bowing to the earth and kissing the ground," he visited and adored the "monument" of the Lord — the Holy Sepulchre. Here he found an infinite display of devotion and countless votive-offerings, giving the tomb the appearance of the "winning-post on a race-course." Among other wonders, developed by generations of sight-seers, was the miracle of the Star; which appeared in heaven precisely when (and whenever) the true Cross was brought out into the church to be worshipped, retiring again when the relic was taken back to its place. The Tower of David, "where he sung the psalter," was next visited; and here pilgrims might discern at midnight a murmur of mysterious voices rising from the valley of Jehoshaphat, "in the places that look towards Sodom and Gomorrah."[1] Mount Sion was likewise rich in marvels,—such as the corner-stone that the builders rejected *because it was so ugly*, which Antoninus put to his ear and found it giving out a sound like the "hum of many men;" or the column of scourging, on which Christ's hands left their imprint, "so that a measure is taken from thence for various weaknesses, and those who wear it round their necks are healed." All the relics seen by earlier pilgrims were shown to this last stranger from Italy, "and many others which I have forgotten," not to omit the skull of the martyr Theodota, "from which many drink water for a blessing; and I drank."

From Sion[2] our pilgrim went to see the hospice with "beds for more than three thousand sick folk," built by Justinian in the temple area; the Prætorium, where the Lord was tried; and the marks of Christ's feet upon the square stone on which the Accused had stood. "And many are

[1] Caps. 18, 20–22.   [2] Caps. 22, 23.

the virtues of that stone; for men take the measure of His footprints, and bind them upon their bodies for divers weaknesses, and are healed." Then, after visiting the "ancient" (or "double"?) gate of the city, the pool of Siloam, and the brook Kedron, which "runs into the *Jordan* below Sodom and Gomorrah,"[1] Antonine next came to the iron chain with which "unhappy Judas" hanged himself, to "the stone that cried out," and to the column of scourging, outside Jerusalem, on the road to Diospolis (Lydda), "which was anciently called *Azotus*." And this column,[2] he tells us, to which Christ was first led, was raised by a cloud, and fled away, and was deposited in this place. The truth of this legend was manifest from the fact that the pillar had no foundation, but merely stood upon the earth; and that it was still endued with the power of casting out demons.

Returning once more to the city, Antoninus now set out for Bethlehem, Hebron, and Mamre, in the south[3] (where his journey is unusually lacking in novelties), and for Gibeah (or, as he calls it, *Gilboa*), Ascalon, and Gaza in the south-west. Twenty miles from Jerusalem, he came to the mount "where David killed Goliath,[4] and Saul died with Jonathan, where rain never falls,[5] and where in the night-watches unclean spirits are seen whirled about like fleeces of wool or the waves of the sea." Gaza "the magnificent" —chaste, liberal, and a lover of pilgrims—he reached after a journey through a country rich in sacred memories, "where Samson slew a thousand with the jawbone of an ass,"[6] "where Zacharias was murdered," and "where Isaiah

---

[1] Caps. 24, 25.
[2] Cf. Theodos. c. 24 (Tobl.); Willibald, c. 25.
[3] Caps. 27–31.
[4] The tomb of Goliath, Antoninus says, was marked by an immense heap of stones, because every passer-by was accustomed to throw three upon the "accursed."
[5] According to David's curse, "Ye mountains of Gilboa."
[6] Caps. 31–33.

was sawn asunder." [1] And now, fairly started upon his further wanderings, Antoninus entered the desert, passed through Abila, Ailah, or Elath,[2] at the head of the gulf of Akabah, and, after eight days, reached Horeb and Sinai. On the way he saw a few men on camels, who fled before him ; and this occurrence somehow reminded him of the "Ethiopians" he once met in Jerusalem with "ears and noses slit," and "rings upon their fingers and their feet," who had told him a strange story of servitude.[3] They were so marked, they said, by the Emperor Trajan, "for a sign." Saracen beggars and idolaters swarmed on this frontier of Arabia; twelve thousand, Antoninus reckoned, were going on festival at this very time "into the greater desert :" but he was consoled for this multitude of sinners all hasting to do evil by the concourse of monks and hermits at Mount Sinai.[4] Yet even here false gods had penetrated. At one place upon the mountain the Saracens had a marble idol, white as snow. At the time of their festival this marble changed colour under the moonlight ; and when they began to worship, it became as black as pitch : but as soon as the pollution of their idolatry was over, the original whiteness returned.

The Bedouin festival had given a certain security to the desert journey that Antoninus was making ; but now it was drawing to an end, and he hastened to return to Elath, then

---

[1] Eleutheropolis was the traditional scene of Samson's victory; Zakariyeh, of Zacharias' martyrdom ; and the tomb beneath Siloam, of Isaiah's sufferings.   Cf. Theodosius, c. 22 (in Tobler).

[2] Caps. 34, 35. This is the Elusa of the Pentinger Table, seventy-one Roman miles south of Jerusalem ; it was converted to Christianity by a mission journey of Jerome's friend Hilarion.

[3] Were these the envoys of King Elesbaan, who visited Jerusalem c. A.D. 550? (vid. supra).

[4] Caps. 35-38. Antoninus tells us, in c. 37, of the chapel at the top of Jebel Mûsa, whose ruins are still to be seen. For the following description cf. Antoninus the Elder, A.D. 303, 304.

a centre of the Indian and Red Sea trade, where the visitor might see ships from India laden with "divers spices." But our pilgrim, who was on his way to Egypt, now turned west, and struggled through Phara (Feiran), Magdalum, Sochot, and the "oratory of Moses" to Clysma, or Suez, "where also come ships from India." [1]

The place of the passage of the Israelites through the Red Sea was now, he tells us, a tidal gulf, and at ebb tide the marks of Pharaoh's army and the tracks of his chariot-wheels were still to be seen, "but all the arms have been turned into marble." Modern wonders, too, were not wanting here to balance the ancient: in Suez, Antoninus ate of fresh green nuts from India, which many believed to come from Paradise; "and such is their goodness that, however many taste of them, they are satisfied." Besides this, the "island of *rock oil*" (*petroleum*), within twelve miles of the port, was famous from its powers of ejecting devils from the sick, calming the sea, and spreading a sulphurous stench for miles around.[2]

From Suez, Antoninus visited a cave of one of the first monks (of "blessed Paul") at Syracumba (Deir Bolos), on the western shore of the Red Sea, and thence made his way through the desert to the Cataracts of the Nile, "where the water rises to a certain mark"—probably the Nilometer at Assouan. At this point his account becomes again, as in central Palestine, extremely confused. He tells us that Babylonia (Old Cairo) is close to the cataracts, and traces his further wandering in Egypt *through* Tanis *to* Memphis and Antinöe, near the modern Beni Hassan. Probably his real course was from the Monastery of St. Paul to Assouan, and thence down the river to the places of the Exodus and the Pyramids or "Barns of Joseph."

[1] Caps. 40, 41. [2] C. 42. Cf. Orosius.

Antoninus seems to have quitted Egypt at Alexandria,[1] which he reached by a boat-journey through a marsh swarming with crocodiles, and declared to be "splendid, but frivolous," a lover of pilgrims, but afflicted with heresies.

The rest of his journey is a bald itinerary of a very extensive wandering—from Alexandria to Jerusalem (where he was detained some time through sickness, tempered by visions), from Jerusalem to Joppa and Cæsarea Philippi (which he confuses with *Strato's tower*, or the Cæsarea on the coast); thence to Damascus, Heliopolis or Baalbec, Emesa, famous for the head of John the Baptist in a glass jar, and Apamea, "most splendid, in which is all the nobility of the Syrians."[2]   Then, after a visit to Greater Antioch, on the Orontes, he, like Silvia, struck east, entered Mesopotamia, and reached as far as Chalcis (Kinnisrin), Carrhæ (Haran), and Sura (Surieh), where he mentions a great bridge crossing the Euphrates, and the martyr-memorials of Sergius and Bacchus, in the neighbouring towns of Barbarissus and Tetrapyrgia.   Here ends the pilgrimage, and Antonine's own record.

The return home is described apparently by a later hand, without a word of detail : " Crossing the sea, we came to Italy, our own country, and to Placentia, our own city."[3]

The remaining notices of pilgrim-travel in the last years of the sixth century are chiefly from Gregory of Tours. About 575 a nameless stranger, just returned from Jerusalem,[4] showed the chronicler a silken vestment, in which he said the Cross had once been wrapped, and which had come into his possession in Jerusalem, while in the service of Futes the Abbot.   Again, in 577, Vuinochus, or Vuanochus,[5]

---

[1] Caps. 43–45.
[2] Caps. 46, 47.
[3] C. 48.

[4] De G. M. i. 6.
[5] Hist. Franc. v. 22, viii. 34.

arrived at Tours from Britain, on his way to Jerusalem, "without clothes, except a sheepskin bared of its wool." He seems to have been hospitably entertained by Gregory himself, and sent on his way with a rather better equipment. Once more, in 578, Gregory,[1] afterwards bishop of Agrigentum (with others), went from Sicily to the holy places of Syria; about 579, an intended journey of an unnamed envoy of Guntram, king of the Franks, to Jerusalem, is reported by Paul the Deacon, the historian of the Lombards;[2] and some time before the year 586, various people who had seen a wonderful amber statue of the Redeemer at the source of the Jordan;[3] a deacon who had visited the miraculous well and star of the Virgin at Nazareth; and a leper named John, who, like many other sufferers of Gregory's acquaintance, had been cured, after the manner of Naaman, by bathing in the Jordan, all related their pilgrimages to the annalist of Tours.

About 587 occurs the somewhat doubtful journey of the Gallic saint Agilus,[4] to fast and pray at the sepulchre of the Lord; and a few years later, a new age of Western history commences with the pontificate of Gregory the Great, who also begins a new era of ecclesiastical intercourse between East and West. In 591 and 595 his legates carry his missives to the patriarchs of Jerusalem and Antioch.[5] In

[1] It. Hi. ii. 243, Migne, P. G. xcviii. etc., 567–579.

[2] Paul. Diac. iii. 33.

[3] Cf. Theodosius, xxviii., in Tobl. (= xiii. in Gildermeister); G. T. De G. MM. i. 1; i. 21; i. 19.

[4] Acta SS., Aug. vi. p. 567.

[5] G. Ep. i. 25. Three notices in It. Hi. ii. p. 253, bear somewhat, if only indirectly, on our subject:—

α. 592, Apr. "Rusticianam patriciam a consilio eundi ad loca sancta deflexise miratur S. Gregorius (Papa)."

β. 591. "Eusebius, Syrus Negociator, Parisiensis fit Episcopus" (Greg. Tours, Hist. Franc. x. 26).

γ. 594. "Cosmas Syrus, ut videtur, mercator in Italia et Sicilia degit" (Greg. P. Ep. iv. 45, iii. 58).

Two notices on It. Hi. p. 254, ditto:

α. 595. "Joannes abbas Persa, qui Romam etiam adierat."

β. 595. "Petrus, presbyter ex Româ" (a doubtful pilgrimage to Palestine).

594 he induces a Roman lady, Rusticiana, to go on pilgrimage to Mount Sinai and Jerusalem, and writes to her while still on her travels.[1] Several return embassies from Syria to Rome—for instance, in 595 and 596—are also recorded. In 597, one Peter, acolyte of the Church of Rome, has fled to the Church of Jerusalem, and his extradition is demanded from the patriarch.

In June, September, and November of the same year, 597, and in April and May of 599, legates bearing Pope Gregory's letters arrive at Antioch and Jerusalem; in the last year of the century, one " Simplicius, a Roman," goes to Mount Sinai (and apparently to Palestine), as appears from two letters of the pope's ; and the same pontiff's letters are conveyed in the same year to the abbot of the great Monastery of St. Catherine on the Mount of God.[2]

In or about the year 600 also occurs the interesting mission of Probus,[3] the abbot sent by Gregory to build a hospice for Latin pilgrims at Jerusalem. John the Deacon, in his life of the pope, declares[4] that he sent an annual supply of food and clothing to the servants of God in the holy city of Palestine, and in the holy mount of Arabia. In all this, he recalls the action of Constantine and Justinian, and their erection of pilgrim churches and hospices. We shall see, later on, how Charles the Great follows the same example.

To the sixth century also belongs the " Notitia " of the patriarchates of Jerusalem and Antioch, a list of all the sees to be found in these two great provinces of the Eastern

---

[1] G. Ep. iv. 46, viii. 22, xi. 43, xiii. 22.

[2] Cf. G. Ep. vii. 27, 32, 34 ; viii. 2, 6 ; ix. 49 ; xi. 1, 2.

[3] G. Ep. xiii. 28; Acta SS. March ii. 150, 157.

[4] ii. 7, § 52 ; ii. 2, § 11. Cf. the note under 600, It. Hi. ii. 257 : " S. Gregorius Magnus pro peregrinis loquitur. 'Peregrini ad hospitium non solum invitandi sunt, sed etiam trahendi.' "   Gregory,   " Evangelical Homilies," II. xxiii. 1.

Church, and interesting as a memorial of their state shortly before the Moslem invasion. The remaining pilgrimages of the pre-Mohammedan time, such as that of the daughters of King Ælla from Britain, are unimportant; and the victory of Islam seems to have discouraged Christian travel of the sort for a long time. But before this, the Holy city had already been stormed, sacked, and terribly injured, by Chosroes of Persia, in 615; most of Constantine's buildings in Jerusalem were now ruined by the fire-worshippers; the true cross was carried away beyond the Tigris; and the victory of the Christian Heraclius in 627 only recovered the place for ten years. In 637 the Patriarch Sophronius surrendered to the Caliph Omar, and, from the time of this final profanation, there is a marked decline in pilgrim records, if not in pilgrim journeys. Waimer, the Duke of Champagne, is said to have gone to Palestine in 678 to expiate his share in the murder of St. Leger; and Wulphlagius, a country priest in the diocese of Amiens, travelled Sionwards about the same time, for the sake of devotion: but neither of these left any account of their wanderings.[1] Till the visit of Arculf, more than a century later than Theodosius, he and Antoninus find no one to follow in their steps, no Western Catholic who both visits and describes the new Palestine—Palestine under the Moslems.

[1] See Acta Sanctorum, June ii. 30; "Histoire Littéraire de la France," vi. 475.

CHAPTER IV.

THE ANGLO-FRANKISH PILGRIMS—CIRC. A.D. 680–870.

I. ARCULF, CIRC. A.D. 680.

THE next period of Christian travel opens with Arculf at the close of the seventh century. And in the interval between Antoninus and Procopius,[1] and this same Arculf there had taken place the third of the revolutions by which we pass from the old Roman world into the mediæval. The first of these changes was the conversion of the Roman State; the second was the collapse of the purely Latin Empire, and the complete conquest of all the provinces to the west of the Adriatic by the barbarians from beyond the Rhine and Danube; the third was the rise of a new race and a new religion. In 622 Mohammed rallied his followers at Medina; and within the first thirty years of the Hegira, under himself and his first two successors, or caliphs, all

---

[1] Procopius does not call for a detailed account in this connection. Here we may notice how much his tone, as that of an educated man of the world, contrasts with that of contemporary pilgrimage. In his most geographical treatise, for instance— that on the "Buildings of Justinian" —there is only one startling remark, the mention of the Nile "which flows from the Indies." In this work Procopius describes both the churches and fortresses of the Empire, especially on the eastern and south-eastern frontier, very carefully, dealing even with erections among the Lazi of Colchis, in the Crimea, beyond the Euphrates and upon the Upper Nile, as well as along the southern border of the African or Carthaginian province; and thus, in giving us a view of the Roman world in the sixth century, reminds us somewhat of Strabo and his description of that same world under Augustus.

the Bible lands were overrun by the Saracens, and Christian pilgrimage at once assumed a new character. It was no longer the same thing—easy, natural, patronised by the State, performed by many if not by most of the religious leaders. "Blessed be the one God," was now the cry of those who ruled in Jerusalem, in Damascus, in Alexandria, and in the Thebaid; "blessed be the undivided Unity, who hath neither consort nor son." Christians were no longer masters; no longer at home in the home of their religion. They came and went, they resided there on sufferance. The servant abideth not in the house for ever.

Deprived of sovereign power in nearly all of Asia, and in the whole of Africa, the Catholic Church, dependent as it was upon the Roman Empire (for only heresies, such as the Nestorian, have ever flourished in a truly natural and healthy manner among the native Asiatic states), became mainly European and Aryan in character, and addressed itself to the vital problem of government and organisation. The local Church of old Rome became the centre of its system. The earlier ideas of democratic or aristocratic government in the spiritual kingdom yielded more and more to the monarchical rule of the Italian popes, and by their efforts the idea of a Crusade, of a holy and perpetual war against the Moslem interloper, was gradually developed,[1] with momentous results to the exploration of the world. But within thirty years of the death of Gregory the Great the intercourse of trade and of friendship, of learning and of religion, between the Levant and Western Europe began to be seriously curtailed; and independent Christendom (the States of Italy, Germany, Gaul, Spain, and Britain, as far as they were saved from northern heathendom and southern

[1] Though it was the Norsemen who made this practical by giving the requisite energy to European society.

Islam) was barbarised for generations by the double attack.
It is true that the civilisation of the converted Empire was
rapidly penetrating the European conquerors, who reverenced
Rome and her faith, and were willing to learn from her.
But the triumph of Mussulman armies in Asia and Africa,
and the persistent danger of their attacks, was a more serious
hindrance.   For the Arabs learnt Greek philosophy and
science with eagerness; but they despised and hated the
Christian theology that had grafted itself upon Plato and
Aristotle.   The intellectual supremacy passed for ages away
from the doctors of the Church to their chief enemies;
and while the armies of Islam overthrew Christian govern-
ments and ravaged Christian lands, and while the corsairs of
the Caliphate destroyed the commerce of Christian nations,
and prevented any development of European enterprise on
the Mediterranean, new schools arose within the Mohammedan world, which made themselves, till the time of the
Crusades, the almost undisputed successors of ancient knowledge and ancient thought.   A crushing defeat was inflicted
for a time, not merely on Roman and Christian and
European empire, but upon the very civilisation or higher
life of that empire, which was thus thrown back into its
Dark Ages.

At the epoch we have now reached,[1] the Saracens had
not yet broken into Europe by way of Spain, but they had
already overrun Northern Africa to the shores of the
Atlantic, they had shut up the Byzantine power to the
regions west of Taurus, they had made their first but futile
dash upon the city of Constantine, and they were yearly
threatening to swoop down again upon the Bosphorus, or to
cross the Western Mediterranean into the Latin Christendom
of Europe.

[1] About A.D. 680–690.

The world in which Arculf travelled was no longer, as it had been to earlier pilgrims, the dominion of one religion, that of the gospel, and of one ruler, the Roman emperor. The greatest State which had taken the place of the Cæsars' kingdom was the Caliphate: and the growth of this new semi-temporal, semi-spiritual monarchy had been rapid almost beyond example.   By A.D. 644, within twelve years of their first attack upon Syria, Egypt, and Persia, the Mussulmans had mastered all the lands between Khiva and Carthage, and before Arculf went on his journey they had established themselves along the whole south and east of the Mediterranean world, in Tangier, in Alexandria, and in Antioch.

Meantime, Christendom, whose broken fragments, at least within the limits of the Old Empire, had seemed likely (for a moment) to be reunited by Justinian, was more hopelessly divided than ever, in political power.   The Byzantines had now lost, by Arculf's day, all their dominion in Africa; while in Asia they could claim nothing east of the Taurus, and in Europe next to nothing west of the Adriatic.   The Isaurians had not yet arisen to give new vigour to the failing State, and the extinction of the "Lower Empire," in the capture of Constantinople itself, looked highly probable. In 675 the first Moslem host came in sight of St. Sophia: and though it fell back baffled, this was only to prepare for another and a more determined siege.

In Western Europe all the more stable political forces centred round two personages, the Bishop of Rome and the King of the Franks.   The Byzantine exarchs or viceroys at Ravenna had been practically insignificant from the time of the Lombard inroads in North Italy, in the latter years of the sixth century; Pope Gregory the Great represented the authority which still clung to the name of Rome far

better than any other potentate in Italy; but from the time
of Clovis (who died in 511) there was apparent the growth
of a new secular power in the Transalpine lands. The
Franks in Gaul and Western Germany were taking upon
themselves more and more an imperial authority. They
were the greatest tribe or race, indeed the only tribe or
race which showed enough stability and organising power
to be called great, between the North Sea and the Mediterranean. Their conversion to orthodoxy made them fitter
than ever to represent Rome: but they were still a long
way from their position under Charles the Great, and his
house had not yet come to the Frankish throne; as yet
they were only mayors of the palace.[1]

The Gothic Kingdom in Spain was to all appearance
more peaceful, settled, and secure than any other State of
Latin Christendom; far less anarchic than Italy, more
united than Britain, not so near as Frank-land to a domestic
revolution—but its hour was nearly come. Suddenly upon
its pretentious weakness fell that Saracen onslaught which
would hardly have been less fatal in the Italy of the seventh
or eighth century. A rotten Government, a disloyal nobility,
a factious church—and an enemy whose fire and subtlety no
Christians had yet resisted with success,—these were the
conditions of the problem whose solution was to be so
rapid and so mysterious.

The English kingdoms were taking shape and had
settled into a fairly definite triple division, of North, South,
and Centre; they had passed through the struggle of their
conversion, and had all accepted Christianity[2] and the
culture that it brought with it. In days that were soon to
come, English missionaries would lead a movement against
the heathendom of Northern and Central Germany, beyond

---

[1] Circ. A.D. 680.　　　　　[2] By 670–680.

the Elbe and the Rhine; but this belongs to the lifetime
of our next pilgrim, Willibald. As yet, in spite of successes
in Britain, and the still unspent energy of the Irish Church,
Christendom was on the whole receding from without, and
showing but faint hope of brighter things within, when
Arculf struggled from France to Syria, and thence, by many
wanderings, to Scotland. We shall not, then, be surprised
if our material decreases very greatly in amount. The
stream of pilgrims has dwindled to a rivulet, and the
memorials of pilgrim-journeys naturally fall away with the
decline of practical enterprise.

We may, indeed, expect that Christian travel, following
the general course of Christian politics and Christian knowledge, will not only lose what little enterprise it may have
had, but will also become more and more superstitious and
confined in outlook. Yet the reality is hardly so bad as the
appearance of things would argue. With all their barbarism,
the Northern nations who took up Christianity, who founded
their States upon the ruins of Rome's Empire, who drove
back the Moslems, and who at last discovered, conquered,
and colonised the best parts of the world, have never been
surpassed for manliness, for daring, and for endurance. With
all their faults, accordingly, we find in the pilgrims of this
time, who are almost entirely Northerners, certain qualities
that may be respected. The Frankish, and English, and
Irish travellers of the new age—Arculf, and Willibald, and
Bernard, and Fidelis—are not altogether without the spirit
of an imperial race; and the same Northern blood, poured
into Italy and the South, is, no doubt, in part the cause
of the fresh commercial and maritime activity awakened in
such ports as Amalphi and Venice, where, in spite of all
dangers from Mussulman attacks, the first essays were soon [1]

---

[1] In the ninth and tenth centuries.

to be made towards a new European trade. In the same spirit Rome had struggled to save the Church, and had made a good beginning in her attack upon the North by the victories in England, where her missionaries gained a fresh starting-point and a powerful flank position for the next campaign in Germany.

The first of our new group of pilgrims has an especial relation to England, and to the dual conversion of our island by Continental and by Irish preachers. It was about A.D. 680 that Arculf, whom we only know as a Gallican bishop and a visitor to the Holy Land, was driven out of his course by storms on his return, and carried to the monastery of Iona, which had long been the capital of the Irish Church and its missions, but was now passing under the obedience of Rome. Here he was entertained by the abbot Adamnan,[1] the biographer and successor of St. Columba; to his host he related the story of his journey; and by him it was written down, and, after some years, presented to King Aldfrith the Wise, last of the great Northumbrian rulers, in his court at York (A.D. 701). The narrative aroused interest. It was read by the first scholar in Christendom, who happened to be a Northumbrian Englishman living at Jarrow; and in the result two summaries of Arculf's, or rather of Adamnan's, record were made by the Church historian of the English for his countrymen. Of these, the shorter was inserted in the "Historia Ecclesiastica;" the longer formed a separate tract; and the name of Bede as

---

[1] " Little Adam," who became abbot in 679. See Adamnan's Prologue, in the full text of Arculf, and Bede's Epilogue (ch. 21) in his abridgment (" De Locis Sanctis "); cf. also T. Wright's Biog. Brit. Lit. Anglo-Sax. Period, p. 202. Arculf must have been in Palestine soon after the death of Moawiyah (661-679), the tolerant and enlightened Caliph whom he mentions, in Book i. ch. 11, under the name of Mavias, and whose capital at Damascus he certainly visited.

the compiler secured a great popularity and a large number of copies for this abridgment of the new work on the Gospel sites.   During the Middle Ages more than one hundred transcripts of it were made, as against some twelve or thirteen only of Adamnan's original account; but it adds hardly anything to the latter, and its work was simply to popularise Arculf's relation.   For an obscure name, then as now, needed a famous man to recommend it to a public which decided by the title of a book to read or not to read.

The full narrative, as told by the abbot of so great a monastery as Iona, is naturally far more literary than most of its class.   It is never a mere itinerary; the information contained is worked up into a certain form, and not ·thrown out just as the memory served, as was clearly the case with the later guide-book of Willibald, or the earlier tract of Theodosius.   Again, it is unique, among these early pilgrim-records, in its illustrations, and in its formal completeness (its division into three books, its invocation of the Trinity,[1] and so forth); while it shares with Willibald's narrative the distinction of being dictated by the traveller himself to a scribe.   But in the case of the latter, the pilgrimage forms merely part of a treatise attempted in commemoration of a master by two very humble disciples; in Arculf's case, his story was set forth with the best skill and culture of the time, and has one only object—a complete account of the holy places of the Levant.

Arculf's first chapter is a general one, about the site of Jerusalem—its walls, with their eighty-four towers and six gates; its "great houses of stone;" and its "famous spot, where once the temple stood in all its splendour," now replaced by the "square-built prayer-house" of the Saracens,

---

[1] "In the Name of the Father, and of the Son, and of the Holy Ghost,   I am about to write a book about the holy places."

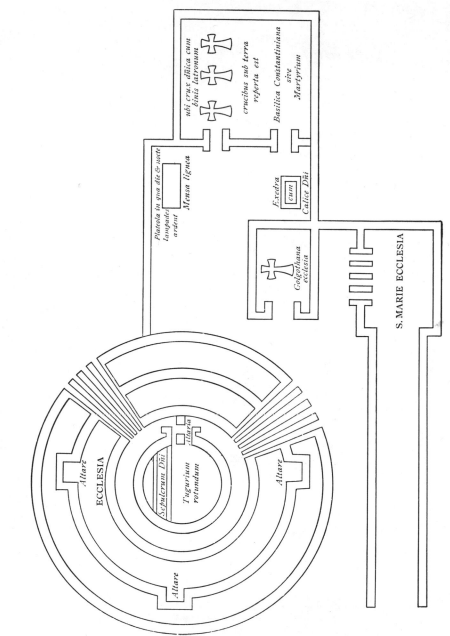

BISHOP ARCULF'S DRAWING OF THE CHURCH OF THE HOLY SEPULCHRE AS IT WAS ABOUT A.D. 680. [To face p. 133.

"able to hold three thousand men at once." More than all these, he speaks of the great annual fair held in the city on the 15th of September, with its "almost countless multitude" of men, and its hosts of camels, asses, and horses; and he looks on the rains that regularly followed it and washed the streets of their refuse as nothing short of a miracle, worked by God "for the glory of His only begotten Son." [1]

From the well-constructed private houses of Jerusalem, Arculf goes on to speak of the sacred buildings, and especially of that centre of pilgrim-devotion, "the round church built over the Sepulchre of the Lord;" and in connection with this, he gives us one of the earliest of Christian plans—a sketch of the Holy Sepulchre in all its parts, as it was at the time of his visit, originally made by himself, at the spot, upon a wax tablet that he carried.

Next, in the long account that follows of the churches of the Resurrection, of Calvary, and of the Invention or Rediscovery of the Cross, we have, for the first time, the story of the column which marked the centre of the world, "on the north side of the holy places, and in the middle of the city," which at the time of the summer solstice cast no shadow at midday,[2] thereby clearly proving Jerusalem to be the "navel of the earth." "Whence also the psalmist sings, 'But God is our King of old, working salvation *in the midst of the earth.*'" [3]

---

[1] Arculf, i. 2, 3. The Caliphs, at the end of the seventh century, greatly fostered a Jerusalem pilgrimage among their Moslem subjects, and this was one reason of the concourse noticed by Arculf. See Delpit, "Essai sur les Anciens Pèlerinages," pp. 271, 272; and De Guignes' "Mémoire sur les Rélations de la Gaule avec l'Orient."

[2] But a slightly increasing shadow from that time on, beginning three days after the solstice (June 24-27).

Arculf, i. 13. Cf. Theodosius, pref. : "In medio autem Judee civitas Iherusolima est, quasi umbilicus regionis totius" (not in Gildemeister's recension).

[3] Ps. lxxiv. 12. Arc. i. 13, 14. Arculf copies from old stories of the column of scourging the thought of Christ's knees "marked upon hard stone, as on wax," and applies the story to a new relic—the stone on which He knelt and prayed in Gethsemane.

A little later, in describing the site of the death of
Judas, Arculf, or Adamnan for him, makes his solitary
quotation from "uninspired writings"—and this is from
the valuable author Juvencus, a "versifying priest" of
St. Jerome's time, who furnishes a line appropriate to the
"suicide from a fig-tree."[1]

In the account of Mount Sion, which immediately
follows, we have another sketch-map given us—a plan of
that "Mother and Mistress of all Churches" under whose
roof were now grouped four of the holy sites—the places
of the Supper of the Lord; of the Descent of the Holy
Ghost; of the Virgin's death; and of the Column of
Scourging;[2] with the rock of the stoning of Stephen just
outside. Arculf now turns from the city itself to describe
its surroundings. He begins this second part of his
"Relation" with a notice of "the rough and stony places
from Jerusalem to Ramah of Samuel," of the vines and
olives of Mount Olivet, and of the rich and fruitful country
stretching towards Cæsarea and the coast—a remark as
unexpected as it is rare in these pilgrim-memoirs, which
as a rule pass by every natural feature of the country
without remark, or only attend to those curiosities that
seem to offer an easy opening for miracle. In speaking
of the round church, " of the Ascension " on Olivet, whose
lights at night cast quite a brilliant glow over Jerusalem,
Arculf gives us his third illustration or ground-plan, a
picture which he tries to fill up by his careful iteration of

[1] "Informem rapuit ficus de vertice
mortem." C. Vettius Aquilinus
Juvencus, a Spanish priest of the
fourth century, wrote an "Historia
Evangelica" in verse. The older
story of the "iron chain" had not
necessarily passed into discredit.

"Unhappy Judas" might have used
both this and the fig-tree.

[2] Arc. i. 19. Arculf only alludes to
Mount Moriah in c. 1. His object
was to describe the *Christian* shrines.
For the references which follow, cf.
Arc. i. 21–23; ii. 7–11, 12–15.

the wonder of the eight glass windows used in that church,
through which the lamp-light streamed over the whole
mountain and all the neighbouring country.   Moving on
to Bethlehem, and describing the wonders of the city of
Christ and St. Jerome, our pilgrim notes the old Royal
Road which connected Jerusalem with the South, and which
was traversed by him, at least as far as "Hebron, which
is also Mamre," and the tombs of the patriarchs.   He was
particularly interested in the tomb of Adam, which was
made, not from stone or marble, but simply from the soil—a
sort of example of earth-to-earth burial—in special allusion
to the threat of his Creator: " Dust thou art, and unto dust
shalt thou return."

Then, after telling us about the oak of Mamre, which
"St. Jerome somewhere says had been there from the
beginning of the world to the time of Constantine," Arculf
comes back to Jerusalem, noticing on his way the mode of
transport by camels, "for in all Judæa it is rare to find
waggons or carriages," before starting again from Jerusalem
on a visit to the gorge of the Jordan and Dead Sea.

Jericho, like Hebron, he found in ruins, only the house
of Rahab standing, and the land on the other side of
Jordan was now all "Arabia"[1]—across that narrow milk-
white stream "over which a strong man could easily hurl
a stone," but which to the Christian pilgrim was Rhone and
Rhine, Tagus and Tiber, Golden Horn and Nile, and all—
more than all the sacred and venerable streams of history
—in one.

The "Dead Sea" of salt suggests to him a curious
disquisition on salts of the earth and sea, on the rock salt

---

[1] The space between Jericho and the Jordan was now inhabited by "sorry fellows of the race of Canaan" —"quorumdum Channanee stirpis homuncionum . . . domus."

dug out of "a mount of Sicily," and on Christ's saying to His disciples, "Ye are the salt of the earth." And as to this land salt, adds Adamnan, Arculf had a right to speak, for he lived some days in Sicily, and by sight, taste, and touch assured himself that this was truly the saltest of salt.[1]

From the Dead Sea the next stage was to the sources of the Jordan in the province of Phœnicia, " at the roots of Lebanon," where the two fountains of Jor and Dan [2] bubbled up from the earth, and sent their waters victoriously through the two Lakes Merom and Gennesaret, only to be absorbed in the third, the "Asphaltic," or Sea of Sodom. Here Arculf stops to correct a topographical mistake, as he views it— " the Jordan rises not at Paneas (Cæsarea Philippi), but in the country of Trachonitis," fifteen miles distant; and he spends a chapter in a full account of the Sea of Galilee,[3] which he describes as fringed all around with woodland— a striking contrast to its present-day condition.

In Central Palestine he visited Nazareth, Mount Tabor, and the great cruciform church over the well of Jacob at Sichem,[4] of which he gives us a plan in the fourth and last of his illustrations. But, as he laments, he could not stay ; he had attached himself to a brother-devotee, one Peter, and

---

[1] In his abridgment "Concerning the Holy Places," Bede adds, in confirmation of what the Gallic pilgrim tells of the buoyancy of the Dead Sea waters, the well-known story, as given by Josephus, of the experiment of Vespasian. At his bidding men had once been thrown into the Asphaltic Lake, who had never learnt to swim, and whose hands were tied; but nothing could make them sink, and they (see Josephus, B. J. iv. 8. 4) floated obsti-nately on the surface of the water.

[2] These represent probably the sources of Baneas (Cæsarea Philippi) and Tell-el-Kâdy (Dan). Cf. Ant. Mart. c. 7. Arculf, whose flash of critical spirit in this place recalls Silyia, traces the real sources in a lake Phiala, 120 stadia from Baneas, flowing thence underground (ii. 17).

[3] ii. 18. "Chinnereth" and "Tiberias" he also names it (ii. 18).

[4] "Improperly named Sichar," ii. 19.

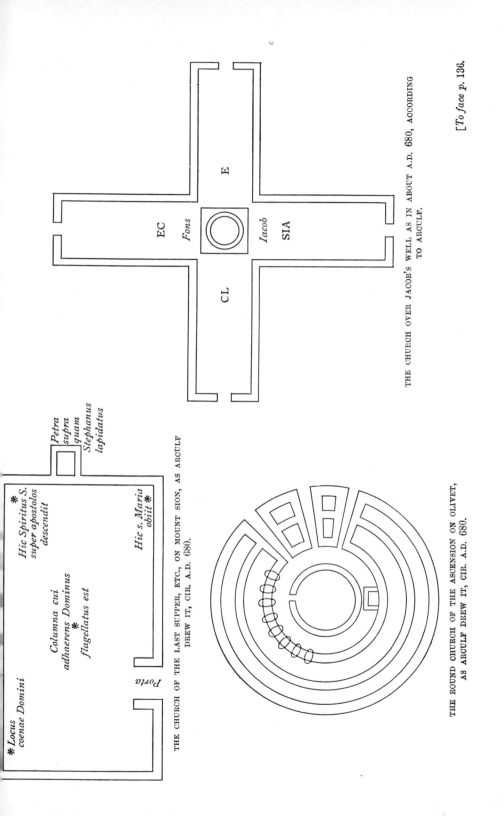

Locus coenae Domini

Hic Spiritus S. super apostolos descendit ✻

✻ *Hic Spiritus S. super apostolos descendit*

Columna cui adhaerens Dominus ✻ *flagellatus est*

Petra supra quam Stephanus lapidatus

✻ *Hic s. Maria obiit*

Porta

THE CHURCH OF THE LAST SUPPER, ETC., ON MOUNT SION, AS ARCULF DREW IT, CIR. A.D. 680.

EC

Fons

CL

E

Iacob

SIA

THE CHURCH OVER JACOB'S WELL AS IN ABOUT A.D. 680, ACCORDING TO ARCULF.

THE ROUND CHURCH OF THE ASCENSION ON OLIVET, AS ARCULF DREW IT, CIR. A.D. 680.

[*To face p.* 136.]

he was now forced to hasten on by the conduct of his companion. This "soldier of Christ, a Burgundian by race, well acquainted with sites," but apparently infirm of temper, seems to have travelled with Arculf for some time, till, at this point, he refused to go any further, and returned "by a roundabout way from Nazareth to the solitary place where he had been before." [1]

The two pilgrims had been together at Mount Tabor, which Adamnan declares,[2] from Arculf's account, to be thirty stadia, or nearly four miles, high—perhaps in reference to the length of the winding path to the summit ; but the Burgundian anchorite would only allow his friend to pass one night in the hospice on the top. Still he had time to see the great monastery of the place and the three handsome churches, "according to the number of the tabernacles of which Peter spoke : " and in this short visit he gained the somewhat wild impression of Tabor's summit as forming a broad expanse three miles across.[3]

Arculf is next to be found in Damascus, which lies "in a plain with olive groves, enclosed by an ample circuit of walls and intersected by four great rivers ; " and from this, his furthest point eastwards, he seems to have come back to Tyre, the "metropolis of Phœnicia," and taken ship for Egypt, where he does not tell us of any extensive travels, but only of journeyings in the lower valley of the Nile.

The voyage from Joppa to the great city of Alexandria, "once the metropolis of Egypt," was a matter of forty days,

[1] Passing over the "plain of the loaves and fishes," north of Tiberias, and through Capernaum. He says nothing to help us to fix the site of the latter. In Nazareth he especially describes the well, the one certain relic of the day of Christ therein.

[2] Adamnan's phrases sometimes suggest that he drew the story slowly and painfully out of his visitor by repeated questioning.

[3] It is really a quarter of a mile in length by one-eighth of a mile in width. Cf. Arc. ii. 24, 25.

he tells us ; and here, as in Damascus and all through Syria
and Egypt, the " King of the Saracens " had now seized the
government.   Except in passing, however, Arculf never
alludes to the great revolution that had so lately befallen
the pilgrim-lands of the Levant, in this contrasting strongly
with Willibald and with Bernard, who also seem to have
suffered much more from Moslem espionage and extortion
than their predecessor.   As to Alexandria, it lay like an
enclosure between Egypt and the great sea.   On the south
it was bounded by the mouths of the Nile, on the north by
Lake Mareotis—an odd inversion of the real facts of the case.
Its port was difficult of access, and something like the human
body in shape.   " For in its head it is ample, at its entrance
very narrow, where it admits the tide of the sea and the
ships ; and by this entrance the means of breathing, as one
may say, are supplied to the harbour.   But when you have
once passed this narrow neck and mouth, the sea stretches
out far and wide," like the human body at the shoulders.   On
the right-hand side of the harbour Arculf saw the Pharos,[1]
the great lighthouse of the Ptolemies, still standing, " and
every night lit up with torches " as a landmark for sailors
far along the coast and out at sea, as well as a guide for
mariners through the narrow, winding, and rocky entrance
of the harbour.   The port itself was always calm, and in size
nearly four miles across.   So calm and so great a haven was
needed for a city used by the whole world as an emporium ;
whither countless people still resorted, in spite of Moslem
rule.   As the country, though very fertile, was almost rainless,
the want was supplied by the "spontaneous showers " of
Nile irrigation.   The river was not only a fertiliser, it was
an invaluable water-way for commerce, always crowded with

[1] Built 280 B.C. and mentioned as existent for 1600 years (to about A.D 1300).

traffickers. So men here could sow without ploughing and
journey without waggons, on the great stream that flowed
through and divided Egypt, and which was navigable, as
they said, to the "town of elephants" (Elephantine).
Beyond this, the cataracts, or hills of water, prevented any
further progress—not from any shallowness of the stream,
but from the headlong fall of the whole river, and a sort
of "ruin," as our pilgrim calls it, of the rushing waters.

The city of Alexandria Arculf found so long and narrow
that he was one entire day in merely passing through it.
Entering one side of the town at the third hour of a day in
October, it was evening before he reached the other.

Along the banks of the Nile he also noticed the dykes
that the Egyptians put up to regulate the yearly overflow.
If these embankments burst, terrible destruction sometimes ensued; so that many of the people living in the
lowlands built their houses on piles standing well above
the high-water mark of the floods.

It was the Canopic mouth of Nile which, to Arculf's mind,
made the geographical division between Asia and Africa,
and up and down the lower reaches of the great river he
passed several times, noticing, as he did so, the ferocious
daring of the crocodiles, "quadrupeds not so large as
ravenous."

Thus ends our pilgrim's account of Egypt.[1] The last
section of his relation opens in Constantinople, which he
reached from Alexandria by way of Crete; and which he
declares, from a personal knowledge of several months, to be

[1] Here, from his allusions to the
Nile, and notably to Elephantine,
we may suppose that he went up
country to visit the monks and solitaries of the desert; but he says
nothing about them, though they
had been standing attractions to
earlier pilgrims; and his silence is
imitated by Bernard, Willibald, and
the other devotees of this Frankish
age of travel.

without doubt the metropolis of the Roman Empire,[1] and by far the greatest city therein. Surrounded by the sea on all sides except the north ("for the Great Sea here breaks in for a space of forty miles "), the place was truly imperial, with walls twelve miles in circuit, and full of splendid stone houses built after the fashion of Rome.

So Arculf speaks : to what he says over and above this general description [2]—" of the first foundation of the city by Constantine," " of that church in which the Lord's cross is kept," and of the story of St. George the Confessor (though the first account of England's patron saint ever circulated in Britain)—we need not attend, except so far as to notice that the "round church which contains the life-giving wood of the Cross " is Saint Sophia, the crowning glory of Justinian's buildings; and that Arculf's whole account of Constantinople is a witness to the seventh-century preponderance of that city in size and splendour over all the other centres of Christian civilisation.

From the New Rome of the East, Arculf sailed to the Old Rome [3] of the West, and on his voyage his curiosity was especially roused by the isle of Volcano in the Liparis, "twelve miles from Sicily," which vomited smoke by day and fire by night, with a noise like thunder—a noise, too, that was always louder on Fridays and Saturdays, and shook the whole of the opposite coast of Sicily ; so, at least, our pilgrim imagined when he was staying there.

II. Willibald,[4] circ. a.d. 721–728.

Arculf, although a Frank, comes before us in an English or Anglo-Irish account, and the chief immediate result of

---

[1] iii. 1, 5 (end).
[2] iii. 2, 3, 5.
[3] iii. 6.

[4] Cf. Tobler-Moliner's pref. xxxix.– xliii., which points out that the narratives of Willibald, Antoninus Martyr,

his journey is to rouse still further the pilgrim-interest among the newly converted English race. The journeys of our devotees had at first been to the shrines of Ireland,[1] in the days when Irish missions controlled the Christianity of Northern and Central England; but now that the Roman cause had triumphed, and the Continental connection had been perfected by Wilfrid and by Theodore, men began to go in numbers from Britain to Rome, and in a few examples as far as Syria.

The next of our Latin pilgrim records is that of a high-born Englishman, Willibald, son of a certain Richard who bore the title of king, and who is supposed to have been himself son of that Hlothere, king of Kent, who died in 685. His mother was Winna, sister of Winfrith, or Boniface of Crediton, afterwards the apostle of Germany and arch-bishop of Mainz. A still more powerful connection of hers was Ini, king of Wessex, the restorer of the West Saxon kingdom and conqueror of Somerset. Willibald's brother[2] Wunebald, and his sister Walburga, or Walpurgis, both became prominent like himself in the German missions of the Church, and the oil of St. Walburga was long the boast of the faithful at Eichstädt, and has been defended in our own day, as a credible miracle, by Cardinal Newman. Both,

and Arculf are the chief pilgrim-records under the Merwings; inclines to the belief that the Spaniard who aided Willibald in Syria was an apostate; and dates the main stages of his journey as follows : Left Rome, Easter, 722; reached Jerusalem, Nov. 724; in Constantinople, about March, 726; 728–9 returned to Italy.

Molinier, p. xli., suggests that the nun of Heydenheim wrote down most of the narrative from Willibald's lips, but that another hand added (after his death) the account of his life as a bishop. At this very point ends the Codex Augiensis, with the Pope's commission to Willibald to join Boniface in Germany. T. Wright (Biog. Brit. Lit. Anglo-Saxon Period, pp. 341, 342) dates Willibald's departure from Rome 721, and from Tyre on his return to Constantinople 724. See also Heinrich Hahn, " Die Reise des Heiligen Willibalds," esp. pp. 1–16.

[1] Cf. Bede, H. E. iii. 27; iv. 4, etc.
[2] Afterwards abbot of Heydenheim.

after Willibald's return from the East, followed their kinsman into central Europe. English as they were, they thus became Frankish subjects, leaders of those religious enterprises which extended the obedience of the Roman Church and the political limits of the Frankish kingdom in exact correspondence.

Willibald especially represents, as it were, the reverse action of the movement which Arculf helped to spread—that strikingly enthusiastic Christianity of the English tribes whose earlier paganism[1] was by comparison so half-hearted, so almost "agnostic" in character.

As the Gallican bishop had aided the progress of spiritual interests in our island by his visit, and his story of pilgrimage, so the English missionary and pilgrim of the next generation helped to give back to the Continent that religious energy which had found as good a material in the English as in the Irish race, and which was now returning to its starting-point, in Continental Christendom, to play its part in that contest for whose sake Rome had struggled to win the allegiance of the heathen island of the North.

The childlike simplicity of Willibald's story, a simplicity which may be both compared and contrasted with that of Antoninus Martyr,[2] must not make us forget the importance and rank of the traveller. His story is recorded first by a nun,[3] "a poor little creature," as she truly calls herself, and

---

[1] Like the paganism, *e.g.*, of Arabs, Berbers and Tartars before their acceptance of Islam.

[2] It is at first sight remarkable that Christian travel and geography is even more wildly credulous, superstitious, and unnatural under Justinian than in the time of Arculf and Willibald, and among races so much less civilised than Byzantines and Italians. But the earlier Christian philosophy was in much the same attitude towards Scripture (and towards science) as the later; and in both there was an amazing indifference towards the tests of observation and material proof. The difference was not so much through any alteration of Christian thought, as through the almost total extinction of the old learning, and the discredit thrown on nature and the knowledge of the world.

[3] In the "Hodœporicon."

secondly by a deacon,[1] who seems to have abstracted the nun's guide-book, adding a few learned and rhetorical touches of his own. Had the noble pilgrim written his own account, it would probably have been much more ornate ; it might have been far less pleasing. We have a specimen of the inflated bombast which an old English noble mistook for fine writing in the Chronicle of Æthelweard. But our present guide-book describes itself, not without pathos, as the work of "a little ignorant child plucking a few flowers here and there from numerous branches rich in foliage and in fruit . . . in order that he that glorieth, may glory in the Lord." [2]

Willibald, as a young man, already tonsured and destined for the ministry of the Church, thought of pilgrimage, as so many others of his nation had done or were doing, in the way of a duty—a kind of seal of his Christian confession. His relative, King Ini, went to Rome as a pilgrim-penitent in 728.[3] King Ceadwalla, of Wessex, had already travelled there to die in 688. About 721, some three years after Boniface started on his mission journeys in Continental Europe, his nephew Willibald first "sought another land by pilgrimage, and tried to explore the unknown regions of foreign places."

His first object was merely Rome.[4] The idea of the further passage to the Holy Land seems to have suggested itself to him in Italy. But even the road to Rome was dangerous. Matters were not better, but worse than they had been a generation before, in the time of Arculf. Islam was stronger ; Christendom was weaker. The Saracen

---

[1] In the "Itinerarium."
[2] Pref. or prologue.
[3] And founded there the "Saxon House."

[4] Thus (Hod. c. vii.) Willibald only urges his father Richard to visit the *limina Petri.* See Heinr. Hahn, "Die Reise des Heiligen Willibald."

attack had simultaneously reached the Bosphorus on one side, and the Garonne on another, in the early years of the eighth century. Saracen brigands scoured Provence, infested the passes of the Alps, threatened both New and Old Rome at once. The whole Mediterranean was overrun by Moslem pirates, and the main body of the Moslem host appeared to be marching on to the conquest of the world.

In 675 and 717 the armies of Islam were thrown back from the walls of Constantinople; but in 711 they had overthrown the Gothic monarchy in Spain; in 721 they were fighting round Toulouse; in 732, exactly a hundred years from Mohammed's death, came the trial day for Latin Christendom and Western Europe on the battle-field of Tours. Desperate indeed appeared the state of the Christian world, with unconquered heathenism sweeping round it on the north along Rhine and Danube, and Islam cutting it short on the south, east, and west, from Armenia to Spain, —when the Isaurian emperors restored somewhat of its old power and glory to the Roman Empire in the East, and the Franks stopped the Saracen advance in Gaul. From a superficial point of view, and taking less account of the social forces underneath than of the show of political and military power, the days of an independent and sovereign Christendom might have seemed numbered, when Willibald started on his journey (720–21).

We have already given a brief outline of the position of affairs, and the effects of the rise of Islam on Europe, down to a date some thirty years anterior,[1] in our last section. There is only one important change to notice, and that, as we have seen, is the passing of the Saracens into Europe and their conquest of nine-tenths of Spain and of nearly all

[1] 680 or 690 to 720.

the Aquitanian lands.[1]   But, meantime, their second attack
on Constantinople has just been foiled; a manly race and
a true leader have come forward among the despised Byzantines; a breathing-space has been given by the victory of
Leo and his Isaurians in 717; and the Frankish race has
begun to recognise a line of real sovereigns in the family of
Charles Martel.   To Christendom, standing at bay against
a ring of foes, every year was of value.   The fanatic zeal
of the Arabs was a force that was bound in time to grow
feebler; while the new European nations, which now seemed
so divided and so undisciplined, only needed a respite.
Then they would reinforce their strength by fresh blood
from the North; they would make head, little by little,
against feudal, or local, misgovernment; they would forget
their differences in a common struggle for the Cross, and
for their own common interests; they would at last show
themselves to be stronger than all their enemies.   Whether
such respite was to be had—all turned on that; and the
future was still undecided when Willibald followed Arculf,
and even when, a century later, Bernard followed Willibald.

The journey of our earliest English pilgrims, as originally planned, ended, we have said, at Rome.   Willibald
started with his father Richard and his brother Wunebald
simply for the "threshold of Peter, prince of the apostles."
The idea that such a desertion of home cares and duties would
be "cruel and dishonourable" was waived[2] as unworthy

[1] To this might be added the collapse of the Northumbrian power in
England since Arculf's day.

[2] It was peculiar to the English,
says Goscelin, in the Bollandist Collection, "to find many saints in one
family together" (Life of St. Richard,
Feb. vii.). Of the two brothers, Willibald was evidently the leading spirit.

The Itinerarium, c. iii., makes him
tell his father that "cruelty for Christ
was better than all affection." "At
this time," says Bede (H. E. v. 7)
of the beginning of the eighth century, "multitudes of the English,
high and low, clergy and laity, men
and women, went on pilgrimage" to
Rome and the Holy Land, etc.

of a "valiant soldier of Christ;" and at a "suitable time
in the summer," probably of 720–21, this family party
took ship upon the river Hamble, "the appointed place,
known by the ancient name of Hamble-Mouth,"[1] which falls
into the sea about six miles below Southampton (Willibald's "Hamwih"). They took with them the means of
livelihood and a band of friends, hoisted sail with favouring
wind and tide,[2] and crossed in safety the "vasty deep" of
the English Channel. Ascending the Seine to Rouen, they
disembarked close to the city, where there was a market,
and "going on thence from place to place," came at last
into Piedmont, and arrived at Lucca, after a passage of the
dangerous and brigand-infested passes of the Alps,[3] which
was indeed fortunate for an eighth-century traveller.

At Lucca, Willibald's father died, and was buried in the
Church of St. Frigidian,[4] where, under the name of St.
Richard, he is to be found working miracles in the twelfth
century, and where his tomb was pointed out to John
Evelyn in 1645 (Diary, May 21st).[5] His sons, however, still

---

[1] "Hamelea Mutha," caps. 7, 8.

[2] As the Tractarian biographer
remarks, in Lives of English Saints
(p. 9 of St. Richard the Saxon),
"the style of the narrative rises as it
comes to the tale of the voyage, and
swells into long, undulating, tremu-
lous words, as though the memory
of its sensations had dwelt in the
mind:—"*Nauta ille cum classibus*
suoque nauclero, *naulo impenso* [fare],
circio flante [wind], *ponte pollenti*
[tide], *remigiis crepitantibus* [row-
ing], *classibus clamantibus*, celocem
ascenderunt. Tumque *transmeatis
maritimis fluctuum formidinibus
periculosique pelagi pressuris*, vas-
tum per equor *citato* celocis *cursu,
prosperis ventis, velata nave* . . .
viderunt terram."

[3] Lucca, reads the text, was in the
"Gorthonic" land. In *Gorthonicum*,
Mabillon and the Bollandists have
conjectured *Dertonicum*, from *Der-
tona*, now *Tortona*, near Alessandria.

[4] St. Frediano, c. 8.

[5] With the epitaph:—

"Hic rex Richardus requiescit, scep-
     tifer, almus,
Rex fuit Anglorum, regnum tenet
     iste Polorum . . .
Hic genitor Sanctæ Walburgæ
     Virginis almæ
Est, Vrillebaldi Sancti simul et
     Vinebaldi,
Suffragium quorum nobis det
     regna Polorum."

persevered, journeying on through the "vast lands of Italy, through the depths of the valleys, over the steep brows of mountains, over the levels of the plains, climbing on foot the difficult passes of the Alps, and directing their steps on high," passing the ice-bound and cloud-capped summits without the loss of one of their companions, and triumphantly "escaping the cunning violence of armed men." [1] About Martinmas they descended upon Rome, the "Ladder of Learning," and entered the "Church of Holy Peter." Till the Easter following—and after—they stayed in the city, and under the protection of Gregory II., still subject in name to the exarchs of Ravenna, and to their master, the heretic, if heroic, Emperor Leo, Isaurian and iconoclast,[2] now struggling to restore the Empire from Constantinople. During the heat of summer the brother suffered from fever, and it may have been the unhealthiness of Rome that suggested further travels. In any case, Willibald, "that illustrious worshipper of the Cross of Christ, sighing for heights of virtue yet unattained, desired a greater and more unknown pilgrimage than that wherein he rested," and determined, whatever the cost, "to reach and to gaze upon the walls of that delectable and desirable city of Jerusalem." [3]

In the spring of 722, accordingly, the pilgrims, now reduced to three, set out for Syria, and, travelling to Naples by way of Terracina and Gaieta, found a ship from Egypt that would serve to take them on their journey. But never before or after was their venture more difficult. Charles the

[1] Liutprand, king of the Lombards, was the most troublesome neighbour for passengers over the Alps, who were not yet in much danger from the Saracens on this side till they reached the Mediterranean coasts.

[2] Canon Brownlow, in his meagre edition of Willibald for the Palestine Pilgrim's Text Society, 1891, remarks, with a certain flavour of injustice to the introducer, or, at least, populariser of Greek Fire, on the "decrepitude and tyranny of the Eastern Empire, then under Leo the Isaurian."

[3] Chs. 8–10 (note).

Great had not yet come to rally Western Christendom, and to give it a new starting-point and new hopes of victory. The old hospitals and hostelries for infirm and unprovided pilgrims in the Holy Land do not seem to have lasted on from the time of Gregory the Great, and their partial restoration by the Frankish princes was still in the future. Throughout the whole extent of the Caliphate, from the Oxus to the Pyrenees, Christians were beaten, dispirited, despised, subjected. And so Christian devotees must expect insult and suspicion.

Of this, Willibald had his full share. As we shall see, his Eastern greeting was a cold one. He was thrown into prison, and in danger of his life as a spy; he suffered the agonies of a long voyage in the torture chamber which men then called a ship; he endured all the wretchedness of a cold and hungry winter in Asia Minor. But his faith was strong "in the aid of a gracious God, and in the support of the saints;" he had renounced the "riches of earth, country, parents, and kindred;" and he did not flinch from hardship. All the way he and his friends seem to move in an atmosphere of wonder and of miracle, the offset to their pathetic sufferings. Thus, in Sicily, his main interest is Catania, "where rests the body of St. Agatha the Virgin.[1] And there is Mount Etna; and when it happens that the fire" of the volcano "wills to pour itself out over the region, then the people of that city take the veil of St. Agatha and place it over against the fire, and it stops."[2] Again, the cave of the seven sleepers at Ephesus,[3] the restoration of sight to Willibald himself in the Holy Land;[4] the miraculous

[1] C. 10.

[2] A wonder, dating from 252, the year after her martyrdom, according to Acta SS., Feb. 5. The miracle frequently occurred in succeeding centuries, e.g. the twelfth—to the eye of faith.

[3] C. 11.

[4] Caps. 24, 25. In his whole journey, Willibald seems to have lived as a beggar-monk.

punishment he records of the wicked Jews,[1] who would have carried off the body of St. Mary; the deliverance of the pilgrim from the lion in the plain of Esdraelon;[2] the hell of Theodoric,[3] where the traveller expected to see and hear the torments of the damned, are all indications of that habit of mind which is ever on the watch for the supernatural to appear through the thin veil that hides it from the eyes of ordinary men, through the shadows of the world of matter.

But to return. From Syracuse, Willibald sailed to the Morea ("Slavinia"), now overrun by the Bulgarians, who had helped to place Leo of Isauria on the throne of Constantinople. Thence he made his way to Chios, Samos, and Ephesus,[4] where his chief interest was the Cave of the Seven Sleepers, though he also paid a visit to the tomb of St. John. From Ephesus the pilgrims walked along the coast [5] to Patara in Lycia, sometimes in the last stages of cold and want and misery.[6]

At Figila,[7] near Ephesus, they begged some bread, and, sitting on the edge of a well in the middle of the town, "dipped the bread in the water, and so ate it." At Patara they had to stay "till the dreadful freezing cold of the winter had passed." Near here, at the Holy Headland of

[1] C. 20.

[2] C. 28.

[3] Caps. 30, 31.

[4] Hodœporicon, c. xi., "Ephesus, an island of Asia," adds the Itinerarium, c. v.

[5] Passing on the way the mountain of the Galliani, or Promontorium Sacum of Lycia, opposite to the Chelidonian Islands.

[6] At Milite, or Militena (Miletus ?), apparently noticed out of its right place, as if east of Lycia. "Two monks lived on a stylite," says Willibald, a late survival from the days of the Simeons and other pillar saints. Cases in Syria and Greece are, however, mentioned as late as the eleventh century. In the Western Church the practice had been smartly repressed. Cf. Greg. of Tours, H. F. vii. 15, for the story of the ascetic Wulfilaich, who tried the *rôle* of a pillar saint in the diocese of Trèves but whose bishop demolished the pillar.

[7] Phygela: cf. Strabo, xiv.; Pliny, v. 29.

Lycia,[1] their "inward parts were so torn with want of food, that they began to fear the day of death was at hand. But the Almighty Pastor of His people deigned to provide food for His poor servants."

At last they got to Cyprus, "lying between the Greeks and the Saracens,"[2] where they seem to have been in rather better quarters, and took their leave of Christendom for what proved a stay of several years among the infidels. Landing at Antaradus (Tharratæ, or Tortosa), in Northern Syria, they walked inland—twenty to twenty-four miles, on their own reckoning—to Emesa,[3] where they were seized and "held in captivity as strangers and unknown men."[4] From this they were rescued by a "man from Spain," who had a brother in the caliph's palace at Damascus, "chamberlain of the king of the Saracens,"—that is, of the Caliph Yezid II. "And when that governor who had put them in prison came to the palace, the Spaniard who had talked with them in prison, and the captain of the vessel in whose ship they came from Cyprus, presented themselves before the king of the Saracens. And when all had been related to the king, he asked whence they came. And they said, 'From the Western shore, where the sun sets, and we know not of any land beyond—nothing but water.'"

This was too far for spies, they pleaded, and the caliph agreed, and gave them a pass for all the pilgrim sites of Syria, still left open to Christian devotees.

With this permission, they "travelled one hundred miles" to Damascus, "walked on to Galilee," visited Nazareth, Cana, Tabor, or Age-Mons,[5] and the city called

---

[1] Cf. the Itinerarium, c. vi., "the place being then ravaged by the storms of war."

[2] "And containing twelve dioceses."

[3] The Itinerarium, c. vi., says Edessa; probably a confusion. The

pilgrims were now eight in number (Hod. c. xii.).

[4] And strangely dressed, adds the Itinerarium, c. vii.

[5] Ἅγιος-Mons. On Tabor Willibald records one church, in opposition

" Tiberiadis," [1] on the shore of the sea " upon which Christ
walked with bare feet, and through which the Jordan
flows ; " [2] and so came to the " villages" of " Magdalene " and
Capernaum, the fountains of Jor and Dan, and the other
favourite sites, such as the place of the baptism of Christ,
and the fountain of Elisha.

In Jerusalem itself, Willibald records various novelties,
which we may notice as indicating the pilgrim's habit of
mind. Thus he refers to the column set up at the place
where the Jews tried to carry off the dead body of the
Virgin ; to the Church of Calvary and the three memorial
crosses outside its eastern wall; and to the stone in front of the
Sepulchre—not the original, as other pilgrims had reported,
but only a copy of the one rolled away by the angel.[3]
Further, he tells us about a supposed connection between
the pool of Bethesda and Solomon's porch ; about a number
of (fifteen) golden bowls standing, probably as votive offerings, upon the couch on which Christ's body was laid ; and
about certain much-venerated pillars in the Church of the
Ascension on Mount Olivet. These last were set up, he
tells us, as a sign of the two angels " in white apparel." [4]
" And that man, adds Willibald with emphasis, who can creep
between those pillars and the wall, is free from all his sins." [5]

The place of the massacre of the Innocents he moves
from Bethlehem to Tekoa (Thecua) ; in Gaza, after visiting

to the three of Ant. Mart. and Arculf.
Probably the others had perished at
Saracen hands.

[1] Hod. cc. 13, 14.

[2] Jor-Dan we have met with in
nearly all our pilgrims since Jerome ;
yet Ambrose, Augustine, and Jerome
himself give the Hebrew derivation of
the name, " Descensio Eorum." Here,
the Itinerary adds (c. ix.), was a

statue of Christ, with one of the
αἱμαῤῥόουσα, which was thrown down
by Julian the Apostate (Cf. Greg.
Tours De Glor. MM. i. 21).

[3] Hod. cc. 18-20.

[4] " Who said, Ye men of Galilee,
why stand ye gazing up into heaven "
(Hod. c. 21).

[5] I.e. Wins plenary indulgence.

the Laura of St. Saba, he tells us of a "holy place," but
without any hint of what had hallowed the town which
earlier pilgrims had only known as a station on the great
road from Syria to Egypt. The town of Hebron appears
in his guide-book as Aframia (Abramia ?),[1] a name which
recalls its crusading title of Abraham's Castle. Again,
Lydda is changed by him to "St. George," from the dedication of a church in the town ; and Tyre and Sidon, on the
"Adriatic" sea, as the Levant was now called, he brings
within six miles of one another.[2] Perhaps he was deceived
by his guides. He had lost his sight for two months before
it was miraculously restored him in the Church of the
Invention of the Cross, and in the guide-book's strange
jumble of routes and places, we cannot be sure of the actual
sequence of his wanderings.[3] We can only tell from the
narrative that he was on four separate occasions in Jerusalem,
and that he traversed the whole length of the Holy Land,
blind or seeing, several times.

For many months he had tried to get his passport for
leaving Syria ;[4] at last, seemingly about the year 726, he
escaped, just in time to save himself from the persecution
begun by Caliph Yezid against the subject Christians of
the East in 727.[5] But before this, while he was still in

---

[1] Castellum Aframiæ, cf. Itin. c.
xiii.

[2] They are really twenty miles
apart.

[3] This may be due to the dictating
method of the narrative. The nun
to whom Willibald was speaking
might be called off every now and
then to meals, or to hours of prayer ;
and, in resuming, some part of the
story might be forgotten.

[4] Among the last places he mentions in Palestine are Tripolis,

Damascus (re) Cæsarea (re) Emesa
(re), Salamaitha or Salameyeh (the
Salamias of the Antonine Itinerary,
eighteen Roman miles from Emesa),
Sebastia, "formerly called Samaria,"
and the wide plain full of olive-trees
(Esdraelon), where he met the lion of
c. 28, who "threatened him with
fearful roaring."

[5] Though not in time to avoid the
winter storms, which gave him a
terrible voyage.

Jerusalem, he had purchased some balsam, and filled a calabash with it, and, to carry this off in safety, he had to resort to smuggling tricks, which brought him once more within measurable distance of martyrdom.

To secure his balsam "he took a cane that was hollow and had a bottom, and filled it with petroleum, and put it inside the calabash, and cut the cane even with the calabash, so that the edges of both seemed alike even, and thus he closed the mouth of the calabash." With this trophy, Willibald and his friends successfully passed the douane at the Tower of Libanus,[1] near Acre. But "when they came to the city of Tyre, the people took them, and bound them, and examined all their luggage to find if they had anything contraband hidden, and if they had found anything they would have made martyrs of them." But they found nothing but the calabash, and when they opened, and smelt it, they only scented the petroleum, and "the balsam they found not. And so they let them go."

Once embarked at Tyre, the pilgrims were sailing from the end of November till Holy Week, when they anchored in the Golden Horn, and Willibald took up his lodging in a cell in the church "where is the body of John Chrysostom." For Greeks and Latins were still in full communion.

Here, in a stay of two years (726–728), the guide-book tells us only of a visit to Nicæa, though the great icono-clast was at this very time reorganising the whole adminis-tration of the State, driving back the Saracens, and struggling to "purify" or puritanise the Church. For all this, intimately as it concerned the people and the religion

---

[1] Hod. c. xxviii. Where that mountain "goes down into the sea, and is a promontory," with a guard-house of the Saracens: viz. the modern Ras el Abyad with its ruined tower.

of Latin Christendom, Willibald had no eye. He does not
even tell us how Leo had threatened Pope Gregory II., and
been excommunicated for his impiety in 728. He only lets
us know incidentally the result of this, when he sailed from
the Bosphorus for Sicily "with the nuncios of the pope
and the emperor"[1] in that very year. But, like Arculf,
he was arrested on his journey by a passing curiosity about
"the isle Vulcano" in the Liparis, now associated with
the full-blown legend of "Theodoric's hell," where Gregory
the Great had told men that the Gothic "tyrant" was to
be seen writhing in the crater of the burning mountain,
damned for the murder of Pope John V., and of the senators
Boethius and Symmachus, as well as for his own impenitent
Arianism.[2]

The pilgrims of Willibald's ship went so far as to land,
in their curiosity to see "what sort of a hell it was." But
they dared not climb the mountain because "the ashes from
the foul Tartarus lay there in heaps at the top like snow,
when it piles up the falling masses of flakes. But they saw
the horrible flame belching out from the pit with a roar
like thunder, and they gazed in awe at the fiery vapour of
smoke ascending to an immense height. And the pumice-
stone, which writers are wont to use,[3] they saw going forth
from the hell, thrown out with the fire, and swallowed up
in the sea, where it fell, and then again thrown out by the
sea upon the shore, where men gathered it."

Such was the view of the known world current in the

---

[1] Hod. c. xxix. These legates
returned to Old Rome in 728, when
Gregory II., as already said, excommunicated the emperor.

[2] At nine o'clock (in the morning?)
a hermit had seen the "king, without shoes and girdle, his hands fast

bound, brought betwixt John the
Pope, and Symmachus the Senator,
and thrown into Vulcan's Gulf"
(Greg. Dialogues, iv. 30). Cf. Hod.
ch. 30.

[3] For cleaning parchment.

eighth century in Latin Christendom, for Willibald's account was published with the imprimatur of Gregory III.,[1] who "turned over all these matters" with the pilgrim "in pleasant and familiar conversation."

Between these events, however, which directly led to Willibald's departure for the German mission, and his return from Syria, ten years elapsed. For travelling from the Liparis by way of Naples, Capua, and Teano, he came to the great monastery of the Benedictines at Monte Cassino. " And when the venerable man (and Tidbert, who had travelled with him through all) came to St. Benedict "—or, in other words, to his successor, the abbot Petronax—" he took up again his old intended profession," and passed ten years among the brethren as sacristan, dean, and porter. When he joined the monastery he had been seven years absent from the West, and it was ten since he quitted England. Twenty years in all had thus passed before Willibald, in escorting a Spanish monk to Rome, found opportunity to publish his journey before the " apostolic " pope.[2]

At the request of his uncle Boniface, he was now sent into Germany to aid him in his work among the heathen ; [3] and, travelling by Lucca, " where his father rested," Ticino, Brescia, and Garda, he came at last to Eichstädt, which Boniface formally resigned to him as his bishopric.[4] His scruples were overcome, it is said, by the trenchant argument that he was fit for the work, and " whoever, like himself, endued with power, refuses the office of a prelate and prefers his own peace to the welfare of others, deserves to suffer the pains of as many of the damned as the number of sinners whose morals he might have corrected as a prelate."

[1] Hod. cc. 33, 34.
[2] Hod. cc. 32, 33.
[3] This request, according to the Itinerarium, cc. xvi.-xvii., was defin-

itely made before Willibald came to Rome with the Spanish monk.
[4] Hod. cc. 35-37 ; Itin. xvii.

Consecrated in 741, and becoming, after his uncle's martyrdom in 754, the leader of the German mission, Willibald survived till 785, and it is evident, from the introductory chapter, that the final touches at any rate were not put to his guide-book till after this, but the main part of the account was dictated by himself on the 23rd of June in a year unnamed.[1]

Willibald is the chief Latin pilgrim in the time between Arculf and the imperial restoration of Charlemagne, but we cannot think that in him we have much of an explorer, discoverer, or scientific observer. Beyond his visits of religious devotion he tells us little. He met a buffalo and a lion in Palestine at different times; he describes the cattle standing in the Syrian pools; and he was interested in the Volcano island of the Liparis—although the last named seems to have attracted him more as Theodoric's hell than as a marvel of nature. These allusions do not prove much of a secular interest, but we must be content with them and a few others—such as the account he gives us of his imprisonment, of the Saracen guard-house on Mount Libanus, of the Customs at Tyre and his own sanctified fraud therein, and of the blackmailing of the Nazareth Christians by the Arabs, who threatened to destroy the local church. His defence before the caliph is put in the ordinary language of Latins, who thought Western Europe was one extreme end of the world of land, beyond which was nothing but a waste of waters.

Once entered into the Caliphate, we may notice, Willibald does not appear to have suffered any definite persecution,[2] though suspected and insulted at his entrance and his exit. The Ommiads were comparatively tolerant, and to

---

[1] So Tobler, xxxix.; pref. to Hod.
[2] Cf. Wilson (C. W.), app. in P.P.T. edit.

that fact we may attribute, in part, the general absence of remarks about the people and government of Syria in our present tractate. It was a case of let well alone on both sides.

The value of Willibald's narrative is of course relative, from the dearth of other notices of pilgrimage in this time. Except for the journey of the monk Fidelis, we have no other narrative of an eighth-century traveller from the Christian West to the Levant.

And we may end this section by reminding ourselves that we must not put too much to Willibald's account, for the form of his record is due, as we have seen, not to himself, but to a nun and a chaplain, whose views, like their experience, are naturally limited.

III. Latin Pilgrims under the Karling Dynasty: Bernard, etc., circ. a.d. 750–870.

The remaining pilgrim-travellers whom we must notice, have this in common—that their journeys are all made in the time of Karling, or Carlovingian rule, between the years in which the father of Charles the Great seized the Frankish sceptre from the Merwings, or house of Clovis, and the abdication of Charles the Fat (751–888). And that abdication was, of course, coincident with the ruin of the dynasty of Pepin and Charlemagne, and with far greater events than the collapse of any one sovereign family. For the close of the ninth century also witnessed the failure of the Frankish attempt to restore the Roman Empire, under Teutonic leadership, among the nations of Western Europe; and it saw the appearance of the heathen Northmen as a " determining quantity " among those same nations—which now first, perhaps, displayed their inborn dislike of a universal

monarchy, and their tendency to group themselves in a
number of independent but powerful states. To all appearance the elements of modern civilisation, prematurely forced
into the mould of the new Holy Roman Empire, were then
thrown out of solution; and the process of the experiment had to be begun over again. As to what specially
concerns us here, the early pilgrim-travel ends with the
same epoch, with the journey of Bernard the Wise—not to
appear again in literature until the twelfth century, and
then as a resultant of the First Crusade, and the consequent
movements of warlike and commercial enterprise.

Here, then, we find a natural stopping-place; but in this
last period of our inquiry, the conditions of Western life are
so changed from what they were in the time of Arculf and
of Willibald, that a word must be said about them. In
732,[1] only a year or two after the nephew of St. Boniface
returned from the Levant, Charles Martel, mayor of the
palace, or chief minister of the Frankish Kingdom, checked
the Saracen invasions of Western and Southern France at
Tours in such a way as to stagger their whole advance upon
this side; and before they could renew the attack, a formidable centralised dominion had arisen to the north of the
Pyrenees, which even threatened them with reprisals in Spain.
For in 751–752 the son of Charles Martel, Pepin, the father
of a still more famous Charles, added the name to the
power of kingship, with the approval of Pope Zacharias;
dethroned Childeric III., the last of the long-haired and
fainéant Merovingian puppets; and founded a new dynasty in
the great Teutonic kingdom. In 754–755 he invaded Italy,
crushed the Lombards, and secured the safety of the papacy
by gifts of land and cities from the conquered territory.
His son and successor, Charles, with the help of the same

[1] And again in 737, elsewhere.

papal alliance on which his father had thriven, strengthened
the Frankish hold on North Italy; and, not content with
practically supplanting the Byzantine authority (now only
existent in name), gained the authority of the Church for a
transference of the imperial title. The Middle Ages had
extraordinary reverence for abstract right; and it was no
light thing for the men of the eighth or ninth century to
say that a lord *de facto* was, or could become, a lord *de jure*—
yet this was what Charlemagne obtained. The Roman
people and the Roman Church, through the mouth of the
bishop of the imperial city, declared, in the year 800, that
to them reverted, in case of abuse, the conferring of the
name, to them so much more awful than the thing or
reality, of Roman Emperor. The Byzantine rulers had
abused their title; a woman, Eirene, the murderess of her
own son, had usurped what was sacred to the nobler sex;
the throne was void; and the electors, reasserting a right
which had never been exercised, gave it to the deliverer of
the holy see, the chief among Christian sovereigns, Charles,
already patrician, now Cæsar and Augustus. He was crowned
on Christmas Day, 800, and for nearly a century his race held
the position he had won for them. It was the first attempt,
by the Teutonic conquerors of Western Europe, to organise
themselves as a political and social whole, analogous to the
religious unity in which they all were now embraced.
Judged by its immediate aims, it was a splendid failure;
but it created a new spirit and a new ideal which, though
realized in forms rather nationalist than imperial, was vital
to the growth of Christendom. The spirit and the ideal
were those of men who were resolved to go forward, to
increase their strength and widen their life—even if it were
in the name of a past which they were leaving more and
more irrevocably behind them.

The new Frankish Kingdom was, perhaps, the first thing which forced upon the Moslem intelligence the unwelcome conviction that there existed in Europe a compact body of resistance, which was not to be broken through by the force or argument of any Asiatic invasion, whether physical or spiritual. A still more alarming power of absorption and adaptation, of taking the best things from strangers without altering its own inner character, was also disclosed with ever greater clearness by that same Europe from this time.

Before his death, in 814, Charles the Great and his Franks rallied the Church militant with considerable effect; driving back the Saracen dominion to the Ebro, conquering the heathen Saxons in the North, and extending Christianity in Upper Germany and along the coasts of the North Sea. And in spite of all the discord, the civil war, and the feudal anarchy, which made head after the control of Charlemagne himself had been removed, some appearance of a united Frankish Empire, guarding Europe from Beneventum to Sleswick, and from the Pyrenees to the Elbe, was maintained for half a century longer (c. 814–888). The only important Mussulman conquests made since the battle of Tours were in the Mediterranean islands. And with the arrest of the Arab advance, the Arab dominion had shown the first symptoms of division. In 750 the Ommiad line of caliphs was brought to a close by the Abbasides; only one of the dispossessed escaped the massacre; but he was welcomed in Spain as the true Commander of the Faithful, and so began the Western Caliphate of Cordova, which lasted to 1038. The Abbasides, indeed, increased the Moslem Empire to east, to north-east, and to south, while they founded a new Moslem capital in Bagdad, and promoted the growth of Moslem commerce and civilisation; but the first confidence of universal victory for Islam was now replaced by more sober ambitions, and the Caliphate little by little grew accustomed to the position of being only one, although the greatest, among the powers of the Earth.

Thus the Byzantine Empire still survived, though its position sank with the decline of the Isaurian revival; but its power was much reduced even in the Balkan peninsula and in Asia Minor, and was practically extinct in the rest of the Mediterranean.

Four states, in the eighth and ninth centuries, had gathered round themselves every race and every country that could be called civilised or progressive—to the west of India and China—with three exceptions. The British Isles, the Asturias, and the Scandinavian lands alone remained outside the two Christian Empires of Franks and Byzantines, and the two Caliphates of Bagdad and of Cordova; and in this time the first of these exceptions was almost included in the third. For between the earlier West-Saxon overlordship of Ecgberht, and the commencement of the later under Ælfred (800–878), the greater part of the British Islands was conquered by the Vikings.

The Spanish Biscayan kingdoms, which alone survived from the Gothic monarchy, were so insignificant that they could hardly be noticed in this bird's-eye view of the world of the Karlings and the Abbassides if it were not for the great future that lay before them.[1] To the south of the barren hills where they had found a refuge, in the lovely regions of Andalus, Mussulman Spain had, by the time of Pepin, already begun to enjoy a higher, more varied, and more refined life than any other society in existence. In the air of that peninsula where Christianity perfected the Inquisition, the ferocity of Islam seemed to evaporate,

---

[1] And for the revival of map-science in that region, with the work of Beatus, in this very time.

and only the purity without the bigotry, only the taste and learning without the literalism of the Arabian faith or philosophy, survived in the Mosque of Cordova or the Giralda of Seville, in the writings of the court of Abderrahman III., or in the speculations and researches of Averroes and of Edrisi.

Under the Karling dynasty there are three principal names associated with pilgrimage—Fidelis (in about 750–760), Bernard (in 867–870), and Frotmund (perhaps in 870–874).[1]

None of these are important, and none except Bernard has left any adequate account of himself.

Fidelis is only known as a traveller in Egypt on his way to Jerusalem, and through the mention of him by a writer who belonged to the next generation—Dicuil, the Irish geographer, in that work of his on "the Measurement of the Earth," which, as we have seen, furnished a brief compendium of geographical knowledge as it stood at the opening of the ninth century.[2] The notice in question is connected with a scientific controversy of the time. Some declared that the Nile on one side flowed into the Red Sea ; others denied this ; and Fidelis is quoted as a witness for the allegation. What his story really proves is, of course (to repeat what we have said before), the continued existence of that fresh-water canal from Memphis to Suez which had been opened by Necho, restored by Hadrian, and again cleared out by Amrou, to aid the Arabs in retaining Egypt. It was not finally blocked up till 767, when a revolt of the people of Medina made men fearful of an attack on Egypt by this very artery. Fidelis, we may fancy, was an Irishman, from his being mentioned only

---

[1] Not to count the anonymous " De Casis Dei " or the " Qualiter sita est Hierusalem."

[2] Finished 825.

in an Irish writing and in connection with Irish churchmen. Thus Dicuil tells us that his story was related to Suibhne, in the presence of the writer, then a pupil of the latter's. "*Brother* Fidelis," he says, was on his way with various clergy and monks to worship in Jerusalem—and it may be presumed that these were a party of the Irish devotees who had already done so much to save Christianity on the Continent, to restore it in Britain, and to connect it with the art and science of the time in their own island. The geographical aspect of the Irish Church movement will be further examined in another chapter. Here we have to deal with the only important pilgrim-record which that movement has left us.

Sailing along the Nile, the travellers were astonished by the sight of the Pyramids, or seven barns of Joseph,[1] "according to the number of the years of plenty." Earlier pilgrims had spoken of twelve; but now facts were being more strictly brought into line with Scripture. There were four of these barns in one place and three in another, and their size was wonderful, "like mountains, all of stone, square at the base, rounded in the upper part, and tapering to a point at the summit."[2] Fidelis, measuring a side of one of these barns, found it almost exactly as we reckon it to-day—four hundred feet; while hard by he noticed a scene of slaughter, a lion and eight men and women, all lying dead. For "the lion had slain them by his strength, and they had slain the lion with their spears and swords; for the place of those barns is desert."

From this point, a little below Memphis, he and his friends started again upon their voyage along the Nile, and sailed on "to the entrance of the Red Sea;" or, in other

[1] Dicuil, vi. 12-20.
[2] "In fine sublimitatis quasi gracile acumen habent." The casing was then on the Great Pyramid.

words, down the canal to Suez; where he found himself close to where Moses crossed with the Israelites. Like earlier devotees,[1] he wished to go and look for Pharaoh's chariot-wheels; but he had given himself up to go whithersoever the mariners listed, and they refused to delay the voyage for any antiquarian researches. Instead of that, they hurried him on, down that western arm of the Red Sea, which Fidelis correctly describes as about six miles in breadth, and as running up far into the north from the main.

No pilgrim-traveller has left us an account of the Levant in the days of Charles the Great; but, in addition to all the other proofs he gave of his care for the holy places, he seems to have inspired the composition of the tract, " On the Houses of God in Jerusalem," which may be dated within his reign (about 808). The writer was possibly not an ordinary priest; he was, some have thought, a man of high rank or office, sent out by the emperor himself to draw up this report, so gloomy in its picture of the increasing wretchedness of Syrian Christians and the decreasing strength of their religion. Whoever the author, and wherever and however he put together his facts and figures, the official tone is unmistakable; but the subject-matter is simply and solely of a religious, and statistical, kind— it is almost a stretch of language to call it geographical.

Fidelis's own account makes it clear that he could not have travelled by the route he describes later than 767. From this time just a century goes by before another pilgrim-record occurs worth noticing. In the course of this long interval the Frankish kingdom grows into the Western Empire, reaches its furthest extent of power and territory, and begins to go to pieces; and our next traveller, Bernard

---

[1] See Orosius, Hist. (i. 10); Philostorgius, iii. 6; Cosmas, Christ. Topog. bk. v.

"the Wise," of Mont St. Michel, does not start for the Levant till this process of dissolution is pretty well advanced.

In 843 the Treaty of Verdun recognised the partition of the grandsons of Charlemagne. Lothair took the Middle Kingdom; Lewis, or Ludwig, the Eastern or (purely) German parts beyond the Rhine; Charles the Bald, the Western districts, which represented the later "France." And in spite of all efforts to the contrary, in spite of all appeals to an older unity, this division proved permanent; Germany, France, and Italy were never again brought together under one central government like that of Charles the Great; for the so-called restoration of the Empire in 884–888 was incomplete in itself, and but a phantom of sovereignty, after all.

Meantime, while the new Christian State was falling asunder, the Northmen were throwing themselves at once upon all sides of it. In 845 they attacked simultaneously the three kingdoms of the creation of 843. Charles the Bald in the West, and Lewis in the East, struggled in vain against their ravages for the next thirty years; while across the Channel the West-Saxon kings were forced to look upon the conquest of all England north of Thames by the same Northmen, and in the South the Mussulmans were slowly establishing themselves in Sicily (827–878), in Crete (823),[1] in Corsica, in Sardinia, and in various points of lower Italy, and even of Provence.[2]

Two great ecclesiastics (Nicholas in Rome (858–867), and Photius in Constantinople) were at the head of the Greek and Latin-speaking branches of the Church : but the

---

[1] First in 750.

[2] Thus, in Fraxinetum (889); on the Garigliano (881); on the pass of the Great St. Bernard (in the tenth century); in Bari (848–875); in Tarentum (856–881). They attacked Marseilles in 838, and Rome in 845, 852, etc. (Cf. Spruner-Menke, Atlas, sheets 21, 22, § Italien, i. and ii.)

wretched Michael the Drunkard was still reigning on the Bosphorus; Lewis the German, Charles the Bald, and Æthelred the West-Saxon were still helplessly witnessing the advances of Northmen and of Moslems; and Christian theologians were just in the midst of their labours in the preparation of the Forged Decretals when our monk of Mont St. Michel was preparing for his pilgrimage.

Bernard started from Rome in 868–869.[1] That is the first we hear of him. But he must have been there before 867, as he obtained the blessing of Pope Nicholas on his journey. He seems to have left Jerusalem before the death of the Patriarch Theodosius, whom he mentions as famous for sanctity. He was again in Italy after the conquest of the people of Beneventum by Lewis the German, in 870. His visit to Bari must have been in the latter days of Saracen dominion within that city; for in 875 it was recaptured, by the united forces of Greeks and Germans, by Lewis and Basil the Macedonian, who had united to pull out this terrible thorn in the flesh of Christendom.

Bernard's narrative may perhaps be compared with Willibald's for the simplicity of its style and the length of its introduction—lengthy, that is, as compared with its very brief account of the holy places themselves. In another respect, it reminds us of Silvia's route. For these two are well-nigh the only examples, among the more important pilgrims (who have left us their own accounts), of the journey to Palestine by way of Egypt. In Bernard's day, this was the regular path of trade and travel.

[1] In the oldest manuscript, B. Mus. Cotton, Faustina, B. 1, the date is given as 970; but every particle of evidence agrees in fixing the true date as in the text. Compare the notices of Pope Nicholas; Theodosius, patriarch of Jerusalem, who died 869; Alexandrinus Michelis, Coptic patriarch, 859 – 871; Lewis (II.), Charles, Lothair, and the sons of Lothair;—all prominent figures in ninth-century history: and see the mention in William of Malmesbury, bk. iv.; Hardy, Eng. Hist. ii. 562, 563

His credulity and ignorance are not greater than those of earlier pilgrims; his sufferings appear to have been less than Willibald's; he shows no inventive faculty, like Antonine or Cosmas, no peculiar breadth of view or culture of style, like Silvia or Arculf.[1] His miracle of the sea retiring on the anniversary festival at Mont St. Michel is like Theodosius' tale of the Euxine paying homage to St. Clement at Cherson; his mention of the barns of Joseph on the Nile banks recalls the language of Fidelis, and of the "Martyr" of Placentia. His recital of the legend of the Archangel Michael himself dedicating the Church at Monte Gargano is characteristic of his class and his time; and so, in another way, is his witness to the extent of the Saracen ravages in Italy, and the hordes of Christian slaves now being shipped to Africa.

The library collected by Charles the Great in Jerusalem, intended, like his hostelry, for the benefit of Catholic travellers, is among Bernard's most valuable memoranda, recording as it does, the care of a true ruler for the civilisation which is the best fruit of victory. Darker days had come now, but the time was not yet forgotten when Saracens had left Christendom in peace for a season; when Frankish king and Moslem caliph exchanged presents and courtesies; and when Haroun Al Rashid sent to Aachen the elephant that Dicuil describes, and the keys of the Holy Sepulchre and of Jerusalem itself.

The "Itinerary of three monks"—of Bernard from Brittany, of one Stephen from Spain, and of a certain Theudemund, whom we may guess to have been a Frank, and who came from the monastery of St. Vincent at Beneventum, starts, as we have said, from Rome. Of the journey from Northern

---

[1] Although he quotes Bede (*i.e.* Arculf) as the standard authority upon the sepulchre of Christ.

France to Italy no record remains. How dangerous it then was may be imagined from Bernard's description of the " land of Rome" itself, or what we should call the Campagna, where "robbers and evil men" so abounded that those who wished to " go to St. Peter " could not pass, save in strong armed bands.

On their way to "the holy places and Babylon" the party first went to Bari, then the chief seat of Saracen power in Italy, by way of Monte Gargano, where they saw the famous sanctuary of the Great Angel of the Guarded Mount, who was also the patron of Bernard's distant home. This church (or cave), made historical in the time of the Norman conquest of Apulia and Calabria by events of the eleventh century, was so small, Bernard tells us, that it was all covered by one rock, from which oaks were growing. There was a monastery here, with sixty brethren, under an abbot Benignatus, and it was probably from these good men that the travellers learnt how the archangel in person was supposed to have hallowed the sanctuary.[1]

The next stage, of one hundred and fifty miles, brought Bernard to Bari, presumably from the want of any other safe port of departure for the Levant. If he sailed from a Christian harbour, such as Marseilles or Amalphi, he would run a greater risk of damage from Moslem ships, and of a bad reception in the Moslem ports for which he was bound.

Bari had been taken by the Saracens, from the hands of the Beneventines, in 848. For, on the death of Charles the Great, as we have pointed out already, the advance of Islam had been taken up with fresh vigour. Mussulman divisions alone prevented a conquest of Italy as complete as that of Spain; the true believers had twice entered the

[1] Ch. 2.

Tiber before Leo IV. fortified the Leonine city against them in 852, and the remembrance of this and the dread of worse may well have left Bernard without hope of success in his undertaking except through the help of his enemies, from start to finish.

So, "finding out the chief man of the city, by name Suldanus" (whatever his name was, his title must have been Emir, as Sultan was the dignity of a superior), the pilgrims "had all their voyage settled by two letters," which gave a statement of their appearance and their intended route to the authorities in Egypt, at Alexandria and at "Babylon," or Old Cairo. But the ruler of all the Saracens, to whom these provincial governors were subject—"Amarmominus," Bernard's version of Emir-al-Mumenin, the commander of the faithful—lived far away beyond Jerusalem, in Bagdad ("Bagada").[1] For since Willibald's day the Ommiads had been supplanted by the Abbassides, who had moved the capital from Damascus at the same time that the Karlings were replacing the Merwings as sovereigns of the Franks.

Bernard got his passports at Bari, but he did not embark there. He was sent on to Tarentum, then likewise in Saracen hands, and put on board a ship bound for Egypt, which, with five others, was engaged in transporting nine thousand Christian slaves to Africa. Two of these were bound for the Barbary coast, two for Tripoli, two for Alexandria; and, sailing with these last, the pilgrims came, in thirty days, within sight of the Pharos. But on trying to land, they were stopped by the "captain of the crew;" permission was only to be won with backsheesh. "For leave to disembark, we paid him six gold pieces."[2]

---

[1] "And Axinarri," adds the manuscript: "Axiam" in Mabillon. See Wright, "Early Travels in Palestine," pp. 21–30.

[2] Cc. 3–5.

The same process had to be gone through with the lord of Alexandria, who ignored the letters of the Soldan of Bari, till he had been paid three hundred denarii, when he suddenly became quite affable, and gave Bernard a letter to the governor of "Babilonia," or Middle Egypt. Insisting as they did on payment by weight, these Moslem princes made even more profit on this money of the road than appeared at first sight: "Three solidi and three denarii among them are six solidi and six denarii among ourselves." "This Alexandria adjoins the sea," Bernard is careful to tell us, and so the Venetians were able, a few years before, "by sailing thither," to steal away the body of St. Mark. For Venice was then just beginning to appear as a power in the Mediterranean, like Amalphi, but unstained by the same disgraceful alliance with Moslems to the damage of Christian lands.

Six days' sail up the river Nile, or "Gighon,"—which flowed, says Bernard, through the midst of Alexandria into the sea—brought the travellers to "Babylon,"[1] the ancient fortress near Fostat, and the "seven granaries of Joseph." Here the whole party, in spite of introductions and certificates, were promptly clapped into prison till each had paid over again the old tax of three hundred denarii, when they were at once released, and under the powerful protection of the governor, who, as Bernard was told, ranked next to the caliph himself, they were safe from all further extortion while in Egypt. Only, in going from place to place, they were obliged to provide themselves with a "parchment or sealed document,"—a passport, in fact, with *visés* constantly redated,—before they were permitted to depart.

---

[1] The governor here was "Adelacham," the "second man in the Empire of Amarmominus."

The subject Christians living under the Moslem rule were all obliged to pay at least thirteen denarii by the year; but, if penniless, the strict law of Koran, tribute, or sword, was not enforced, and the defaulter was only sent to prison " till, either, by the love of God, he is delivered by His angel, or else brought out by other good Christians."

Descending the Nile to Damietta and Tanis, where he found " very religious Christians, burning with hospitality," the pilgrim now set out for Palestine across the desert; noticing, near the " entrance of Egypt," three of " the bodies of those who were rooted out in the time of Moses, huge as walls—three of the Colossi, in other words, of ancient Egypt.[1]

From hence to Gaza, at the " entrance of Syria," there were only two oases, Albara and Albachara,[2] but these were furnished with hospices and bazaars for the purchase of supplies, for rest, and for refreshment.   Before reaching Gaza, too, there was a piece of fertile country : the remainder was total desert ; " and well is it called a desert, for it brings forth no herb nor anything grown from seed, save palm-trees, but is white like the earth in time of snow."   Through this Bernard painfully made his way, and at Gaza, " Samson's town, a city exceeding rich in everything," [3] he at last reached the sacred ground of Palestine.

But here his account (which though brief has been hitherto fairly ample) dwindles into a bare enumeration of sites and churches, and only details one or two marvels, such as that of the Holy Fire, which, though probably as old as the second century in one form or another, and noticed by

---

[1] Bernard, ch. 8.

[2] " The well " and " the pulley." These two are made into one by Clermont Ganneau, " Révue Critique," 1876, ii. p. 394—rather unreason-ably, as it seems.   Bernard's route lay through Farama and Alariza (Pelusium and Al-Arish).

[3] As Antonius Martyr had found it. Bernard, ch. 9.

Gregory of Tours at the end of the sixth, was now beginning to attract wider attention.

"On Easter Eve," says Bernard, "after the office is done, Kyrie Eleison is chanted; till, by the coming of an angel, the light is kindled in the lamps that hang before the sepulchre of the Lord;" and these words of his are quoted by William of Malmesbury as an evidence of the antiquity of the miracle. The twelfth century relies on the word of the ninth.

In Jerusalem the pilgrims were comfortably lodged in the "hostel of the glorious Emperor Charles,"[1] which he had built for all who came there to worship, "speaking the Roman tongue;" and enjoyed the use of the library in the Church of St. Mary close by, collected by the care of the same great prince. Yet they seem to have made but a short stay. At least they recorded little. Bernard tells us, indeed, of four "pre-eminent" churches, built round the Holy Sepulchre; of the place said to be the centre of the world and marked out with chains, in the midst of the court-yard between the same four churches; of the stone that the angel rolled away from the tomb—for only the original, and no mere copy, will satisfy travellers in this age; of Solomon's Temple, which contained the synagogue of the Saracens; of the iron gates through which the angel led forth St. Peter, never opened afterwards; of the four round tables of the Last Supper; of the writing on the marble which Christ traced with His finger, and which

---

[1] In Charlemagne's day, there was friendship between the (Eastern) Caliphate and the Frankish Kingdom, so he was naturally allowed to provide for the better reception of travellers from his own land. The Caliph Haroun Al Rashid is also said to have sent Charles (1) the keys of the Holy Sepulchre and of Jerusalem, (2) an elephant, and (3) dogs. Cf. Dicuil, vii. 35; Einhardt Vita Car. 16; Mon. Sangal. Gesta Carolina, ii. 9; Pertz Script. ii. 752. The story of Charles's pilgrimage is found in an Anglo-Norman poem of the twelfth century.

was now to be seen, after centuries of forgetting; and of the pool in which Lazarus washed after his resurrection;—but his catalogue is, after all, a meagre one, and for many of his details he seems to refer to Arculf's book, which he had certainly read in Bede's abridgment.

Near Bethlehem, Bernard was shown a curious memorial —the field where Habakkuk was working when the angel bade him carry his dinner to Daniel in Babylon.[1] And as to this Babylon, he adds, it is to the south of Jerusalem, a different place from the Babylon of Egypt, but now unapproachable; serpents and wild animals alone inhabit it.[2]

With this his journey begins to point again towards home. After visiting a few of the monasteries of Judæa, but apparently without any exploration of Central or Northern Syria, Bernard came down "from Jerusalem to the sea," took ship, and, after sixty days of tempestuous sailing, landed at Mons Aureus in Italy, and so made his way to Rome.

Here, in the Lateran, the proper seat of the "apostolic;" in St. Peter's, "on the west side of the city, that for size had no equal in the world;" and among the "countless" relics of saints which Rome even then contained, Bernard found solace after his toils: but, in spite of his Christian loyalty, his thoughts seem to go back to the peace and strong government of Islam with a sort of regret, when face to face with the thieves and robbers of Italy. For fear of these, as well as of Saracen corsairs, the keys of Rome, he noticed, were brought every night to the pope himself; in the absence or paralysis of the secular power, the bishop of the city had to provide for its defence, and the pontiffs of the ninth century did their duty manfully.

But in the duchy of Beneventum, in the Campagna, in

[1] Bell and Dragon, 34; Bernard, chs. 11–16.   [2] Cf. Theodosius, ch. 83 (Gild).

Lombardy, and in Brittany, the fight with misrule was a hard one. The people of Beneventum, in murdering their prince Sichard " for his pride " (A.D. 839), had been just in time to prevent his murdering them, but in the result they had abandoned most of South Italy to the Saracens; here and in Lombardy Lewis the German had now undertaken to restore order, and had done some good; but anarchy still prevailed near Rome itself, and the state of his native Brittany Bernard indicates clearly enough by one remark. The blood-feud was so savage that the chance passer-by, in the absence of a kinsman, was bound to avenge the injured, and death was the punishment for any theft above four denarii.[1] There must have been, then and there, as many sturdy beggars as in England in the days when, if a man stole aught above thirteenpence halfpenny, the law said he should hang for it.

About the same time as the pilgrimage of Bernard a noble Breton, of the name of Frotmund, who had " incurred blood-guiltiness," submitted himself to an extraordinary penance. Bare-footed, with ashes on his head, covered with a coarse robe of penitence, and bearing round arms and waist a heavy chain, he started in the year 870, on a sort of perpetual pilgrimage. That is, he was to wander from one holy place to another till God should relieve him of his sin, and of the material load he bore in evidence of that sin. He first went to Syria, and stayed some time in Jerusalem; next to Egypt, where he lived with the monks of the Thebaid; next, we are told, he was found praying at the tomb of Cyprian, outside Carthage; then he returned to Rome, and tried to win pardon from Pope Benedict III. Condemned to further expiation, he again travelled to Jerusalem, to Cana in Galilee, to the Red Sea, Mount Sinai,

---

[1] Chs. 20–23.

and the site of the resting-place of the Ark in the Mountains of Armenia, suffering unnumbered tortures by the way, sometimes stopped and scourged along the roads by the infidels, sometimes by his own austerities bringing himself near his end,—destitute, afflicted, tormented ; till finally, in the fourth year of his wanderings, he was " delivered from his chains of sin and iron " at the tomb of St. Marcellinus, in the monastery of Redon.[1]

The downward limits of our present section are the closing years of the ninth century ; but (in a volume confined to the earlier Middle Ages) we do not lose much by stopping at this point.   For the remaining two hundred years of pre-crusading history hardly furnish us with more than one other memorial of Christian pilgrimage, beyond the scattered references of chroniclers ; and the exception in question, the little treatise " On the Situation of Jerusalem '' (which some have plausibly tried to fix to the year 975, and John Tzimiskes' brief re-conquest of the Holy City), is, from its solitary position, a confirmation of the natural fitness of our boundary.   For now the field of exploring activity is practically abandoned by the religious travellers : and—

> " The old order changeth, giving place to new ;
> And God fulfils Himself in many ways,
> Lest one good custom should corrupt the world."

---

[1] Cf. Tobl. Bibl. Geog. Pal. 26 (edit. of 1875).

THE ROUND WORLD AS REPRESENTED IN MEROVINGIAN COINS.
(*From B. Mus. Coin Dept.*)

CHAPTER V.

COMMERCIAL AND MISSIONARY TRAVEL.

I. COMMERCIAL.

THE commercial intercourse of Christendom with the non-Christian world of this time lies partly inside and partly outside the story of exploration and geographical advance.

In this chapter we shall find ourselves at a loss from the absence of those personal notices, those accounts of individual travel, which we have been able to use for the history of early pilgrimage, or which illuminate the progress of trade from the Crusading Age. We shall also notice with disappointment how the chief commercial routes remain unaltered, except to decline; how discovery, such as marked the transition from the mediæval to the modern world, is either unknown, or merely transitory (as in the case of fresh caravan routes over thoroughly well-known countries); and we must be careful not to overrate the importance of traditional and stationary trade upon our subject. We are only concerned with matters which helped to enlarge or stimulate, in some way, the knowledge of the world possessed by Christendom; and, as we have warned ourselves before, it will not aid us to attend to a simply decadent or unprogressive intercourse, either of traffic or religion, unless it leaves, for instance, some landmarks, like the pilgrim-records we have examined, by which we may check our position.

But a word must be said about the great routes, as they existed from Constantine to the fall of the Karlings; about the attempts made from time to time to modify or alter them; about the manner in which they were, or were not maintained, at their earlier efficiency; and about the more important notices bearing upon Western enterprise, however little of real novelty there may be in any of them. We must welcome and make something of even the smallest satisfactory proof of a Christian interest in the vast tracts beyond the Roman civilisation. Thus, for example, we shall not be at any pains to chronicle the coming and going of the regular silk-merchants from Central Asia, through Persia, to the Levant: but the two attempts made by Justinian and his successors to open other lines of traffic in the same precious article will be more to the point. Yet there is a charm about the very dimness of the outlook. It is true we have often to rely upon suggestions, hints, indications covering large masses of unknown or forgotten detail; we are forced to frame our picture of the movement of life to and fro upon the world-surface with the vagueness of an unfinished, barely outlined sketch; a mist is upon the face of the earth, for us;—through it we see some prominent objects, perhaps even trace the lie of the country, but we cannot follow from point to point those who are moving up and down, from east to west, from north to south. The merchant floating down the stream; the caravan crossing the steppe, mounting the defile, looking out upon the sea and its harbours; the ferry passing the river; the mariners in their little ship,—they are real figures, yet they are nameless, all but a few : they suffer, and they succeed without having ever found a voice for their story. On the desert, perhaps, a cloud of robber-horse bursts upon them; on the river their boat sinks overladen; in the mountain gorges they drop with cold ; in the dirty lanes of the mart they die of disease. Commerce is not organised, safeguarded, universalised as at present ; but such as it is, its reach is wide, and its life never quite extinct. And though the picture may be misty, we must try and see our way through the haze. The value of the whole, after all, depends on the meaning that the several parts supply.

And first of all as to the general tendency. In these earlier Middle Ages, contrasting somewhat with the Cæsars' time, contrasting absolutely with our own, the centre of trade-energy is in Asia, and not in Europe :—

> " The seër from the West was then in shade ;
> The seër from the East was then in light."

As the Oriental reaction, rising up against the tide of Greek and Roman influence which poured in with Alexander and with Cæsar, added strength to strength in the Persian and Arabian revivals of Asiatic Empire ; as the Mediterranean civilisation seemed to decay ; and as Gaul, Spain, Italy, and Britain were brought face to face with barbarism ;—the old world, as it had been before Marathon, appeared almost to have returned. The wheel had come half-circle round.

But to go back a little. What were the trade routes that the Roman world, when it became Christian, carried on from its pre-Christian time ? for they continued the same, only under varying control, through the earlier Middle Ages.

They were mostly from east to west, or from west to east ; for, on the north, beyond the Elbe and the Carpathians—as well as on the south, beyond the Sahara and the Arabian desert,—there was not much commerce to be had, with two exceptions. The amber trade of the Baltic coasts, and the gold, ivory, and slave trade of the Zanzibar coast, beyond Guardafui, were the only important flank diversions

of the mercantile activity which moved, like the course
of the great mountain ranges, across the length or longitude
of the Old World.   For the Red Sea channel, so important
for East African, Arabian, and Indian products, was mainly
along the same line, along the same " path of the sun " as
the Central Asian track.   From the Indus to the straits
of Bab-el-Mandeb, its direction was parallel to the overland and caravan route followed by the chief part of the
same Indian commerce; from Aden to Suez, and up the
canal[1] from Suez to the Nile, the straight line from east to
west was bent, as it were, to run north-west; but it was
only in the by-path along East Africa that a flank movement, similar to the northern, was really followed.

Meantime, from the Levantine coasts the Mediterranean
Empire had choice enough for the extension of its traffic
into Asia, both in the way of imports and of exports.   There
was the route from Byzantium and Trebizond, which crossed
the isthmus of the Caucasus, traversed the Caspian, and
ascended the Oxus to Bokhara and Samarcand; still proceeding eastwards, it forked—one branch turned north-east
to China, another south-east to India.   There was the
Euphrates waterway, starting from Callinicum or Rakka in
Syria, and bringing the traveller through the Persian Gulf,
and along the coasts of the Gulf of Oman and Baluchistan
to the Indus.   And there was also the main Persian road,[2]
which, crossing the upper Euphrates near Birrah, and passing
Nisibis, ran on steadily, first due east, then north-east, to
the Oxus, where, like the first-named track, it divided, to
seek both the treasure-houses of Further Asia.

[1] Cf. Heyd, Commerce du Levant
(edit. of Soc. de L'Or. Lat., 1885–86),
i. 10–11.   Open at intervals, e.g. (1)
under Necho, (2) under [some of]
the Ptolemies, (3) under Hadrian
and Trajan, (4) in the early sixth
century, (5) from Amrou's conquest
to 767.

[2] Cf. Pliny, vi. 17; Heyd, Commerce du Levant, i. 4, 5.

Viewed again, from the Chinese or Turkish standpoint, there were three separate ways from the Roof of the World to the Levant: the first, from Lake Balkash by Talas, the main seat of trade between the Jaxartes and the Wall of China, and thence across Sogdiana and the Caspian to the Black Sea; the second, from Kashgar by Merv, and so through Persia to the south of the Caspian; the third from Khotan and Yarkand, across the Pamir and the Hindu Kûsh to the Indus valley, from which men either went by sea along the coast to the Persian Gulf, or followed a land route parallel to this.

A path of minor importance, and connected with the main Black Sea avenues of commerce, ran from the lower Danube round the north of the Euxine, and was employed by the Scythian and Græco-Roman settlements in the Crimea; while the Red Sea outlet, already noticed, though deriving most of its value from the Indian trade, carried the more daring merchant along the shore of Africa to the equator, and possibly beyond, to the islands of Pemba and Zanzibar. The northern amber and fur trade, such as it was, probably followed the course of one of those great rivers, the Dnieper, the Oder, or the Vistula, which formed the natural roads between Baltic and Mediterranean lands.

These were the main arteries of the commerce of that ancient world, which reached its highest development and its clearest interconnection in the time of Ptolemy, in the second century after Christ; when the Antonines [1] sent their

[1] In the Chinese records both the Antonines (ANTUN) in A.D. 166; and the sovereign reigning in A.D. 282–3, viz. Carus, sent embassies to the Celestials (the latter arriving in 284); and in the Roman records, envoys from the Central Flowery Kingdom are said to have appeared before Augustus (Florus, iv. 12) probably for trade negotiations. Later on, Cosmas in the sixth century, Theophylact Simocatta in the seventh, were possibly acquainted, although only by hearsay, with China (or Cochin-China); and the Chinese speak of Byzantine ambassadors ap-

mission to the Court of China, and when the furthest extension of Greek and Roman knowledge and influence, to east, south, and north, had been accomplished. It was a world bounded by the inland of China and Further India on the east; by the Gobi Desert, the Kirghiz Steppes, the plains of " Great " or Central Russia, the Baltic, and the German Ocean on the north; by the Atlantic on the west; and by the Sahara, the marshes of the Nile, the Arabian Desert, and the Indian Ocean on the south. On this side, however, occasional glimpses had been caught, both of the Soudan countries beyond the Sahara, of Southern Arabia,[1] and of the shore lands of East Africa stretching far beyond the furthest south of continental or inland knowledge. But, with these exceptions, the limits we have sketched were final even for Ptolemy; and, without committing ancient knowledge in general to his peculiar theories and extraordinary misconceptions, we may say pretty confidently that the horizon, both of ordinary men and of geographers, was narrower than his, down to the age of Viking discovery.

---

pearing in 643, 711, 719, 742, perhaps to ask for aid against the Arabs, such as was sought in vain by Yezdegerd, the last king of Sassanid Persia.

[1] As by Ælius Gallus (with whom went Strabo) in his march to Marsiaba, possibly Yemen, in B.C. 24 (Strabo, xvi. 4, §§ 22–24); by Petronius, in his capture of Premnis and Napata, probably Abou Hammed on the Upper Nile, below Khartoum, c. B.C. 20 (Strabo, xvii. 1; Dion Cassius, liv. 5; Pliny, H. N. vi. 29); by Cornelius Balbus, in his conquest of the Garamantes, in the modern Fezzan, B.C. 20 (Pliny, H. N. v. 36; cf. Virgil, Æneid, vi. 795); by Septimius Flaccus and Julius Maternus, in their expeditions to Agisymba, possibly the region of Lake Tchad, at a date unfixed, but probably in the time of Trajan, A.D. 97–117 (Ptolemy, Geog. i. 8, § 5); by Trajan himself, in his march against the Æthiopians, in one tradition preserved by Antoninus Martyr in Justinian's day (Ant. c. 35); by the centurions of [? Julius Cæsar and of] Nero, in their journey up the Nile valley in search of the river's sources, which seemed to them to lie where we now find the Great Marshes in about 9° N. Lat. (Pliny, H. N. vi. 29, and Seneca, Nat. Quæst. vi. 8); cf. the journey of the Knight Julianus under Nero to the Baltic in search of amber (Pliny, H. N. xxxvii. 3).

Yet, narrower or wider, the commercial outlook and intercourse of the Cæsars and their subjects was very extensive;
compared with that of the earlier mediæval period, it may
fairly be called immense; and yet, perhaps, the successes
already gained were an obstacle to greater. In one sense, the
light that was in them proved to be darkness. The Roman
world, gathered round the great inland sea, was so rich,
so highly organised, so self-content, that it made no serious
effort to explore the ocean, or to follow up barren and
unknown coasts, in hope of treasures beyond. There was
no commercial need for trying to open up the waterway
round Africa, as the Phœnicians claimed once to have done
six centuries before Christ.[1] When the caravan routes and
river highways to India and further Asia were in such good
order, even the most adventurous would not embark on the
perilous voyage from West to East, from Spain to the Ganges,
which was certainly believed as possible by the more
advanced of ancient geographers fifteen hundred years
before it was realised in the American and Pacific voyages
of 1492 and 1520.   Columbus and Diaz, Da Gama and
Magellan were not anticipated, chiefly because the same
suggestions of gain did not occur to men who were living
in the splendid and proud society of the Julian or Flavian
or Antonine emperors. There was the added reason that
the compass [2] and quadrant were unknown, and nautical
science in its childhood; but this fact in itself forces us to
look for an explanation. If Greek thought had cared to
give its attention to ocean voyaging, it would soon have
made headway. But it was interested in the theory of the
world, its shape and size, far more than in the practical

[1] That ancient commercial enterprise was pretty far advanced (down
the East African coast) is proved by
the Mashonaland gold mines of the
Sofala shore, and the " ruined cities "
of that region. But these were almost
undoubtedly pre-Roman.

[2] Though not the magnet stone.

exploration of the same; and while Eratosthenes[1] could calculate pretty accurately the circumference of the globe, and while Ptolemy could discuss with admirable thoroughness the mathematical and astronomical basis of geography, the maps even of the last-named gave only an approximate account of lands already well known; discovery and travel hardly ever pushed beyond a limited part of the north temperate zone; even the West African islands were practically unvisited; and the most daring of Greek navigators[2] declared that all progress in the North Sea was barred, about the latitude of the Shetlands, by an impenetrable black mollusc.

We have noticed that the ancient trade routes continue far into the Middle Ages, with only a change of masters. Between Constantine and Justinian there is nothing that calls for notice in the Roman, or Western, or Christian commerce on these lines, except a decreasing activity, a lowered scale of demand,[3] if not of supply, and an enfeebled control. The reverence of the outside world for Rome, which outlasted the third century with all its terrible revelations of weakness and anarchy; which led the Chinese, as Vopiscus boasts, to look upon Aurelian as almost divine; which brought embassies from India and Ethiopia to the court of Constantine; and made the ruler of Ceylon anxious for the friendship of Julian,—had dwindled to a shadow of its former self in the dismal time that witnessed the break-up of the Western Empire.[4] But in the sixth century two

---

[1] Followed by Marinus and Ptolemy with rather less success.

[2] Pytheas.

[3] In the time of Pliny, the Roman world spent one hundred million sesterces a year in the Asiatic trade (H. N. vi. 26, xii. 41); the Christen-dom of Charlemagne probably not a tenth of this sum, even including Byzantine commerce.

[4] See Vopiscus, "Aurelian," ch. 41; Eusebius, "Life of Constantine," iv., chs. 7, 50; Ammianus Marcellinus, xxii. 7. The portraits and busts of

important attempts were made towards new developments of trade by changing the old mercantile routes from the Levant to Further Asia, or rather by bringing into a place of primary value certain ways which before had only held a secondary place. Further, in this same time, during the last revival of an Empire which could still be called Roman, a valuable industry was introduced into Christendom; and several merchant travellers of unusual experience journeyed and wrote (or told) their story. In other words, the Byzantine rulers tried to divert the overland commerce of the far East from its regular course through Persia,—first by the help of Abyssinian middlemen; and, secondly, by an alliance with the Turks and Sogdians beyond the Oxus. Both these attempts arose out of the question of the silk traffic. The monopoly of the carrying trade for this product had long been in Persian hands; but now the Mediterranean receivers, dissatisfied with their intermediaries, tried to open a more direct traffic with the original makers and vendors.

Christian Abyssinia, or " Æthiopia," Justinian hoped, in alliance with its Christian sub-kingdom in Yemen, with the Nestorians of Persia, and with the Church of St. Thomas in Malabar, might open anew for the main branch of Eastern commerce a route long followed by a certain number of

Constantine, according to Eusebius, were taken back by the Indian deputies to their own country, and there honoured as likenesses of " their Master and their Lord." The rhetorical verses of Claudian—

("... Totam pater undique secum Moverat Auroram, ... " etc.); the equally rhetorical prose of the Orator Pacatus (A.D. 389), which describes Medians, Sacæ, Indians, and other Eastern peoples, as the subjects or allies of the Great Theo-dosius, are obvious extravagances (see Panegyrici Veteres, ii. 316). Precisely similar bombast is talked by Avitus of Vienne, in A.D. 516, in reference to the Emperor Anastasius, to whom Parthian and Indian must alike submit. See Reinaud, " Rélations de l'Empire Romain avec l'Asie Orientale," pp. 280–284. Still more extravagant are the terms in which Sidonius Apollinaris addresses Majorian at Lyon, in 458, and Anthemius at Rome, in 468.

traders. This diversion, if successful, would have involved
a considerable increase of maritime activity; for it made
necessary a long sea voyage from Scinde to the mouth of
the Persian Gulf (the course of Nearchus), before sailors
could bring their wares to South-west Arabia, and through
the straits of Bab-el-Mandeb to Adulis and Axum, or to
Suez and Elath.[1] It is curious to notice the possibilities
opened to Western enterprise by this far-reaching Christian
alliance, which sanctified the delights of monetary gain by
its apparent zeal for the propagation of the faith. Had it
succeeded, it might, for one thing, have given a new impulse
to discovery. It might have developed a powerful Christian
State in the South. And in particular, by strengthening
Christianity on the east of the Red Sea, it might have
rendered impossible the rise of Islam. The decisive advantage in world-commerce which the Christian allies might
have gained would have certainly carried with it an advantage—possibly decisive, possibly illusory—in political power
as well. As it was, the Christian kingdom of Yemen came
near to conquering Mecca and the holy land of Arabia in
Mohammed's infancy. The defeat of Abrahah's army by
the Koreish in the battle of the Elephant was a turning-
point in the history of Southern Europe, of Western Asia,
of Northern Africa; by it the field was cleared for the birth
and the rearing of a giant whose strength would one day be
felt. But how small a force might have turned the scale in
570. And, before Mohammed, where was the unity, the
fiery alacrity, the mission of the Arabian people? Without
the bond and the inspiration of their common faith, they
were as sheep without a shepherd. It was in the light of

[1] Cf. Theophanes, i. 218, who
mentions a Roman Customs-station
near the Isle of Jotaba (Tirân), in
the Red Sea, for the Suez goods; cf.
also Procopius, De Bell. Pers. i. 19;
Anecdota, p. 564; and Heyd, Commerce du Levant, i. 10.

religion that they saw, as a revelation, their power and their right, to combine, to conquer, to govern, and to civilise.

But Justinian found the Abyssinians lacking in the enterprise and persistence necessary to oust the Persians from the marts of this "Erythrean" route, and thus his plan collapsed with the failure of its initial step. The alternative, of a northern *détour*, analogous to the north-east passage of later days (as the southern digression suggests the Portuguese curve round Africa to reach the Indian coasts), was equally futile in the long run, but for a time it seemed to promise better results. The way was opened by a quarrel that broke out between Touran and Iran, between the Persians of Chosroes Nushirvan and the Turks beyond the Oxus. These last, by their conquest of Sogdiana, in the middle of the sixth century, now controlled the western avenue of the trade of Central and Further Asia; but the Persian king, fearing that their warriors would infallibly attend their caravans, refused admittance for all alike on the Oxus border. Accordingly, in 568, a Turkish embassy arrived at the court of Justin II. (Justinian's successor) "to cultivate the friendship of the Romans, and transfer the sale of silk to them." The alliance was eagerly accepted; [1] and, in August of the same year, Zemarchus the Cilician, "prefect of the cities of the East," left Byzantium for Samarcand, by way of Kertch and the plains of Astrakhan.

The embassy was under the guidance of Maniach, "Chief of the people of Sogdiana," who had first suggested to Dizabul, the Turkish khan, this Roman alliance, and had himself come to Byzantium to negotiate the same. On crossing the frontiers of Sogdiana the travellers were solemnly exorcised; Zemarchus was made to pass through the fire; and strange

---

[1] Cf. Procopius, De Bell. Pers. i. 19, 20, etc., on the Southern Venture; Menander excerpt. p. 295, 397; Theophan. p. 484, etc., on the Northern.

ceremonies were performed over the baggage of the expedition—certain " Turks ringing a bell and beating a drum over this ; while others ran round it carrying leaves of incense flaming and crackling, raging like mad men, and gesticulating as if they were repelling evil spirits." After these precautions the Roman envoys arrived in the camp of Dizabul, " in a hollow encompassed by the Golden[1] Mountain,"— apparently somewhere in the district of the Seven Rivers, near Lake Iyssk-Kul, to the west of Tengri Khan. They found him in his tent, seated on a golden chair, and surrounded with rich hangings of silk ; another of his gilded thrones rested on four golden peacocks, a precursor of the peacock throne of the great Mogul at Delhi. His gold and silver plate, his clothing of flowered silk, the drinking powers of himself and his court, astonished the ambassadors,— who accompanied Dizabul soon afterwards in an attack upon Persia. On the march the Romans passed through Talas or Turkestan on the north side of the Jaxartes, the very country where Hiouen-Thsang, on his way from China to India, sixty years later, met with Dizabul's successor. Zemarchus was present at a banquet in Talas, where the Turkish chief, forgetting his politeness in his cups, insulted and reviled the Persian envoy who had come to stay his hand ; but the Byzantine does not seem to have actually gone into battle with his ally. Near the river Oech (Jaxartes?), he was sent back to Byzantium with all honour, accompanied by a Turkish embassy. Halting by the "huge, wide lagoon"

[1] Aktag, or Ektag, *i.e.* the " White Mount," mistranslated "Golden" by Menander. The Golden Mountain of the Mongols, in later time, was the Altai, and this may be meant here, but it seems rather too distant, and does not quite suit the narrative. See the fragments of Menander Protector in Müller, Fragment. Histor. Græc., iv. p. 235 ; De Guignes, "Huns," i. 226, 227 ; ii. 380–395, 463. Also see Theophylact Simocatta, vii. 8. Hugues ("Il Lago d'Aral," 1874) thinks Dizabul's camp was near Khokand.

of the Sea of Aral,[1] Zemarchus sent off an express, under a lieutenant named George, to announce to the emperor "the return of the party from the Turks." George hurried on by a route which was "without water and altogether desert, but was the shortest way," apparently across the steppes to the north of the Caspian and Euxine; and his superior, following more slowly, marched twelve days by the sandy shores of the Aral Sea; crossed the Emba, the Ural, the Volga, and the Caucasus; and, triumphantly eluding the Persians who tried to stop him on the Kuban, made his way in safety to Trebizond and Constantinople. For some twelve years, this north Caspian track seems to have been followed, while the Turkish alliance subsisted; and, about 580, another embassy was despatched by the Emperor Tiberius II. under one Valentine, to Tardu Khan, the Tateu of the Chinese.[2]

But at last, in the reign of the same Tiberius (II.), dissensions [3] broke out; the Turks attacked and took Kherson: and when the Turkish dominion itself fell to pieces, early in the seventh century, the people of Bokhara

---

[1] So Hugues, "Lake of Aral," pp. 21, etc. (1874). Yule, "Cathay," prelim. essay (suppl. note viii.); Vivien de St. Martin, "Histoire de la Géographie, etc." (p. 235); Peschel, "Geschichte der Erdkunde," pp. 92, 93; Marinelli (Neumann), "Die Erdkunde bei den Kirchen Vätern," pp. 6-8;—all treat of Zemarchus' route and agree on the main points, as given in text. After passing along the Aral Sea, he crossed (1) the Ich = the Emba, flowing into the Caspian at north-east corner; (2) the Daïch = the Ural, called Γεήχ by Constantine Porphyrogenitus in the tenth century, (De Adm. Imperii. ch. 37); (3) the Attila, Athil, or Volga; (4) the Land of the Ugurs, where he was warned of 4,000 Persian enemies lying in wait for him near the river Kophen, or Kuban (?), which flows into the Sea of Azov near the Gulf of Kertch.

[2] Menander Protector (another fragment, in Bonn edit., 1835) and De Guignes, as last cited.

One might have expected that these repeated journeys to the north of the Caspian might have done something to break down the time-honoured superstition of this Water as an inlet of the Northern Ocean, but they seem to have had no effect on the Latin world.

[3] From A.D. 579.

and Samarcand resumed the old Persian route, which had only been closed on account of their Tartar lords.

But in the lifetime of Justinian these failures to divert the trade routes were compensated for by the introduction of a new culture, which might in its turn make the Mediterranean lands the starting-point of an independent line of commerce. The secret of silk manufacture was brought either from China or from the halfway station of Sogdiana, by two Persian monks, in the interests of their religion rather than of their Government, in 552.[1]

About this time, as we may gather from Procopius, these monks arrived—" from India ; and, learning that the emperor had it much at heart that the Romans should no longer buy silk from the Persians, promised to manage so that Romans should not have to purchase the article from Persians or any others." They explained to Justinian that silk was not combed from trees (as Virgil and nearly all Westerns, except Pausanias,[2] had supposed), but that it was spun by a caterpillar, whose eggs might be transported, and whose habitat might thus be changed. With this purpose, they now journeyed to Khotan, if not to China;[3] and returned with the eggs stored in a hollow cane, and mulberry leaves to feed the worms when hatched. The folly of the Government, which tried to enforce a State monopoly in the manufacture of silk, hampered the progress of the new industry in the West, and helped to keep Christendom in dependence on outside products. More than that, it drove

---

[1] Procop. De Bell. Goth. iv. 17. Theoph. excerpt. p. 484 (Bonn edit.); also cf. Prelim. Essay in Yule's Cathay; Gibbon, ch. xl.

[2] Paus. vi. 26 (see Zonaras Annal. xiv.).

[3] Theophanes says the "land of the Seres," which is almost certainly one or the other in his pages; Procopius, more loosely, "India." But, as we shall see in other connections, some part of Further India is constantly in the mind of Western writers when they speak of "Serica."

many nimble-fingered artisans to emigrate into Persia; and so, by the time of Heraclius, the last state of the Empire (in commerce as in many other things) was worse than the first, a century earlier, when the imperial restoration began, and before Justinian's experiment had been tried and finally found wanting.

It was possibly, though by no means certainly, in connection with the Southern or Abyssinian enterprise already noticed that Cosmas and Sopater travelled to Ceylon about this time. These two merchant-travellers are perhaps the most distinct figures in the story of the commercial enterprise of their day; for the Persian monks who brought the silk-worms' eggs are nameless, and Zemarchus is a rather shadowy figure. Ceylon, the Taprobana of the Greek mariners and of Ptolemy, the Sielediva of the natives, was then, as in other times, a great meeting-place of trade. It had been visited by sailors of the Red Sea ports, and apparently brought into connection with the Mediterranean world, in the time of Claudius; its king, three centuries after, took pains to send an embassy (for commercial alliance) to the Emperor Julian; still later, probably in the fifth century, an Egyptian or Coptic Christian, named Scholasticus, voyaged both to Malabar and to Ceylon, where he fell under suspicion as a spy, and was kept in prison for six years; for the " Roman name " had now lost its old prestige in the Far East and South, and pelf and power alike had passed into the hands of Abyssinians and Persians.[1] In days of Chinese activity,[2] such as the years just before

[1] See Pliny, H. N. vi. 24; Ammianus Marcellinus, xxii. 7; Emerson Tennent's "Ceylon," i. 532; Palladius, in the work "De Gentibus Indiæ et Bragmanibus" (London, 1665), pp. 3, 59, etc.; Letronne, Recueil de l'Acad. des Insc. x. 223, and Reinaud, "Rélations de l'Empire Romain avec l'Asie Orientale," pp. 217, 292, etc.

[2] Under the Han and Thang dynasties. Fa-Hien travelled there (399–414). Cf. Heyd, i. §§ 1, 2, pp. 3, 6, 8, 9, 28, 33.

and just after the birth of Christ, or the time of the
undivided Caliphate (c. 650–750), the junks of the Yellow
Sea came regularly to the island. Fa-Hien had visited it, in
search of the Buddhist books of discipline, at the epoch of
Alaric's capture of Rome (c. 410). In the eighth century
it became a central market of Arab or Moslem traffic : now
Rome and Persia are found competing for supremacy in its
harbours.

Sopater is only known to us from Cosmas' mention of
him. He was, we are told, a Roman merchant who was
engaged in trade between Ceylon and the Red Sea during
the early years of the sixth century. Sailing once in an
Abyssinian ship from Adule, he found himself challenged [1]
before the native ruler of Ceylon by a Persian rival, who
declared his sovereign to be the most powerful on earth.
" Produce your king," said Sopater, at last breaking silence.
" You have in your hands," he continued, addressing the
Indian prince, " the coins of both sovereigns. Compare
them." The gold *byzant* of the Roman was put alongside
the silver *dirhem* [2] of his enemy, and the first easily won.

. From Sopater, it has been conjectured, Cosmas derived
all his knowledge of Ceylon; and although this is unlikely,
he is at any rate an interesting witness to the commercial

---

[1] This was " thirty-five years, at
least," before Cosmas wrote his
eleventh book in c. 545 ? (*i.e. =*
c. 510). Sopater had been dead all
this time, according to Cosmas.
Possibly Cosmas is inaccurate, or our
information misleading. Sopater probably travelled *after* Justinian's accession (527). Cf. Cosmas, xi. (Montf.
pp. 331–339); Vincent, " Erythræan
Sea," ii. 506, 510.

[2] (1) Nomisma ; (2) Miliaresion.
The Nomisma was doubtless the
aureus coined by Constantine, of
which seventy-two went to the
pound of gold. The Miliaresion
was probably the drachm, of which
twenty went to the Daric. Cf. the
Periplus of the Erythræan Sea, § 42,
etc. ; Pliny, " Natural History," vi.
24. The whole story has a suspicious
likeness to the similar one in Pliny
(*loc. cit.*) about the Cinghalese
envoys to Claudius and their admiration of Roman denarii.

struggle of the time, and to the importance of the Abyssinian
alliance for the Christian world of the Mediterranean.

But Cosmas himself is, of course, the principal character
among the traders, as he is among the geographers or theorists of Justinian's Age. Here we are only concerned with
his practical and far more satisfactory work. Scattered up and
down through the " continent of mud " which his ingenious
orthodoxy spread over the true face of the earth, there are,
as we have suggested before, a few pieces of solid ground.
In other words, we get some useful notices of Eastern Africa,
of Hither, or even of Further India, and some insight into
the south-coast trade route, from various passages in that
ever-memorable " Christian Topography," which tried to
work out a scheme of the visible world from the teachings
of the invisible contained in the Jewish and Christian
Scriptures.

As to the extent of his travels, he tells us expressly that
he sailed upon the Mediterranean and upon the " Arabian "
and Persian gulfs; but he makes the Caspian flow into the
Arctic Sea; and as to the ocean, he is ignorant.[1] He
declares, indeed, that this cannot be navigated, from the
currents and fogs here met with, as well as from its illimit-
able area.[2] But he refers to the Christianity of Ceylon and

[1] Top. Ch. ii. p. 132 (Montf.).

[2] Cf. his account of how, while sailing on the Red Sea, towards the land
of Zinj (beyond Guardafui), he and
the whole crew were terrified by a
current setting in from the ocean,
and threatening to sweep them out of
the narrow sea (ii. p. 132–3; Montf.).
The Zinj or Zanz[ibar] of Cosmas included the whole east coast of Africa
beyond the Straits of Bab-el-Mandeb.
We may notice that Cosmas, like the
" Periplus of the Erythræan Sea,"
makes Cape Aromata or Guardafui the
end of " Barbaria ; " while Ptolemy,
on the other hand, prolongs Barbary
from here to Rhapta and Cape
Prasum (Zanzibar Islands ?), i. 17;
iv. 7. With Cosmas' account of the
gold trade on this coast, as quoted
below (pp. 194–196), we may compare
Cadamosto's description of a similar
barter-traffic in North-West Africa,
at the time of his voyages in the
service of Prince Henry of Portugal,
A.D. 1455, etc.

of Malabar as if among the things he had himself inspected;
he tells us how he sailed by Socotra,[1] though he did not
land there; he describes the buffalo of India and even the
yak of the upland; he correctly traces the main lines of
the voyage to Further India,[2] and gives the position of the
country with striking accuracy, "on the extreme east coast
of Asia, compassed by the ocean,"—a far better account than
Ptolemy's. Further, he is minutely observant of the
wonders of "Ethiopia," or the Abyssinian country—both
beasts, palaces, and ancient remains; and his description of
Ceylon is too detailed and lively for a second-hand account.[3]
The island, he rightly says, might be considered to occupy
a sort of central position between India, Persia, Ethiopia
and "Tzinista" (Cochin-China?), on the side of the sea;
and so ships came to it from all these parts. But the
overland route was a much nearer way from Persia to the
extremities of Asia than the maritime; and especially in
going to Tzinista, it could hardly be believed from an

---

[1] Top. Ch. iii. 178 (Montf.).

[2] *E.g.* a ship sailing to the Tzinistæ, he says, is obliged, after going east for a long way, to turn north, at least as far as a ship bound for Chaldæa would have to run up the Persian gulf to the mouth of the Euphrates. But his "Tzinista," in which Col. Yule insists on recognizing the name of China, is probably only a dim notion of Malaya or Cochin-China; the northern bend he describes is probably that of the Gulf of Siam; and this shadowy account does not at all anticipate the real discovery of these regions, for Europe, by Marco Polo, or, for the Caliphate, by the Arabs.

[3] *E.g.* in his statements — (1) that it lies on the "other side" of the pepper country of Malabar; (2) that it has many small islands with cocoanuts near it—apparently the Maldives, though somewhat loosely placed; (3) that measures of length in Taprobane are reckoned in "gaudia"—"gaou" is still in use, viz. "an hour's walking-distance;" (4) that hyacinths or rubies are found in it; (5) that it has a church of Persian Christians (Nestorians); (6) that one of the native temples has a famous ruby ("hyacinth") as big as a pine cone—apparently the same that Hiouen-Tthsang saw on the Buddha Tooth Temple near Anurajapura, c. A.D. 630; (7) that Taprobane exports to Malabar, Sindu on the Indus, Persia, Yemen, and the Red Sea. (Bk. xi. pp. 336–340, Montf.)

experience of the coasting voyage how much more expeditious the caravan route would be found. Nothing could be truer, in view of the commerce and shipping of that time; and it was only the dilemma of Persian dues, or no imports, that had set the emperor and his people upon a trial of the roundabout ocean way.

Of the country between Ceylon and Tzinista, Cosmas disclaims any knowledge, except that cloves were grown there; and it would be extravagant to suppose that he ever crossed the bay of Bengal or worked his passage through the Straits of Malacca. From his terror of the open sea, it may also be conjectured that most traders had now, for a time at least, forgotten or disused other than coasting voyages. Hippalus' discovery (c. A.D. 120) of the use of the monsoon in wafting sailors from Africa to India and back again, was to wait perhaps for the Arabs to revive it in general use: but, even as a shore-traffic, and less important than the Persian caravan trade, the Erythrean commerce was respectable in these last days of its Roman time; and the Indian ships that Antoninus Martyr[1] and other pilgrims saw in the gulfs of Suez and Akabah, might have never ceased bringing their freight direct to Christian lands if it had not been for Islam and the Arabs.

Lastly, from the equatorial or "incense" coasts of Africa, condiments and spices were exported in great quantities. So Cosmas tells us, in a remarkable passage[2] that has in it something of the flavour of personal experience. The trade went by sea; and the products were taken to Adulis or Adule in Abyssinia, to the Homerites of Yemen in Arabia, to Persia, and to India. But besides spices, he adds, this land of Barbary (bordering on the Ocean of the Blacks or Zanj, as they call themselves) brings forth gold

[1] Ant. M. c. 41, etc.   [2] Top. Christ. bk. ii. pp. 138, 139, Montf.

in abundance, and year by year the King of Axum
(in Abyssinia) sends merchants to procure what they can
of it.

Their business was performed by an extraordinary method
of barter—on a principle exactly similar to what we find
recorded as in vogue among the natives of the West Sahara
and Soudan, after the lapse of a thousand years. The gold
caravan, says Cosmas, is usually made up of about five hundred traders. With them they take a good quantity of cattle,
salt, and iron. And when they are close to the gold land,
they rest awhile, and make a great thorn hedge. Then they
kill the cattle, cut them up, and spit their joints upon the
thorns, while they put out the salt and iron at the foot of
the hedge. This done, they retire to a certain distance. Now
come up the natives with their gold, in little lumps; and
each places what he thinks sufficient above the beef, the
salt, or the iron which he fancies. Then they, too, go away.
Next return the merchants, and inspect the price offered
for their goods. If content, they take away the gold and
leave the flesh, salt, or iron thus paid for. If not content,
they leave both gold and other things together, and again
retire. A second visit is then paid by the blacks; and either
more gold is added, or it is removed altogether, according as
the purchaser thinks worth while.

"And thus," exclaims the traveller, "do they get over the
difference of language and the want of interpreters." The
caravans generally stayed about five days; and their chief
danger was on returning, when, armed to the teeth, and
loaded with gold, they hurried back, in daily fear of robbery
and murder. The whole journey was finished within six
months; and most of this time was consumed on the way
out, as the cattle moved but slowly, and on the homeward
route haste was the only safety. "And so distant is that

land, that the founts of the Nile [1] are near to it; and in winter the traders are often stopped by floods. But what is winter on that coast is summer with us." [2]

Ethiopia, we have said, plays an important part in Cosmas' record of travel; and by this name he generally designates the whole of Eastern Africa from Egypt to the Equator; but a narrower use of the same term is to be found in his pages, answering to the kingdom of Meroe or Khartoum, between the Abyssinian Mountains to the east and the Libyan Desert to the west. Here, in very early times, had probably settled a colony from South-West Arabia; here Christian missionaries had now penetrated; and here, as in Abyssinia itself, Justinian was now looking for allies. From the Blemmyes of Ethiopia the Axumite traders of Cosmas' day obtained emeralds, which they shipped from Adule for the Indian and "Roman" markets.

So much for the early Byzantine trade. The independent commerce of *Western* Europe in this age is far more difficult to follow. In most countries, now overrun by the Teutonic herdsman and hunter-warriors, trade with distant lands was almost extinct; and we get nothing more to guide us than occasional entries in such writers as Gregory of Tours, who tells us now and then (for instance) of merchants going to the Levant from "France." [3] From some of these he must have gathered his information about Egypt; about the Nile running through the country; about "the Babylon

---

[1] *I.e.* the Blue or Abyssinian Nile, whose sources near Geesh were rediscovered in modern times: (1) by Portuguese travellers of the sixteenth century; (2) by Jesuit missionaries of later time; (3) by Bruce, at the close of the eighteenth century.

[2] "Torrents of rain," adds Cosmas, "here fall for three months together, and make a number of rivers, which all flow into the Nile."

[3] Cf. Hist. Franc. i. 10. Gregory of Tours' life was from 538 to 595.

in which Joseph built his barns" on the banks of the river; about the arm of the Red Sea "projecting towards the east," and Clysma or Suez at the end of it; and about the Indian ships that came there, "for the sake of the merchandise that, from this point, is dispersed throughout all Egypt."

Jerome and Salvian, indeed, speak of men from the Latin provinces coming to seek their fortune in Syria and Egypt; but, on the whole, it seems probable that after this time—the earlier fifth century—there was a far greater influx of trade and traders from the Eastern Mediterranean into Gaul, Spain, and Italy than could be maintained in the opposite direction. Under the Merovingians, Syrian trade-colonies, for example, were established in Narbonne, Bordeaux, Orleans, and Tours; the wine of Gaza, the papyrus of Egypt, were brought to Marseilles, even in the sixth century. In the commercial stagnation of the Latin world, Marseilles indeed retained some movement, on the edge, as it were, of the current; and it seems, at the darkest times, to have kept up a certain trade with Byzantium and the Levantine coasts.[1] The mariners of the Venetian lagunes were also winning a name as skilful seamen, but as to the details, objects, or extent of their voyages we do not as yet find any certain information; though a later story (in the ninth-century chronicle of Altino) brings them to Antioch and other Syrian ports before the appearance of the Saracens. But the intercourse was, in any case, very slight, and almost wholly one-sided. Many Eastern products were valued and sought after in the west of Europe, even in the days of Clovis, but there was nothing to offer in exchange but money and furs. The trickle of Oriental commerce into the lands beyond the Adriatic was answered by no corresponding stream from the same Western countries.

[1] Greg. Tours, Hist. Franc. v. 5; vi. 2, 24; vii. ?6; Agathias, i. 2.

So much, or so little, for Christian trade routes and merchant travel before the Arab conquests; after this, the commercial importance of the Caliphate is overwhelming, and until the Viking Age, our European traffic humbly depends upon the leavings of the new Empire, upon the crumbs that fall from the table of Islam.

The great highways, indeed, are not changed, except that the Moslems are now masters of the same; in possession of the whole carrying trade that in earlier time Romans, Abyssinians, Persians, and Bokhariots had divided. The Red Sea is cut off from Christendom, like the Caspian; the south-coast, like the overland, routes, pass into new hands; and receive from them a wonderful development. While the Empire of Charles the Great is falling into anarchy, Arab merchants have passed all the shores and islands of Further India, have opened marts in China, and are sailing in the Sea of Pitchy Darkness, beyond the mainland of Asia.[1]

From the days of their first attack, the Saracens showed a care for the trade and the material prosperity of the lands they swept over.[2] The Levant of Haroun al Raschid was far wealthier, and had a much wider commercial outlook, than the realm of Heraclius or even of Justinian. We have seen how Arculf and others bear witness to the continued splendour of such ports as Alexandria; but this well-being was now largely independent of Christendom and its wants. The Moslem world was self-contained and self-satisfying—at

[1] Heyd, I. i. pp. 29-32.
[2] The care they took, for example, in Syria and Egypt to prevent the ruin of the crops, to guard the non-combatants, and to organise their new dominion with an eye to the well-being of agriculture and manu-factures, proves this. The temporary discouragement of vine-culture was perhaps their most reactionary deed, unless the story of Omar and the Alexandrian Library can be re-established (cf. Heyd, i. 25).

least, so far as it looked towards the west; to north and east, and even to south, it showed a different spirit.

We cannot here enter upon the fascinating subject of Arabic enterprise and science, although it is here certainly that the human intelligence finds its best expression, both in geography and other branches of knowledge, between the Age of Ptolemy and that of Marco Polo; we must attend to the corresponding movement, or lack of movement, in the Christendom of the early Middle Ages.

1. Greek or Byzantine commerce with Asia and Africa, after languishing through the time of the first Saracen irruption and settlement, seems to have revived early in the ninth century. Leo the Armenian (Leo V., A.D. 813–820), in consequence of rumoured outrages at the holy places, forbade his subjects to visit Syria and Egypt; but this restriction was soon removed, and under his successors the trade with the Caliphate greatly increased.[1] Antioch, Alexandria, and Trebizond were the principal marts; but Thessalonica and Cherson—Saloniki and the Crimea—had a certain, though smaller, share in this traffic.

Yet however much Constantinople imported articles of luxury, it did little to develop its own manufacture of silk, and almost nothing to awaken a commerce among its more backward Christian neighbours. Immense wealth might have rewarded Greek merchants in the rising Italian ports, but the chance was missed; and, worse than all, the carrying trade of the European nations was allowed to slip into the hands of Venetians and Amalphitans. For the Byzantines sacrificed power to show, as consistently as old Rome disregarded appearance for reality. They liked to

---

[1] From Moslem brokers this same Leo V. must have obtained the Indian aromatics Cedrenus speaks of (ii. 54, Ed. Bonn.; see Theophanes, Contin. p. 457). (Cf. Heyd, I. ii. pp. 52, 53, 110.)

dazzle the eyes of barbarians with magnificent presents and spectacles; they were ever on the watch to make a good profit on valuable imports, and they exacted a heavy tax (of ten per cent.) on all exports: but they did not understand the advantage of a liberal and enterprising commerce. It was undignified, to their mind, to go and seek out trade with other nations; let these come to the queen of cities, and pay highly for the privilege of access: but, above all, let not the Empire part with anything really precious in exchange. The Byzantine idea of commerce was to get everything and to give nothing; and their short-sighted and ruinous selfishness was but rarely visited by glimpses of comparative sanity. Such an exception appeared now and then in the course of the Slav traffic with Constantinople; we find Greek merchants among the Bulgarians [1] of the Lower Danube, in Southern Russia, and in the Crimea; but this commerce belongs almost entirely to a later time, to the tenth and eleventh centuries, and is partly inspired by a later movement—that of the Norsemen.

2. In the Frankish kingdom, in Germany and France, Slavs and Italians were the principal traders, although native markets existed at Mainz, Magdeburg, Erfurt, and at various points along the line of the Elbe and Saale, the limits of the German people and of Christendom alike on this side. Teuton merchants resorted to the town of Jumna,[2] eight days' journey east of Hamburg, from the time of its foundation at the end of the ninth century, but the settled inhabitants of this town long remained heathen and Sclavonian.

The modern finds of Oriental, and especially of Arab, coins in Germany [3] point to some actual traffic, though

---

[1] Cf. Theophanes, i. 175. Constantine Porphyrogenitus, De Adm. Imp. p. 77.

[2] Adam of Bremen, in Pertz, Scriptores, vii. 312; cf. Heyd, I. ii. pp. 63, 77.

[3] Of surprising amount, numbering many thousands of pieces.

unrecorded, upon the route described by the Caliph's post-
master, Ibn Khordadbeh. Writing about 880, he tells us
how merchants could pass to and fro between the lands of
the Franks and the Oxus, by a track from the Elbe to the
Volga, and so round the north of the Caspian to Samarcand,
and even to China. But this way seems to have been
chiefly used by Jewish brokers and dealers, and it was more
on the side of Italy and the Adriatic that native German
enterprise was called out, by the alliance with the Venetian
merchants.

The canal begun by Charles the Great between Rhine
and Danube[1] was immediately intended to aid his military
operations against the Avars. His successes opened the
way for the hucksters who followed in the wake of the
army, from Ratisbon or from Lorsch; but the Black Swarm
of the Hungarians soon put an end to this line of trade
(c. 880), and till the end of the first millennium the overland
commerce of Western Europe was thrown back into its
North German channel, and prisoned there.

Nearly all Latin trade with the outer world, however,
now flowed through the Mediterranean, and this naturally
fell to the share of Italy, as Spain was Mussulman and
Southern France both more distant and more backward.
The men of Ratisbon appear to have been the first Teutons
to discover the truth of this; and they and the Augsburgers
were to be seen in the markets of Venice at a very early
day,[2] in the same way that Lombard merchants frequented
St. Denis' fair in Paris, before the death of Mohammed.[3]

In Gaul, or the western Frankish land, an indirect commerce, generally passing through Italian hands, continued

---

[1] More exactly, between Altmühl
and Rednitz (Heyd, I. ii. pp. 80, 81,
and authorities as above).

[2] Ninth and tenth centuries.
[3] From the time of Dagobert I., c.
A.D. 629.

with Syria and Egypt, under the house of Pepin and of Charles, as under the descendants of Clovis. Pepper, spices, dates, and paper are all mentioned[1] among the imports of the eighth century; and in the reign of Charlemagne himself this traffic, for a time at least, grew apace. Arab caliph and Teuton king were sworn friends, so long as Aachen was at a safe distance from Bagdad. On his side, Charles sent Frisian cloth, possibly with furs and amber.[2] Haroun al Raschid returned his presents by others, of rare animals, musical instruments, silk stuffs, perfumes, and drugs; and both the Moslem prince and the Christian Churches of Asia gave some sort of sanction to a favourite title of the Frankish emperor. As Protector of the holy places, he built a hospice, organised a market, and afforded protection to Christian pilgrims and traders "of the Roman tongue" in Jerusalem.[3] His name and his foundations were still respected, half a century after his death, when Bernard the Wise of Mont St. Michel arrived in Syria (c. 868–870).

But the same record which tells of the "hostelry of the glorious Charles" in the Holy City, gives us proof enough, like all other records of the time, that Latin commerce did not survive him like his benefactions. The Arab corsairs, who throve upon the decline of the Frank kingdom, were now destroying all traffic but their own, or their allies', over the Mediterranean; and, till far on in the tenth century, the

---

[1] As in the grant of Chilperic III. to the abbey of Corbie of an annual duty upon the douane receipts of Fos. This town, on the Fossæ Maritimæ, or old canal of Provence, constructed to aid the communications of the Lower Rhone districts with the Mediterranean, appears for a time as a rival to Marseilles.

[2] Charles even went so far as to wish there were no sea between the Franks and the Bagdad Saracens— "O utinam non esset ille gurgitulus inter nos" (Monk of St. Gall. 743. Also cf. Einhardt, Vita Caroli, cc. 23, 24, 27, etc.; Monk of St. Gall, 752, 761, in Dümmler's collection; cf. Heyd, I. pp. 87n, 90, 91, etc.).

[3] Cf. Bernard the Wise, ch. x.

only safe mode of transit was in Saracen vessels, and under Saracen protection.

3. The British Islands, before the appearance and settlement of the Northmen, had scarcely any intercourse with the outside world, except of a purely religious kind. The Irish and Northumbrian art and culture of the eighth and ninth centuries, the journeys of early English saints to Iona or to Rome, are connected, not with commerce, but with missionary and pilgrim travel. Willibald and Boniface, Columba and Columban, St. Gall and Virgil, Fidelis and Dicuil, Wilfrid and Benedict—scarcely any one of these ever figures as a trader.[1] Never did the " isles of saints " look less towards the national destiny, the national instinct, of shopkeeping. The feeble beginnings of our commerce are only to be discovered in the Viking Age; perhaps the first traces are apparent in the journeys[2] of Sighelm and Æthelstan (c. 883), of Ohthere and Wulfstan (c. 895) to the far East, the White Sea, and the Baltic in the service of Ælfred the Great.[3]

4. It was in Italy that the most active mercantile life was aroused during this time (c. 600–900); and its development would have been still more rapid, but for the harassing trouble of Moslem raiders, and the constantly recurring danger of a Mussulman dominion throughout the peninsula. With the instinct of self-preservation, the rising commercial republics of South Italy—Salerno, Amalphi, Naples, and Gaieta—allied themselves, to the scandal of other Christian States, with the Saracens whom they dared not defy. They were even accused, and with justice, of aiding and abetting in the slave-hunts of the African corsairs,[4] sure of

---

[1] But cf. the curious story of Bede's bequest of pepper to a friend.

[2] Cf. O.E. Chron. *sub.* an. 883; Æfred's Orosius.

[3] See p. 214 of this vol.

[4] Thus Sichard of Beneventum, in 836, binds them not to kidnap and enslave any of his people; see Capitulare Sichardi in Pertz Legg. iv. 218; cf. Heyd, I. ii. p. 99, etc.

a percentage on the profits. Thus Lewis the German, in 870, exclaims that Naples has become a second Palermo, an outpost of Islam and a depôt for its booty. Pope John VIII., in 875, repeats the charge against the whole group of towns, which, in that year, had again joined the Saracens in carrying fire and sword into Central Italy. But he thundered in vain. Not till the tenth century, and then by military force rather than Church censures, were these ravages checked and the infamous league dissolved.

Yet it was probably by this channel that quantities of Oriental goods poured into Italy; for, in comparison with other Latin countries, it was richly supplied. Byzantine stuffs may have been brought in by the Venetians, for the most part; but the riches imported from Alexandria must have entered almost entirely through the traffic of Amalphi with North Africa.[1]

The place of this city, as helping in some degree to bridge the interval between two great ages of progress, the classical and the crusading, for the south of Europe, is tantalising in its interest and its vagueness. Not less so is its position in later time, as a claimant for the honour of nautical invention in the West. "Prima dedit nautis usum *magnetis* Amalphis." [2]

Parallel to the precocious growth of Amalphi is that of Venice. In both cities the lists of doges, or sovereign mayors —practically independent, though, in name, vassals of Byzantium,—begin at much the same time, about the year

---

[1] It was not till later that Amalphi had direct intercourse with the Levant—973 is the earliest instance known. But even in the ninth century we find a family from Antioch (that of "Maurus Vicarius") at the head of the government of Amalphi. This does not prove direct intercourse of the two cities, but it is a curious fact. We may also recall how Willibald, in 722, saw a ship from Egypt in the port of Naples.

[2] Antony of Bologna, surnamed "of Palermo."

700. In both cities a commerce with North Africa was developed before the end of the ninth century. But the Venetians were soon further afield than their rivals. Direct intercourse, though slight and intermittent, was established between the Adriatic and the Levant in the lifetime of Charles the Great, or soon after his death. When Leo V. (813–820) forbade the Byzantines to visit Syria and Egypt, Venice, as a "Roman" town, followed the emperor's lead. But in 827 or 828 they appear again at Alexandria, and commit a sacred robbery. As Bernard the Wise tells us, it was now they carried off the relics of St. Mark, who seems to have become their patron as the guardian of Christian Egypt, and as their protector on the long and dangerous voyage to this their earliest distant market.

Their European trade seems also to have been a creation of the time of Charlemagne. It was through his friendship, through his grants of entire freedom of trade in the Frankish empire, that they were able to win the position of middle-men between Western Europe and the Levant. By the Padus and the Adige they transported their wares into the heart of Italy. By the Brenner and other passes of Tyrol they made their way to the chief towns of the Karling States. As wellnigh the only traders of Latin Christendom who dealt directly with the Eastern harbours of the great inland sea, they were almost beyond competition, until first Amalphi and then Pisa and Genoa entered upon the same field.

II. MISSIONARY TRAVEL.

Stories of extensive missionary travel are connected with the earliest days of Christianity. St. Thomas and St. Bartholomew were said to have preached in India and in Central Asia according to a disputed tradition; the "blessed presbyter," Pantænus of Alexandria, more certainly visited

Hindostan in the second century (A.D. 189); and the Gospel was carried far into Africa and Arabia, before the conversion of the Roman Empire. In the same way, Gregory the Illuminator travelled and taught in Armenia as early as the reign of Valerian (A.D. 257); while Licinius was still reigning in the East, Bishop Hermon of Jerusalem (about 311) despatched Ephraim on a mission journey to "Scythia," and Basil on a similar errand to the Crimea: and these are only samples of a widespread activity, called out by the proselytizing zeal of the early Church. But the two chief extensions of the new religion beyond the Mediterranean world, to South and East, followed upon, and did not precede, the primary and fundamental success of the imperial alliance it had gained with Constantine.[1]

1. The Abyssinian Church was founded, or at least became the religion of the people, in the fourth century, through the labours of missionaries from Alexandria. About A.D. 330, Frumentius, who, according to the oldest form of the story,[2] had sailed for India with one Meropius, was stopped and plundered on the Red Sea coast; he found a refuge among the Abyssinians, through the help of Christian merchants trading in the country; and, at last returning to Egypt, received the commission and consecration of Athanasius as bishop of Ethiopia, or Hither India. Such was the account given to Rufinus by Edesius, the friend and companion of the new "apostle," who, however, did not return with him to Ethiopia.

The first orthodox mission was soon followed by an

---

[1] See Jerome, "De Viris Illustribus," c. 36, letters, Ad Marcellam (No. 148, in old edd. = Migne, lix.), and Ad Magnum; Eusebius, H. E., v. 10; La Croze, "Christianisme des Indes," i. 57–70; Rae, "Syrian Church in India," especially pp. 62–78; Gibbon, ch. xlvii.; Neale, "Holy Eastern Church" (Patriarchates of Antioch and Alexandria); Baronius, "Annales," under years referred to.

[2] As given by Rufinus, i. 9. See Socrates, i. 19; Sozomen, ii. 24; Theodoret, i. 23.

heretical one.   In 356, the Arian Emperor Constantius sent
the "Indian" Theophilus, possibly a native of Socotra,[1] with
letters to the Princes of Axum, as lords of the sacred city
of the Abyssinians, urging the expulsion of Frumentius, and
an alliance with himself in the interests of Arianism.   This
was part of a far-reaching scheme of Arian proselytism and
imperial ambition, especially aimed at "those formerly
called Sabæans, but now known as Homeritæ," in Arabia
Felix.   The conquest of this Happy Land had been a favourite
object of Roman policy since the days of Augustus, when
Strabo accompanied Ælius Gallus on his march against that
very same region of spices.   Theophilus, the present envoy,
had been sent to Rome while "very young," as a hostage
from the islanders of Divus (? Diu or more probably Socotra),
when Constantine was at the head of the Empire.   He did
not succeed in his commission against Frumentius; but he
visited not only Abyssinia, but the Homerites of Yemen,
and apparently most of the Southern coast of Asia, from the
Straits of Babel Mandeb to the Indus, or even beyond; he
is recorded to have built churches at Aden, at Sana (Zaphar,
or Tapharum), the "metropolis" of the Sabæans, and "where
the mart of Persian commerce stands hard by the mouth of
the Persian Sea;" finally he returned through the land of
the Axumites,[2] to the Roman Empire.   Everywhere he promoted his own sect, either the true faith or the damnablest

[1] See Letronne, "Christianisme en
Nubie, etc." The use of the term
"India" for many parts of East
Africa and Southern Arabia (as in
Marco Polo) is common enough.
See Letronne, also, in Receuil Acad.
Inscr., etc., ix. 158; x. 235, etc.; and
in *Journal des Savants*, 1842, p. 665;
Reinaud, "Relations de l'Empire
Romain avec l'Asie, etc.," p. 175, etc.

[2] See Letronne, "Christianisme en
Nubie, Abyssinie, etc.;" Philostorgius
in Photius, Biblioth., Cod. xl., and his
abridgment of Phil. iii. 4–6; Athanasius, "Apology to Constantius," § 31;
Nicephorus Callistes, ix. 12. The
letter of Constantius to the Axumites is given in Baronius, "Annales,"
A.D. 356.

of heresies; on the fact friends and enemies are agreed, with only a slight change of epithets.

In the course of the next (fifth) century, and probably about 460, at a time coincident with the schism in the Church of Egypt which followed upon the Council of Chalcedon, "many monks" are said to have come to Abyssinia from "Rome," or the Roman world; and, among these, nine are mentioned by the Chronicle of Axum, under more or less Ethiopic names. From these, however, may still be recovered the Greek forms of Pantaleon and Michael;[1] and to their labours may be ascribed the stubborn adherence of the Abyssinian, in alliance with the Coptic, Church to the doctrine of the One nature in Jesus Christ, against the decrees of the Council of Chalcedon.

Early in the sixth century we come upon another notice of intercourse between the Empire, and the Ethiopian Christians. To avenge the cruel persecution of the faithful of Najran, by the Jew tyrant, Dhu Nowas,[2] King Kaleb, or Elesbaan, made war upon the Homerites in 522. With an army of 120,000 men, he crossed the Straits, conquered Yemen, and set up a Christian sub-kingdom on the other side of the Red Sea. On his victory, he sent the news of it to Justin, apparently with a request for some "Roman" ecclesiastic to set in order the affairs of the Abyssinian Church,[3] or, perhaps more exactly, to organize the Christianity

[1] See Ludolphus, Hist. Æthiop., III. iii.

[2] To this, perhaps, Mohammed alludes in the eighty-fifth chapter of the Koran: "Cursed were the contrivers of the pit of fire, when they sat over against it, and were witnesses of what they inflicted on the believers. . . . They hated them for their faith in God." It is by this war of Elesbaan against the Homerites that Cosmas dates, in his "Christian Topography." Ludolphus (Hist. Æthiop. ii. 4) says Kaleb transported his army in 423 ships across the Red Sea, and gives some triumphant verses on his success. See T. Wright, "Early Christianity in Arabia," pp. 49, etc.; John of Ephesus in Assemani B. O.; John Malalas, pt. ii.; Theoph. Chronog.

[3] Procop., De Bell. Persic. i. 19.

of the newly conquered country.   For this purpose, Bishop
Gregentius was now sent to be the Samuel of the new
Saul.

Following close upon this came Justinian's attempt,
already noticed, for a closer political and commercial as well
as religious alliance between the Empire and Ethiopia, with
the mission of Nonnosus in 533.   Nonnosus was something
of an observer, and Photius[1] has preserved to us a few of
his memoranda upon Axum and Adule, the chief centres
in his time of Abyssinian trade, faith, and government.   It
was with Adule merchants that Cosmas, a few years earlier
or later, travelled to the incense-bearing coast of Barbary
or East Africa, beyond Guardafui.

The conversion of the Blemmyes[2] of Nubia at about the
same time (in the reign of Justinian) may be, to a certain
extent, connected with Christian missionary travel, although
no names are preserved to us of wandering preachers who
" broke up Æthiopia with the ploughshare of personal

---

[1] Photius, Biblioth. cod. 3; John
Malalas, part ii. pp. 193–196; Procopius, De Bell. Pers. chs. 19, 20;
Wright, "Christianity in Arabia,"87–
89. Nonnosus' father and grandfather
had both been sent on diplomatic journeys to Arab princes—the Mondar of
Ghassan, and the King of Kenda.
He himself, after ascending the Nile,
crossed the Red Sea,landed in Arabia,
and visited Kenda.   From the harbour
of Bulicas, in Yemen, he sailed to
Adule.   Thence he went up to Axum,
by way of Aua, or Aueen, where he
saw a herd of a thousand elephants.
At Axum the Negus gave him
audience in an open field.   The
Abyssinian ruler was seated on a
lofty, four-wheeled chariot, drawn
by four elephants, caparisoned with
plates of gold; and was dressed in
a tunic set with pearls and gems,
and a lower garment of linen and
gold thread.   His diadem was a
linen cap crusted with gold, from
which hung four chains; on his
arms were bracelets and chains of
gold; in his hands were two spears
and a gilded shield.   His nobles
were dressed in the same way, but
with less magnificence ; a band of
musicians attended the court.   The
"Roman" letters and presents were
received with great respect, and the
advice of Justinian was instantly
adopted; the Negus brandished his
arms, and vowed undying enmity
against the idolaters of Persia.

[2] Cosmas (ii.) mentions the intercourse of the Axumites with the
Blemmyes.   See additional note on
page 242.

exhortation," [1] and it must remain doubtful from which side, the Egyptian or Abyssinian, these tribes of the Upper Nile were more strongly influenced. In any case, they were caught between two fires. Axumite kings, such as he who contributed so large a share to the Adule inscription, and who records his conquest of Kasou,[2] near Meroe or Khartoum, were threatening on the south; the might and name of Rome, and the chief resources of the Church, would more naturally be employed on the north. In this relation we may notice the inscription (of the sixth century) set up by King Silco of Nubia in the temple of Talmis as a monument of his victory over the surrounding idolaters; and the evidence of the survival of Christianity in the upper valley of the Nile far down into the eighth century, when Islam began to exterminate its rival. Not without interest in this connection are the letters of Isaac and of Michael, patriarchs of Alexandria, in 687 and 737 respectively, to the Christian kings of Nubia, exhorting them to concord with their Abyssinian brethren, and dissuading them from intended attacks upon Moslem Egypt.

The Abyssinian Empire of Elasbaan had once threatened, as we have seen, to create a great Southern or Ethiopic Church. But this passed away like a dream, for the success of Islam in Arabia itself first of all expelled Christian warriors and missionaries from the native land of the Prophet; and after his death, the war was soon carried into the aggressor's home. The Ethiopian coasts and the Nile Valley, right up to the Abyssinian highlands, were alike conquered by the Saracens, and only distance and obscurity saved the Negus from submission to the Caliphs. For eight hundred years

---

[1] See Letronne, "Christianism en Nubie, etc.;" Ludolphus, Hist. Æthiop. (iii. 2); Rufinus (x. 9, etc.).

[2] Such is Glaser's emendation for *Sasou*. See "Die Abessinier in Arabien und Africa."

the Abyssinian Church remained cut off and almost wholly forgotten by the rest of Christendom—except only the schismatical Copts of Egypt,—till "Prester John"[1] was rediscovered (in a new continent) by the Portuguese (from A.D. 1486), and the "sheep of Æthiopia" were attacked, in the words of the native anthem, by the "hyænas of the West."[2]

2. The hope of a far-reaching, wealthy, and powerful Southern Church thus proved a delusion; but an Eastern Communion was formed by the Nestorian missions, which at one time probably outnumbered the whole Catholic body, and for centuries was the chief representative of Christianity to Asia, the honoured teacher of early Arabic science, and the strongest link between Greek and Moslem knowledge.

To its general history—to the part this great heresy once played in the intercourse of the Further and the Nearer East—we can only allude. But a word more must be said of the travels of those Nestorian missionaries who preached and baptized under the shadow of the wall of China, and on the shores of the Yellow Sea, the Caspian, and the Indian Ocean.

A hundred years before Nestorius, an orthodox mission had been extended far into Central Asia—at the very time when the religious travel of the Latin West was beginning with the journey of the Bordeaux pilgrim, and when Constantine had given fresh vigour to the Church, in East and West alike, by his adoption of Christianity as the religion of the Empire. Bishop John "of Persia and Great India"

---

[1] At first, in the eleventh century, a central Asiatic potentate, traditionally converted by the Nestorians in 1008.

[2] See Bent, "Sacred City of the Abyssinians," especially pages 49, 176, 181, 190, 192, 194, etc. From his conclusions we may gather that Ludolphus is not likely to be soon superseded, or any very striking discoveries added to knowledge from Abyssinian sources (see especially p. 49, on the question of possible manuscript finds). Ethiopic literature, so far as known, appears to be almost entirely of a secondary character, e.g. translations from Greek and Syriac.

attended the Nicene Council in 325; in 334, one Barsabas was travelling in Khorasan as Bishop of Merv; in the same period Christians were so largely increasing in Persia as to bring upon themselves the cruel persecution of King Sapor and his Magians.[1] At the beginning of the next century the missionary travels of Samuel, bishop of Tusa, and the presence of a (unnamed) Bishop of Merv at a synod in 410, prove the continued life of Catholic Christianity in the same distant region.[2] But this early venture was ruined or absorbed by the still greater activity and larger scope of the heretical movement that followed it. Nestorius was "made anathema" by the Council of Ephesus in 431; fifty years after, in 498, his followers, already widely spread in Persia, formally severed themselves from Byzantine orthodoxy and obedience, and set up an independent patriarchate at Ctesiphon, which, in 762, followed the Abbasside Caliphs to Bagdad. This rather improved their position than otherwise; for the Persian kings no longer looked on them as Roman spies: yet both under the Sassanides and the Arabs, who conquered Sassanid Persia, Christians were "always liable to be treated with capricious outbursts of severity." But the need of standing or falling alone, roused the Nestorian Church to a wonderful activity; and this activity expressed itself in missionary enterprise.

In the sixth century, and seemingly before A.D. 540, Nestorian bishoprics were founded in Herat and Samarcand. In 635 the first attempt was made for the conversion of China.[3] Meantime, equal progress had been made in the

---

[1] The line of "Metropolitans of Babylon" (= Ctesiphon and Seleucia) begins in the fourth century (see Sozomen, H. E., ii. 9).

[2] Assemani, Bibl. Orient., iii., pt. ii. p. 426.

[3] Arnobius, Contra Gentes II., speaks vaguely of Christianity having been preached to the Seres (? China) before Constantine, in the third century; but no satisfactory evidence of this is forthcoming.

OLD "SYRIAN" CHURCH AT CARANYACHIRRA (AFTER BISHOP D. WILSON).

THE OLD CHURCH OF PARUR ON THE COAST OF MALABAR (AFTER CLAUDIUS BUCHANAN).

[*To face p.* 213.

South. In or about 650 the patriarch Jesu Jabus writes bitterly to the Bishop of Fars upon his neglect of duty. It was owing to his slackness, we are told, that the people of Khorasan had lapsed from the faith, and that India, from the Persian coast to Travancore, was now being deprived of a regular ministry.[1] The same Father of Fathers, in the course of his short popedom of ten years, also addresses himself to the Christians of Socotra and of Balkh, and undertakes to provide a fresh supply of bishops for his spiritual subjects in the Upper Oxus valley. His successor, the Patriarch George, was not content with exhortation. In order to appease a standing quarrel between the Bactrians and the Metropolitan of Persia, he visited Balkh in person about A.D. 661.[2] The next century witnessed an increase of Nestorian energy. We shall see presently what progress was now being made on the side of China; but in Western India the ancient Church of Malabar was also quickened into fresh life at this time. As early as the sixth century a Christian named Theodore, who had come from the Sepulchre of St. Thomas, presumably at Maliapur, told Gregory of Tours [3] about this famous monument and its wondrous size; and whether Nestorian or not, his travels from the Deccan to France, could not easily be paralleled in the Christian world of that day. In 745, according to the native tradition, a company of Christians from Bagdad, Nineveh, and Jerusalem, under orders from the arch-priest at Edessa, arrived in India with the merchant Thomas; [4] and in 774 the Hindu

[1] "India from Fars to Colon," says the patriarch. Colon is Quilon in Travancore, near Cape Comorin, the "Columbum" of Bishop Jordanus in the fourteenth century (see Assemani, iii., pt. i. pp. 130, 131; pt. ii. pp. 133, 437; Yule's "Jordanus," xii.–xvii.).

[2] Assemani, Bibl. Orient., iii., pt. ii. pp. 81, 82, etc.

[3] Greg. Tours, "De Gloria Martyrum," ch. xxxi.

[4] The "Armenian (Aramæan) Merchant" of Gibbon, ch. xlvii. Jerome's letters to Marcella and

ruler of the Malabar Coast granted a charter, engraven on copper, to the Worshippers of the Cross in his dominion. Much the same process was repeated in 824. Two missionaries, Mar Sapor and Mar Peroz, now arrived from Persia, and another charter of liberties was immediately granted to the native Christians—probably by the famous "Zamorin" Kerman Permal himself, who, in 827, embarked for Arabia at the spot where Calicut now stands, and ended his life as a Moslem saint in the holy land of Islam. In both these cases it is possible that the charter was the result of the immigration just preceding. The Permal dynasty was in difficulties; and out of their troubles the Christians of Malabar made their profit.[1]

Recent discoveries in the district of the Séven Rivers, near Samarcand, have brought to light some inscriptions on Nestorian tombs, which illustrate the obscure history of these missions in Central Asia by certain details. Under the years 547, 600, 956, and so forth, departed members of the Church,—priests, laymen, and women,—are commemorated. One of these was an ecclesiastic "sent round to visit the Churches;" another was a celebrated Exegete and preacher, "who made all monasteries bright with his light," and was

---

Magnus defeat the modern attempt to trace the Thomas legend of India to this person. According to Theodoret (Hæret. Fab., i., 26), Manes sent another Thomas, one of his disciples, to India in the third century; but neither can he be fairly considered as the original of the story. Pantænus had already carried a more orthodox Christianity to India in A.D. 189 (see p. 206 of this vol.).

[1] See Rae, "Syrian Church in India," pp. 172–174. The mission of King Ælfred, who in 883 sent gifts to "Rome and St. Thomas in India" in charge of Sighelm and Æthelstan, belongs to the Norse or Viking movement of European travel, and will be dealt with later, in its place. 'The Life of Bishop D. Wilson' and the 'Travels of Claudius Buchanan' give several sketches of old Syrian Churches in Southern India, three of which are reproduced here. (See Yule, "Marco Polo," ii., 365:) (1) at Caranyachirra; (2) at Cotteiyam in Travancore; (3) at Parur, near Cranganore. A fourth is said to be still standing at Quilon.

EXTERIOR OF OLD "SYRIAN" CHURCH AT COTTEIYAM IN TRAVANCORE
(AFTER BISHOP D. WILSON)

INTERIOR OF CHURCH AT COTTEIYAM (AFTER WILSON).

celebrated for his wisdom; a third was the wife of an assistant bishop.[1]

But the crowning achievements of Nestorian enterprise were in China, and of these we have an account in the famous monument of Singanfu. This curious record, discovered in 1625, and now, after many disputes, generally accepted as authentic, gives the history of Chinese Christianity for the first century and a half of its existence· Opening with a sketch of Christian doctrine in which no mention is made of the death or resurrection of Jesus, though His birth,[2] epiphany and ascension are referred to, the inscription goes on to record how the "Luminous Doctrine" (of the Gospel) had been "propagated in the Central Kingdom" of the Celestials. It relates how, in the ninth year of the Emperor Taitsung, A.D. 635-6, there was a man of lofty virtue named Olopan, who came from Great China (the Roman Empire), "directed by the blue clouds, observing the signs of the winds, and traversing perilous countries." Olopan, the record continues, arrived in safety at Singanfu, then the capital of the Empire; he was received with favour; his teaching was examined and approved; his scriptures were translated for the Imperial Library; and within three years an edict of the Son of Heaven declared Christianity a tolerated religion, A.D. 638. With the speculative fairness of his race, Taitsung was disposed to welcome any religion whose spirit, in the words of his edict, was

---

[1] These monuments were discovered by Dr. Chwolson in 1885–86 in the Semiretchensk, to the southeast of Lake Balkash, and are described and illustrated in the *Transactions of the Russian Archeological Society* (Oriental section), vol. i. pt. 1, 1886–87. See the plates fronting p. 160 (in that vol.), and cuts on pp. 88, 102, etc. The monuments outside the limits of our period are of 956, 962, 978, 981, 985, 996, 1002, 1005, 1007, 1013, 1016, 1022, 1023, 1027.

[2] In strikingly heretical language: "Our Triune God communicated His substance to the Messiah, who appeared in the world in the likeness of a man."

" virtuous, mysterious, and pacific." The " radical principle " of the new Faith, he thought, " gave birth to perfection, and fixed the will. It was exempt from verbosity, and considered only good results." Therefore it was " useful to man, and should be published under the whole extent of the heavens. And I command the magistrates," concludes the emperor, " to erect a temple of this religion in the Quarter of Justice and Mercy [1] in the Imperial City, and twenty-one religious men shall be installed therein."

The inscription goes on to relate how the Christian faith spread and prospered in China for the next half century; how it had then been for a time depressed by Buddhism; and how, from about 740 to the time of writing (in 781), there had been a revival, dating from the travels of a new missionary, Kiho, who had come, like his predecessors, from the West. Taitsung's successor,[2] according to the monument, was still more friendly to the Church. " He fertilized the Truth, and raised Luminous Temples (Christian churches) in all the provinces," till they " filled a hundred cities." " The Households (of faith) were enriched with marvellous joy ; " Olopan himself became a " Guardian of the Empire, and Lord of the Great Law." Then followed, from about A.D. 683, a time of disfavour and oppression. The two rulers who had done so much for the Christians were, after all, like Kublai Khan, Akbar, or our early English pagans,[3] agnostic at heart. Reason was one, faiths were many; suited to various races, times, and climates ; each containing some truth, no one exclusive of the others :—this was their position, and their " conversion " did not go beyond. So a reaction was always possible.

[1] I-ning.
[2] Kao-Tsung, A.D. 650–683.
[3] Compare the tone, half vacillating, half indifferent, of King Raed- wald of East Anglia, and so many others of the old English princes and people at the time of the conversion (597–664, etc.), Bede, H. E., ii 5, 15.

Taitsung behaved as a devout Buddhist at the same time that he ordered the building of Luminous Temples; and his successor heaped grander titles and more honour upon Hiouen-Thsang than he did upon Olopan. After his death Chinese conservatism rose up against the new-fangled worship. The Buddhists [1] "resorted to violence, and spread their calumnies; low-class men of letters put forth jests" (against the Cross). But after a time the Nestorian Church in China, as in India, was revived, apparently by a fresh influx of believers. In A.D. 744 "there was a religious man of Great China (the Roman Orient), named Kiho, who travelled for the conversion of men," and directly after his arrival, "illustrious persons united to restore the fallen Law." In 747 the Emperor Hiouen-tsung brought back "the venerable images to the Temple of Felicity, and firmly raised its altars;" with his own hand he "wrote a tablet," probably for the great church of the capital. Three rulers followed him upon the throne before the end of our record (in 781), and all of these "honoured the Luminous Multitude." One [2] observed the Festival of Christmas by burning incense; another "instituted Nine Rules for the propagation of the doctrine" (of Christ); various high officials of their court, a member of the Council of War, and several governors of provinces, "rendered perpetual service to the Luminous Gate."

The inscription closes with words of praise and thankfulness: never had the mission been more fortunate than when, "in the year of the Greeks, 1092 (A.D. 781), in the days of the Father of Fathers, the Patriarch Anan-Yeschouah,[3]

[1] "Children of Che."

[2] Sutsung, A.D. 756–762.

[3] This is technically wrong, for this patriarch (Anan-Jesus II. 774–778) died in 778; but the news of his death (probably in or near Bagdad) might well take some years to reach Singanfu; communication was not necessarily constant, and Anan-Yeschouah's successor may not have notified his accession to such a distant mission for a considerable time (see Assemani, III. i. 155–157).

this marble tablet was set up with the history of the Dispensation of our Saviour and the preaching of our fathers before the kings of the Chinese."

The "son of a priest from Balkh," a bishop in Singanfu itself, and a "councillor of the palace," took part among others in the work of composing and erecting this extraordinary monument, which is perhaps the most remarkable witness both of Christian activity in the earlier Middle Ages, and of forgotten intercourse[1] between China and the Western world. Its general truthfulness is well borne out by what we know of the Chinese mission from other sources. Between 714 and 728 the Nestorian Patriarch Salibazacha appointed the first Metropolitan[2] for China; in 745 the Emperor Hiouen-Tsung, the protector of the Church, decreed the name of Roman Temples to the Christian Churches of his Empire, in allusion to their Byzantine origin; in or

[1] The monument consists of about 1780 characters in Chinese, on a dark-coloured marble tablet, 7½ feet high by 3¾ broad, with some additional notes in Syriac on the left side and at the base of the main text. These latter give the name of the patriarch, and of various bishops, priests, and deacons who apparently combine in setting forth this record. Tracings of the inscription were long ago sent to the Jesuit house in Rome, and the Bibliothèque Nationale at Paris; and a rubbing was taken by Baron Richthofen on a visit to Singan, which is used by Yule in his "Marco Polo" (2nd edition, ii. 22), and is here reproduced. The long controversy about its genuineness may now be regarded as settled. Gibbon, in his day, with his almost infallible judgment, declined (ch. xlvii.) to follow Voltaire and La Croze in the tempting pastime of refuting a valuable, if astonishing, proof of early Christian energy; and Stanislas Julien is the only scholar of weight who has disputed it in recent years. See Pauthier, " De l'Authenticité de l'Inscription de Singanfu;" Klaproth, "Tableaux Historiques de l'Asie;" and Abel Rémusat (Mélanges Asiatiques and Nouv. Mél. Asiat., esp. ii. 189, etc., all strenuous defenders of its genuineness; also Huc, " Christianisme en Chine," i. chs. i., ii.,iii. (1857); Legge, "On the Singanfu Inscription" (1888); Hirth, "China and the Roman Orient" (1885); Yule's "Cathay," prelim. essay, § 6; Marco Polo, ii. 22, etc. ; Calcutta Review, July, 1889; Richthofen, "China" (1876). The idea of such a monument was familiar enough in Buddhism, and may have been borrowed by the Christian missionaries, either from native parallels or from reminiscences of Rome.

[2] Assemani, III. i. pp. 522.

THE CHRISTIAN [NESTORIAN] INSCRIPTION AT SIN-GAN-FU,
FROM A RUBBING BY BARON RICHTHOFEN.

[*To face p.* 218.

about 790 the Patriarch Timothy sent a monk named Subchal-Jesu, from the famous monastery of Beth-Hobeh in Assyria, to preach in the Caspian shore-lands, in Tartary, and in China; and after his murder at the hands of robbers, the same pontiff despatched David to succeed him as Metropolitan of Singanfu, together with six other bishops and nine monks, for the further conversion of Central Asia. It was probably about this time that Bishop Abraham went from Bassora to the Celestial Kingdom; and some evidence of the same kind is given us by the Arabs. Thus Abou Zeyd Hassan of Siraf speaks of Nazarenes as still numerous among the people of Khanfu down to the sack of 878, and records how Ibn Vahab, his contemporary and informant, had been shown a picture of "Jesus, the Son of Mary, and His Apostles," by the Chinese emperor a little time before. On the same occasion (about A.D. 875), the Arab visitor and his royal host discussed the stories of the various prophets from Noah to Mohammed, and the emperor seemed well aware of the shortness of Christ's ministry,[1] and other things, which one would suppose he must have learnt from native Christians.

By the ninth century the Nestorian Communion had perhaps reached the height of its power. Ever since the days of Jesu-Jabus, who speaks especially of Merv as a "falling Church" (c. A.D. 650), the patriarchs had had to deplore a slow but steady defection of the Faithful to Islam, although they generally speak of the kindly and tolerant behaviour of their Mohammedan rulers.[2] The Moslem conquest did not depress them in Western Asia, as it depressed the Catholics of Syria and Africa. The Nestorians were in high favour with the Abbasside caliphs as their guides to the

[1] "All He did was transacted in the space of . . . thirty months." See   p. 420 of this volume.
[2] See Assemani, III. i. 130, 131.

Greek treasures of science and letters; and although they could not proselytize from Mussulmans, they made many converts from among the conquered fire-worshippers, as well as from the idolaters beyond the Caliphate.

In 850 we find the line of metropolitans still continuing in China, India, Merv, and Arabia; for these distant prelates are now excused, with others, from attending the central councils of the Nestorian Church in Mesopotamia, on account of the length and difficulties of their various journeys. They could not be expected, it was said, to come from the ends of the earth to Bagdad every four years.

But in the course of the ninth century this widespread activity began to be seriously checked: on the one side, the spread of Islam tended more and more to contract the area still left open in the home-field of Persia and the Levant; on another side, in both the great mission off-shoots of India and China, the preaching of the Gospel broke vainly on the stubborn wall of native distrust and local custom. The domestic disorders of 878, and subsequent years, produced a great change in the spirit of the Chinese Government towards alien importations of all kinds. The baleful effects of civil war were attributed to foreign devilry, and, in the course of the next century, Chinese Christianity became almost extinct. As early as 845, the Emperor Wutsung dealt it a heavy blow by his ordinance against excessive monasticism, both Buddhist and other; when he ordered that all the foreign bonzes, Christian, Magian, and other, should return to secular life, and cease to pervert the institutions of the Central Flowery Land. It was little more than one hundred years after the Revolution of 878, that the scene closes for a time upon the Chinese episode in this early missionary travel, and the last word, it is significant, has to be spoken by an Arab. In A.D. 987

Mohammed Ibn Ishak, surnamed Abulfaragius, author of a celebrated Bibliography (the Kitáb-al-Fihrist), tells how he met with a Christian monk from Najran, behind the principal Church of 'Bagdad, who had been sent to the Celestials seven years before, but had returned in despair on finding but one person of his faith still extant in the land.

Yet, till the eleventh century, the Nestorian worship retained a great hold over many parts of Asia, between the Euphrates and the Gobi Desert, and its ministers seem to have travelled incessantly, wherever we can catch a glimpse of their history. Here and there have been preserved the name and the journey of one of their spiritual envoys—of John of Mosul, sent as metropolitan to Hamadan in the ninth century; of Mark, despatched to Raja in 893; of Joseph, "Metropolitan of Turkestan," A.D. 900; or of John and Sabar-Jesus, Metropolitans of Kashgar at the same epoch: but this is all,—and from such fragments it is impossible to construct a connected story.

When Marco Polo crossed Asia in the later thirteenth century, he found the Nestorian missions, existing indeed, but on a very slender scale beyond the Bolor,—in Yarkand, in Tangut, in Kamul, and in various places of China itself. As a matter of fact, this struggling Christianity had begun to raise its head afresh under the tolerant and inquisitive Mongol rulers, who, like the early caliphs, took many a lesson in science from their Nestorian subjects;[1] yet this revival was but partial, as we shall see in its place. Here we must not enter upon the later traditions, lying as they do outside this period,[2] which attest the continued, though

---

[1] Whom Albyrouny (c. A.D. 1000), in his "Chronology of Ancient Nations" (pp. 282, 306, in Sachau's edition), praises for their mental activity, and especially for their use of logic and analogy.

[2] Circ. A.D. 300–900.

declining life of Nestorian enterprise ; and which tell us of the conversion, in A.D. 1008, of a Tartar chieftain,[1] who perhaps was the Asiatic original of the story of Prester John ; or of the twenty-five metropolitans still subject to the patriarch in the same eleventh century.[2] The Pontificate of Timothy (778–820) apparently marked the zenith of Nestorianism in nearly every field ; and it never raised another monument of success like the Tablet of Singanfu.[3]

In all, however, taking one time with another, it had four Metropolitan sees in China, or Mongolia, of which Singanfu, Zeytun, and Pekin were the chief ;[4] one in Malabar ; four in Central Asia, between the Oxus and the Gobi desert ; five or six in the Levant proper, west of the Zagros Mountains and the Tigris ; eleven or twelve in Persia, and one at least (Socotra) on the East African coast. Its adherents, in the Age of Charles the Great, must have been numbered by millions ;—probably a greater following

[1] By Ebed-Jesus, Metropolitan of Khorasan.

[2] Neale's " Eastern Church," gen. introd. i. 143–146, conjectures this period to have been the culmination of Nestorián power—surely not a well-founded view.

[3] When Layard visited the valley of Jelu in Kurdistan (see his " Nineveh and Babylon," p. 433) he was shown in an old Nestorian church, a number of China bowls, blackened with age and smoke and dust, hanging from the roof. These he was told had been brought from Cathay in very early times ; possibly they reached back to the age of the Singanfu inscription. On the whole subject of the Nestorian missions, see Assemani, " Bibl. Orient.," iii., pt. ii. pp. 77–175, 413–617 passim, the chief collection of material. Also his " De Catholicis seu Patriarchis

. . . Nestorianum Commentarius " (Rome, 1675); Mosheim's " Memoirs of the Church in China " (1862); and Huc, Yule (Cathay, Friar Jordanus, and Marco Polo), Gibbon's references and other studies, as cited. L. A. Waddell, " Buddhism in Thibet " (especially pp. 421, 422), considers it certain, from grounds other than the Nestorian records, that Christian communities existed in West China, near the borders of Thibet, in the seventh century, where Marco Polo found some survivors in the thirteenth.

[4] Otherwise Kambaluc, with which Zeytun disputed primacy ; cf. Assemani, B. O. ii. 458, 459 ; Robertson, Ch. Hist. vol. iii. ; and Yule's " Cathay," Prelim. Essay, § 6 ; and especially his map of the Nestorian bishoprics, and Supplem. Note, pp. ccxliv., ccxlv.

then looked up to the patriarch of Bagdad than to any Catholic pontiff; and the scope of its activity was, beyond comparison, more widespread.

Cosmas, who was possibly a Nestorian himself, describes the vast extent of an Oriental Christianity, which can hardly have been any other than Nestorianism, at a time when from other sources we know that these missions were in a flourishing state (c. 550). Churches were then to be found, he declares, in Ceylon, Malabar, and Socotra (with a bishop and clergy "ordained and sent from Persia"); in Bactria and among the Huns; in Mesopotamia, Scythia, Hyrcania, Lazica, and the lands to the east of the Black Sea,—as well as in all the countries where more orthodox communion[1] existed. He is, indeed, passing in review the whole of Christendom, from "Southern Gades," or Ceuta, to Central Asia, and from the Indian Ocean to the Caspian; and he says not a word of any difference of creed between the Franks and the most outlying Christian Churches; but his purpose is only to set forth the fulfilment of the prophecy that the gospel should be proclaimed in every district under heaven, and it was not in such an ecstasy that he would call attention to the rents and divisions of the once seamless garment.

He had reason to exult. For perhaps never before or after was Christianity of one kind or another so widely spread in the Old World—the world of Europe, of Asia, and of Africa—as in his day.

The bearing of these Eastern missions on geography is obvious enough. Had they left a fair account of themselves men's knowledge of the world could not but have been strengthened and deepened. But in the West, the limits of the old Empire were far more nearly coextensive with the

---

[1] Bk. iii. and bk. xi. (esp. p. 178, Montf.). Cf. Assemani, De Cath. Nestor; "Bibl. Orient.," ii. 458, 459. In 893 Elias, Metropolitan of Damascus, reckoned thirteen metropolitan sees. See p. 242.

limits of *terra firma*, and it is not till the ninth century and
the journeys of Ansgar in the Scandinavian and North
German lands that Latin missionary travel does much for
the exploration of the unknown or forgotten.

But Ulphilas among the Goths and Patrick among the
Celtic Irish were the pioneers of this religious discovery at
a far earlier time.

Ulphilas, who, as early as 340, appears as a Christian
teacher to his own people beyond the Danube, died in 381,
within the limits which had so long been fixed for the
Roman civilisation.   But his translation of the Bible prepared the way for missionary enterprise to penetrate among
the heathen of Central Europe; and by his work the conquerors of Adrianople (378) were made more accessible to
civilising influences and more unlikely to destroy the
Mediterranean culture; which included of course all the
geographical knowledge hitherto put together, with such
tedious and painful toil.

Again, Patrick's conversion of Ireland (c. 430) opened to
Christendom a country that had never been Roman, and
was practically unknown to Continental Europe after
Honorius withdrew his legions from Britain (c. 409).   Merchants had found their way to its shores in the second
century, and Ptolemy had a fair notion of its harbours and
its general shape, but the full discovery of the island was
the work of Christian missionaries.   More than that, Patrick
had only been dead a century, when the Irish themselves,
with a fervour like that of the early Saracens, took up a vast
mission work of their own.   A wedge of heathendom had
thrust itself in upon Britain and the Continent, when the
Catholics of Italy and France were joined by these new
allies.   To Rome their help, independent and self-reliant as
it was, proved embarrassing; and after a time the two

Churches began to struggle for the allegiance of North-Western Europe: but to Christendom, and to progress in general, they were true pioneers. They preached with striking success among the English who had overrun all the eastern plains of Britain.[1] Their cause triumphed at last over the enmity of the Midlands and of Penda. They carried the gospel further into Caledonia than Agricola had ever carried the Roman eagles. They sent their more daring devotees to the Orkneys, the Färoes, and even to Iceland. They founded houses of learning and religion in North Italy, in Burgundy, in Switzerland, and in Bavaria.[2] Their influence was felt in every Christian or semi-Christian country, and in many lands outside the pale of the shrunken Church of the seventh century.

Further, they developed an art, a literature, a culture of their own which, with all its fantasies, had extraordinary beauty and merit, if it is judged by its age and its opportunities—or its lack of them; and among these memorials of a noble fight with barbarism we have left to us at least two,[3] which have direct and useful relation both with the history of travel and the science of geography.

The most brilliant work of the Irish missions was done in one hundred years (560–660); but it was kept up in a sense for five centuries, and for at least half that time it is worth our notice, if we would attend to anything which helped to keep the world from getting darker.

St. Columba crossed from Ireland to Iona in 560; and with this begins the new Celtic enterprise and travel. In 565 he converted the King of the Picts, Brude or Bruidi,

---

[1] Cf. Bede, Hist. Eccl., bks. iii. iv. v., passim.

[2] Those of Bobbio and St. Gall became especially valuable, from their scholarship, which prompted collections of manuscripts hardly equalled in any monastic library of the Dark Ages.

[3] Dicuil and Virgil.

in his royal town on the site of Inverness; and from this point he spread the Christian faith through the most northerly parts of Britain. He even despatched a party of his monks to convert the Orkneys, of which Bruidi was overlord. "Some of our brethren," he announced to his powerful convert, " have lately sailed to discover a desert in the pathless sea.[1] If they shòuld wander to the Orcadian islands, do thou shield them from harm."

On the other side, to the south and south-east, Columba's followers travelled into the English kingdoms, saved the Christianity of Northumbria after the overthrow of Eadwine (633), and made themselves, in the course of the next generation, the religious teachers of all the English race north of the Thames. Beyond the Channel, Columban reached as far as Bobbio and the Apennines in his missionary wanderings; and was celebrated as the Apostle of the Juras, and the Elijah of the two Frankish Jezebels, Brunehaut and Fredegund (600–615). St. Gall in Switzerland, where he drove out the spirits of the lakes and mountains over the Boden See (600–627); St. Catald in the south of Italy; St. Fridolin in Glarus; St. Colman in Austria, St. Kilian in Franconia,—all of these and many others, in the sixth and seventh centuries, followed up the exploring achievements of Columban. Even the devils were subject unto them. "Come and help me," one demon was heard crying to another over the Lake of Constance, "help me to break the nets of these strangers, for they are too hard for me."[2] And while they pressed heathendom so vigorously, these Irish missionaries seemed to think of wresting from Rome the religious leadership she was doing so little to assert.[3] They would not wait for a pope's commission to journey and to evangelise.

[1] Adamnan's Life of Columba, ed. Reeves, p. 366.
[2] Life of St. Gall.
[3] Between St. Leo and St. Gregory, c. A.D. 450–600.

Columban bluntly told Gregory the Great, when he quoted the words of Pope Leo I., that a living dog was better than a dead *lion*. The Celts had given way to Romans and Teutons on the battle-field and in civil life ; was their turn now to come in the religious moulding of the new nations ?

Time was to show that enthusiasm, in the long run, must yield, even in the Church, to the power of governing and of organising ; that the emotional cannot rule the stronger and more persistent elements of human nature : but this intensely emotional movement of Irish missionary energy did not pass away without leaving some permanent results.

In geographical discovery, the hermit-instinct, to which we have had an allusion in Columba's words—the longing to fly from men, and discover a desert in the ocean, where God only might be served—was responsible for the first voyages to the Färoes, and to Iceland.

Writing in 825, in one of those Irish monastery schools[1] which had welcomed learning as it fled from the new barbarism of the Continent, and thus become "Universities of the West," Dicuil stops his description of the earth's measurements and marvels, to tell us about the latest of these ventures.[2] Thirty years before, he says, in the year of Christ 795, a party of his countrymen, solitaries, or in search of solitude, visited "Thule," and stayed there from the first of February to the first of August. Unlike the hermit of the East, to whom all nature—human and other— seemed full of hidden or open devilry, and who therefore hated and feared every kind of useful knowledge—these Irishmen noticed things that a geographer, like Dicuil himself, found very interesting. They said that in the island they discovered the setting sun, during that summer,

[1] Such as Durrow or Armagh.
[2] De Mensura Orbis Terræ, vii.

11–13 (ed. Parthey, 1870).

"not only at the solstice, but for many days in the year, seemed merely to hide itself behind a little mound, so that there was no darkness to hide a man from doing what he liked, even from picking lice out of his clothes."[1]

They thought, indeed, if they had been on top of a mountain, they would never have lost sight of the sun at all.[2] From this Dicuil was disposed to believe that the exact opposite occurred in winter—not indeed for half the year, but just as in summer, for a few days before and after the solstice. About the sea round Thule, the brethren reported it was not frozen, as had been falsely said—even of more southern latitudes. At the end of January they had found it perfectly open; but on going one day's sail to the north, they had come to the ice-wall.[3]

These were not the only Arctic explorations of Irish saints. Dicuil tells us nothing about the legendary, yet possibly not altogether fictitious, voyages of St. Brandan; but he knew of many journeys among the islands to the north and West of Britain. Some of these, he was informed— probably the Färoes—were two days' sail from the "northern islands" of the same Britain, and a "certain priest who was also a monk" had come in two summer days and a night to one of the aforesaid. To Dicuil's own knowledge, "Scottish" hermits had frequented such solitudes for nearly a hundred years (c. 750–820). From the creation of the world these had lain waste without inhabitant, and now (by 825) the Northmen had desolated them afresh. It was wonderful that no record had ever been made of them before. And other islands there are, proceeds the geographer, around Britain and around Ireland: some he had visited himself; all of them he knew by hearsay or by

---

[1] "Peduculos de camisia abstra-here."

[2] D., vii. 11–13.

[3] D., vii. 14. Cf. Solinus, xxii. 9.

reading, and he could not compare the Irish satellites with the British—for the first-named were mere rocks, while the latter made a far better show. The Hebrides are certainly larger and more habitable than the Skerries or the Blaskets.

Dicuil's story of the pilgrimage of Fidelis to the Levant has been already noticed; in connection with this it is curious to see how many recondite and unconvincing but suggestive evidences have been collected by Irish antiquarians to prove an intercourse between Syria and Ireland in this age. The schools of the younger Church were modelled, it is said, after the Laura of the older; and the cell-buildings of the Eastern monks were exactly copied in various Celtic monasteries.[1] But this question is architectural in the main, and of extreme obscurity.

What Irishmen did for the theory of geography will be examined in the next chapter, in a view of the science of the whole period. We have seen something already of Dicuil, and how much he contributed to knowledge by the accounts he preserved of practical travel; we shall have to add some appreciation of another "Scot,"[2] Virgil, the bishop of Saltzburg (A.D. 750–784), who dared to prefer the guidance of pagan Greeks to that of St. Augustine in forming a doctrine of the world's shape, and ignored the axioms of Cosmas against the sphericity of the earth and the existence of antipodes. He was, indeed, rebuked and silenced by the pope, but in this he only shared the fate of Roger Bacon.

[1] Cf. G. T. Stokes ("Ireland and the Celtic Church," lect. xii.), Dunraven's "Notes on Irish Architecture," and De Vogüé's "Syrie Centrale."

[2] Virgil hadn't learnt, says Rev. G. T. Stokes, in his excellent lectures ("Ireland and the Celtic Church," p. 224), the secret of all safe and most successful men, never to startle one's hearers by advocating any novel or unpopular view,—a curious doctrine for the minister of a religion which was once, in Pilate's Prætorium and in the Roman amphitheatre, both novel and unpopular—and certainly professes, even now, to teach a body of truth rather than a body of conventionalities. But certainly neither Christ nor St. Paul would have been called safe or successful by the Jews.

It remains to see whether Brandan and his story adds anything real to the credit of Irish explorers. Like St. Malo, the Abbot of Clonfert is still supposed by many to have made some genuine discovery of land in the Western or Northern Ocean about A.D. 565. There is nothing to prevent us believing that he may have sighted one of the outlying Hebrides, or even the Färoes; but a voyage to America, Iceland, or Greenland is quite out of the question, and yet there is no nearer land to account for the legend, unless it be Rockall Island, a speck of firm ground planted, like St. Helena on Ascension, in the mid-ocean, without any attendant group, about 150 miles north-west of Donegal. In itself, a voyage like Brandan's is possible, but the tradition is late and closely connected with fable, of a venerable but not the less childish kind; such as it is, it does not perhaps forbid us to look in the south for his discovery—among the Azores, the Canaries, or the Madeira group. But the legend cannot really be verified or disproved. We are in absolutely uncertain and fabulous regions, as much as when we try to follow the journeys of the three Calendars in the Arabian Nights. We may feel it likely that a germ of truth exists in a body of unsubstantial romance, but we cannot extract it; for we are uncertain in what part of the tale to detect the historical fact, or even if such fact is to be discerned at all. The balance of likelihood is almost even, and we can only be sure of one thing—that the floating or vanishing island,[1] which many a man of later time was said to have found and chased in vain, is a myth. Down to the end of the Middle Ages, and in the sixteenth century, Brandan's isle was marked on maps, usually due west of Ireland; it was sighted again and again by determined and devout people who went out to look for it; it was associated with similar discoveries

---

[1] Cf. Vincent of Beauvais, Spec. Hist. xxii. 81.

of St. Malo in the sixth century, of the seven Spanish
bishops in the eighth, of the Basques in the tenth; on the
success of Columbus, it was turned, of course, like the rest,
into a claim for a prior discovery of America : but it began
in twelfth-century poetry or poetic hagiology, and it
obstinately remains in a poetic mirage.[1]   It gives us,
perhaps, a picture of the shuddering interest of these
missionary travellers in the wildness, the power, and the
infinitude of nature, as it could be tasted on the ocean; it
does not give us anything more definite.

In its complete form, the legend gave this account.
Brandan was an Irish monk who died on May 16, 578, in
the abbey of Clonfert, which he had founded.   One day,
when entertaining a brother monk named Barinth, he was
told by him of his recent voyage on the Ocean, and of an
isle called the Delicious, where his disciple Mernoc had
retired with several religious men.   Barinth had been to
visit him, and Mernoc had taken him to a more distant isle
in the West, which was reached through a thick fog, beyond
which shone an eternal clearness—this was the promised
Land of the Saints.   Brandan, seized with a pious desire

[1] Cf. Matthew Arnold's "St. Brandan":—

> "Saint Brandan sails the Northern Main,
>   The brotherhood of saints are glad.
> He greets them once, he sails again :
>   So late ! such storms ! the saint is mad !
> He heard across the howling seas
>   Chime convent bells on wintry nights;
> He saw, on spray-swept Hebrides,
>   Twinkle the monastery lights :
> But north, still north, Saint Brandan steered,
>   And now no bells, no convents more,
> The hurtling Polar lights are reached,
>   The sea without a human shore."

For a discussion of the later mediæval evidence on this point of "The
Legendary Western Voyages"—and its worthlessness—we must refer to the
monograph of M. de Goeje and other studies, as cited on p. 239, note 2.

to see this Isle of the Blessed, embarked in an osier boat covered with tanned hides and carefully greased, and took with him seventeen other monks, among whom was St. Malo, then a young man. After forty days at sea they reached an island with steep scarped sides, furrowed by streamlets, where they received hospitality,[1] and took in fresh provisions.

Thence they were carried by the winds towards another island, cut up by rivers that were full of fish, and covered with countless flocks of sheep as large as heifers. From these they took a lamb without blemish wherewith to celebrate the Easter festival on another island close by, —bare, without vegetation or rising ground. Here they landed to cook their lamb, but no sooner had they set the pot and lighted the fire than the island began to move. They fled to their ship, where St. Brandan had stayed; and he showed them that what they had taken for a solid island, was nothing but a whale.[2] They regained the former isle (of sheep) and saw the fire they had kindled, flaming upon the monster's back, two miles off.

From the summit of the island they had now returned to, they discerned another, wooded and fertile; whither they repaired, and found a multitude of birds, who sang with them the praises of the Lord: this was the Paradise of Birds. Here the Pious travellers remained till Pentecost, then, again embarking, they wandered several months upon the Ocean. At last they came to another isle, inhabited by Cœnobites, who had for their patrons St. Patrick and St. Ailbhé; with these they celebrated Christmas, and took ship again after the Octave of the Epiphany.

[1] In a deserted palace, from angelic hands, by one account.

[2] "The beast Jasconius (in one version), greatest of things that swim, which laboureth night and day to put his tail in his mouth, but for greatness he may not."

A year had passed in these journeys, and during the next six they continued the same round with certain variations (such as their visit to the island of the Hermit Paul,[1] and their meeting with Judas Iscariot); finding themselves always at St. Patrick's Isle for Christmas, at the Isle of Sheep for Holy Week, on the Back of the Whale (which now displayed no uneasiness) for Easter, and at the Isle of Birds for Pentecost.

But during the seventh year, especial trials were reserved for them; they were nearly destroyed by a whale, by a gryphon, by Cyclops. But they also saw several other islands. One was large and wooded; another flat, with great red fruit, inhabited by a race called the Strong Men; another full of rich orchards, the trees bending beneath their load; and to the north they came to the rocky, treeless, barren island of the Cyclops' forges; close by which was a lofty mountain with summit veiled in clouds, vomiting flames—this was the mouth of hell.

And now as the end of their attempt had come, they embarked afresh with provisions for forty days, entered the zone of mist and darkness which enclosed the Isle of Saints, and, having traversed it, found themselves on the shore of the island they had so long been seeking, bathed in light. This was an extensive land, sown as it were with precious stones, covered with fruit as in the season of autumn, and enjoying perpetual day. Here they stayed and explored the abode of the blest for forty days, without reaching the end of it. But at last, on arriving at a great river, that flowed through the midst of it, an angel appeared to them to tell them they could go no further, and that they must return to their country; bearing with them some of the

---

[1] A little round and barren island, on the summit of which dwelt the hermit who gave them his benediction.

fruits and precious stones of the land, reserved to the saints against that time when God should have subdued to the true faith all the nations of the universe. St. Brandan and his companions again entered into their vessel, traversed afresh the margin of darkness, and came to the Island of Delight. Thence they returned directly to Ireland.[1]

This is the legend which has served as the basis of the claim for an Irish or British discovery of America in the sixth century, and upon this model were formed the similar tales of Western voyages by the seven Spanish bishops in the eighth century, or by the Basques of the tenth.

The alleged discovery of the seven bishops is associated with the names of Antillia and the Seven Cities, but the earliest form of the latter story does not go back before the year 1492; when Martin Behaim placed the following inscription on his famous globe designed for the city of Nuremburg in that ever-memorable summer: " In the year 734, after the birth of Christ, when all Spain was overrun by the miscreants of Africa, this Island of Antillia, called also the Isle of the Seven Cities, was peopled by the Archbishop of Oporto with six other bishops, and certain companions, male and female, who fled from Spain with their cattle and property. In the year 1414 a Spanish ship approached very near this Island." A somewhat fuller account is given by Ferdinand Columbus, who also identifies the names of Antillia and Seven Cities as referring to the same spot, but dates the flight from Spain in A.D. 714, and describes how a Portuguese ship professed (but with highly

[1] In the twelfth century Sigebert de Gemblours found these marvels insufficient, and added that the name of the isle so much sought for was Ima; that St. Malo there raised a giant to life, instructed him in the true faith, and baptized him under the name of Mildus, after which he allowed him to die again immediately.

suspicious circumstances[1]) to have discovered the colony in the time of Prince Henry the Navigator.

The first remark that naturally occurs in regard to the Brandan story and its imitations is, that the record is very late; the second is, that it shows in many places signs of being concocted from other narratives. In other words, as to the first point, although Brandan is supposed to have sailed in or about A.D. 565, no trace is found of his story before the eleventh century; while, as to the next matter, the voyage of the Moslem Wanderers (or Maghrurins) of Lisbon, as recorded by Edrisi, and those of Sindbad the Sailor, as preserved in the "Arabian Nights," are clearly related in some way to the Brandan narrative. This can hardly be in the way of copy to original, for the Christian record is undoubtedly much later as well as much more fabulous than that, for instance, of the ninth-century Soleyman the Merchant, the main source of Sindbad; or even than that of the Lisbon Wanderers, whose journey probably took place at some time before A.D. 1000, and who certainly appear to have reached some of the West African islands. Their adventure belongs to a subsequent period of our history, but we may notice here one striking resemblance of their story with the Brandan legend. Their tradition of the Isle of El Ghanam[2] abounding in sheep, whose flesh had a bitter taste, from a herb on which the animals fed—does not this recall St. Brandan's Island of Fat Sheep? Once more, the Arabic Islands of El Toyour (or of birds); of the Wizards, Sherham and Shabram; and of the whale where Sindbad's companions kindled a fire

---

[1] Thus the captain was unable to offer any proofs of his visit, and when the prince ordered him to return, and bring home more certain intelligence, he promptly took to flight.

[2] Which has been identified with our Madeira.

with even more disastrous results, find their parallels in St. Brandan's Islands of Pious Birds, of the Solitary Hermit, and of the great fish; while his volcano, or Island of Hell's Mouth, and his Isles of Delights and of Paradise are traditional expressions, both in classical and mediæval geography (Arab and Christian), for the fiery mountain of Teneriffe and the lovely climate of the Canary or Fortunate Islands. Even the Griffin of Brandan's story, and the whale that attacks his boat, may be borrowed from the Roc and the aggressive sea-monsters of the Sindbad Saga; while the very number of the years of travel in the Christian legend correspond to the sevenfold ventures of the navigator in the "Arabian Nights." In the case of the latter, the seven years of travel are arrived at naturally enough by seven successive voyages; in the case of Brandan, the time assigned to the adventure is purely arbitrary and artificial, as would be the case in a borrowed narrative. There is no reason at all why the saint should not reach the Isle of Paradise in his first year's sail, as his precursors Barinth and Mernoc seem to have done; no reason why he should be compelled to perform his curious round of visits for six years without reaching further; except, indeed, the charming explanation of a later insertion[1] in the eleventh century narrative, that Brandan was thus punished for having disbelieved and destroyed a book of marvellous stories which had come into his hands. He was condemned to wander, according to this, during a sacred cycle of years, till he should have seen with his own eyes all the wonders he had refused to credit; and, as a crowning penance, he was forced to describe them for the instruction of others.

As we might expect in a narrative so made up of borrowed details as Brandan's "Navigation," the inconsistencies of the

[1] Of the twelfth century.

story are not merely in the unreasonable and unexplained
delay of the saint in reaching his goal in the Isle of Paradise; the Whale Island is treated in an entirely different
manner in the first and the subsequent years; in the one it
behaves (as in the Sindbad story) naturally and wickedly—it
resents the fire kindled on its back, and tries to get rid of its
visitors; but in all following years it shows the utmost
docility, puts itself completely at the disposal of the holy
men, allows them to celebrate their services on its back, and
charitably conveys them to the Isle of Birds. Again, the
Brandan legend, in telling us of this same Whale Island,
first describes it as barren, and then alludes, in the manner
of Sindbad, to the woodland growing upon it. On the other
hand, the conception of the land promised to the saints, as
set forth in the " Navigation," belongs rather to a Christian,
a European, and, more narrowly, a Northern idea of Paradise
than to anything Oriental; but, in the main, the Brandan
legend is penetrated by Eastern influence. We may see
this more fully, if it be worth while to multiply instances, in
many minor details of the " Navigation "—in the empty
palace which Brandan finds in his first-discovered island, the
devil[1] who afterwards comes to light in that same palace,
the soporific spring in the Isle of Birds, and the speechless
man[2] of the Isle of Ailbhé, " who only answered by gestures," in the Christian narrative, compared with the similar
incidents of the second and third voyages of Sindbad.
Again, the giants who threaten both the Arab and Irish
adventurers by aiming huge blocks of stone at their frail
vessels, probably come into both narratives from the Cyclops
story of the Odyssey; the river and precious stones in
Brandan's Isle of Paradise irresistibly recall the charms of
the island in the sixth Sindbad voyage; and just as the

[1] The Negro Cannibal of the Arab.   [2] The Old Man of the Sea.

latter's companions are roasted and eaten by the demon Black of Sindbad's third adventure, so on the shore of the Burning Isle one of Brandan's monks is caught away by devils, and burnt up to a cinder.

In any attempt, therefore, to resolve this story into its historical elements, so as to see what bearing (if any) it has on geographical thought and enterprise within this period, it seems necessary to assume that the compiler of the "Navigation" owed his principal inspiration to the Sindbad "romances of fact." Perhaps we may suppose the real state of the case was as follows: First of all, there was a real Brandan, who lived at the beginning of the age of Irish mission enterprise, and took part in that national movement. A tradition of an actual voyage made by him was preserved in Ireland from the sixth century; but in this tradition there was an almost absolute want of detail (from the later "Navigation," it is evident that there was just as much authority for making Brandan's course an eastward as there was for making it a westward one); and the voyage itself was of a modest scope, only reaching some such island as Rockall, near to the Irish coast. As time went on, Brandan's voyage, which owed its comparative importance simply to the spiritual fame of its leader, was enriched with various, but slender details; thus the saint was credited in the ninth century "Life of St. Malo"[1] with having sought *in vain* for Paradise.

Then, either shortly before or after the year 900, an Irish or Frankish monk, going on pilgrimage to Syria, heard or read the Sindbad story in some form, and witnessed the miracle of the holy fire at Jerusalem; which appears in the Brandan story of the lamps lighted by an angel's hand on the Isle of St. Ailbhé, and which was first made widely

[1] By Bili.

known in the time of Bernard the Wise, about A.D. 870.
Now, and not till now (say in the course of the tenth
century), the Brandan story was thrown into the form we
have (in all its main incidents), by the unknown pilgrim we
have supposed, on his return from the East; and before the
narrative had reached the state even of the oldest manuscript
we possess, the Brandan romance, thus Orientalized, had
received a good many additions from other sources, especially
from the Spanish voyages of the Young Man of Cordova, and
the Wanderers of Lisbon, as well as from lives of other
Christian ˜saints and Christianized fragments of classical
myth.[1]   In its final shape, the legend aimed at giving not
merely a Christian Odyssey, but a picture of monastic life
and worship; and by thus combining the edifying element
with the adventurous, strove to win that popularity which, as
a matter of fact, it gained.[2]

And if the Brandan story proper wears so doubtful and
unreal a semblance, still less satisfactory are its copies.   As

[1] The meeting with Judas and
with Paul the Hermit are examples
of Christian—the encounters with
the talking birds, the friendly fish,
and the crystal column in the sea are,
perhaps, specimens of classical—loans
to the Brandan story.

[2] See Avezac, "Iles Fantastiques
de l'Ocean Occidental" (1845); and
Goeje, "La Légende de Saint Brandan" (1890), by far the most important of recent studies on this question;
also Schirmer, "Zur Brendanus
Legende" (1888), which attempts to
prove that the "Navigation," as we
have it, is of the ninth century; Gaston
Paris, "Terre de l'Éternelle Jeu-
nesse;" and the editions of the text
in one or more versions by Jubinal
("Légende de Saint Brandon"),
1836; by Thomas Wright, Percy

Society Publics. (1844); by Francis
Michel ("Les Voyages Merveilleux
de Saint Brandan"), 1878; by P. F.
(Cardinal) Moran (Acta Sti. B.),
1872; by W. T. Rees, in the "Lives
of the Cambro-British Saints," 1853;
and by Schröder, 1871, who essays
the difficult task of proving the Irish
narrative to be an original, from
which Sindbad and others copied.
There is also a study by Paul
Gaffarel of 1881, embodied in his
"Histoire de la Découverte de
l'Amérique" (1892); and one by
Zimmer of 1889, in the Zeitschrift
für Deutsch. Alterth. xxiii. pp. 129–
220, 257–338.   The Rev. Denis
O'Donoghue's "Brendaniana" (Dublin, 1893) gives an English version
of the principal Brandan episodes.

to the chief of these, the Antillia story, as far as it is not
an essay in purely fantastic geography, seems to rest on
nothing earlier or better than the tale of the Portuguese
mariners of 1414, which may have referred to some distant
and imperfect view of the Azores, or may have been only
the transference into Christian phrase of the Western
Dragon Island of some Arabic writers, or of the Atlantis of
Plato. With this last, Antillia is expressly identified by
an inscription of 1455, which says nothing of the Spanish
bishops or the Seven Cities, and only repeats the tradition of
the Timæus.

The real achievements of the Northmen make these
earlier traditions of similar ocean voyaging almost ludicrous. In 790 the black boats of the Vikings were first seen
off the Irish coast; within fifty years the newcomers had
dealt the Irish Church and its enterprise a blow from
which it never recovered: and with their advent, here as
elsewhere, we reach a natural close of this early religious
geography.

In the introductory chapter, we have already noticed
the Continental counterpart of the Irish missionary movement. For while this was still in its prime, Gregory the
Great commenced a Roman enterprise of a similar kind ;—
which met and worsted the Celtic preachers, won back the
best part of Britain to its old communion, returned from
England upon heathen Germany with added force, and
absorbing into itself all other activities of Western religion,
at last completed the conversion of Europe, by the gain of
the Northmen and the Hungarians, just a thousand years
after the gospel had been brought over into Macedonia by
St. Paul.

In its later stages this expansion of the Church carried
with it a decided expansion of the civilised world, and so of

geography. Within the limits of our period (to the end of
the ninth century) it did not accomplish much more than a
defensive work; but here and there it made exploring
conquests, even from the seventh century.

Thus, the Bavarians, the Thuringians, the Frisians, and
other tribes beyond the lower course of the Rhine were
converted by Frankish, Irish, and English missionaries in
the obedience of Rome before the time of Boniface, who
pressed home their work into the central heathen land of
Germany (716–755). But it was not till the middle of the
ninth century that any great advance was made in widening
the bounds of Christendom, if we except Charles the Great's
compulsory baptism of the old Saxons between the Ems
and the Elbe. About 850 the Catholic attack was resumed
in a less violent and more Evangelical manner. Ansgar
in the far north, had already made his way to Denmark and
to Sweden (822–829); Cyril and Methodius had begun
their mission work in the south-east a few years before: but
it was now that some result was first clearly traceable along
these two lines of progress. It was under the protection of
Eric of Denmark that Ansgar founded the earliest permanent Churches among Danes and Swedes.[1] It was under
the auspices and in the pontificate of Nicholas I. that the
Moravians as a people became Christian (c. 863). In the
next generation the gospel was carried into Bohemia (c.
894). These successes bore on geography as well as on
religion. They widened the horizon of Christendom; they
brought large tracts of half-known country within the view
of the Western world; they even threw a light into the
black darkness of heathen Scandinavia and Sclavonia. They
prepared the way for the conversion of those races who were
to be the foremost champions, the most daring expanders

[1] 848–853. Cf. Rimbert's St. Ansgar, in Migne, P. L. cxviii.

of the Europe and Christendom to which they joined themselves.[1]

ADDITIONAL NOTE TO PAGE 209.

As to Christian mission journeys in the Sahara and Northern Soudan, we may add, from Tertullian (Adv. Judæos, 7), that at the beginning of the third century the faith had already been preached among some of the Gætulian and Moorish tribes to the south of the Syrtes. The Blemmyes and Nobades of (? Napata in) Nubia were not converted till about A.D. 548, when the Priest Julian undertook his evangelizing travels from Alexandria, under the patronage of the Empress Theodora (John of Ephesus, Hist. Eccl. iv. 5–9). Julian won over Silco, King of the Nobades; in 569 he was followed by Longinus, also of Alexandria (John of Eph. iv. 49). The Alodes living to the south of the Nobades—in Meroe proper?—were evangelized by the latter in 579. The Maccuritæ, who about 573 sent ivory and a camelopard to Justin II., were then still heathen, and threatened the mission travellers; where they lived is rather uncertain, except that they were south of the Nobades. See Letronne in "Mémoires de l'Acad. des Inscriptions," ix. 128; x. 168, 218; E. Revillout, "Mémoire sur les Blemmyes," in Mém. presentés à l'Acad. des Inscr. VIII., ii. 371; A. Dillmann, "Uber die Anfänge des Axumitischen, Reiches," 1878; Duchesne, "Églises Séparées," 280–300; and refs. as noticed above, especially to John of Ephesus.

ADDITIONAL NOTE TO PAGE 223.

METROPOLITAN SEES OF THE NESTORIAN CHURCH.—The thirteen metropolitan sees mentioned by Elias of Damascus in 893 are: 1. Bagdad, the province of the patriarch. 2. Djondesabour, the seat of the great medical college, between Bagdad and Ispahan. 3. Nisibis. 4. Mosul (Nineveh). 5. Bethgarma, or Bajarma, the present Eski-Bagdad, east of the Tigris, below Dur. 6. Damascus. 7. Rai, in Tabaristan, east of Teheran. 8. Herat. 9. Armenia. 10. Kand (? Samarcand). 11. Fars, on the east of the Persian gulf. 12. Bardara, metropolis of the province of Ar-Ran on the Kur, south-east of the modern Elisabetpol, at the south-west end of the Caspian. 13. Halwan, close to Bagdad, on the north-east, a summer residence of the caliphs. To these may be added, even within the limits of our period and Elias' own life-time: 14. Hind, or India, for the Malabar churches. 15. Sin, or China, for the Singanfu and other churches beyond the Great Wall. [15A. Khambalik, Cambalu, or Pekin, and 15B., Zeytun, are probably of later creation, after 900, and point to a Nestorian revival in China in the crusading time, just as the Nestorian archbishopric of Jerusalem begins in 1200.] 16. Merv, or Tus, for the missions on the east side of the Caspian. 17. Halaha, or Balkh (?). 18. Kashimghar, or Kashgar (?). 19. Sejistan (? metrop. of Persia). 20. Kotrobah, or Socotra (?).

---

[1] Historical judgment is always in danger of over-satisfaction with the comfortable doctrine that whatever is, is right. We shall never know whether Europe, conquered and heathenised by the Northmen, would have been at last (say in the twelfth century) more or less backward than it actually found itself. It is curious that the Norse genius for exploration, though not for conquest, seemed to die out with its conversion: but we must not forget that the impulse of the crusading movement was due to them; and if the Vikings grew tamer within the Church, we must not regret it. They would not have received the Catholic system if they had felt that it cramped and enfeebled their life.

CHAPTER VI.

GEOGRAPHICAL THEORY.

I.—SOLINUS AND THE FABULISTS.

WE have now to look at the theories and the theorists of our earlier mediæval, or patristic, geography. We have followed the steps of the travellers, of the practical explorers of this time, from the age of Constantine to the age of the Vikings; we must now try to realize what students had made of the science which the pilgrims represented in its active and matter-of-fact relations.

And here we shall be even more roughly awakened to the decline which had taken place from the high-water mark of classical knowledge. Whereas Strabo, Ptolemy, the Peutinger Table, and many less important and prominent works, all bear witness to the fulness and the extent of Roman and Greek acquaintance, under the Empire, with a large portion of the Eastern Hemisphere, and with the shape and size of the world as a whole; whereas the reckonings of Eratosthenes shows how a fairly accurate measurement of the circumference of the earth was possible in the time of Hannibal; and whereas the writings of Herodotus are evidence of correct ideas, even in the time of Pericles, upon such a distant and difficult region as the Caspian Sea, and tell us of attempts in map-making five hundred years before Christ—now, after the lapse of a thousand, or even of thirteen

hundred summers,[1] the history of European thought seems
only to display, as a permanent result, the savings of a
wreckage. The ill-chosen and often misunderstood fragments of pre-Christian work—the extracts from Pliny, or
Mela, or the traditional surveys of Cæsar and Augustus,
which we find in the patristic and ecclesiastical geographers
before the Crusades—appear to be almost the sole antidotes
to ignorance. Of independent work in geographical theory,
except for scripturists like Cosmas, there is scarcely anything; as a substitute for this, we have little more than
compilations from the more fanciful and less trustworthy
pagan authors. Till the Mediæval Renaissance begins, in
the Crusading Age, we must be content with abridgments
of Pliny, lists transcribed with many blunders from ancient
itineraries, and maps drawn partly from the Jewish
Scriptures, partly from late and secondhand repositories
of general knowledge. Early Christian science seemed often
to avoid, as if on principle, the better sources of information,
the geography of Claudius Ptolemy, the description of all
known lands by Strabo, the narratives of authentic travel
to be found in the ancient Peripli or Coastings, such as that
of the " Red " or Indian Sea.[2] These dry records were unpala-
table; they must be taken with a pleasant mixture of natural
history (as in Pliny), or of grammatical fancy (as in
Servius and Varro), òr of theological dogma (as in the
Catholic Encyclopædists, Orosius, Isidore, and the rest).
And besides this instinctive preference for the legendary
as against the commonplace, the Christian science in question had two other prepossessions which were scarcely
helpful to the progress of knowledge. It delighted in any
suggestions of geographical symmetry, however fanciful; [3]

---

[1] Viz. from Herodot., 450 B.C., to
A.D. 900.

[2] The " Erythræan " Periplus,
prob. of c. A.D. 80.

[3] *E.g.* of the length of the οἰκουμενή
as double the breadth.

and it was anxious to square its ideas of the world with those which had been held by the Hebrew race at various periods, and which were enshrined in the Old or New Testament. Under the impulse of this last and very natural desire, it even ventured into something like original work. It was impressed by the idea that science was governed by revelation, and so, confronting various passages of Scripture with the discoveries and assertions of pagan geographers and astronomers, it subjected the latter as far as possible to the tests of an infallible Word and of an infallible Church directed by that Word. As we have pointed out already, one theologian at least proceeded even further. Cosmas, the monk, by a daring literalism, and a still more daring mysticism, in his interpretation of Bible texts, constructed a complete religious system of geography. In the manner of his class, he illustrated this with stories of marvels, animal, mineral, or architectural, in various parts, and with definite statements intended to illustrate the symmetrical harmony and suggestiveness of nature.

His work, however, must be discussed in its proper place, like that of the other Christian theorists of the later Empire and the earlier Middle Ages; and among these we shall find three schools, all of which are sometimes represented in the same writer, and whose characteristics we have attempted to illustrate by certain leading examples.[1]

First come the *Fabulists*, the copyists of the classical curiosities of literature, whose happy hunting-ground lay in the tales that had gradually collected about distant countries.

After these, and standing in the same dependent relation

---

[1] Viz. Solinus for the Fabulists; Cosmas for the Cosmographers; the Ravennese geographer for the Statisticians; together with Dicuil and some of the minor geographers of the Dark Ages as representing a blend of all.

to pre-Christian work, but interested also in a less romantic part of that same work, are the *Statisticians;* who transcribe for us many of the ancient road measurements and place-names; not without adding, in some cases, pleasant stories which show their close connection with the Fabulists. Their primary object, however, is to give us facts and figures about every country, its people, and its natural features; and the title of Dicuil's work, "On the Measurement of the Earth," applies to every one of these arithmetical geographers. Had their labours been in any way original, and in the few instances where this is the case, they would have been, they are, useful and valuable; but they are nearly always content to extract and to compile from non-Christian sources.

Lastly come the *Cosmographers,* those who attempted in maps and in writings to draw a picture of the world as they conceived it. Beginning with Cosmas, or even with Lactantius, this school possessed an undoubted though rather mournful independence. It aimed at being separate from profane and non-Biblical speculation; it was proud of owing so little to pagan workers, and of differing so sharply from the conclusions of the unaided reason. With the help of faith and the holy books of Christianity, it sought, as Ptolemy had once tried on his own account, to reconstruct, to "put right" the ancient charts; and with its results we may finish this survey of that religious age of thought which we have been attempting to describe in its travel and now have to question about its science—its organized knowledge and its reasoning.

It is unnecessary to ransack the literature of the Dark Ages in search of examples of the geographical fable or myth. Much of this sort of thing is scattered through the writings of those who are really to be classed among the

collectors of statistics or the draughtsmen, whose object, like
that of Ptolemy, was above all, if not to delineate, at least to
give material for the delineation of, a world-picture. But
the representative of the class in question which alone needs
any detailed study is the work of Julius Solinus, surnamed
Polyhistor.[1] In his "Collectanea," or gallery of wonderful
things, he has brought together from Pliny's natural history,
from Pomponius Mela, and from other sources, that body of
travellers' tales which became the standard of geographical
myth between the fourth and the fourteenth centuries. By
the side of this all similar collections are insignificant;
from it directly come most of the fables in works of object
so different as those of Dicuil, Isidore, Capella, and Priscian.
He is quoted and used by a considerable number of
Christian writers from Augustine downwards; his more
striking and picturesque narratives are transferred almost
in their entirety to mediæval maps as late as the Hereford
example (c. 1300); but he is himself in all probability
a pagan, and in no sense original. Three-quarters of his
material comes from Pliny, and the remaining fourth is
nearly all derived from other writers, more classical than
himself. Even fragments of Varro[2] are to be found in his
museum. But it would be wrong to refuse him a place in
the history of Christian geography, for no one ever influenced
it more profoundly or more mischievously. And it would
also be wrong to go back at once to Pliny and disregard his
imitator; for the copy differed in important respects from
the original, and it was the copy and not the original which

---

[1] Or the varied narrator.

[2] From the lost book De Litorali-
bus, *e.g.* Sol. xi. 6, 30. As he stands,
however, Solinus has apparently been
revised at a considerably later date,
by some one who has added details
relative to the British Isles, and who
therefore was presumably a Briton or
Irishman (an Irish monk, some have
conjectured). Cf. Mommsen's Sol.,
pref. new edit., 1895.

was known to and studied by the Christian West for so long.
Pliny's natural history contained a great amount of curious
and mythical matter, but this was only a fraction of the
whole, which on a general view was not altogether unscientific.
Solinus made it his business to extract the dross and leave
the gold, transcribing every marvellous tale for a book that
did not amount to one-seventh of the size of the older
encyclopædia. To this end he combined with his Plinian
anecdotes, a number of stories differently fathered; and
a few he seems to have contributed himself. For his
object and spirit were quite different from the writers he
copied. They, in however confused a manner, were attempting some kind of description in agreement with observed
facts; his collection was one of marvels, different from the
ordinary humdrum course of nature.

Of the life, date, or creed of Solinus we have only approximate knowledge. But it may be stated with confidence
that he wrote at some time in the third or fourth century,
A.D.; it is probable that he belonged to the earlier of these
periods; it is certain that he wrote before the time of
Theodosius II. (408–450), in whose reign a copy was made
of his "Collectanea." The traditional date of his work is
generally given as about A.D. 230–240, in the age of confusion that followed the death of Alexander Severus; we
can only suppose it probable, from the total absence of any
Christian reference, that it was written in any case before
the conversion of Constantine (c. 312). From the character
of the language we shall be justified in bringing down its
composition to the latest period consistent with other
limitations; and we may notice that St. Augustine[1] is the
oldest known authority to make use of this collection
(c. A.D. 426), and that Priscian is the first to quote him by
name (c. 450).

[1] De Civ. Dei, xvi. 8; xviii. 17; xxi. 4. 4; 5. 1.

It has been pointed out[1] that Solinus speaks of Byzantium, but never of Constantinople; that he shows no knowledge of the Diocletian divisions of the Empire; that his mention of silk as now used, not only by women, but also by men, points, on the other hand, to a time after Elagabalus first made this luxury popular among the male sex in Rome (A.D. 218–222);[2] and that his compilation may therefore be fixed within a limit of sixty years (c. 220–280): but we must not forget that a book of excerpts, such as his, need not often or ever reflect the views, the habits, or the life of the collector's time, but only of those from whom he draws. Weak, however, as are the arguments[3] in a positive direction, they are hardly met by any that point against so general a conclusion, and until fresh and better evidence appears, we may take it as probable that before the close of the third century and the Diocletian persecution the "Collectanea rerum memorabilium" was already in men's hands.

The whole work, divided into fifty-six sections or chapters, is dedicated to one Adventus, whom the author assures of the credibility of his book, as following the most reliable authorities. Its pompous and inflated style helps us to believe in the probability of a tradition, which makes him a grammarian.[4] On the other hand, it is clear that he could not have studied geography, except as a naturalist or a

[1] As by Mommsen, in his admirable preface, which has left little to be said, except in the explanation of various difficult expressions in the text, e.g. the "Thunder-stones" of the German coast.

[2] Also Caius, his prænomen, was rare in the fourth century.

[3] We may add that he names the Emperors Caius, Claudius, and Vespasian; refers to Suetonius and the destruction of Jerusalem, and speaks of Persia in a way that points to a time after the Sassanian Revival (see chs. liii., xlv., xxix., xxiv., xxxv.

[4] To the same purpose is his mention of Varro, and most of his first part, "Of Man." Cf. Bunbury, Anc. Geog. ii. 676, etc.; and Ramsay, in Dict. Class. Biog., who gives a peculiar meaning to his title of Polyhistor.

lapidary. He shows no acquaintance with Ptolemy, mentions Strabo only once, and is constantly using expressions which convey an entirely wrong idea of the countries he describes. In knowledge of the earth-surface, he is far behind Herodotus, though pretending to cover a really wider field.

The business of Solinus was to put together, from all available sources, a number of marvellous tales,—tales of monstrous races, strange animals, curious minerals and precious stones; tales, also, of natural wonders by sea and by land,—but his method of treating them was strictly geographical. Thus he first of all describes Italy,[1] after detailing the wonders, past and present, of the Eternal City itself; then he narrates the marvels of South-Eastern Europe, and especially of Greece; thirdly, he takes us through Pontica and Scythia, the Black Sea lands and Russia; from this point he turns back and traverses Northern and Western Europe, from Germany to Spain. The last two sections of his book are concerned with Africa and Asia.[2]

Of his main sources we have already spoken. His nickname of " Pliny's ape " is justified, for what it is worth, by nearly every page of his work;[3] but he did not use the Natural History, as we have suggested, without discrimination. It was his quarry for a certain kind of treasure, and he only laid under contribution those portions which contained good store of marvels. Thus he turned especially to the geographical books (iii.–vi.), and to the passages " Concerning Man " (bk. vii.), " Concerning Animals " (bks. viii.–xi.), " Concerning Trees " (bk. xii.), and " Concerning

----

[1] After his long introductory chapter, " De Homine," which is largely occupied with the wonders of Rome and its history. Cf. cc. 1–19.

[2] Cf. cc. 20–56.

[3] Yet though his whole work is based on Pliny, he never names him.

Gems" (bk. xxxvii.) in that great treatise, from which he makes over seven hundred extracts.   In the same way, most of the thirty-nine chapters of Pomponius Mela which re-appear in Solinus are from the second book of that com-pendium, where the manners and monsters of outlying countries are particularly dwelt upon.   Varro's book, "On Shore-lands," is repeatedly quoted; and, besides the autho-rity of Homer and Virgil, Solinus invokes the philosopher Democritus, the King Juba, the sage Zoroaster, and the writers of the "Punic Books," with the still more famous names of Aristotle, Cato, Cicero, and Sallust, in his support. But though his sources were thus exclusively classical,[1]

---

[1] It was probably from lost classical works that he drew most of his addi-tional facts or fancies, unknown to Pliny and Mela, *e.g.* his isles of Thanet (first named by him), and of the Silures, separated by the sea from Britain; his story of the visit of Ulysses to the extreme point of Caledonia, and dedication of an altar there; his tale of the snake-destroy-ing properties of Irish and Thanet soil, and his adjectival use of the term Mediterranean, for the great inland sea, for which his proper name is "Ours" (Nostrum Mare). St. Isi-dore, c. 600, is the first who distinctly calls it by the new name (Mediter-raneum Mare). The authors named by Solinus are (with references to pp. and lines in Mommsen's edit. of 1895): —Agathocles, 3. 10; Amometus, 183. 6; Anaximander, 72. 8; M. Antonius, 34. 12; Apollodorus, 7. 6; Apol-lonides, 26. 3; King Archelaus, 186. 15; Aristotle, 112. 10; Bæton, 186. 2; Bocchus, 25. 9; 34. 11; 36. 2; Calli-demus, 74. 6; Callimachus, 76. 19; M. Cato, 31. 9; 33. 3; 117. 9; Cicero, 25. 19; 7. 8; Cincius, 7. 5; Cœlius, 39. 3; Corn. Nepos, 7. 6; cf. 220. 31; 173. 6; Cosconius, 35. 4; Crates, 72. 9; Cremutius, 169. 16; Crispus (= Sal-lust), 46. 4; Ctesias, 187. 19; Demo-critus, 13. 4; cf. 45. 15; Demodamas, 180. 14; Dionysius, 183. 16; Dosi-ades, 72. 7; Eratosthenes, 7. 6; Fabianus, 79. 6; Gellius, 4. 5; Gra-nius Licinianus, 34. 14; 41. 7; Hanno, 110. 16; Hecatæus, 92. 13; Hegesi-demus, 79. 17; Hemina, 34. 7; 35. 7; Heracleides, 3. 6; Homer, 36. 3; 45. 3; 61. 10; 62. 4; King Juba, 110. 17; 119. 10, and in five more places; Lutatius, 7. 6; Mæcenas, 79. 6; "Mantuan Poems" (Virgil), 178. 1; Megasthenes, 183. 14; 187. 16; Me-trodorus, 42. 1; Philemon, 92. 14; Pictor, 7. 5; Pomponius Atticus, 7. 7; Pesidonius, 183. 11; "Prænestin. Books," 33. 13; "Punic Books," 138. 4; Statius Sebosus, 112. 1; 190. 16; Sextius, 33. 4; Silenus, 5. 11; Sotacus, 133. 8; Tarruntius, 5. 23; Theo-phrastus, 41. 2; 87. 2; Theopompus, 55. 3; Timæus, 46. 3; Trogus, 12. 19; Varro, 5. 16; 19. 2; 25. 17; 37. 15; 57. 8, and in seven more places; Xenophon of Lampsacus, 39. 11; 210. 5; Zenodotus, 33. 12; Zoroaster, 41. 16; 159. 9.

Solinus' readers seem to have been almost as exclusively Christian. Starting with the four references of Augustine in his "City of God," we go on from strength to strength, through the five of Ealdhelm, the two of Bede and of "Jordanis," to the half-century of Priscian, the two hundred of Isidore and the thirty-six of Dicuil, or the transcripts that cover the Hereford map.

Yet scarcely any of the imitations of the "Collectanea," with one exception, occupy quite the same position or have really the same object. The exception is to be found in the mediæval Bestiaries, or story-books of animals. Even later and more famous travellers' tales, like Mandeville's, do not cover quite the same ground, and take a rather more scientific attitude. They do not aim so simply at extracting the marvellous from the ordinary world. They delight to enliven their pages with wonderful tales; but Solinus goes far beyond this. With rare intervals, he steadily avoids naturalism altogether. His work is perhaps the most completely miraculous view of the world ever put forth in Europe; and it is paralleled only by the scientific supernaturalism of Cosmas' geography. Where the pagan narrator gave relations of marvellous but supposed fact, the Christian monk attempted to prove a systematic basis for the government of the world, independent of natural law and essentially matter of faith. The latter generalised where the former merely instanced; but the mental attitude of the two was very similar; and they appealed for favour and for acceptance on much the same ground, and to much the same kind of people. They both came into fashion, in their different degrees, with the rise of theological interests; they both passed out of serious notice when the exclusive power of those interests was disturbed.

The work of Solinus opens with a collection of stories

mainly about people, chiefly taken from classical mythology, and dignified with the title of an essay on man.

From this he returns, as Arthur Golding paraphrases him, to his "before determined purpose in the recital of places," beginning with Italy "and the praise thereof." Unluckily, this hub of the universe had been so often and so thoroughly described, especially by Marcus Cato, "that there could not be found there the thing which the diligence of former authors had not related." "For who knoweth not that Janiculum was either named or builded by Janus;" or, again, that Caieta took its name from Æneas' nurse? These facts were granted by all and known to all; but it might give his readers a new and improved idea of geography, Solinus appears to think, if he described Italy's shape as like an oaken leaf—a curiously perverse comparison.[1] In spite of his complaint, we do not find that familiarity has bred contempt in the fabulist. He stocks the best-known country of his race and language with marvels worthy of the most distant and romantic lands. Thus the people who sacrificed to Apollo at Soracte, and in their yearly festival frisked and danced upon the burning wood without harm, being a "kindred privileged from hurt of fire;" their compeers, who were more dangerous to serpents than serpents to them, like the Jean Fréron of the French proverb;[2] the boas, or pythons, of Calabria, who fattened upon the udders of milch kine; the wolves that made men dumb if they saw without being seen; above all, the lynxes, whose urine congealed into "the hardness of a precious stone,"[3]—prevented Italy from being entirely condemned as prosaic.

[1] Sol. ii. 20.

[2] "Un serpent mordit Jean Fréron.
    Eh bien, le serpent en
        mourut."
And cf. a similar Greek proverb

about the Cappadocians. Cf. Sol. ii. 26, 27, 33; Pl. vii. 15, 19.

[3] The sagacity and malevolence of these same lynxes were as remarkable as their natural wealth. "As soon

The grasshoppers of Rhegium, adds Solinus, were dumb; and this silence of theirs was especially curious, as the same insects at Locri, the very next place, were noisier than all others. The real cause of the marvel was, of course, Hercules, and nothing else. He was bored by the noise the crickets made one day, and ordered them to hold their peace. They stopped at once; but, from resentment or forgetfulness, he neglected to take off the embargo, and so it still continued in force. These were the chief marvels of Italy; besides them, it had not much to show, except coral in its seas—" a shrub like a gristle "—and devoutly religious birds in its temples.

Among the islands near, notably Corsica, Sardinia, and Sicily, Solinus finds magnetic stones, once turned to good account by Democritus of Abdera, in his " contests with the wizards; " poisonous worms, that lie in the shade and sting those that sit down upon them; " sardonic " plants, that kill men with a horrible grinning lockjaw; and valuable springs, that knit up broken bones, expel poison, drive away diseases of the eyes, and discover thieves.[1]

The volcanic marvels of Sicily;[2] the sacrifices on Vulcan's hill, " which take fire of themselves; " the wonderful fountains, child-productive or -destructive; the underground ways, which carry the fire of Ætna to the Liparis and elsewhere, are more in the ordinary course of pseudo-science, and scarcely add much to Solinus' reputation.

Perhaps his description of the milk-stones of Greece [3] is more creditable to his, or rather Pliny's, imagination. These treasures, we are told, tied about a woman that giveth

as the water is passed from them, by-and-by they cover it over with heaps of sand—verily of spite, as Theophrastus avoucheth. This stone hath the colour of amber, and draweth to it things that be near at hand."

[1] Sol. iii. 4, 5; Pl.xxxvii. 152; also Sol. iv. 1–3, 47.
[2] Sol. v. 1–23.
[3] Sol. vii. 4; Pl. xxxvii. 162.

suck, make her breasts full of milk; tied to a child, they
"cause more abundant swallowing of spittle;" received into
the mouth, they melt, but "therewithal perisheth the gift
of memory." Yet in Greece, as in Italy, the fabulist is
worried and hampered. He has not got a free hand. There
is too much of the dry light of fact. All the country is so
well known, that the only marvel is (as Arthur Golding
translates the Silver-Latin into Elizabethan English), "how
it should be kept in Hugger-mugger." Yet Hugger-mugger
was the true atmosphere for the wonder-weaver. The best
fairy stories of an enchanted world could only be put
together with confidence and grace when the artist knew
himself to be safe from detection.

To escape from the unpleasantly searching light of
plains and cities, Solinus now takes us up to the top of
Olympus,[1] and tells us pleasant tales about the altar there.[2]
"There is no land under heaven," he is positive, "that may
worthily be compared thereto in height, and hereunto the
rage of water never attained when the flood overwhelmed all
things." Even in the lower ground there were still to be
seen traces of this same flood—"prints of no small credit."
In the dark caves of the hills, for instance, one could see
the shells of fishes, which must have been left there by the
deluge.

Under the head of Thrace[3] we get some improvements
upon the old and true tale of the migratory cranes. When
these fly south for their yearly fight with the pygmies, lest
the wind should drive them out of their course, they gorge
themselves with sand and stones, and keep watch at night,

---

[1] Sol. viii. 6; Me. II. ii. 10.

[2] Any educated man, adds a later
text, translated in Golding, but not
found in Mommsen's edition, is well
aware that letters written in the
ashes of that altar continue till the
ceremonies of the next year.

[3] Sol. x. 1–12; Pl. x. 59, 60.

holding little weights in their claws,[1] till they are past the Great Sea.

The mention of Delos and Quail Island (Ortygia) gives a fine opening for quail stories, especially in Bœotia, where the bird is *not* found, but where it is held in honour for its peculiar properties, since "this animal alone, of all beasts, excepting man, suffers the falling sickness;" and with Mount Athos, which casts his shadow to Lemnos, fifty-six miles away, and is reckoned higher than where the rains come from, we are back again on the continent of Europe.[2] Here, as we have seen, life is too confined for anything like free play of the imagination, and Solinus hurries on to Scythia (Russia and Tartary),[3] where begins the third main division of his work, on more congenial and productive soil.

In the waters to the south (as in the Black Sea) the dolphins show extraordinary activity, being often known to leap quite over the mainsails of passing ships; in the steppes themselves monsters of every kind delight the searcher after truth.

Besides the beavers (who, like the lynxes of Italy, try to cheat their hunters by cunning devices), there are tribes of loupgaroux—of men who, at certain times, turn into wolves, returning to their former shape after a short holiday among the brutes; of horse-footed and long-eared men, who need no other apparel to clothe or to sleep withal than their own flaps; of cannibals, whose cruel outrages have made all the land a desert, "even till you come to the silk-country;" of

[1] Sol. x. 16.

[2] Sol. xi. 19, 33; Pl. iv. 72; Me. II. ii. 10.

[3] Sol. xii. 2; Pl. iv. 76. He returns later—in xviii. 1 (cf. Pl. iv. 93)—to discuss the question of the Mediterranean and its origin. Some think it starts with the inrush of the ocean at the straits of Gades, or Gibraltar, the agitation of which causes the ebb and flow of the tide to be felt as far as Italy. Others, however, think its source is in the Pontus, or Black Sea, and prove their theory by the fact that the tide from this quarter has no ebb.

savages, who devour huge feasts of human flesh by way of
burial festivals, and quaff mead and wine from drinking
cups made of the skulls of their dead parents. Others there
are who offer strangers in sacrifice ; others, again, who live
at the back of the north wind ; and a third race, who hunt
better with one eye than most men with two—the one-eyed
Arimaspians of older fabulists.[1]

In the far north is the land of feathers,[2] where Solinus
makes the snow fall as if Pagan Jupiter, in the words of
the French jest, were plucking geese upon Olympus. "A
damned part of the world is this, drowned by the nature
of things in a cloud of endless darkness, and utterly shut up
in extreme cold as in a prison, even under the very north pole.
Alone, of all lands, it knoweth no distinction of times, neither
receiveth it anything else of the air than endless winter." [3]

In the Asiatic Scythia there are rich lands, he continues,
and one might hope to gain a footing there, but no such
thing was possible. Although they abound in gold and
precious stones,[4] the Gryphons, "a most fierce kind of fowl
and cruel beyond all cruelness," tear in pieces any intruder,
"as creatures made of purpose to punish the rashness of
covetous folk."

The far Northern lands beyond were placed by some, says
Solinus doubtfully, between sunrising and sunset, between
the west of our Antipodes and our east, but this was against
reason, considering what a waste sea ran between the two
worlds. In any case the poles or hinges of the earth were

---

[1] Cf. Sol. xiii. 2 ; Pl. viii. 109. Also
Sol. xv. 1, 2 ; Pl. iv. 88 ; Me. II. i. 6,
13 : Sol. xv. 4 ; Me. II. i. 13 ; Pl. vi.
53, 54 : Sol. xv. 13, 14, xvi. 2 ; Me.
II. i. 9.

[2] Sol. xv. 20, 21 ; Pl. vii. 10.

[3] A little later, however (xvi. 3),

he speaks of the same country as
blessed, according to some, with six
months' continual sun.

[4] Sol. xv. 22 ; Pl. vii. 10. Especially
emeralds, says Solinus,—a startling
novelty.

commonly thought to be there, and the uttermost circuit of the stars.

Among the Cimmerians, Amazons, and other races of these parts lies the Caspian Sea, which falls into the Icy Sea, or Scythian Ocean; is sweetened by the multitude of fresh-water streams that flow into it;[1] and has the curious property of growing emptier with rain and fuller with drought. Thus Solinus repeats the mistakes of so many ancient geographers, between Herodotus who first corrected the popular notions, and Ptolemy who described and drew the great Salt Lake with only an error of direction, twisting its length round, as it were, and making it lie in a direction from east to west, instead of from north to south.

A long way from hence, the Hyrcanians,[2] we are told, possess the mouths of the Oxus, in a country where the tigers are peculiarly obnoxious; and about these and the panthers and "libbards" of the same region Solinus expatiates for some time, collecting many facts interesting to the mediæval Bestiaries. Thus the cat-like tenacity of such big felines is illustrated by the difficulty of killing them—"for they live a great while after their bowels be taken out,"— and the rest of the description of Scythia and the far North (save for certain legends of the journeys of Alexander the Great—from India to Bactria in eight days, and to the frozen and dead seas of the Arctic regions beyond the remotest "featherland") is almost entirely taken up with minerals, and the natural history of curious animals, such as the goat-stags, for whom later mythologists depended upon Solinus himself.[3]

[1] About the sweetness and whole-someness of the Caspian water there can be no possible doubt, as both Alexander and Pompey drank of it to see if this tale were true (Sol. xix. 3; Pl. vi. 50–52).

[2] Sol. xvii. 3, 4, 10; Pl. viii. 62, 66, 100.

[3] Cf. Sol. xix. 2, 4, 5, 9–19; Pl. vi. 39, iv. 94, viii. 113–120, xxviii. 149, 150, 226.

The fourth part of this collection[1] brings us back to Europe, and begins with Germany, proceeding on to treat of Gaul, Britain, Spain, and the furthest West.

Germany stretches, according to our present guide, between the Hercynian Wood and the Sarmatian rocks. "Where it beginneth, it is watered by Danube, and where it endeth, by Rhine," while from the heart of this land Elbe and Vistula run into the ocean. Chief of German wonders are the Hercynian birds, whose feathers give light in the dark, "be the night never so close and cloudy;" likewise an exquisite creature, like a mule, with such a long upper lip that he "cannot feed except walking backward;"[2] and the thunder-stones ("ceraunies"), which "draw the brightness of the stars to themselves," and were evidently some kind of felspar or silicate.[3]

Over against Germany is Scandinavia—the "isle Gangavia"—greatest of all the German isles, but "having nothing great except itself"—no marvels, no pleasant legends.[4]

Crystal and amber, called by the natives "glass"[5] (glæsum), came from another part of the German Sea—the island Glesaria,—and this, Solinus adds, was the best amber in the world, though he warns us with conscientious care that India produced it also, but of inferior quality.

From Germany we come to Gaul, between Rhine and Pyrenees, between the ocean and the Jura Mountains. About the customs of the country, Solinus only mentions in a doubtful way the human sacrifices of the Druids. In fact, his mythology almost deserts him here; he merely tells us that from Gaul we may "go into what part of the world we

---

[1] Sol. xx., etc.; Pl. iv. 80, etc.

[2] His counterfeit is pourtrayed with beautiful fidelity on the map of Hereford.

[3] *E.g.* "double silicate."

[4] Sol. xx. 7, 8–13; Pl. viii. 39, xxxvii. 23, 37–50; iv. 36, 37, 97.

[5] So Golding.

will," and at once takes us across the Channel into Britain.[1]

The sea coast of Gaul, he declares, would have been the end of the earth, but that the isle of Britain had almost deserved the name of another world. In length it was eight hundred miles, measuring to the extremity of Caledonia, "in which nook an altar engraven with Greek letters bore witness that Ulysses arrived there."

Of the many and not unrenowned islands that surrounded Britain, Ireland was chief, with "uncivil inhabiters," and fat pastures—so fat, indeed, that the Irish cattle would burst if not sometimes forcibly kept from feeding. No snakes lived there, and few birds. Those Irish warriors who loved to be fine, trimmed their sword hilts with the teeth of sea monsters. Right and wrong were all one in Ireland. The sea between Britain and its chief satellite, one hundred and twenty miles in breadth, was so rough and stormy that it could only be sailed for a few days in summer time. The troublous sea also cut off Britain from the Isle of Man, where every one, man and woman alike, could foretell future events; just as Thanet[2] "upon the strait of Gaul," which had the same anti-venomous properties as Ireland, was separated from Britain by an arm of the same ocean. Of the other islands round Britain, Thyle or Ultima Thule (Shetlands?) was the furthest, the last point of known land towards the north, where the summer sun almost totally destroyed the night, and the winter darkness scarcely allowed any daylight to exist. Beyond Thule there was only the sluggish and frozen sea;[3] but further south, and nearer to Britain, Solinus mentions the Hebrides and the Orkneys; the latter he

---

[1] Sol. xxi. 1–xxii. 1; Pl. iv. 105.

[2] Not only would no snakes live in it, but a little Thanet earth always expelled snakes from any other part of the world.

[3] Sol. xxii. 9. Cf. Dicuil on Iceland, vii. 11–13.

describes as uninhabited, and puts altogether out of place between the main land and the Hebrides, at a point much further from Thule than the northernmost promontory of Caledonia.[1]

The circuit of Britain Solinus gives, after Pliny, at 4875 miles; and of the marvels of its " inner country " he notices the excellent rivers, the hot springs at Bath, the black jewel called jet, and the customs of tattoo and flesh embroidery.

Coming back to the Continent, Solinus next treats of Spain and the isles thereof; of the ocean; of the " Midland," or " Roman," Sea; and of the tides.

In Lusitania (Portugal) he notes especially a promontory, which is called by some Olisipo (Lisbon), "dividing heaven, earth, and sea," and forming the natural end of Spain on one side. At the circuit of it beginneth the sea of Gaul and the north coast, and at the same endeth the Atlantic Ocean. Here was Olisipo founded by Ulysses; here flows the Tagus, preferred before all streams for its golden sands; hereby the mares conceived by the breath of the south wind—thus Solinus wrings the poetry out of the old myth of the Spanish jennets, which were " swift as children of the wind." [2]

The Tin Islands, or Cassiterides, fertile in lead, proceeds the compiler, are opposite to Celtiberia, as are also the Fortunate Islands, which have nothing remarkable but their name.[3]

At the head of Baetica, the later Andalus, where is the end of the known world, is an island, Gades, the modern Cadiz, seven hundred feet only from the mainland, " which the Tyrians, setting out from the Red Sea, called Eryth, and the Carthaginians, in their own language, named Gadir—

[1] Sol. xxii. 2–9; Pl. iv. 102–104; Me. III. vi. 6.
[2] Sol. xxiii. 1–8; Pl. iv. 113–119,
viii. 166; Me. II. vi. 2.
[3] Sol. xxiii. 10; Pl. iv. 119.

that is, a hedge ; " and here, at the Strait of Gades, is the point where the Atlantic tides rush in and divide "our" (Mediterranean) world. For the ocean, which the Greeks so call because of its swiftness, breaking in at the sunset place, tears away Europe on the left, from Africa on the right ; having cut asunder Calpe and Abyla, "which are called Hercules his Pillars." At this strait, which is in length fifteen miles, but in breadth scarce seven, the ocean opens the bars of the inner sea like a gate, mingling with the Mediterranean gulf, and pressing on towards the east in the very "lap or groin" of the world.[1]

From the ocean we come next to its most remarkable phenomenon—the tides. As to their nature and cause, Solinus is disposed to think them the breath, as it were, of the nostrils of the great deep—conceiving of the world as a living creature,—though he mentions the opinion of others, that the ebb and flow were governed by the changes of the moon.[2]

The fifth part of the "Collectanea" brings us to Africa ; and we enter an enchanted land, from the Orchards of the Sisters called Hesperides, to the Pyramids of Egypt, and from the Mount Atlas to the monstrous tribes with which Solinus fringes the Southern Ocean.

First, however, as to the Hesperides and their Orchard, Solinus begins by being a little critical. The encircling dragon is nothing but an arm of the sea, with serpentine windings. The golden apples are as much a fable as the dragon. "But this is a greater wonder than the fruit trees or leafy gold, that though the ground be lower than the level of the sea, the tide never overflows it, but the waves, of their own accord, stand still in a circle at the innermost of the sea banks."[3]

---

[1] Sol. xxiii. 12–17 ; Pl. iii. 3 ; iv. 119, 120.

[2] Sol. xxiii. 17–22 ; Me. III. i. 1, 2.
[3] Sol. xxiv. 1–8 ; Pl. v. 2–6.

Mount Atlas rises from the sandy wastes, and, reaching close to the moon, hides its head above the clouds. He is bare towards the ocean, fruitful towards the inland; his head is always covered with snow, his sides swarm with wild beasts. "All day long there is no noise, but all is whist, not without a horror; but in the night he blazes with fire, and resounds on every side with the choirs of satyrs, and all along the seashore is heard the sound of shawms and playing upon cymbals." [1]

The rivers about Atlas, Solinus declares, are not to be wholly passed over; especially Bambotum, which swarms with river-horses and crocodiles; and the Black Stream of Niger beyond, which flows through the scorching deserts, that are boiled perpetually with immeasurable heat of the parching sun, burning hotter than any fire.[2]

In the Moorland of Tangiers, Solinus chiefly "entreats of elephants," with a precision and critical care that would be interesting if it were not all too daringly "hypothetical;" and a certainty quite as great, and as little supported by facts, follows him in his next discourse—"Of Numidia and the Bears thereof." [3]

The next marvel of Africa is found in the sandbanks of the Syrtes, where the ground, as Varro related, is so rotten that "the air alters the upper part of it;" and then, after mentioning the Niger, "which brings forth the Nile," and separates all this region from Ethiopia and Asia,[4] Solinus plunges again into his bestiary. And now we hear of lions, "who never look asquint, and cannot bear that any should look asquint upon them;" and of hyenas, whose backbones are without joints, whose very shadows rob dogs of their

---

[1] Sol. xxiv. 9; Pl. v. 14, 15.

[2] Sol. xxiv. 14, 15; Pl. v. 8, 10, 13–15.

[3] Sol. xxv. 1–xxvii. 1; Pl. viii.

(*passim*), esp. 1–34, 100.

[4] Sol. xxvii. 1–5; Pl. v. 23, 30, 32; ii. 218, etc.

bark, and in whose eyes lies a wondrous stone, which, put under any man's tongue, "doth give him power to tell of things to come." As to other features of the animal kingdom, "Africa swarmeth in such wise with serpents, that it may worthily challenge the pre-eminence in that mischief from all the world." [1]

In the great Oases of Fezzan, south of the Syrtes, are the "Charmers," who cannot die from snake-bites—at least, the genuine members of the race. "But if their women bear offspring of adultery," they perish in this way. So an easy test of virtue is in vogue. They throw all their new-born babes to serpents, and the sin of the mothers, or the privilege of the fathers' blood, is punished or proved accordingly. Unhappily, this interesting people has long since been exterminated. [2] Nobody can be allowed to have any doubts about the lotus-eaters; for they are really found, according to Solinus, in the innermost recesses of the great Syrtes; and with this [3] our author "falleth again to discourse of" beasts, plants, and minerals; and is specially instructive upon the cockatrice, or basilisk, that unique horror, "which dries up and destroys the very earth, and infecteth the very air." No bird can fly over him; all other serpents are horribly afraid to hear his hissing. What he killeth no fowl and no beast will touch. His motion is as terrible as his bite and breath—"with one half he creepeth, with the other he avaunceth himself aloft. And yet, for all this, he is overcome of weasels." God, exclaims the pious translator exultingly, hath provided a remedy for every mischief. [4]

Passing on to the apes of the "land between Egypt, Ethiopia, and Libya" (wherever that may be), Solinus begs

[1] Sol. xxvii. 6–28; Pl. viii. 85; xxvii. 23; and v. *passim*, esp. 5, 22–24, 28.

[2] Sol. xxvii. 41, 42; Pl. v. 27, etc.
[3] Sol. xxvii. 43; Pl. v. 28.
[4] Sol. xxvii. 50–53; Pl. viii. 78, 79.

his readers not to be vexed at a little digression about these animals, " for it is not expedient to omit anything in which the providence of nature is seen." [1]　Besides the common variety who daub their eyes with bird-lime, in imitation of hunters washing theirs with water, " and so are more easily taken," is also a species of jovial ape, which makes merry at the new of the moon, and becomes sad when she is in the wane; together with the Dog-headed Simians of Ethiopia, " never so tame but that they be more rather wild," and the shaggy-haired sphinxes and satyrs, gentle and docile, and " easily taught to forget their wildness, very sweet faced, and full of toying continually." [2]

The " salt houses," built with salt blocks as if with stone, of the inland tribes that traffic with the Troglodites, are next described; [3] and then the Ethiopians claim attention, divided from the tribes of Atlas by the river Niger, which is " thought to be part of the Nile," [4] for it has the same papyrus, it is fringed with the same rushes, it brings forth the same animals, and it overflows at the same time of year.

From the queer animals we come to the queer peoples of Ethiopia; and among these are the Nomades, who live on the milk of the dog-headed apes—a rather feeble and uncertain sustenance, one would think; the Syrbots, " lazy things of twelve feet long; " the race that has a dog for king; and the people of the coast who are said to have four eyes apiece, but whose peculiar advantages are explained away as only meaning that their sight is a good deal sharper than other folks'.

By way of contrast, perhaps, their near neighbours, the " wild- (or wolfish-) eaters," are endowed with a sovereign who

---

[1] Sol. xxvii. 55, 56; Pl. viii. 215.
[2] Sol. xxvii. 57, 60; Pl. viii. 72, 216.
[3] Sol. xxviii. 1; Pl. v. 34.
[4] Sol. xxx. 1; Pl. v. 30, 44, 45, 53.

After a notice of the Garamantes of Fezzan and their marvellous (? Herodotean) fountain at Debris, cold by day and boiling hot by night.

has only one eye, in the middle of his forehead; and beyond
this tribe are several equally voracious—the "Eat-alls," who
"feed of all things that may be chewed;" the Cannibals; the
Bitch-milkers, "who have long snouts and chaps like dogs;"
and the Locust-eaters,[1] whose food has the disastrous effect of
shortening life to a maximum of forty years.

From the Ocean or Atlantic to Meroe on the Nubian Nile
is a distance, we learn, of only 620 miles, about three-quarters
of the length of Britain; further to the east, beyond the
great river, are the long-lived or blameless Ethiopians of
Homer and Herodotus (with their standing repast at the
Table of the Sun), and the deserts that stretch onwards to
Arabia.[2]　And then, in the furthest point of Africa towards
the sunrise, we come to the monstrous tribes that fringe the
torrid zone in our own Psalter and Hereford mappemondes;
some with their ugly faces wholly "plain without a nose;"
others without tongues, who use gesture instead of speech;
others with mouths all grown together, save for a little hole
by which they suck in sustenance through an oaten pipe.
The South of Ethiopia is "set thick with woods," and on this
side is a burning mountain, in whose fires thrive many
dragons. It is a great point, adds Solinus, to distinguish
the true dragons from the false; the real ones have small
mouths, and sting through their tails. Likewise true information is much to be desired about the camelopards or
giraffes of these parts; about the ants of the Niger, as big
as mastiffs, who dig in its sands of gold; about the chameleons
"with their thin smug skins like glass;" and especially
about the "bird Pegasus," which has nothing of a horse
except its ears.[3]

---

[1] Sol. xxx. 4–8; Pl. vi. 190–194.
[2] Sol. xxx. 9–12; Pl. vi. 196; Me.
III. ix. 1–3.

[3] Sol. xxx. 13–29; Pl. vi. 197; viii.
69, 122; ix. 87, etc.: Me. III. ix. 4.

Again reverting to the people of the desert, Solinus gives us a list of tribes " withdrawn into the pathless wilderness," all with something unusual and inhuman about them ;—the men of Atlas who curse the sun that galls them from dawn to dusk, who never dream, have no language, and are quite void of civility ; the Troglodytes, devoted to poverty, who live without coveting ; the devil-worshippers ; the headless Blemmyes, with eyes and mouth in breast ; and last of all, the Crooklegs, who " rather slide than walk."[1]

The mention of Egypt now brings Solinus to his account of the Nile. It rises, he tells us almost in Pliny's words, close to the Western Ocean, forms a lake called Nilides at a little distance from its source, is then lost for a while in the sands, emerges again in the " Cæsarean cave," again sinks below the ground, and reappears among the Ethiopians, where it throws off the arm of the Niger[2] and forms many great islands.[3] Then rushing down the Cataracts, it turns finally to the north, encircles the South of Egypt, and runs into the sea by seven mouths. As to the causes of the yearly Nile flood (between July 19th and August 11th), Solinus tells us that the Egyptian priests considered this time to be an anniversary of the world's birthday. The marvels of the stream—the crocodiles without tongues, who keep truce with men for the seven days of the Apis festival, allow their jaws to be cleaned by a little bird, and are killed by Pharaoh's rats (the ichneumons); the bold men of low stature, living on an island in the Nile, who train the crocodiles to be their river-horses; the ibises, who guard men from the winged snakes of Arabia; and all the other wonders—are lovingly and lengthily described, and something is added about a

---

[1] Sol. xxxi. 1-6; Pl. v. 43, 45, 128; xxxvii. 167.

[2] The Western Nile, or Nile of the Blacks.

[3] Such as Meroe.

human portent, a race living on the borders of Egypt, who
tell the New Year by the motions of animals.[1]

From the Nile it is but a short step to the Pyramids.
And these, Solinus tells us, are towers lofty beyond the reach
of man, and with a singular characteristic. "Forasmuch as
they pass the measure of shadows, they have no shadows at
all."[2]

Here we leave Africa, and enter the sixth and last portion
of our Survey with Asia. Passing by Arabia and its phœnix,
spices, and flying snakes or dragons,[3] we pass into Syria at
Joppa, the oldest town in the world, built before the flood,
where Andromeda's monster was long preserved. The people
of the place enjoyed the privilege of measuring it at their
pleasure, and certified its ribs to be forty feet long.[4] From
Joppa to Jerusalem, " the old head of Judea, now destroyed,"[5]
we come to the Dead Sea, or Lake Asphaltitis, which contains
no living thing, but in which nothing can sink, and to the
" sorrowful coast, once stricken from heaven," where grow
only the apples of Sodom on the black ash-covered soil.
This fruit looks ripe enough without, but within " is a cinder-
soot, which at every light touch puffs forth like a smoke,
and crumbles into loose dust."[6] After this story, which is
also alluded to by Josephus and Tacitus, and by several of
the Christian pilgrim-travellers in later time, the fabulist,
proceeding northward through Scythopolis (founded by
Bacchus, where he buried his nurse), brings us to Antioch
and Mount Casius, and romances at some length about the

---

[1] Sol. xxxii. 1–33; Pl. v. 51–59;
viii. 89–97; Me. III. viii. 9.

[2] Sol. xxxii. 44.

[3] Sol. xxxiii.; Pl. v., vi., and esp.
xii. passim.

[4] Sol. xxxiv. 1–3; Pl. v. 68, 69;
ix. 11.

[5] As by Titus in A.D. 70. But
probably Solinus' words referred to the
complete extinction of the old city
and name by Hadrian (135–6).

[6] Sol. xxxv. 8; Joseph. B. J. IV
viii. 4; Tac. Hist. v. 7.

height of this mountain, from the top of which day still appeared on one side while deep night had come up on the other.[1]   Hence to the Euphrates, rich in gems, and having the selfsame source as the Nile, situated under the same parallel, and rising into flood at the same time of year; to the Tigris, coming from a different spring; and to the lake Arethusa, that can bear any weight, sinks twice below the ground, and runs just as swiftly as an arrow flies.[2]

Here Solinus,[3] after a long progress eastward, abruptly turns to the west, and details the marvels of Asia Minor; the Cydnus of Cilicia, which derived its sweetness from the same source as the Choaspes streamlet in Persia; Mount Taurus, where ends the backbone of the world,—the Imaus, the Niphates, the Caucasus of Further Asia; the volcano Chimæra of Lycia; and the beast Bonacus of Phrygia, able to discharge its ordure over two acres of ground, whose "lively portraiture" in the Hereford map is one of the features of that serio-comic geography in which Solinus reigned supreme.[4]   Asia Minor abounded also in Chameleons,[5] who could not only change colour at will, but fed on air, and had the raven for their mortal enemy, and the bay-leaf as an antidote for the poison of their flesh.   Cappadocia, in particular, was famous also for horses, some born of the wind, "but these never live above three years."[6]

From Media comes the medicine tree, "enemy to venom," a possible source (among others) of the Dry Tree or Arbre Sec of mediæval travellers; and north of this, in the Caspian Gates, is another miracle of nature.   The rocks sweat salt which the heat forms into a sort of "summer ice."[7]

[1] Sol. xxxvi. 1, 3; Pl. v. 74, 80, etc.
[2] Sol. xxxvii. 14–16; Pl. v. 83, 85, 90; vi. 127–130.
[3] Sol. xxxviii., xxxix.; Pl. v., esp. 92, 97–99, 100, etc.; Me. I. xiii. 3.
[4] Sol. xl. 10–11; Pl. viii. 40.

[5] Often alluded to before by Solinus, but now first fully described, after Pliny, xl. 21–24; cf. Pl. viii. 120–122, etc.
[6] Sol. xlv. 5–18; Pl. viii. 155–166.
[7] Sol. xlvii. 1; Pl. vi. 43–46.

Crossing the Oxus and the Jaxartes, and passing the furthest point of Alexander's march, we now traverse the snows and deserts of Scythia, (skirting the Cannibal-land we have already sighted once before, and various tracts full of outrageous wild beasts,[1]) before coming at last to the Seres and the Land of Silk on the western side of China. Like Virgil, Solinus believed the soft and precious " wool " was combed off the leaves of trees. Then, as now, its " Celestial " possessors kept their secrets closely, avoided all import traffic, and jealously excluded strangers.[2]

But, to our compiler, Silkland was not the end of the Continent, as it is to us; that place he reserves for India,[3] which he seems to put (according to the guidance of his authorities) [4] directly opposite Gaul. " Of old it was believed to be the third part of the world." In marvels it was prodigal. The famous islands of gold and silver [5]— Chryse and Argyre—were to be found at the mouth of the Indus; and among strange people the imagination could revel.

There were many so tall that they could vault over elephants as if they were horses; there were the Fakirs, or Gymnosophists,—philosophers who went stark naked; there were tribes who had their feet turned backwards, with eight toes on each; others living in the hills, who had dogs' heads and talons for fingers, and ".barked for speech ;" others, again, with one leg, but feet so huge, to atone for this deficiency, that they could use them for shade against the sun; others, at the sources of the Ganges, who lived by the smell of fruit.[6]

Suttee is described by Solinus, apparently from some

---

[1] Sol. xlix.; Pl. vi. 22, 49–54.

[2] Sol. l. 2–4, Pl. vi. 54, 88.

[3] Sol. lii.; Pl. vi.

[4] Especially Posidonius.

[5] Sol. lii. 17, Pl. vi. 80. Cf. Mela,

III.

[6] Sol. lii. 20–30; Pl. vi. 79; vii. 22–28. On these Cynocephali, Skiapods, etc., see pp. 335–338.

independent source, and from monstrous men we wander off
again to monstrous animals,—the eels and the yellow oxen
with flexible horns, the unicorns, the "worms with arms six
cubits long (? octopuses), who hold elephants under water;"
the whales that cover four acres of ground, and the rest of
Pliny's wonders.[1]   Among trees, there are the pepper-plants,
that look towards the sunrising; among gems, the diamond
or adamant, which will counteract the loadstone[2] in its
power of attracting iron.[3]

Till the courage of great Alexander discovered and
explored Taprobane, or Ceylon, we are told, this island was
believed to be the other world of the Antipodes.   Now it is
known to lie only seven days' sail from the coast of India,
in full view of Canopus, though entirely outside the circle
of the Northern stars, and having sunrise upon its right and
sunset upon its left.   As the stars are no good here, birds
indicate the mariner's route during the four months in which
alone their seas can be navigated.   The greater part of the
island is a wilderness parched with heat—a cruel libel upon
one of the richest of all countries—but its mountains are so
lofty that from their summits the sea-coast of the Seres or of
Silkland may be seen.[4]

Here we draw towards a conclusion.   Briefly indicating
the main routes from Persia and Egypt to India; and
noticing a few marvels in the Southern Ocean, such as the
ever-glowing and unapproachable Island of the Sun;[5] Solinus
ends his work with a description of the Outer Sea, "where it
begins to be called Atlantic."[6]   With remarkable caution,

---

[1] Sol. lii. 34–42; Pl. viii. 72–76;
ix. 4, 8, 46.

[2] So fa. he magnet was known to
the ancie. .s, but not its polar properties.   Cf. Claudian, Idyl v.

[3] Sol. lii. 50–64; Pl. xii. and xxxvii.
passim; esp. xii. 26, xxxvii. 61.

[4] Sol. liii. 1–21; Pl. vi. 82–91.

[5] Sol. liv. 4; Pl. vi. 97–98.

[6] Sol. lvi. 4; Pl. vi. *pass.*

he ventures to doubt the common assertion that no one could sail in the tropical and burning waters beyond Ethiopia. For King Juba, he had read, maintained that the water-way was open from India to Spain: and merchants attempting the passage had found these parched coasts far from destitute of inhabitants; besides the harmless fish-eaters and Troglodytes, there were the troublesome Arab pirates, who harassed strangers not a little.[1]

To Solinus this tale was interesting, not so much because it challenged the common tradition as because it added another marvel to his stock. Men were not then accustomed to sail round Africa, or to believe in the possibility of this feat; so he dwells affectionately on statements in favour of it.

To the same end are his stories of the Gorgon islands, over against the Western Horn of Africa, whence Hanno brought back the Gorgon or gorilla-skins to Carthage; of the Hesperian Island, a sail of forty days from the Continent[2]; and of the Fortunate Islands, on the left side of Mauritania or Barbary, where the thick fogs and snowstorms ever abide over Nivaria or Teneriffe (?), and where, in the island of Canaria, the huge dogs are found who give their name to the Canary Group.[3]

Those who care to believe that in this tradition Solinus preserves a memory of the West African islands may, of course, do so. They must be easily satisfied, if they can recognise, in a description that would apply to Iceland, the eternal summer of any of those " Fortunate " islands which we know as Canaries, Azores, Cape Verdes or Madeiras.

Solinus retains the ancient names—Junonia, Capraria, Nivaria, Canaria—the isle of Juno, the isle of goats, the isle

---

[1] Sol. lvi. 6-8; Pl. vi. 7, 175, 176.

[2] As Statius Sebosus (? the friend of Catulus) affirmed. Cf. Cicero,

Letters to Atticus, ii. 14, 15.

[3] Sol. lvi. 10-19; Pl. vi. 200-205.

of snows, the isle of dogs, and the rest,—but the men of his time had quite lost the dim knowledge once possessed of Teneriffe and its attendants; which had given the Greeks their story of the giant Atlas that held the heavens and the earth apart; which had afforded Ptolemy his first meridian; but of which nothing but the vaguest notions ever obtained in the Mediterranean world of old.

II. Cosmas.

We have already made the acquaintance of Cosmas as a practical traveller, in the interests of trade; now we must hear what he has to say about scientific geography. Unfortunately, the book which he devoted to a description of countries, and which would have given his really excellent qualities of observation a better chance, has perished, like all his other works[1]—his "Astronomical Tables," his Commentaries on the Psalms, on the Song of Songs, and on the Gospels. We have only the "Christian Topography," and in this his object is essentially controversial. To demolish false doctrines about the Universe, and to establish the true one, to harmonize science and religion by proving the same things from Scripture and common sense —this was what he set before himself. The aim was thus at starting the same as that of every Christian thinker. It was in the details of execution that Cosmas displayed his surpassing extravagances.

In germ, much of what he said had been already advanced by some of the Fathers, and in after times the schoolmen long continued to follow very similar lines of thought.

[1] Except for a few fragments of his treatises On Difficult Places in the Psalms, and On the Arguments (or Course of Narrative) of the Four Gospels.

"Can any one be so foolish," asked Lactantius (the "Christian Cicero") in the third century,[1] "as to believe that there are men whose feet are higher than their heads, or places where things may be hanging downwards, trees growing backwards, or rain falling upwards? Where is the marvel of the hanging gardens of Babylon if we are to allow of a hanging world at the Antipodes?" Augustine and Chrysostom felt and spoke in the same way, though in more measured language, and nearly all early Christian writers who touched upon the matter did so to echo the voice of authorities so unquestioned.

And not only upon the question of Antipodes. For this last was commonly connected with a far more serious controversy, to which Cosmas in particular devotes his energies —the controversy on the world's shape and position in the Universe. Yet in thought the two points were perfectly distinct, and it was quite consistent for a Christian Doctor (like Raban Maur under the Karlings) to hold to the one and reject the other; to accept as possible the sphericity of the earth, and to deny with scorn the very conception of antipodean peoples. The torrid zone being, in the opinion of most men of the Patristic age, impassable from the heat, it was plain that the "opposite peoples of the South," if existing, could not be of the race of Adam, or among the redeemed of the dispensation of Christ. And from such heresy men naturally shrank.

But though there was not the same unanimity among the Patristics against the spherical theory of antiquity as against the special point of the antipodean races, yet a very strong preponderance of opinion declared itself in favour of substituting for "sphericism" the obvious truths of a flat earth, vaulted over by the arch of heaven; and some, even

[1] Inst. Div. iii. 24. About 290–300 A.D.

in the lifetime of Augustine, faintly conjectured what Cosmas illustrated and established, beyond question from obedient believers. Diodore of Tarsus and Severian of Gabala had already suggested the comparison of the Universe with a two-storied or three-storied house, divided by the firmament, and roofed by the Heaven of Heavens,— 150 years before Cosmas; and on other points, such as the " glueing together " of the rims of heaven and earth, the Terrestrial Paradise beyond the encircling Ocean, the multiplicity of Heavens, the Waters above the Firmament, and the ministry of angels as the Lamp-bearers of the sky, the monk of Alexandria was not without forerunners.[1]

[1] Cf. Augustine, De Civ. Dei, xvi. 9; " Confessions," xi. 23; Chrysostom, Hom. xiv., on Hebrews; Diodore of Tarsus, Fragment in Photius, Bibliotheca, cod. 223, and " On Genesis," in Migne, Pat. Græc. xxxiii. cc. 1562–1580; Severian of Gabala, " Orations on Creation," esp. no. iii.; in Photius, Bibliotheca, references in cods. 59, 96, 231, 232; Procopius of Gaza, " On Genesis;" Athanasius (Contra Gentes); Cæsarius, Dial. i., respons. ad interrog.; Theodore of Mopsuestia in John Philoponus, " On Creation," iii. 9, etc.; cf. in the fourth century, St. Basil (Hexæm. Hom. iii. 3, 9); Cyril of Jerusalem (Hieros. Catech. ix. 76), who seems to think that rain is derived from the reservoir of waters above the firmament, and hence, like Cosmas, disbelieves in clouds sucking up moisture from the earth; and Eusebius of Cæsarea (c. 340), who likewise conceives the universe as a two- or three-storied house; see also Avitus (c. 523), who, almost in the very language of Cosmas, places Paradise in the far East, beyond India, for ever shut off from man among inaccessible mountains, close to the rim where the confines of heaven and earth unite. Similar passages are to be found in St. Ambrose, Justin Martyr, and others as cited by Letronne, " Des Opinions Cosmographiques des Pères." Most of these (except to a certain extent St. Augustine, who is willing to concede, for argument's sake, *figurâ conglobatâ et rotundâ mundus esse*) are distinctly anti-spherical, as well as opposed to antipodean peoples, etc. The more cautious method of Augustine is imitated by Isidore of Seville (" Origins," iii., xi., xiv., 1, 2, 5, etc.). See Letronne's " Opinions . . . des Pères," *Revue des Deux Mondes*, Mar. 15, 1834 (p. 601, etc.); Marinelli (tr. Neumann, " Erdkunde bei den Kirchen-Vätern,") especially part ii.; Santarem, " Essai sur Cosmographie," etc., vol. i., especially pp. 314, 315; Peschel, " Geschichte der Erdkunde " (pp. 85–90); Charton, " Voyageurs Anciens et Mod." ii. 1, 3, 7, etc.; Ferd. Denis, " Le Monde Enchanté;" and, for a fuller treatment of the same, part v. of this chapter, " The Minor Geographers."

Even in pre-Christian thought, from Herodotus to Cicero, there was plenty of doubt and hesitation in accepting the word of astronomers about the roundness of the earth; the vulgar belief in a flat plain, which even Plutarch to some extent supported,[1] was still the vulgar or common belief when Christianity was rising to power. Some who were ready enough to grant that the world was spherically shaped in the parts known to man, imagined that it might be cut off flat in the middle, resembling the upper half only of a ball. Others, again, thought at any rate no life could exist in an Antipodes beyond the regions of intolerable heat in the middle of that "globe," which otherwise they were ready to accept.

But the really scientific geographers of the old world— men like Eratosthenes and Ptolemy—left no possible doubt on the truth of the spherical doctrine to any one who could understand their arguments and appreciate their facts;[2] and the mind of educated pagan society was too plainly declared, for all the theologians to remain quite happy in denying what was said by the infidels. In a misty sort of way, men like Clement of Alexandria, Origen, or St. Basil the Great felt there was some reason on the other side; and so the last-named avoided the difficulty by declaring that religion was not concerned with the shape of the earth,

---

[1] In his tract On the Face in the Moon (De Facie in Orbe Lunæ), formally written against the spherical doctrine.

[2] The case was different with the Heliocentric or Copernican School of Antiquity, which received much greater support than is often supposed (*e.g.* Seneca will not pronounce against it, Nat. Quæst. vii. 2), and was at least known to Aristotle and Ptolemy; but, on the whole, was regarded as impossible even by educated opinion. See Schiaparelli, "Precursors of Copernicus in Antiquity." The chief Sphericists of the old world were Aristotle ("De Cælo," ii. 14); Strabo (bk. ii.); Thales and Pythagoras (in Diogenes Laertius' "Lives" of Thales, i. 1, of Pythagoras, viii. 26); Cicero (De Nat. Deor. ii. 18, 19); Pliny (Hist. Nat. ii. 65); Seneca (Nat. Quæst.).

and that it did not matter to faith whether it were formed
like a sphere, a cylinder, or a disc. This careless attitude
was hateful to Cosmas, who not only carried the popular
tradition to the furthest extreme, but elaborated a counter
theory. He professed to find the truth in St. Paul's utter-
ance, that the tabernacle of Moses was a figure of this
world. With astonishing courage he attempted to follow
the comparison into every detail. In the proportions and
furniture, in the four walls, the roof, the floor, of the tent
of the wilderness; in the candlestick, the ark of the covenant,
and the table of shewbread, he found in small compass the
whole of nature; except for that upper vault representing
the world to come, which lay above the firmament or flat
roof of the present earth. The best comparison of this
scheme is no doubt to be found in the time-honoured parallel
of a modern travelling-trunk, where, of course, the false roof
within answers to Cosmas' firmament, and the curved and
fixed lid to the arch of the upper heaven, while the oblong
form of the whole trunk is exactly the tabernacle-shape
assigned to the world. In all this Cosmas passed beyond
the position of most of the theologians who preceded him.
Where they had only denied, he affirmed; and affirmed with
definiteness and decision. For his system was demonstrated
from Scripture, and no Christian could doubt it. The faithful in earlier times had been content to doubt or dispute the
theory of a round world, and the monstrous fallacies connected with this error, but they had hardly ever been
offered the clear alternative—God's word for man's.

Similarly, in his doctrines of the land beyond the ocean,
containing Paradise, the world of the patriarchs, and the
sources of the four great rivers;—of the courses of these
rivers by underground passages, from the outer to the inner
earth;—and of the barrenness of that older home of man,

the new Christian topographer had an advantage over
nearly all his forerunners.

Once more, in his explanation of the Deluge, which was
sent, not so much to destroy man, as to bring those of the
fittest who survived, over sea from the desert of the antediluvian lands to the garden of the present earth; in his
assumption of gigantic mountains to the north of the world,
on which day and night depended; and in his resolute
attempt to find a place for the angels (in controlling all
natural phenomena), the monk of Alexandria, though using
fragments of Patristic and Rabbinical tradition, showed a
well-nigh unrivalled ingenuity in subjecting the fancies of
profane science to the sure word of sacred authority.[1]

Cosmas, as we have seen, was a merchant in earlier life,
when he traded to India and Abyssinia; learnt of, and perhaps visited, the sources of the Blue Nile; and found out for
himself into how many lands both the faith and money of
Rome had spread.[2]

But it was only after he became a monk that he entered
the noble army of writers. Naturally enough, he first put
down what we may call his "Memories of Travel," and
"treated of all the regions of the world, of coast-lands and
islands and others; of the countries of the South, from Alexandria to the ocean; of the Nile and its tributaries; of the
Arabian Gulf; and of the peoples of Ethiopia and Egypt."
Controversies about this earlier work, and especially about
his account of the burning desert of central Africa, led to
the "Christian Topography." The derivative has survived

[1] Exactly the same spirit is shown
in his account of the invention of
writing, which was discovered at
Sinai when the Law was revealed.
The forty years' wandering was to
allow the Hebrews a sufficient amount
of learned leisure to profit by the
new gift.

[2] Every country in the world, he
says, trades in Roman money, p. 148
(Montf.).

where the original has perished; and, as it proceeded, this apologetic treatise lost all connection with the geography of observation.   It is possible, however, that its descriptive portions, dealing with Ceylon, the Nile, the negro gold-trade, the Malabar coast, and other matters, are really extracted from the older "Description."   They are almost always introduced to illustrate some point in the argument, but their character is essentially independent.   They are far too long merely to support general views; they are in their nature extracts from a different kind of work; they are Strabonian and not Ptolemaic.

The "Christian Topography" seems to have been written between 535 and 547.[1]   It is dedicated, in its original form, to one Pamphilus a monk; in parts subsequently added, to a friend named Peter and a certain Anastasius, who had reported to Cosmas the compromises of some Christian geographers.   Nearly seventy authorities are quoted in all, among philosophers, historians, travellers, doctors of the Church, soldiers, and statesmen.   Aristotle is three times refuted; Berosus, Ephorus, Eudoxus, Manetho, Plato, Claudius Ptolemy, and Pytheas of Marseilles, with many other well-known names, find a place in the pages, and usually in the pillory, of Cosmas, whose reading was as

---

The eleventh book, and some other parts, were apparently composed during the exile of Theodosius, ex-patriarch of Alexandria, which began in 536 A.D.   Again, Timothy the Cat is mentioned elsewhere (at end of bk. x.) as if till very lately patriarch of Alexandria; and he died 535.   Once more, other parts, e.g. bk. ii., of the Top. Christ. are dated twenty-five years after the war of Elesbaan against the Homerites, which was in 522.   Cf. Pagi ad ann. 522.   Bks. i.–vi. are addressed to Pamphilus, the seventh to Anastasius, the eighth to Peter; the remaining four are without dedication.   Cf. Photius ("Bibliotheca," Cod. 36), who knew of no author for the Top. Christ., but remarks on its love of the marvellous ("as if man were fonder of myth than of truth"), and describes its diction as humble and its style of composition as beneath the common level.   See also the § "Cosmas" in Charton's Voyageurs Anciens et Mod. vol. ii. [esp. for its bibliography].

wide as his reflection was infantile.[1] In the first book he
demolishes the heresy of the roundness of the world. In

[1] It may be useful to add a list of the chief names, especially of authors, mentioned by Cosmas, with the references to Montfaucon's edition. (1) Amphilochius, a friend of St. Basil, bk. vii. p. 292; (2) Anastasius, a lover of Christ and of toil, vi. 264, vii. 274, 275; (3) Apion, grammarian and writer on matters Egyptian, xii. p. 341. He was nicknamed by the Emperor Tiberius, "Cymbalum Mundi," for his boasting. He wrote against the Jews, and was replied to by Josephus; (4) Apollinaris, heretic, v. 242; (5) Apollonius, (Molo) Egyptologist, xii. 341; (6) Archimedes, iii. 182—an incomparable geometer and arithmetician, "squarer of the circle;" (7) Aristotle, i. 121, iii. 177, 9; i. 117, 123; (8) Arius the heretic, v. 242; (9) Athanasius, bishop of Alexandria, vii. 292, x. 316–319. His " Festal Epistles," Nos. 2, 5, 6, 22, 24, 28, 29, 40, 42, 43, 45 are quoted; (10) Athenians, not belonging to the Faith (οἱ ἔξωθεν 'Αττικοί), v. 197; (11) Babylonians, on the Spherical heaven, viii. 305; (12) Basil, friend of Amphilochius, vii. 292; (13) Berosus, xii. 340; (14) Brahmins, ii. 137; (15) Cadmus, v. 206, xii. 343; (16) Chæremon, writer on matters Egyptian, xii. 341; (17) Chaldæans, teachers of Spherical heresy to Egyptians, iii. 159; (18) Christian Sphericist, vii. 274, 299; (19) Dius and Menander, translation of Tyrian Antiquities into Greek, xii. 342; (20) Ephorus, fragment quoted from bk. iv. of his history, ii. 148; (21) Epiphanius, x. 326; (22) Epistles, Catholic, vii. 292, disputed by some Churches; (23) "External," i.e. adverse, writers οἱ ἔξω, etc., iii. 175, iv. 190, ix. 310;

(24) Euclid, geometer, iii. 182; (25) Eudoxus of Cnidus, iii. 159; (26) Eusebius, iii. 174, vii. 292; (27) Eutyches, heretic, v. 242; (28) Greeks, vi. 260, 272; (29) Gregory of Nazianzen, x. 319; (30) Epistle to Hebrews, St. Paul its author, v. 254, 255; (31) Hebrews taught writing at Sinai by God, v. 205. Here Cosmas refers to the Nabathæan and old Egyptian inscriptions near Mount Sinai; of which most belong to the early centuries A.D., though a few date back to Rameses the Great. We may notice that Cosmas always makes his Old Testament quotations from the Septuagint; (32) Homer, xii. 343; (33) Hyperides, v. 197; (34) John the Evangelist, v. 248; (35) St. John Chrysostom, x. 327, 328; (36) Josephus, perhaps his chief authority in matters secular, iii. 174; (37) Irenæus, vii. 292; (38) Jews and Messiah, vi. 271; (39) Lycurgus, legislator, xii. 342; (40) Lysimachus, writer on matters Egyptian, xii. 341; (41) Manetho, xii. 341; (42) Manichæans, v. 242, 262, xii. 271, 272, 273; (43) Marcionists, v. 242; (44) Menander (and Dius), xii. 342; (45) Menander, comedian, v. 198; (46) Montanists, v. 262; (47) Moses, iii. 174; (48) Origen, vii. 298, 299; (49) Pamphilus of Jerusalem, to whom Cosmas inscribes his first six books, i. 114, ii. 124, viii. 305, vi. 260, 266; (50) Patricius, mathematician and bishop, viii. 306, cf. ii. 132 (perhaps same?). v. 192, ii. 125; (51) Peter, to whom bk. viii. is inscribed, viii. 300, 307, 308; (52) Philo, x. 329, 330; (53) Plato, iii. 177, 179, xii. 341; (54) Proclus (cf. Timæus), xii. 341; (55) Ptolemy

the subsequent books (ii.–xii.) he explains his own system, which, in the second, third, and following sections, he confirms from Scripture, in book x. from the Fathers, in book xii. from non-Christian sources. The eleventh book, as we have seen before, is entirely practical, and belongs, like parts of books i., ii., and iii., to the commercial geography of the time.

There is, as we have said before,[1] another interest about the "Topography." It contains, in all probability, the oldest Christian maps that have survived. There is little reason to doubt that the numerous sketches—of the world, of the northern mountains, of the antipodes in derision, and the rest—which are to be found in the Florentine manuscript of the tenth century were really drawn by Cosmas himself (or under his direction) in the sixth; and are thus at least two centuries earlier than the map of Albi, or the original sketch of the Spanish monk Beatus.

From his apparent wealth of information about the Nestorian Church and its missions, it was long ago[2] conjectured that Cosmas was himself a Nestorian. It was

(king or kings), vi. 267, ii. 141, etc. (Adule monument); (56) Ptolemy, Claudius, iii. 177, 182; (57) Pythagoras, iii. 179; (58) Pytheas of Marseilles, ii. 149; (59) Salamon or Solon, xii. 342; (60) Samaritans, v. 262, vi. 271, 272; (61) Severian of Gabala, his Hexæmeron, bks. i. ii. iii. iv. vi. in x. 320, also cf. vii. 292; (62) Socrates, iii. 179; (63) Sopater, merchant, xi. 338; (64) Stephen of Antioch, priest and mathematician, vi. 264; (65) Syrians, vii. 292; (66) Story-tellers (Τερατολογοί), v. 205, 213; (67) Teucer, lawgiver of Locri, xii. 342; (68) Theodosius of Alexandria, schismatic, x. 331; (69)

Theophilus of Alexandria, x. 320; (70) Thomas of Edessa, Catholic of Persia, disciple of Patricius, ii. 125; (71) Timæus the philosopher, xii. 340 (cf. Plato); (72) Timothy the younger of Alexandria, x. 332; (73) Tryphon, xii. 344 [adviser of Ptolemy Philadelphus in translation of Septuagint]; (74) Xenophanes, ii. 149.

[1] Cf. the introductory chapter.

[2] By La Croze, "Christianisme des Indes," cf. pp. 27–37 of that work. The strongest evidence is his professed friendship with Thomas of Edessa, which would have been impossible, one would think, for an orthodox monk at that time.

pointed out how he praised the semi-Nestorian bishops
Patricius of Persia and Thomas of Edessa ; how in his lists
of heretics he never included Nestorians ; how he referred to
the authority of Theodore of Mopsuestia, and Diodorus of
Tarsus, the lights of Nestorian theology ; and how his
expressions upon the Incarnation were never inconsistent
with Nestorian views.[1]   We may add to this, that the
knowledge he shows of the Nestorian discipline and of
its successes in far distant parts, from India to Socotra,
was quite out of the range of the orthodox monk ; but
this, like all the other indications of partiality for the
"Protestantism of the East," may be a survival from
an earlier time.   The Nestorian merchant may have become
an orthodox ascetic.   The famous passage where he runs
over all the Christian Churches of the world, without a
word of condemnation for the Catholics of the West and
North ; his quotation, in one place, of the very phrase,
"Mother of God," on which the whole Nestorian controversy
first arose ; and his constant use of Catholic divines, point
perhaps to this conclusion.   Whether schismatic or no,
Cosmas made little of the divisions among Christians compared to the gulf which separated them all from the atheists
of pagan science.

Lastly, just as the nickname of " Indian Traveller " was
gained by his commercial journeys of the earlier time, so it
is probable that his writings on cosmography in the later
years of his life have changed his own proper name into
a title. " Cosmas " is hardly likely to have been his Christian
or family name ; like " Polyhistor," it has been added as
a description ; but whereas the full name of Solinus has

---

[1] Cf. on these points, pp. 124, 125,
146, 151, 175, 209, 217, 223, 242, 262,
269, 283, 286, etc. of Cosmas (Montfaucon's edit.). But note his use of
Θεοτοκός in bk. v.

THE PLANS OF COSMAS.

i. The World and the Firmament.

survived, all of Cosmas' has perished, except his designations.

The place of Cosmas in history has been sometimes misconceived. His work is not, as it has been called (in the earlier years of this century), the "chief authority" of the Middle Ages in geography. For, on the whole, its influence is only slightly, and occasionally, traceable. Its author stated his position as an article of Christian faith; but even in those times there was anything but a general agreement with his positive conclusions. St. Isidore of Seville at the end of the sixth century, and Virgil of Salzburg, the Irish missionary of the eighth, both maintained the belief of Basil and Ambrose, that the question of the Antipodes was not closed by the Church. The subtleties of Cosmas were left to the Greeks, for the most part; the Western geographers who pursued his line of thought were usually content to stop short at the merely negative dogmas of the Latin fathers; and no great support was given to the constructive tabernacle-system of the Indian merchant.

Yet, after all, the "Christian Topography" must always be remarkable. It is perhaps the final warning of a certain habit of mind—of that religious dogmatizing which fears nothing but want of faith. Quite apart from the useful notes it contains of commercial and missionary travel, it is also one of the earliest important essays in scientific or strictly theoretic geography, within the Christian era, written by a Christian thinker. It is extraordinary that Cosmas should have really done some work in astronomy, and yet should have denied every lesson that astronomy teaches and nearly every assumption on which its progress has been based—yet so stand the facts; and in the Topography we have to deal, not with a mere fabulist like Solinus, still less with a servile

statistician or tabulator, but with a bold and independent
cosmographer.   Had he not set out with the purpose of
making facts bend to pre-judgments and forcing the heavens
to tell the glory of God, Cosmas might have advanced
the science he set himself to overthrow: but it was this
very destructive purpose that led him to write; he recognised no good in knowledge apart from the word of the
Scriptures; and the observations which are to be found
like fossils scattered among the layers of his arguments
are in part merely to illustrate the latter—in part, as we
have said, are probably taken over from a treatise with a
largely different object.   In the "Topography" his interest
was mainly in constructing a theological system of the
universe: never before or since was so complete and so ambitious an attempt made in this direction; but considerable
knowledge, many opportunities, and some education were
here allied to fervent piety.   It was not because of ignorance or through living in Dark Ages that Cosmas wrote as
he did: he flourished at the time when Christianity perhaps
most entirely and exclusively controlled civilisation and the
whole area of the civilised world; and he seems conscious,
not of a feeble and barbarised mind, but rather of having all
knowledge for his province.   He was not without profane
science, but he now saw it (and saw through it) in the light
of theology, the crown of sciences.

Was not the arrogance, as well as the intricacy and the
pettiness, of the Egyptian monk and his doctrines significant
of the coming overthrow of his religion and his race in its own
homelands, where it had turned the search after the truth of
nature into a chase after fantastic and delusive mysteries?
Islam at least brought back more of the sense of respect for
things as they are, a revived interest in the physical world,
a more balanced use of tradition, and a greater restraint of

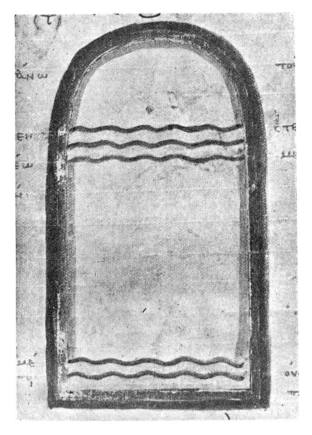

THE PLANS OF COSMAS.
ii. The waters above and below the Firmament.

fancy to its own proper sphere—to the task of amusing, without compelling, belief.

Cosmas starts with an attack upon the Spherical theory of heaven and earth from an astronomical standpoint. He then proceeds, after demolishing the false, to give the true, the Christian doctrine of the shape of the universe, as evidenced by Holy Scripture. "In the Name of the Father, and of the Son, and of the Holy Ghost, One consubstantial and life-controlling God, from Whom cometh down every good and perfect gift,"—so runs the author's invocation,— "I open my stammering and unready lips, trusting in my Lord that He would vouchsafe me of His spirit of wisdom."

In the two prologues which are prefixed to the Topography, we are recommended to study its arguments very carefully as a preparation for the "Descriptive Geography," which, as we have seen, is probably incorporated to some extent in the present work, as it was finally expanded and arranged. The kind offices of Pamphilus and of the "very religious man" Homologus the Deacon are commemorated; the humble and unequal style of the treatise before us is vindicated—"for a Christian wants right thoughts rather than neat phrases;"—and an outline of the argument, divided under five books, is added for the information of the reader. The first of these deals especially with the inconsistencies of those Christians who have discarded the Biblical truth of a flat and immovable world. It is only those who deride with superabundant scorn all the holy men of old as mere scatterers of empty phrases; it is only they who can afford to believe in the spherical shape and circular motion of the universe.[1] But who can say that he ever saw the sky moved up or down[2] at any time? And as we know that it must

---

[1] Cosmas, pp. 116–117 (Montf.).

[2] Cosmas insists (p. 118, Montf.) that the Pagan heaven, *i.e.* "the so-called spheres," must be either moved

either be attracted downwards, forced upwards, or stationary, the disproof of the first two involves the acceptance of the last. But, oh! the darkness of those who prate about the courses and retrogressions of the stars;[1] who dream of the planets' motion as contrary to that of the universe. If the heavenly bodies have their motion from their own nature, whence these vagaries? What force compels them to a motion contrary to themselves? The blasphemy of these triflers recoils upon their own head. In their struggles to get rid of the direct action of the Creator, they are given over to every kind of contradiction and absurdity. Would it not be well, ye wisest of men, exclaims Cosmas with an attempt at Socratic irony, to make an end of this folly; and, though late in the day, to learn of the Divine Word, and distrust the guidance of your own futile judgment?

Let us Christians ask these wiseacres, who babble about the world revolving on its own axis, one or two simple but searching questions. Who is it that sustains this infallible axis of theirs? How has it been driven through the earth for us to revolve upon, and what is it made of?[2] And do not let us be drawn aside by the dishonest conceit of some of these Sphericists, that our world may be moved by the volume of air pent up within it. Let us for one moment consult fact and common sense. If a man were filled with air, would he be kept moving? We know what would really happen. He would burst, before he got very far in his movement. How much more, then, would the earth perish, if it had ever been turned into this kind of windbag?[3] Can there be any question, concludes this first part of our refutation, about the central truths of nature; that

down "by a prevailing gravity," or borne up by the action of the contrary.

[1] Pages 118, 119 (Montf.).
[2] Pages 119, 120 (Montf.).
[3] Page 121 (Montf.).

THE PLANS OF COSMAS.
iii. The World and the Pillars of Heaven.

the sky is fixed, that the earth is the centre of the universe, and that sun, moon, stars and this same earth of ours are all sustained by God alone ?

A popular error is next disproved about the source of rain.[1] It does not come from heat drawing up moisture into clouds; for the effect of heat is not to attract upwards, but the reverse, as Cosmas proves triumphantly from several instances—a bath, a wet log on the fire, a garment newly washed and drying in the sun. Does not the moisture of damp wood run down into the flame ? Does not the perspiration of the body trickle downwards ?[2]

So much for a first essay in scattering the clouds of error. Cosmas now turns[3] with some expressions of relief to the pleasanter part of his work, that of directing his readers towards the light of truth. He reminds his friend Pamphilus how the whole of the " Christian Topography " is due to his advice and his encouragement; how the distinguished author, when " sick in body, weak in eyesight, unversed in rhetoric, involved in business," was roused to undertake this stupendous task. It was Pamphilus who first appreciated the importance of the analogy between the Tabernacle of Moses and the material universe.[4] It was Pamphilus who first insisted how useful such a work must be for the training

---

[1] Page 122 (Montf.).

[2] Cf. pp. 122, 123 (Montf.), which is followed at once by the first statement of an often-recurring crux for the Sphericists who try to keep in touch with religion to some extent by leaving angels, demons, and the souls of men un-included in their spheres. These wicked men, as St. Paul says of the pagans, are really transferring the " glory of the immeasurable God " to His creatures, in placing their souls outside the spheres of being; and from such who have the form of godliness and deny the power thereof, we must strictly turn away.

[3] Bk. ii. pp. 124, etc. (Montf.).

[4] As we have already suggested, this achievement belongs in all probability to the great Nestorian doctor Theodore of Mopsuestia, c. A.D. 330–429. See John Philoponus' attack on his Cosmical Theories in the seventh century (" De Creatione Mundi ").

of young Christians; for the breaking off of that unhallowed alliance of the self-opinionated orthodox with atheist deceivers, Sphericists, and asserters of antipodes. It was Pamphilus who showed how much more important it would be to set forth the true basis of Christian science than to please the world by remaining silent for fear of calumny.

But besides Pamphilus, Cosmas had also a debt of gratitude to the great masters Patricius of Chaldæa and Thomas of Edessa; for all the insight he had gained into the hidden meaning of the Scriptures—an insight beyond the common, as men must grant—he owed to their instruction.[1] He follows this interesting personal reference by drawing out his texts in serried lines, on behalf of the true relation and distinction of heaven and earth which the legend of the Antipodes would confuse in one;[2] and of the foundation of our world upon the immovability of God. To these favourite points, as we shall see, he again and again returns, as he does to other matters now first discussed,—the Tabernacle pattern and the heavens on both sides of the firmament;[3]—but here we will not stop to notice what is more fully thrashed out in later books. In the same way as to the description of the world that follows; its division into two parts, present and antediluvian; its four seas or gulfs, Mediterranean, Persian, Arabian, and Caspian; and its continents or conventional distinctions of Europe, Asia, and Africa, it is not necessary to make a long story in this place.

[1] Patricius, says Cosmas (p. 125, Montf.), when he had fulfilled the Abrahamic order and course, went to Byzantium with his disciple Thomas of Edessa, " who now fills the Archiepiscopal throne of all Persia as Catholic bishop."

[2] Against this, several sacred testimonies are cited, e.g. (1) Moses, " the divine Cosmographer," (2) Melchizedek, (3) Hosea, (4) Zacharias, (5) Daniel, and (6) Christ Himself—" I thank Thee, O Father, Lord of Heaven and Earth " (pp. 126, 127. Montf.).

[3] E.g. pp. 129, 130 (Montf.).

[4] Cf. pp. 131, 132 (Montf.).

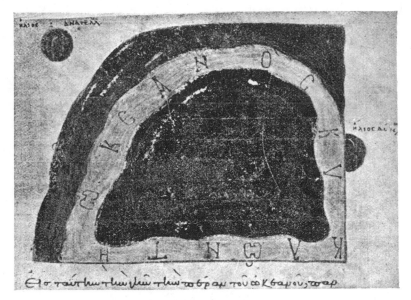

THE PLANS OF COSMAS.

iv. The Present and Antediluvian Worlds, with Ocean between.

But we may perhaps except for a more special notice the doctrine here laid down that, in the northern and western parts of the earth, both land is higher and sea is deeper than in the southern and eastern tracts. What clearer evidence of this could there be than the furious rushing stream of Tigris from the north contrasted with the even flow of Nile from the south ? [1] What clearer contradiction, we may add, could Cosmas furnish to his own arguments against Antipodes? Could not the rain fall *up* to them (however paradoxical it might sound) if the river of Egypt could run up from south to north, from Ethiopia to the " Roman " Sea ?

We next have the scriptural account of the sun's movements. It rises in the east, towards the south, and so ascends to the more western parts, where it turns and retraces its course behind the screen of the great mountain in the north, which now makes night " even to the ocean beyond our earth, and thence to the land on the other side of the ocean." [2]

This is not a mere matter of observation. It is proved by the furniture of the Tabernacle, where the candlestick, placed to the south of the table of shrewbread, typified the heavenly luminaries shining upon the earth. By the moulding also that Moses put round about the same table of shewbread was signified the ocean that encompasses our present world, and by the " crown of a palm's width " beyond the moulding was plainly indicated the former world of the patriarchs on the other side of ocean, where man lived before the flood.

Hence Cosmas naturally floats off into one of his favourite digressions, on that primæval earth which contained

---

[1] Cf. p. 133 (Montf.).

[2] Day therefore equals a course of the sun from east to west by the south ; night a similar course from west to east by the north. Cf. bk. ii. pp. 134, 135 (Montf.).

Paradise, but was otherwise barren and inhospitable and securely shut off from us by the waste of waters, which only the ark of Noah had ever crossed.

And this, again, brings him to the Silk Country of further Asia; "for if, on account of a miserable trade, men now try to go to the 'Seres,' would they not much rather go far beyond, for the sake of Paradise, if there were any hope of reaching it?" The Seric or Silk land, indeed, lay in the most distant recesses of India, away past the Persian Gulf, past the island of Ceylon. It was also called Sina,[1] and just as Barbary or Somaliland had the ocean on its right, so this remote country was washed by the ocean on the left.

And so the Brahmin philosophers declared that if you stretched a cord from Sina, through Persia, to the Roman Empire, you would exactly cut the world in half—and perhaps they said true.

"Moreover, forasmuch as beyond Sina on the east, and beyond Cadiz on the west, there is no navigation, it is between these points that we can best measure the length of the world;" just as from the land of the Hyperboreans "living behind the north wind," and from the Caspian, that flows in from the Arctic waters, to the Southern Ocean and the extremest coasts of Ethiopia, one may estimate the breadth. The first will be found to be about four hundred stages; the second about two hundred.[2] So that Holy Scripture rightly tells us that the earth is twice as long as it is broad.

[1] *I.e.*? Malaya. But cf. Yule, Cathay, i.

[2] That is, reckoning: 1. The length—from Sina to Persia, 150 stages; from Persia to Roman Empire, at Nisibis, 80 stages; from Nisibis to Seleucia, 13 stages; from Seleucia to Cadiz, more than 150 stages. 2. The breadth—from Northern Ocean to Byzantium, 50 stages; from Byzantium to Alexandria, 50 stages; from Alexandria to the Cataracts, 30 stages; from the Cataracts to Axum, 30; from Axum to the incense-bearing coast of Barbary, a district called Sasou, about 50. The Adule inscription (140–144) is made to confirm this. Cf. pp. 136–144 (Montf.).

THE PLANS OF COSMAS.

v. The universe, according to Cosmas, with the Walls and arch of Heaven. Above, the Creator surveying His works. The rising and setting sun are moving round the great mountain in the north.

Cosmas then proceeds to describe the monument of Ptolemy Euergetes at Adule [1] and its vaunting inscriptions, which he thinks an additional proof of his belief that the breadth of earth is not more than two hundred stages. And thus, he concludes triumphantly, is Scripture confirmed by the most accurate travel; thus may we discount the liars who babble of another southern zone beyond the central region of intolerable heat. Are not Greek and Roman and Egyptian history and modern observation at one with the Vision of Daniel in establishing the truth?

The four extremes of the world, continues the geographer, are occupied by four nations. [2] In the East are the Indians, in the South the Ethiops, in the West the Celts, in the North the Scythians. But their regions are not of equal extent. As the world is an oblong, and the length of it is from east to west, the nations dwelling upon these sides have a far wider range than those which are placed at the two ends. [3]

In this, Holy Scripture is agreed with not a few profane and pagan writers, who cannot resist the truth; thus Pytheas, the old voyager of Marseilles in the time of Alexander the Great, tells how he reached the extremities of the North; and how the Barbarians of those unhappy regions, shrouded in eternal night, yet showed him the cradle of the sun, whose rays they never could enjoy. [4]

[1] And of an Abyssinian (Axumite) king, who lived apparently in the later years of the third century, A.D. (in the second, according to V. St. Martin; in the first, according to Dillmann). Cf. Ed. Glaser Die Abessinier in Arabien und Afrika (Munich, 1895); Gesch. und Geog. Arab. (Anhang) 1890.

[2] Page 148 (Montf.).

[3] The Scythians occupy what is left over from the course of the sun, i.e. the North; the Ethiopians over against them extend from the "winter East" to the "shortest West."

[4] Pytheas of Marseilles (c. B.C. 300), who sailed north to the Shetlands and north-east to the Elbe, left two works: (1) "Concerning the Ocean;" (2) "A Periplus, or Coast Description from Gades to the Tanais (Elbe?)." Though Strabo bespattered

The true shape of earth is also established by the well-known courses of the four great rivers, that flow across the ocean into our world—the Phison, Indus, or Ganges, pouring itself into India, and enjoying nearly all the same products as the Nile, from crocodiles to lotus flowers; the Gihon, or Nile, that flows through Ethiopia to Egypt; and the Tigris and Euphrates, that water Mesopotamia—all with a common source, in Paradise.

Seeing then—resumes the astronomical argument, pressing on to its theological conclusion—how stable a mark of night and day, how sure a guide to sailors and travellers are the luminaries of heaven, we may be certain that they are not moved by any spherical motion, but by certain rational virtues that sustain the light—princes of the powers of the air. But, as Paul the apostle teaches,[1] he who once had this power—the devil—is now deprived of it; and his rights are divided among many angels. And some of these move the air; some the sun; others the moon, the stars, and the clouds of the sky. For the work of angels is clearly to minister to the benefit of God's image, which is man; just as the work of devils is to injure the Divine likeness.[2]

By the angels, therefore, the whole framework of the universe is kept in order for our advantage by the ordinance of God, which seemed to them at first vain and burdensome. For after the Fall, might they not think that the damnation

him with calumny, no single traveller of the Old World deserved more gratitude from geographers. Ephorus is also quoted by Cosmas, and Xenophanes of Colophon—valuable for another reason. He (like Ptolemy) thought the known world was terminated, not by water, but by unlimited land, and therefore (unlike Ptolemy) he rejected the Spherical doctrine.

[1] Ephes. ii. 2; Cosmas, 150 (Montf.). So St. Isidore copying (?) Cosmas.

[2] St. Paul makes it clear (1 Cor. iv. 9) that angels, devils, and the souls of men are all included in this world. "We are made a spectacle to angels and to men." Cf. Cosmas, 157 Montf.

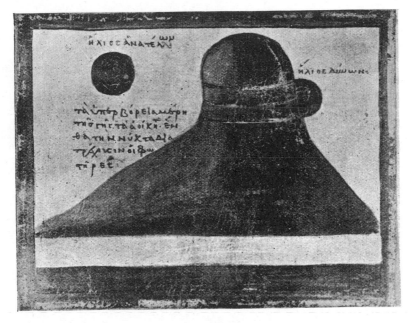

THE PLANS OF COSMAS.

vi. The Great Mountain in the North, with the rising and setting sun.

of man was hopeless, and that the expectation of the creature [1] would wait in vain for the manifestation of the sons of God ? [2] It was vanity, they thought, this work in man's behalf ; and so, as it is said, they were subject to the same unwillingly by the might of Him who subjected them to their task in hope.[3] And that hope of theirs is twofold. First of all, they look forward to man's redemption ; again, for themselves they expect the day when they, the "creatures," shall become equal to men, the children of God ; when their bondage of corruption shall be exchanged for the liberty of the redeemed.[4]

Great will be the amazement, therefore, adds Cosmas, with grim irony, of these new legislators of our world, of these wiseacres who think that all the lights of heaven revolve with the natural and uniform motion of a sphere, when at the last day they discover the truth, when the angels cease their ministry, and every star falls from its place. Greater still will be their horror when they, who have denied the "blessed hope and coming of the great God and our Saviour," will hear the sentence, "Depart from Me, ye who work iniquity." [5] For this is, indeed, wickedness,—to believe in a Universe where nature stands for God, impersonal force for personal agency, and the spherical doctrines of men for the truth revealed in Scripture.[6]

But let us leave these men, laughs our philosopher, whose arguments are as much in a circle as their system ; and let us see what the Divine Word teaches us about the four elements of matter.

---

[1] Themselves, the angels.

[2] Pages 151–154 (Montf.).

[3] Rom. viii. 19–22.

[4] Just as each private person, indeed, has his angel, so races and kingdoms have archangels told off to look after them (Cosmas, p. 154 ; cf. Dan. x. 13 ; Acts xii. 15 ; Matt. xviii. 10).

[5] Page 155 (Montf.).

[6] I.e. of the Tabernacle and its symbolism.

First in the order of creation was the arid element of earth as the base of all things;[1] upon the stable element was then laid its corrective, the humid element of water; upon the humid, the cold dry principle of air; upon the cold, the heat of fire. Thus the mixture was complete, and the two opposites, earth and fire, whose coming together would reduce the world to ashes, were securely separated by the intermediates. It was by the interaction of these elements that rains and earthquakes, like eclipses, were brought about; but as these were effected through angelical virtues acting on the command of God, they were not to be curiously investigated. Faith must believe, not question how.

And just as by referring to Scripture Cosmas has cleared his own mind upon the great laws of nature, so in the special question of the Antipodes, the same guide is at hand, sufficient and decisive. The Bible will not allow us even to hear or speak of such an absurdity as a world facing downwards. There is only one "face" of earth, that which God has given man to dwell on—*the* face we know. It is not "upon every face," upon more than one face, or upon the back or side of the world that man has been planted; he can know no other than that which was from the beginning. In particular, this blasphemous theory of Antipodes makes Christ a liar and His Word not in us. For how could we possibly exercise the power He gave us of treading on serpents and scorpions when walking reversed?[2] It is plain that our only safe way in geography and in all science (as in our common life) is to follow the Word of God, and steadily refuse to be carried about with every wind of doctrine.

[1] A good deal of this is from the Timæus of Plato in a more or less distorted shape.

[2] Page 157 (Montf.).

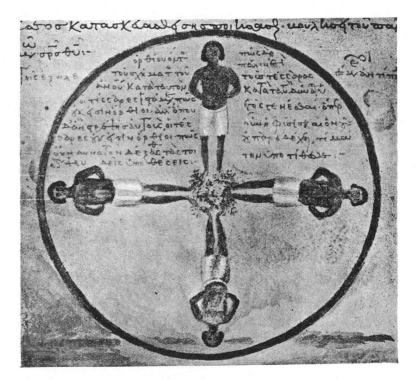

THE PLANS OF COSMAS.

vii. The Antipodes in Derision.

In his next section [1] Cosmas goes on to explain more at length what he has hinted at already, and what was so clearly taught in the history of the chosen people, that the Tabernacle was an exact image of the universe—"see thou make all things according to the pattern [2] shown thee in the mount." He also illustrates his doctrines about the firmament and the shape of this world by some rather startling applications of well-known texts.   Thus the Tower of Babel was built in the mistaken belief that the heaven was spherical; the parting of the Red Sea proved the truth of that division which God made in the beginning between the waters above and below the firmament; the distribution of creation over six days was for the instruction and edification of the angels.[3] On the other hand, the fall of the devil [4] was a direct result of the angelic power over nature.   Entrusted with the care of earth and sea and sky in the service of man, who was the "bond of the universe and the flower of creation," the head of Lucifer was turned by this overwhelming honour, and he rebelled against his Maker.

From the figure of the Tabernacle, which on its outside typified earth and on its inside heaven, it was also apparent that only two heavens existed in nature answering to the two holy places, and not seven or eight or nine, as some had impiously said.

Cosmas then turns again to his polemics with the "sphericists," and indignantly asks them to explain away,

[1] Bk. iii.

[2] *I.e.* of the creation just revealed to Moses in its six days or parts (pp. 162, 163 (Montf.).

[3] Pages 166, 167 (Montf.).

[4] A striking picture is drawn (pp. 167, 168, Montf.) of the angels on their first creation looking with wonder upon one another: "Who brought us here?" Then, as God called up the light, the truth dawned on them—He who created this from nothing must have created them. And just as light was brought into being to teach the angels, so woman was created to instruct man as to who was his Creator (cf. p. 172, 173, Montf.).

if they can, six passages of Scripture which plainly disproved their heresy.[1] One slight difficulty of his own he promptly dismisses. When St. Paul was caught up into the third heaven, this only meant one-third of the space between heaven and earth, and did not impair the great truth he had just stated. Only two heavens could be proved from Holy Writ.

Then, with a few words of contempt for the arts and sciences of the Greeks, which had led them to assert the damnable doctrines of the eternity of the world and of matter,[2] the Christian Topographer, quoting a number of texts in support of his own system, passes on to recapitulate[3] the Scriptural teaching about the shape of this world.

And the result of this is as follows :[4] First of all, we must picture the flat earth hung on nothing, as Job said, but founded on God's stability, and over it the arched heaven joined or "glued "[5] to the earth along its extremities. This great dome is cut in two by the firmament; from the earth to the firmament is the present dispensation of angels and men; from the firmament to the arch of the second heaven is the kingdom of the blessed into which Christ has entered.[6] To illustrate all this, Cosmas gives several maps or pictures of his system; and with infinite repetitions tells us again about the encircling ocean, the world beyond the ocean, and the great mountains in the North, whose summits at night intercept the light of the sun.

[1] Among these the most important are : (1) the sun and moon standing still at the command of Joshua; (2) the shadow going back ten degrees on the dial of Ahaz (p. 176, Montf.).

[2] Cf. p. 182 (Montf.).

[3] Cf. pp. 186–189 (Montf.).

[4] Bk. iv.

[5] Conglutinavi, κεκόλληκα in Job xxxviii. 38 (Septuagint).

[6] Of this second heaven, the firmament is, of course, the floor, as the earth is of the lower region. From some passages in bk. ix. it may be guessed that Cosmas reckoned the distance from the earth to the firmament as double the distance from the firmament to the summit of the Upper Heaven (Mc. Cr.).

His fourth section concludes with some more problems for the unhappy "sphericists."   First, he begs to be informed how they propose to impart motion to their rich assortment of spheres, of which they are so proud.   For, according to them, no place, body, or element can exist outside the sphere: whence, then, its motive power?   Again, these fancied spheres are mobile: how can these possibly retain water, such as we have in seas, rivers, and lakes?

In fact, the whole thing is nonsense; the only marvel is, how a Christian can believe this pagan rubbish.   The teaching of his own Scriptures is perfectly clear; and it would be well for him not to try and serve two masters, or to eat at the table of the Lord and the table of devils.[1]

Both the prophets and the apostles, we have seen,[2] agree on this point—that the Tabernacle is a true copy of the universe, the express image of the visible world.   Cosmas now undertakes (with much else) to explain the symbolism of that Tabernacle in detail.   In all this, repeating at great length[3] what has been said before, we will not follow him here.   But his conclusion, though only a restatement of earlier rhapsodies, is fuller and more emphatic.

Every true Christian, believing in the Old and New Testaments, is bound to reject the Satanic errors of the Greeks in geography, just as he would reject infidelity in religion; for the fancy of a round world abolishes the kingdom of heaven and the future state, and makes of none effect the resurrection of Christ.[4]   The assertors of

[1] Cf. pp. 190–192 (Montf.).

[2] Bk. v.; cf. p. 192, etc. (Montf.).

[3] Cf. pp. 194–260 (Montf.).

[4] Cf. pp. 260–263 (Montf.).   This ends bk. v., with which bk. x. is closely connected, both in subject-matter and because the former is almost entirely composed of Scriptural quotations, the latter of patristic—with applications even more removed, if possible, from the precincts of common sense.   Bk. x. concludes with another passionate outburst: "Oh, wonderful agreement of the Church, of the doctors, of the mysteries of God.   Oh, unity in things least

Antipodes are only to be classed with Jews, Manicheans, Samaritans, and other heretics.

Cosmas next [1] devotes his genius to answering an ugly question raised by some infidels—"How can the sun be hidden as you say behind the northern parts of the earth, when it is many times bigger than the earth?"[2] False, he replies, is this figment of theirs; so far from being greater than our world, the sun is only equal to two of the seven belts or climates [3] of the same. This is proved by his own observations on the length and inclination of shadows at midday in Abyssinia and in Egypt, and by similar reckonings of his friend Stephen the priest in Antioch and in Constantinople. For if in the third climate, at the beginning of the summer,[4] the shadow declines, as in fact it does, only one foot to the north (viz. at Alexandria), in the second half a foot (viz. at Siene), and in the first (at Meroe) not at all, is it not plain that the bulk of the sun can only be equal to this much of our earth? The same truth is evident from similar measurements north of Egypt; for at Rhodes, in

agreed upon. Oh, involuntary concord of schismatics. Oh, unwilling praise of revilers of the faith. Who can escape damnation that contradicts so great a cloud of witnesses? (Cf. pp. 329, 334, Montf.)

[1] Bk. vi.

[2] Page 264 (Montf.).

[3] This use of the term was secondary. *Klima* meant, first, the supposed slope of the earth from a higher north to a lower south, or *vice versâ*; secondly, from Hipparchus' day, B.C. 160, the different belts or zones of the curved or spherical earth-surface as determined by the different lengths of the longest day; thirdly, the average temperature, etc., of each zone. Cosmas' argument from the breadth of the climates is quite at

variance with that from the length of shadows. The former would require the sun to be about 66,260 miles from us, the latter about 4,400 miles. The shadow-arguments which he advances in this book in support of his flat earth are curiously perverse. He had noticed that shadows of identical objects were of different lengths in different latitudes; this variation of course proceeds from the curvature of the earth; but Cosmas, assuming the sun to be a *little object*, close at hand, uses this point against the very thing it really establishes. The shadow-reckonings of Stephen at Antioch, which Cosmas quotes, would require a human figure somewhere about six feet nine inches in height. (Mc. Cr.)

[4] Solstice? lit. summer change.

the fourth climate, the shadow declines a foot and a half; near Byzantium, in the fifth, two feet; and so on. How, then, can they, who babble of the sun being larger than the earth, prevent their opinions from being proved most false and fabulous?[1]   How is it, if the earth be spherical, as they pretend, that the shadow does not vary on this convex surface?   Still more pitiable is their plight when they are examined in a common-sense way about the form of these shadows.   For they assert that when the illuminating body is greater, and the illuminated less, but both round, the shadow cast must be conical, as the rays of the larger sphere pass beyond the smaller.   Cosmas proceeds, both by recounting his own observation, and by demonstrations illustrated with diagrams from a "wooden sphere" and a "conical vessel,"[2] to demolish this error, by a curious process of reasoning which really depends upon two assumptions — first, that the sun is very near the earth; and, secondly, that the size of the luminary is very small.[3]   He then returns to discuss the two worlds of his system—upper and lower—answering to the present and future states of man.   As if this were not already sufficiently established, he overwhelms us with fresh proofs.   From the duality of human nature, with its body and soul, from the two trees in the middle of Paradise, from the two sons of Abraham and of Isaac, from the Jewish tabernacle and temple, and from the word of the angels to the shepherds ("Glory to God *in the highest,* and *on earth* peace"), the two chambers of the universe are made manifest once more.[4]

The next point to be decided is the duration of the

[1] Pages 264, 265 (Montf.).

[2] Page 266 (Montf.).

[3] In modern figures Cosmas' sun should be about 4400 miles from us, and its diameter about forty-two miles, to give effect to some of his arguments in this book. (Mc. Cr.)

[4] Pages 268, 269 (Montf.).

heavens; and here, as before, Cosmas [1] assures us there is no way of meeting the heresies of the Greeks, save by going to the root of the matter, and destroying their assumptions by the letter of Scripture and the voice of common sense. Any other method is but a building on the sand.

Thus, by the syllogism,[2] the Greeks have proved that if spherical and revolving, the heaven must be eternal; and those weak and foolish Christians who admit the roundness and the motion, are, of course, obliged to accept the eternity. Whereas the true answer is this. Scripture tells us plainly that the heaven, like the earth, is to be dissolved. Therefore we cannot believe that it is spherical or in motion. Because, being endowed with ordinary reasoning powers, we cannot accept the monstrous position of the neutral, who maintains that the world may be round and yet come to an end.

A friend of Cosmas, one Anastasius, had told him of the existence of such a person; and he was indeed deserving of great pity. Like an ignorant and unskilful traveller, he had lost his way, and was wandering among brambles and pitfalls in the pathless wastes of a science, falsely so called.

Yet there is an eternal heaven,[3] indissoluble and invisible; so countless texts make evident, and they blaspheme who think that this heaven of heavens shall ever pass away.

Another vital truth now awaits a further exposition—the separate generation of heaven and earth.[4] The Book of Genesis, with the true instinct of Biblical science, leaves no doubt as to their twofold and independent being. For it tells us of the generation of the "heaven *and* the earth,"

---

[1] Bk. vii., p. 274, etc. (Montf.).

[2] Arguing thus: What is spherical and revolving must be eternal; the heaven is spherical and revolving: therefore the heaven must be eternal.

[3] Pages 278, 279 (Montf.); cf. Matt. xx. 23; 1 Cor. xv. 12, 13, 15, 16, etc. This is the Upper Heaven.

[4] Pages 296, 297 (Montf.), repetition from bk. i.

that is, obviously, of everything contained in both. But
the old wives' fable of the Antipodes would make the heaven
surround and include the earth, and God's Word would have
to be changed ;—"These are the generations of the sky."

In support of the same truth, Cosmas quotes the added
testimony of Abraham, David, Hosea, Isaiah, Zachariah, and
Melchizedek, who clenched the case against the Antipodes
—"For how, indeed, could even rain be described as 'falling' or 'descending' in regions where it could only be said
to 'come up'?"   Over against these disproofs of folly and
error stands the countless array of evidences for the true
tabernacle theory, for the flatness and immutability of earth,
founded upon God's stability, and for the shape of heaven,
stretched like a skin-covering over our world, and glued to
the edges of it at the horizon.

To illustrate these points, the " man of science and of
the Church " here inserts a plan of the universe, showing its
exact adaptation to the tent of the wilderness, and accompanies it with a learned discourse on the human womb, as a
type of the world, containing the four elements—of heat,
cold, dryness, and humidity.[1]

He then returns with wonderful iteration to confute the
infidel doctrine of the spheres—of the moon, planets, and
fixed stars, whom the heretics make into deities ; and with
which they empty of meaning the ascension of Christ.   For
how could He mount " above every principality and power "
when the " towers " of the zodiac remained outside ?   Such
errors make Him a liar, like His apostle ; they bring in both
equality and plurality of gods, and are soul-destroying.[2]

The weak and wandering Christians who allege the
authority of Origen, " that marvellous man," to condone the
folly of these dreamers ; who fancy that after death the souls

---

[1] Page 295 (Montf.).   [2] Pages 297, 298 (Montf.).

of men are whirled round with the spheres; or who declare
the world to be without beginning or end, ever passing
through generation and corruption,—virtually blaspheme
God in so doing, and make Him powerless, non-existent, or
a lover of evil.

Cosmas passes again from these deplorable compromises
with the spirit of worldly vanity, and dwells long and
tenderly upon the story of the lengthening of Hezekiah's
life, signified by the return of the shadow upon the dial of
Ahaz—that convincing proof to Jews and Gentiles alike,
of the true cosmography; where God "sitteth upon the
circle of the earth," the immovable arch of heaven, where
He "stretcheth out the skies as the curtains" of the
Tabernacle, and "spreadeth them as a tent to dwell in." [1]

The last point [2] that remains to be cleared up in Christian
science is the course of the heavenly bodies. There is, we
are told, an upper and a lower movement. That of the twelve
months is the upper; that of sun and moon is the lower.
This needs no proof. It is fully typified in the candlestick
of the Tabernacle. Still less does it call for curious
scrutiny. For it is all effected by the invisible power of
God.

Some details, however, Cosmas does supply. He tells
how the circuit of the sun gains on that of the moon twelve
portions daily in its course of thirty days; how the " months "
again pass the sun by one portion daily; he adds a plan to
depict the cycle of the months; and he closes his work
with testimonies—from the Fathers of the Church and from
many pagan doctors, Chaldæan, Egyptian, Greek, and other,
—to the truth of that doctrine of geography which he has
already built up out of Holy Scripture.[3]

---

[1] Bk. viii. 300–306, etc. (Montf.);
Isa. xl. 21, 22.

[2] Bk. ix. 309, 310, etc. (Montf.).
[3] Bks. x. and xii. Cf. 315–334, 340–

His last words seem to show a quiet satisfaction in a great task manfully accomplished. He felt himself to be the apostle of full supernatural theory in science. He knew that his work was unique. And such it has always been recognised—by some with rapture, by others with consternation, by most with derision. At least it is a monument of infinite, because quite unconscious, humour. "For neither before him was any like unto him, neither shall be after."

III.—THE RAVENNESE GEOGRAPHER.

It was apparently about a century after Cosmas—about A.D. 650—that the next important work of Christian geography, and that one of purely statistical object, was compiled in the West. An anonymous student, living at Ravenna, then set forth the result of his studies in a series of tables professing to give the contents of every country under heaven, the political divisions, the towns and the chief natural features of each. These tables, however, were confessedly abstracted from older writers, even for the author's own land of Italy ; and the only original part of the new treatise, in any sense, was contained in the introductory section upon the general divisions of the earth (in correspondence with the divisions of day and night by hours), and in some of the remarks upon the boundaries of the continents and greater kingdoms. Even their originality is nevertheless but nominal, and lies in their being rather adapted than literally copied from the authorities followed throughout.

345 (Montf.). Bk. xi. is occupied with practical notes on Ceylon, etc.—See "Commercial Travel." Bk. xii. is not in the oldest (Vatican) manuscript, and is imperfect in the Florentine. It contains Cosmas' vindication (from *secular* learning) of his Scriptural geography. Cf. list of authors quoted by him in note 1, to p. 280.

Two centuries later, the compilation of the Ravennese was itself abstracted and plundered by one Guido, also a native of Ravenna (c. 850). But whereas the "Anonymous" at least attempted a description of the whole world, Guido's tables only included Italy and the neighbouring islands; with a brief survey of the Mediterranean coasts and ports, and some notes upon the boundaries of Europe, Asia, and Africa.

The main interest of the Ravennese geographer, as of Guido, consists in the question of his sources. And even a cursory reference to these shows us that he rather belongs to the survivals of ancient science than to the mediæval workers, in the proper sense. He thus offers a singular contrast to Solinus. Whereas the latter, though a pagan, is of primary importance for the geographical ideas of the Dark Ages,—the Ravennese, on the other hand, devout Christian as he was, scarcely belongs, except for the fact of his creed and time, to Christian geography at all. His place is as a copyist of the old pre-Christian itineraries; even more than of those writers who belonged comparatively to his own time, such as the "Gothic philosophers" he so constantly produces. Thus Ptolemy, whose elaborate scientific work was naturally outside the range of geographers dependent on and content with Solinus and the pilgrim-travellers, appears to have been used, at least in reference to some of his catalogues of place-names, by the Ravennese.[1] The latter, therefore, must have been a good way removed from the spirit of his time in the material which he transcribed: although his use of that material is pretty much on a level with his contemporaries'. If he had the enterprise to seek out better guides, his stupidity and ignorance prevented his gaining much profit from their

---

[1] Cf. the numerous identifications (between the Ravennese and Pto-lemy's names) in Pinder and Parthey's edit. of Raven., e.g. pp. 104, 105.

guidance. The Ptolemy he quotes is always confused with the "King of the Macedonians in Egypt;" Jornandes, the historian of the Goths, though professedly one of his main authorities for Northern Europe, regularly appears as Jordanis; and the blunders of his place-name transcripts too often prove him equally servile and ignorant.[1]

Yet his advantages were apparently great. He seems to have known Greek, as he not only refers in many places to the works of Greek philosophers, but in the case of Persia acknowledges his debt to a description of that country written in the Greek language; Greek words he quotes in Latinised and often barbarised forms with almost Ciceronian frequency.[2]

But besides Greek, which gave him Ptolemy and so many others to draw from, he had several new and valuable records of the Teutonic conquerors from the North ("Gothic Cosmographies"), and several Roman itineraries of the Imperial time, probably illustrated by road maps, such as was recovered for modern study in the Peutinger Table. The identical table of Conrad Peutinger has been recognised by some [3] in the work of Castorius, which forms the Anonymous Geographer's main authority, is cited thirty-eight times as officially responsible for more than half the entire compilation, and is probably the chief source of much that is not expressly assigned to any one.

---

[1] Thus in "Britain," v. 31, we have Durobrabis and Durobrisin for (?) Durobrivæ (Rochester); Venta Velgarom for V. Belgarum (Winchester); Caleba Arbatium for Calleva Atrebatium (Silchester); Deva Vic*tris*, Utriconion, *Virolani*um. The name of one city, too, is constantly made to do duty for several: thus Londinis, Landini, Londinium Augusti; Tamaris, Tamion, etc.

[2] Thus Britain is a little world of its own, a veritable "micosm"—such is his business-like shortening of the famous "Microcosm" proverb, so flattering to British pride. Such a knowledge of Greek was natural enough to a subject of the Byzantine Empire, living in the most Byzantine town of the Western Exarchate.

[3] Cf. Konrad Miller, Weltkarte des Castorius.

On comparing the Ravennese with the Peutinger Table, as we have it, we see that the definite quotations from Castorius, in every case except that of Arabia, agree with the indications of the table. The language of the Anonymous Compiler also seems to prove that he had some sort of a map before him.[1] And if a map at all, it was unquestionably one of roads, stations, and marked distances, such as the Table, which, in pursuit of its primary object, altogether distorts the shape of the Roman world, and, following with scrupulous care the course of the great highways from east and west, assumes the shape of a narrow and vastly elongated parallelogram. Down to very minute details, the correspondence of the two may be traced: Ancyra, in Galatia, which in the map is only represented by a picture without a name, is passed over without mention by the Ravennese, professedly copying Castorius; on the other hand, the smallest stations are constantly reproduced —so obscure and so unimportant that our Anonymous Geographer would never have been tempted to insert them, if he had not been copying an itinerary.[2] Again, those places—for instance, Rome, Antioch, Ravenna, Constantinople—which are dignified with the largest and most imposing pictures or vignettes on the Peutinger Table, are distinguished by some title, "most famous" or "most noble," in the work of the Anonymous.

But, on the other hand, the world of Castorius is larger than that of the Table, and he gives his copyist a far greater number of place-names in distant countries such as India, and even in lands nearer home, than we find in the famous ribbon-map.[3] Both in the East and the North, our

[1] Rav. i. 18; v. 34.

[2] Miller, however, is wrong in saying (p. 42) that Castorius is not used by Rav. in Burgundy.

[3] *E.g.* in Corsica one town is marked in the Tab. Peut., five in the Ravennese, who is probably copying Castorius. Cf. the case of Arabia,

Anonymous Compiler had other sources than the material represented in the Table; and the authority of Castorius is made to cover too much ground for him to be identified with a reviser, still less with the original draughtsman, of the Tabula. All that can be safely asserted, therefore, is that in Castorius and his other Roman authorities—Lollianus, Maximus, and the rest,—the Ravennese geographer had authorities in the nature of route-guides or itineraries; that some, or all of these, were probably accompanied by or embodied in road maps; and that these road maps bore a very close relation to the Peutinger Table, over a large part of the known world.

In answer to the question, Who was Castorius? there is nothing but conjecture; and this difficulty has, of course, brought upon the Ravennese the charge of forging his authority.[1] But Lollianus, at any rate, is an ascertainable quantity, as he is known to have written about geography (or lent his patronage to such writings) in the course of the fourth century after Christ (c. 340). He is quoted eleven times, over a wide extent, including nearly the whole of the Roman world in Europe and Africa; on Egypt and on Sicily he would seem to have been especially consulted. His other guides, with the exception

not in Tab. Peut. at all; of India Dimirica—in Rav. (quoting Cast.), containing sixty-two cities and two rivers—only a fraction of which are in Tab. Peut.; of India Serica and India Major, which in the Ravennese have close on seventy cities and three rivers [about forty is the Peut. Tab.'s allowance of towns for all India].

[1] As by Wesseling, in 1738; by Mommsen and de Rossi in our own day. The last-named has pointed out that, among the authorities quoted by the Ravennese, Lollianus and Arbitrio were consuls in 355, Probinus and Marcellus in 341. Their names may have been inscribed as consuls on maps which had, e.g., Castorius for author. See Mommsen, in Sitzungberichte der kgl. sächs. Gesellschaft der Wiss., Phil.-hist. Classe iii. (Leipzig, 1851), pp. 80–117; G. B. de Rossi, in Giornale Arcadico, xxiv. (Rome, 1852), pp. 259–281; Wattenbach, Deutschlands Geschichtsquellen, 6 Aufl, i. (1883), p. 67.

of Jornandes, who is quoted ten times, and one or two
others of the "Gothic" geographers of doubtful authenticity,
are employed much more sparingly by our Anonymous
Statistician; they are also, for the most part, non-Roman.
The well-known Greek philosophers, Porphyry, Iamblichus,
and Aristarchus are cited five times, four times, and six
times respectively. Among the other authorities are several
who, apart from their mention in the pages of the Ravennese,
are, as he says himself of the Indian deserts, "Known only
unto our God."

But, on the whole, it seems unnecessary to suspect him,
so vehemently as Mommsen has done. Wherever his
quotations can be traced, they are accurate enough for
practical purposes; his interests in geography are not those
of the fabulist, but of the arithmetician.

The geographer begins with a rhapsody upon the im-
mensity of God's world. Who has measured the height of
heaven, the breadth of earth, the depth of the abyss? "How
great are Thy works, O Lord—in wisdom hast thou done
them all. As for me," he proceeds, "though not born in
India, nor brought up in Scotland,—though I have never
travelled over Barbary, nor examined Tartary,—yet I have
gained a mental knowledge of the whole world and the
dwelling-places of its various peoples, as that world has been
described in books under many emperors. For so Augustus
decreed that every land should be taxed; and so the
doctrine of Christ's apostles has been spread to the ends of
the earth." What this amounts to, our author goes on to
explain. The world stretches, in his conception, from
Britain to India, and is to be divided into twelve parts,
commencing in the east, and ending in the west, according
to the twelve hours of the day. Between the two extremities are to be found the lands of Persians, Arabs,

Ethiops,[1] Moors, Spaniards, Aquitanians and others, and upon them blow the " six winds of the treasuries of God."

The writer next meets the objection that this division cannot be allowed, in that the sun, though it may appear to stand just over India at the first hour of the day, yet really looks upon all the world at the same time. He replies that, first of all, this expression—of the sun shining upon a particular country—is a figure of speech, equally true or equally false of every part of its course ; and that, in the next place, there is a real sense in which the sun stands at a particular place in the heaven at a particular time of the day ; not in the sense of only enlightening a certain country, or being only visible from a limited region ; but as the Divine Scriptures tell of Joshua's commands, " Sun, stand thou still over Gibeon, and thou, Moon, over the valley of Ajalon."

Did not the sun, then, asks the indignant Ravennese, when it stood over Gibeon, yet look over all the world just the same. And " if by the horologium of metal (the clock of the seventh century) we can discern accurately each part of the day in the reckoning of hours, how much more can prudent and wise men reckon what countries are to be taken into account as they go over the world hour by hour ? "

And if perchance some contentious person should question in what way the sun could be said to look upon India at the beginning of the day, especially when it is allowed that an impassable desert lies at the back of the same India, he may be confronted with the common consent of all philosophers, both of the Church and " of this world," that the sun rises and sets over India and over Britain. West of Scotia or Ireland is another impassable tract, the Northern

[1] " Qui Æthiopes plerique dracone vescuntur, ut testatur psalmigraphus," i. 2.

Ocean,[1] beyond which no land has ever been discovered; but to attempt to pry beyond these limits of the earth is flat blasphemy for Christians. It is clear, from Scripture, that no mortal man can penetrate to the hidden paradise of God, which is in the furthest East.

And, if that were not enough, did not the Indian Stoics, did not the Demons themselves warn Alexander, when he reached the Indus, of this boundless waste beyond their country? Did he not then bear witness to the truth by turning back? Nothing is told us, in the story of his conquests, about an ocean beyond the desert; and, indeed, such an idea is quite outrageous. Paradise cannot possibly be placed in Armenia, a land quite well known; and with this heresy must fall the companion error of supposing Tigris and Euphrates to rise in that country. They are known to come out of Paradise: now, Paradise is in the furthest East, beyond all known land; the sources, therefore, of these rivers must be hidden as well.[2] As to the Northern parts of the world, it is clear, from the sayings of philosophers, that there, beyond the sea of ocean, are mighty mountains, placed by the command of God, which (as Cosmas had said in Justinian's day) make day and night by forming the screen behind which sun and moon disappear in their courses.[3] Some, indeed, deny the existence of these mountains, declaring the ocean to be the end of the world, and even asking impudent and awkward questions;—Who ever saw these mountains with his own eyes? Where are they

---

[1] In support of this, Rav. quotes (i. 5) St. Basil, Bishop of Cæsarea in Cappadocia, in his Hexæmeron; Isidore of Seville; and among "philosophers of this world," Liginius, Cathon, and Iamblichus.

[2] Of course, adds the geographer, the idea of an immaterial and in-visible Eden in some well-known country is ridiculous.

[3] It is hard to believe that the Ravennese had: (1) neither seen nor heard of Cosmas' writings, nor (2) read the patristic speculations on this subject which helped Cosmas to form his theory.

named in Scripture? Where indeed? Is it not clear that, although known to the Creator, they have been forbidden by Him to human knowledge, and are therefore inaccessible? And as to the Scriptural difficulty, is there not a plain reference in the book of Genesis, "The sun came up over the land, and Lot entered into Segor?" The sun rises and sets and goes to its own place, the East himself proceeds both to South and North.[1] But the manner and the cause of this "are known only unto God." [2]

To the twelve divisions of the day correspond other twelve—of the night; beginning on the west with the land of the Franks, and continuing to Bactria or the land of Bokhara and Samarcand in Central Asia. This list of countries, with the remarks attached to each, is copied in the main from the historian of the Goths, Jornandes, "wisest of cosmographers," and presents no feature of interest, either for comparative wisdom or comparative folly. In proof of the rightness of his divisions, our geographer appeals to the story of Trajan's march "along the whole northern coast of the ocean;" from Holy Scripture he demonstrates that it was possible to divide the time of darkness as accurately as the time of daylight (for "at the third hour of the night they took Paul to Festus the governor"); and, lastly, in answer to the charge that his scheme magnified Europe (or the portion of Japhet) to an equality with Asia and Africa (or the shares of Shem and Ham) together,—he denies the accusation absolutely. "Europe is far narrower and less extensive than Asia, and that is answer enough for you,

[1] The "coming up" of the sun proves a height to be surmounted, Rav. i. 9, cf. Eccles. i. 5-6.

[2] In i. 9, Liginius and Ptolemy are quoted in support of the argument and the hymn of Rigilinus, which brings the sun at night behind the Northern Mounts, "Zozaico itinere, ac per immensos latices." The notice of "rex Ægyptiorum ex stirpe Macedonum arctoæ partis descriptor" is, almost beyond doubt, one of Claudius Ptolemy confused with the Dynasty.

my inquisitor," exclaims the Ravennese, apostrophising, as
he is fond of doing, his critical reader.

The geographer now passes to the central part of his
work[1]—an enumeration of all the chief seas, towns, rivers,
islands and peninsulas in the world, as known to him;
and accordingly from this point we have merely catalogues
of names, copied with many blunders from previous
writings, mainly of the itinerary class, and divided into
countries. Each list, as we move from land to land, is
introduced by a few brief remarks upon the general nature
of the districts to be considered, and upon the authority
who vouches for the names given. The most usual reference is to "Castorius,"[2] the possible reviser and editor of
some ancient road map like our own rediscovered Peutinger
Table; but, as we have seen, he is only one out of many
sources on whom the Ravennese depends.[3]

---

[1] Rav. i. 17.

[2] Cosmographus Romanorum.

[3] In a work so entirely derivative,
it may be well to mention the chief
references to former writers, and the
alleged source of each part: *Basil*
of Cæsarea, *Isidore* of Seville, and
the "philosophers of this world,"
Liginius, Cathon, and *Iamblichus*, in
i. 5, on the Northern Ocean; *Rigilinus* the Christian poet on the
secrets of creation, in i. 9; *Orosius*
is referred to in ii. 4 and v. 29,—
wisest of Orientalists, "sapientissi-
mus Orientis perscrutator," as he is
called, in reference to Ceylon; *Arsatius* and *Afroditianus* (Persians who
wrote in Greek) are referred to in ii.
12; *S. Gregory's* Homilies in iii. 9, on
Gætulia; also in section on Æthiopia
Biboblatis (iii. 5), *Provinus* (or Probinus) and *Melitianus* "genere Afros"
as authorities, additional to Castorius

the philosopher; in sections on
Northern Europe, *e.g.* iv. 3, besides
Porphyry, Iamblichus (cf. ii 16), and
Lollianus, he names *Livanius* the
Greek and *Arbitrio* the Roman
"philosophers;" " *Pentesileus* philosophus" in iv. 4, with *Marpesius*,
and *Ptolemy*, "rex Ægyptiorum
Macedonum;" and in iv. 5, *Eutropius*;
in iv. 8, 9, etc., *Aristarchus*, "Græ-
corum philosophus;" in iv. 9, *Hylas*;
in iv. 11, *Sardonius*; in iv. 12, 13,
Aithanarit or *Aitanaridus*, *Elde-
valdus* and *Marcomirus* (iv. 17, *Marcusmirus*), "Gothorum philosophi;"
in iv. 14, *Menelac* and *Sardatius*;
in iv. 15, *Marcellus and Maximus*
the Roman; in ii. 21, v. 16, *Epiphanius* of Cyprus ("ter beatissi-
mus"); in v. 33, *Virgil*.

From ii. 1–iii. 2, though "many
philosophers" are constantly referred
to, *Castorius* is the only authority

Beginning with the four chief gulfs of the sea best known to him, those of Issus, Lyons, the Black Sea and the Adriatic, he proceeds to devote the rest of his second part to Asia, his third to Africa, his fourth to Europe, while in his fifth and concluding section he gives a "coaster" or periplus of the Mediterranean, and a summary of islands both inside and outside the "Roman Sea." Under each country we have first a list of provinces, then one of cities, then another of rivers, in the regular order, to which is sometimes added a short description of mountains, and if the land lies upon the sea-coast, we are often told something about that part of the ocean or other water on which it borders. But the

for ASIA (cited) except for the *additional* witness of *Orosius* on the Indus (ii. 4); of *Arsatius* and *Afroditianus* on Persia and Media (ii. 12); of *Porphyry*, etc. on the "Mesogeon" of Asia Minor (ii. 16), and of *Epiphanius* on the position of Rinocorura(os) in ii. 21. ·Always, however, the text is *secundum Castorium*; till in iii. 2, *Lollianus* is followed, on Egypt. From iii. 5–iii. 8, *Castorius* again reigns alone, though others are mentioned as confirmatory; in iii. 8, *Castorius* and *Lollianus* are coupled as authorities. From iii. 11 to the end of bk. iii. *Castorius* again alone, for the rest of AFRICA ; next, for EUROPE, in iv. 1, *Jordanis or Jornandes*, for Scythia ; in iv. 2, *Iamblichus ;* iv. 3, *Livanius*, for Black Sea coasts, though several others are cited ; iv. 4, *Pentesileus* and others, especially "*King*" *Ptolemy*, for modern Prussia, etc.; iv. 5, *Livanius* again, for Dardania, for Thrace, iv. 6, for Mysia, iv. 7; iv. 8, 9, 10, *Aristarchus*, for Epirus, Macedonia, Hellas, etc.; iv. 11, *Sardonius*, for Sarmatia ; iv. 12, 13, *Aithanarit* and others on Dania, etc.;

iv. 14, *Sardatius* (= Sardonius ?) on Datia ; iv. 15, 16, *Maximus* on Illyricum, and Dalmatia ; iv. 17–iv. 23, *Marcusmirus* (Marcom–) on Saxony, Pannonia, Valeria, Carneola, Liburnia, Frisia ; iv. 24–26, *Anaridus*, or *Aitnaridus*, on Francia, Thuringia, Suabia ; iv. 26– iv. 38, *Castorius* again, on Burgundy, Septiman(i)a, Italy; iv. 39, *Eldebaldus*, on Brittany ; iv. 40, *Aitnaridus* (Anar-) on Gascony ; iv. 41, *Eldebaldus* on Spanish Gascony ; iv. 42–45, *Castorius* again on Spain.

No authorities are named for the periplus of v. 1–15, round the Mediterranean coasts ; nor for most of the islands that fill up the rest of v. ; but, in v. 16, *Epiphanius* is quoted on the portions of the sons of Noah ; in v. 29, *Orosius* on the ten cities of Taprobane or Ceylon ; in v. 33, *Virgil* ("Mantuanus") on Thule.

After this we may perhaps prefer Avezac's more charitable description of the Ravennese, as an "ignorant érudit," to the contemptuous language of Letronne, "cette effroyable rhapsodie," etc.

whole, from first to last, is derived, if not from Castorius, then from Orosius, St. Basil, Pope Gregory, Jornandes, or one of the other "Gothic" chroniclers; or from pagan philosophers, such as "most wicked Porphyry." Of original or independent value, this geography has practically none : and it would therefore be sheer waste of time to summarise its contents, from our point of view. To the local antiquarian and the philologist, the contents of this tract are of very different value ; but as we have already tried to show whence the Ravennese got his materials and in what proportion, it remains only to give a specimen of his method, and to notice one or two points in his collection that may have some special interest.

As an example, let us see what is told us about Egypt.[1] "Many philosophers," says our compiler, "have described this country, and among these I have read Cinchris and Blantasis, who are natives of the land, and have described the southern parts of it, as well as Lollianus the Roman ; but these authors have not enumerated the cities of Egypt in the same manner; each has had recourse to his own method. But I have followed Lollianus in my list of the same. And these are, etc."

This is the invariable formula of introduction; though, of course, the names are often changed, and Lollianus in particular is only an authority of the second class. The material thus subdivided and prefaced also follows an extremely dry and regular order : it is only rarely that any remarks are added to the place-names which make up the bulk of the work ; one such is found at the mention [2] of Ravenna, "that most noble city where I was born, who with the aid of Christ do now attempt to set forth this geography ; " but most of these comments are absolutely stale, flat, and

---

[1] Rav. iii. 2.   [2] Rav. iv. 31.

unprofitable, without either the daring of Solinus or the practical knowledge and fresh information of Dicuil.

Here and there, however, we come to something more suggestive. The "silken" or "Seric" division of *India*, where so many philosophers are found called Brahmins, proves the Ravennese guiltless of any clear ideas of China. To him, as to most of the early Christian and to so many of the pagan scientists, the Ganges or the Bay of Bengal was the eastern end of all things.

The Indus our compiler supposes to flow into the ocean near Ceylon; he quotes Orosius for this, and blames as ignorant and foolish people [1] those who traced the stream to an estuary in the Persian gulf. The Caspian [2] he connects with the Northern Ocean by the Gulf of Hyrcania. Egypt he conceives as stretching from the Southern Ocean to the Delta; in "Ethiopia" he notices the famous stream of "Ger," which has been made to figure so conspicuously in modern conjecture as a possible ancient synonym for the Niger,—a river far outside the ken of the Ravennese. His books told him of certain islands in the ocean, west of Tangier; and he confusedly repeats the tradition of the Fortunate Islands, now utterly forgotten, except as a name, in Europe.[3] The "Moor land of Cadiz" he illustrates by a curious story. It was there the Vandals fled after their defeat by Belisarius. Although he seems to have used some of the catalogues, at any rate, of place-names in Ptolemy, the Ravennese geographer shows nothing Ptolemaic in his description of the limits of Africa. To his mind the dark continent was bounded on the south by the same ocean that stretched up to the Straits of Cadiz, not

[1] Rav. ii. 4.
[2] Rav. ii. 8, 12, 20, etc. Ptolemy, who with Herodotus, was one of the very few ancient geographers acquainted with the true shape of the Caspian, would have saved him from this, if he had ever read him carefully.
[3] Rav. iii. 11.

by interminable desert land that on the west forbade any
water-way between Spain and India, and on the other side
stretched round to join Asia in Further India, making the
Erythræan Sea a greater Mediterranean.

In Europe we find a rather startling picture[1] of the
Saxon race, "daring and *most learned,* but not so quick in
movement as the Danes;" and a curious notice of the
infant Venice, "so named by a certain king,"[2] is given us
in Italy, which is naturally described with unusual fulness,
from the "Titanic Alps" to the "Ionic," Gallic, and Adriatic
Seas. In the far distant corner of Gaul, Brittany[3] lies
"among the marshes by the Western Ocean." On the com-
pletion of his survey of all the lands and ports[4] on the
shore of the "Greek" or Roman or Mediterranean Sea, the
Ravennese stops to declare his agreement with the doctrine
of Epiphanius, "thrice-blessed Archbishop of Cyprus," on
the equality of the three continents, Europe, Asia, and
Africa (as being alike portions of the equally favoured sons
of Noah), before he turns to say a few last words upon the
coasts and islands of the outer ocean. Thule and the Orkneys
(Dorcades insula) he places east of Britain;[5] and with a
mention of Ireland or Scotia, which, like Strabo, the geographer locates to the north of the same Britain, and of
islands in the Southern Ocean ("near the Strait of Cades")
in whose hideously distorted names we may recognise the
"Fortunate Isles" of ancient geography, or the Canaries of
modern time, this singular catalogue is brought to an end.

[1] Rav. iv. 17.
[2] Rav. iv. 29, 30. Possibly a confused reference to Attila.
[3] Rav. iv. 40.
[4] Rav. v. 15–17.
[5] Rav. v. 32. In v. 31 he refers
to the Saxon invasions and settlements in Britain. These began long

ago, he says, and have lately been
consummated under a chief named
Ansehis. ["Olim gens Saxonum
veniens ab antiqua Saxonia, cum
principe Ansehis modo habitare
videtur."] Somewhat similar is his
reference to Scandinavia, or Scanza,
as *ancient Scythia.*

IV. Dicuil.

Last among the important geographers of the Dark Ages is Dicuil,[1] the Irish scholar of the ninth century ; who has told us already about the first discovery of Iceland, the pilgrimages of his countrymen in the Levant, the fresh-water canal between the Nile and the Red Sea, and the commercial or ceremonial intercourse between the chiefs of Christendom and Islam in the time of Charlemagne. We have seen something of the place which Dicuil occupied in the great missionary and civilising movement of the early Irish Church. Here we have to ask about his position in the progress or decline of science at this time. His " Book of Measurements," which, as we are expressly told, was finished in the " 825th year of the Lord of Earth and Heaven and Hell," falls into nine sections. The first three are occupied with the three continents, Europe, Asia, and Africa, which (he thinks) had always been considered as separate since the Julian and Augustan survey, eight hundred years before. A fourth section deals with a special part of our Africa— Egypt and Ethiopia. The fifth chapter sums up the length and breadth of the known world. The last four are devoted to special subjects ; and treat successively of the five greater rivers and other smaller ones, " certain islands," the length and breadth of the Tyrrhene Sea, or Western Mediter-ranean, and the six highest mountains.

In the course of these chapters, which, as we have seen, are mainly reproduced from older writings, Dicuil

[1] Who is also known as the author of a (lost) tract on grammar. The survey to which Dicuil so constantly alludes in his first five chapters was probably one undertaken two years before the death of Theodosius the Great, thinks Parthey, p. xiii. ; but of this we have no other account, and it must remain an open question whether Dicuil was relying on a forgery or not.

introduces three dissertations of his own.   Each of these
comes in to illustrate some contention of his argument, either
in support or in refutation of some statement of his authorities. In the first place, the story of Fidelis helps, as he thinks,
to prove the truthfulness of Cæsar's surveyors, when they
said [1] that an arm of the Nile flowed into the Red Sea near
the camp of Moses.   Again, the narratives of the voyage
of the Irish hermits to Iceland in 795, and of similar
ventures among the Orkneys, the Shetlands, the Färoes,
and the Hebrides are introduced [2] partly to confirm, partly
to correct, the bald note of Solinus on Ultima Thule, "where
there was no night at the summer solstice, and no day at the
winter."   Lastly, the account of Charlemagne's elephant, so
lately seen in Dicuil's own lifetime, is meant to rebut the rash
assertion of the same Solinus that no elephants could lie down.

Dicuil had not the speculative instinct of Virgil of
Salzburg, his fellow-countryman and predecessor ; he had
too much reverence for the learned men whose books he
studied to enter on a regular campaign even against their
wilder theories; for the most part he is content with the
office of a transcriber, and as Solinus copied Pliny, as Isidore
copied Solinus, so he, at the end of the ages, copied from
each of his forerunners.

Yet he was not without some visitations of common
sense and independent judgment, both on matters which
did and did not fall within his own immediate observation.

He had his own ideas of what was good evidence and what
was bad.   He ventured sometimes, we know, to criticise and
even to reject the statements of his authorities on certain
details.   To our lasting benefit, he set a high value upon
first-hand evidence, such as he got from the travellers of his
own acquaintance.

[1] Dic. vi. 20 (ed. Parthey).   [2] Dic. vii. 10, etc.

But we have already seen the best of Dicuil in his notes upon the practical travel of his time. As a man of science, a writer upon geographical theory, he is really of small moment. His position is not in any way independent; his measurements are all derived, with scarcely any exercise of judgment, from the ordinary and misleading encyclopædists or compilers on whom his age relied; and he only contributes, for his own share, upon general reckonings and definitions, some citations from otherwise unknown or highly mythical sources. His reading was unusually wide; he quotes or refers to no fewer than thirty Greek and Latin writers;[1] and among them are Herodotus, Thucydides, Pytheas of Marseilles, and Eudoxus of Cyzicus, all of whom gave solid

[1] The full list of these is : Agrippa, Artemidorus, Augustus's Chorography, Cæsar's Cosmography, Clitarchus, Dicæarchus, Ephorus, Eudoxus, Fabianus, Fidelis, Hecatæus, Herodotus, Homer, Isidore of Seville, Juba, Onesicritus, Orosius, Philemon, Pliny, Priscian, Pytheas, Sedulius, Servius, Solinus, Statius Sebosus, Theodosius' Commissioners, Thucydides, Timosthenes, Virgil, Xenophon of Lampsacus.

To Pliny (in all) there are 21 quotations attributed and 37 references made; to Solinus, 40 references (36 quotations); to Isidore, 18 references; to Pytheas, 3; to Herodotus, 1 (on the Nile-flood); to Thucydides (Tuchidides), 1, on the name Sicania, for Sicily (viii. 3). Eight pieces of ancient poetry are quoted, the first being the twelve verses of the Missi of Theodosius; the second, third, fourth, sixth, and eighth, from Priscian; the fifth and seventh, from Virgil's Æneid, iii. 571, 572; iv. 245-251. The lines at the end of the ninth chapter are Dicuil's own fare-

well to his readers, and give us his exact date (cf. chs. v. 4; vii. 9, 31, 50; viii. 10, 11; ix. 9, 12, 13). He is careful to mark the authority of Virgil as exceptional. The Theodosian verses are considered elsewhere, in their proper place. The writer's native country, Ireland, is fixed by vii. 1–15, esp. § 6; as his date by ix. 13. The name Dicuil, Dicul, or Dichull (as Letronne points out, p. 8, etc., of his edition of 1814). is common to several Irish ecclesiastics and missionaries, e.g. (1) a pupil of St. Fursey, who wrote (c. A.D. 650) "Institutiones ad Monachos" ("Acta Sanctorum," Jan. ii. 40, under name Tidulla); (2) a hermit who died in 700, author of "Exhortations to the Western Saxons;" (3) an abbot of Bosenham (Bosham); (4) an abbot of Pahlacht of uncertain date; (5) an abbot of Kilmor, who died about 889; (6) an abbot of Innis Muredaich, who died in 871. Our Dicuil, if he can be identified with any of these, probably answers to Nos. 4 or 6.

material for geographical work; but he usually prefers the guidance of the fabulists or of the commissioners of Theodosius, who are unmentioned by any other writer, and whose historical reality cannot be assumed as certain.

More than half of his little treatise is composed of Plinian excerpts, either direct or through the medium of Solinus, which is his more usual course; next in amount come the references to Isidore of Seville and to Priscian's version of the meagre Periegesis of Dionysius; a bare notice suffices for the ancient geographers of real worth. Two of his most trusted guides, the "Cosmography" of Julius Cæsar and the "Chorography" of Augustus, are probably based upon the same fact—that survey of the resources, defences, and communications of the empire which was conceived by the Dictator, and resulted in the census, at the beginning of the Christian Era, when all the world was enrolled. What the originals may have been, we cannot tell; we can only identify, for practical purposes, the work quoted by Dicuil with the vitiated tradition known as that of Julius Æthicus,[1] and reaching back only to the fifth century. No true record of the first emperors could have been found to refer, as here quoted (vi. 20), to the camp of Moses on the Red Sea; where issued the arm of the Nile, or fresh-water canal, along which Fidelis sailed.

Further, although a great reader, Dicuil was far from being a good scholar. He repeatedly owns (*e.g.* vi. 27 ; ix. 11) that he has forgotten his references; his quotations are

---

[1] This is only an inference from Julius Æthicus and later writers (cf. Æthic., Procemium to the Cosmography), but Dicuil's statement is probably connected with some earlier reports of similar surveys, as in Pliny's account of Agrippa's roads in Gaul, and his measurements in that and other provinces, embodied in his map, and painted on the wall of the portico of Octavia in Rome (H. N. iii. 2, § 17; iv. 12, § 81; iv. 14, §§ 98, 102). Cf. Bunbury, Anc. Geog. ii. 177, 178, 693, 701.

often inaccurate, often quite beyond verification. His Greek was probably second-hand; and however much it may surprise us, there is no evidence of any knowledge of Ptolemy,[1] or any sympathy with his particular theories. Of some of the contradictions and shortcomings of his essay he was well aware. In his preface he warns us not to expect complete agreement between the reckonings of Pliny and those of Theodosius; we are only to be careful to give the preference to the latter, as a more thorough and reliable work.

Dicuil begins by telling us how the Emperor Saint Theodosius, in the fifteenth year of his reign,[2] sent out his commissioners to measure the length and breadth of the provinces of the empire; and how he himself proposes [3] to set forth their results, with the aid of what he has learnt from the younger Pliny.

Accepting the usual division of the world into three parts, as having come down from Augustus' Chorography or Survey, the Irish geographer proceeds to deal with Europe, and takes us through the provinces of the same from east to west, from Spain to Byzantium, giving the measurements of each. In all this, fortified as it is by the authority of Pliny, there is little to notice; except perhaps that the "Sea of Pontus" is made the eastern boundary of Italy; that the "Tuscan Sea,"[4] in like manner, becomes the southern limit of Achaia; and that the earliest name of New Rome is given us as "Logos."

In the next part of his first section or chapter, and before he moves off into Asia, Dicuil says a little about the

---

[1] For he considers the world, to east and south, as bounded by seas, and not by deserts; and following Plinian rather than Ptolemaic ideas of Africa, he brings up the Southern Ocean to the border of the Moorish country.

[2] Dic. i. 1.

[3] Prologue.

[4] "Egeo-Tuscan," Dic. i. 12.

countries to the north and north-east of the old empire,
from Germany and "Gothia" to Scythia, the Caspian lands,
and the Arctic and Seric Oceans.[1]

In Asia, to which the second chapter is given, we have
the "sea between Cyprus and Antioch" brought right
round to the north of Syria; "Arabia" in its wider meaning is extended westward to the Nile; the Taurus range is
made to stretch, as usual, across the whole length of the
continent in its prolongations of Caucasus, Elburz, and
Hindu Kush; and the Ganges with the Indian Ocean is
fixed as the term of the furthest east.

In Africa (the third chapter), the land of the Moors,
Numidians, and other North Sahara peoples, is said to run
out immediately to the Ethiopian or Southern Ocean; while
the common traditions (ultimately derived from the voyage
of Hanno of Carthage down the North-West Coast of Africa
more than a thousand years before) are duly recited—of
the Western Horn,[2] the Gorgon or Gorilla islands, and the
lofty mountain burning with eternal fires, called the Chariot
of the Gods. On the other hand, the story of the Satyrs
inhabiting these coasts is not related[3] with much confidence,
and doubt is thrown upon the alleged existence of anything
like an archipelago "throughout the whole of that sea."

We are next told[4] of the length and breadth of the
known world, from India to the Straits of Cadiz, and from the
Southern to the Northern Ocean,—a world which is considered

---

[1] But though this might be called
a tradition of the China Sea, under
its right name and place "the Ocean
of the Silk Country, in the Furthest
East," he shows no knowledge of
China itself; and a little later ex-
plicitly declares that India is the
limit of Asia towards the sunrising.
This is the implicit or explicit belief
of almost all early Christian science.

[2] Cf. Solinus (56. 10), who, like
Pliny, mistook the meaning of *keras*
in this connection, making it "headland," instead of "estuary." See
Letronne, Dicuil, p. 80; Casaubon
on Strabo, x. p. 704.

[3] Dic. iv. 3.

[4] Dic. v.

as "surrounded by water, and so to say swimming in it;"
and the result of this is very nearly the symmetrical
equation demanded by Cosmas, and favoured by most of
the lights of early mediæval science. The "longitude" of
6630 miles is almost exactly twice the 3348 of the earth's
"latitude." With this ends Dicuil's "Book of Measurements" properly speaking; and it is commended to the
reader with twelve Latin verses, professedly taken from the
original work of the commissioners of Theodosius, who
declare themselves in all their labours, to have followed
ancient precedents.[1]

In the next (sixth) chapter, on the principal rivers of
the world—the Nile, Euphrates, Tigris, Ganges, Indus, and
others—Dicuil begins to quote Solinus, and drops his
allusions to the Theodosian survey, though he continues to
make great use of Pliny and the catalogues of Julius
Æthicus. Herodotus[2] is referred to upon the question of
the annual Nile flood, and a strictly Plinian account is
given of the course of the great African river[3] from the
Atlantic to the Mediterranean.

As to the vexed point of the connection of the Nile with
the Red Sea, we have already seen how the narrative of the

[1] "Veterum Monumenta Secuti."
Cf. their lines :—

"Hoc opus egregium, quo mundi
　　summa tenetur,
Æquora, quo montes, fluvii, portus,
　　freta et urbes
Signantur, cunctis ut sit cognoscere
　　promptum,
Quicquid ubique latet, clemens
　　genus, inclita proles,
Ac per sæcla pius, totus quem vix
　　capit orbis,
Theodosius princeps venerando jus-
　　sit ab ore,

Confici, ter quinis aperit cum
　　fascibus annum . . .," etc.

The authorship of these lines was
attributed to the priest Sedulius, who
flourished about A.D. 410. Cf. "An-
thologia Vet. Lat." (1773), ii. 391,
etc.; Miller, "Weltkarte des Castorius," p. 66.

[2] Dic. vi. 4.

[3] Dic. vi. 7. On which Dicuil
quotes the same authorities as Solinus, viz. Pliny, the Punic Books (of
Hanno ?), and King Juba.

pilgrim Fidelis helped to establish the case in favour of this theory; another and a more mythical authority is also quoted in its support [1]—"the cosmography made in the consulship of Julius Cæsar and Mark Antony."

On the great rivers of Mesopotamia and India, Dicuil has not much to tell us, except in the way of extracts from Pliny and Solinus, which deal largely with the monsters of these distant regions; but as to the smaller streams, which are described from the "aforesaid cosmography" [2] recently discovered by the author, we have some independent and curious figuring.[3]

Thus the Jordan's 722 miles, the 897 of the Meander, the 825 of the Eurotas, contrast oddly with the 453 of the Ganges, or the 210 of the Dnieper (Borysthenes); and the Rhine, "rising in the Apennine Alps, and falling into the Western Ocean," though its length is more fairly stated at 552 miles, also gives colour to Dicuil's geography of rivers. So does the source of Ebro, in the "Assyrian (Asturian) Mountains" of Pyrenees.[4]

In the next chapter (the seventh), "on certain islands," which is the largest in the whole book, St. Isidore is added to the works of reference, notably as to the West African Islands (of which Dicuil knows no more than Solinus), and as to that Ultima Thule about which, as we have already seen, the Irish of this very time had gained so much new knowledge. Returning from its digression on the late discoveries in the Northern Ocean, our "Book of Measurements" becomes more and more exclusively a transcript of Solinus, St. Isidore, and Priscian's version of the old Greek Periegesis of Dionysius. Sometimes, however, the copyist is roused to protest. The

---

[1] Dic. vi. 20.
[2] Dic. vi. 37.
[3] Of the great rivers, Dicuil reckons

Euphrates at 862, Tigris at 895. Danube at 923, Ganges at 453.
[4] Dic. vi. 38–54.

statement of Julius Solinus, in his description of Germany, that elephants were unable to lie down, though clearly stated in authorities of such weight, could not pass.[1] For, says Dicuil, " the people of the Frankish kingdom certainly saw an elephant in the time of the Emperor Charles," when Haroun Al Rashid [2] sent the great beast (" Abu-Lubabah "), with his other presents,[3] to the court of his Christian ally. The arrival of these gifts was an event too recent and too striking to be yet forgotten ; and it is mentioned by several of the chroniclers. A Jew named Isaac, one of the envoys sent by Charles to the caliph, brought back the elephant to Italy in October, 801. It passed the winter at Vercelli, and did not attempt the passage of the Alps till the summer of 802. In July of that year it arrived at Aachen ; for eight years it accompanied the emperor in his marches and progresses ; and in 810 it died at " Lippia," on an expedition against the Danes.

Again, Dicuil disputes the statement that no part of the Nile flowed into the Red Sea, and relates the journey of Fidelis in disproof. A similar lack of faith is shown (viii. 25) towards the report of one Fabian, recorded by Pliny, on the depth of the deepest sea. He said, reported Dicuil, that it was a mile and a half (fifteen stadia) to the bottom of the waters—but who was to believe that Fabian could have sounded all the depths of the ocean ?

In the same way, a little later, the statement of Solinus,[4]

---

[1] Dic. vii. 35.

[2] Cf. Burton, Arab. Nights, Terminal Essay, iii. 1, lib. edit. viii. 123.

[3] Among them a dog (" Becerillo ") and a clepsydra, and fine stuffs. Cf. Einhardt; "Vita Caroli," cc. 16, 23, 24, 27, etc.; "Monk of St. Gall," 752, 761 (Dümmler); Annales Met-

tenses ad ann. 802, 810 ; and " Chroniques de St. Denys," ii. 1, 6 ; Annal. Francor. Fuldens. ad ann. 802; Fragm. Annal. Franc. and Annal Tiliani (Bouquet), as cited in Letronne's Dicuil, 150–152.

[4] Dicuil, bk. ix. 6.

about the " snowy summit of Atlas hidden above the clouds,"
is sharply criticised.   How could the offspring lie behind its
source ?   Snow, falling as it does from the clouds of heaven,
could be indeed a fine sight, laughs Dicuil, up above those
same clouds.

On the other hand, this rationalistic spirit deserts him
sometimes where it might have been more useful.   He
repeats contentedly enough the statement of Isidore [1] about
the narrow strait which alone separates Sardinia from the
" Land of the Phœnix " (Africa ?) ; he raises no protest
against the stories of the wolf-men of Scythia ; he seems
to fancy the Straits of Gibraltar must be of the same width
as those of Messina [2]—it was part of the symmetry of
geography that Spain and Africa, Italy and Sicily, should
be separated by a precisely similar channel.

Again, in his last chapter, " On the Highest Mountains,"
Dicuil gravely tells us that Pelion is two hundred and fifty
miles from base to summit, as had been measured by a
very learned man ; [3] and even if allowance be made for all
the *détours* of a winding path, along which the reckoning
may have been taken, this must remain among the curiosities
of legend.[4]   The height given for the Alps is not quite so
preposterous : the compiler had read in a book that he had
now forgotten, of an altitude of fifty miles.

Lastly, the curious table of the Seven Chief Things [5] in
the visible world, standing for all the invisible things that
are not expressly mentioned, is quite in the same spirit
of studious credulity which had nearly as strong a hold

---

[1] Dic. vii. 49.   Dic. viii. 13, 14, is
inconsistent with this; so vi. 28
clashes with vii. 36, etc. (*vide* Parthey's preface).

[2] Dic. viii. 18.

[3] Dicæarchus. See Pliny, H.N. ii.

65, which gives D.'s measurement as
1250 *paces*.

[4] Dic. ix. 10, 11.

[5] In Dicuil literally, " Of the
Seven Things that follow in the
Cosmography " (viii. 26–31).

over Dicuil as it had over his models, Solinus, Isidore, and the rest.

There were, he declares, exactly 2 seas, 72 islands, 40 mountains, 65 provinces, 281 towns, 55 rivers, and 116 peoples,—for so he had read in the "Cosmography" of Julius Cæsar and Mark Antony. Still more curious, perhaps, is his dependence [1] on Solinus for the measurements of Britain, when from his own knowledge—a knowledge so comparatively full and original about the coasts and islands of Scotland—he might have supplied a better account of the great island only separated from him by the "restless and billowy" waters of St. George's Channel. [2]

V. The Minor Geographers.

We have now had examples of all the principal types of Christian theory or science in geography during this time—the first six hundred years of Christian supremacy. The fabulists, the statisticians, and the cosmographers have come before us in certain instances more completely than we could find elsewhere. Solinus and Cosmas in particular transcend all their rivals and imitators. It will be convenient, however, in this place to supplement the testimony of our principals by that of their seconds, to improve our understanding of the duel then being fought out between the forces of free thought and belief. For this purpose we shall have to notice some of the scientific references of writers who are not properly geographers; but who, in attempting to make their system of theology universal, were obliged, among other things, to offer some kind of answer to the questions of geography. The result of such an inquiry will not be very different from the preceding. As

[1] Dic. viii. 20.   [2] Dic. viii. 22.

the interest of the time was turned away altogether from
observations of natural fact, we cannot expect more from
the amateur geography of professed theologians than we
have already had from the professional geography of amateur
divines. Men like Augustine are entirely concerned with
human nature as a moral problem; and so their utterances
upon physical questions bear little relation to the ability
of the thinker. For these utterances of theirs are not
merely traditional, but represent a tradition of ignorance,
and even of popular prejudice against scientific naturalism.
In other words, the Fathers of the Church were both un-
trained in scientific method and hostile to it, and with but
few exceptions declared for a cosmography, not of reason,
but of revelation.

Among the earlier Christian doctors three points of
view may be distinguished. A few, like Origen, tried to
reconcile pagan and scriptural views by allegorical inter-
pretations of the sacred text. A few others professed to
abstain altogether from profane discussions.[1] But nearly
all the Fathers rejected every kind of compromise; and
their general view and temper may be sufficiently gathered,
in the first place, from their language on the fundamental
question of the Shape of our Earth. Thus Lactantius, as we
have seen before, repudiates the idea of a round world, and
consequent antipodes, as flying in the face of the Bible and
reason alike (c. A.D. 300).[2] Augustine and Isidore repeat
his objections in more measured language, like Chrysostom,

[1] Cf. John Philoponus, "On the Creation of the World," iii. 13, 58, 79, 114, 119, 120, 134, 135.

[2] "Divine Institutions," iii. 9, 24. Cf. also Santarem, Essai sur Cosm., i. 314, 315; and Brooke Montain, "Summary of the Writings of Lactantius." Philostorgius, in his fifth-century Ecclesiastical History, was said to reproduce one of the main points of Lactantius—the impossibility of connection between the north and south temperate zones, across the ocean which separated them; but this does not appear in the epitome that Photius has preserved.

Athanasius, and Procopius of Gaza; while Diodorus of Tarsus, and Severianus of Galaba anticipate Cosmas in an attempt to replace the spherical heresies, which they rejected, by a Christian system (c. A.D. 378–380).[1]   Again, Eusebius of Cæsarea, St. Basil the Great, and St. Ambrose, like St. Augustine, hold fast by the literal interpretation of the Biblical Heaven of Heavens, Windows of the Sky, and Waters above the Firmament.[2]   Basil, indeed, challenges any one to prove that the double heaven of the Christians, so ingeniously arranged as a reservoir for the waters, is not easier to believe than the spheres of his pagan friends, boxed up one within the other.   Cyril of Jerusalem bursts into praise of the Divine wisdom which kept the rain stored up above the firmament for the use of the creation;[3] others (e.g. St. Isidore and St. Basil) admire the forethought which tempered the heat of the upper region of ethereal fire with the cold of these waters.[4]   And just as the theologians derived from the Bible their constantly repeated language about the plurality of the heavens and the shape of the world, so, from various texts in the Psalms and the Prophets, they developed doctrines upon the movements of the stars, and the place of angels in the government of the universe— doctrines which, as we have seen, were pushed to their furthest extreme by Cosmas.   The disciple was not before

[1] Cf., for Diodorus, in Photius, Biblioth., cod. 223; for Severianus, ibid., cods. 59, 96, 231, 232, and his "Six Orations on the Creation" in Migne, Pat. Græc. lvi.

[2] Cf. Euseb., Comment. on Isaiah (Col. Nov. Patr., ii. 511B); Basil, Hexæm. Hom. iii. 3; iii. 7; Ambrose, On Gen. ii. 4 : also, for classical suggestions, Plato, Rep., x. 616; Aristophanes, "Clouds," ver. 372.

[3] Cyril, Catech., ix. p. 76.

[4] In his usual way, Origen tried to explain away the upper waters as angelic powers; but Augustine, though conscious that the texts in question, if understood literally, were above reason and experience, declared them to be insoluble and necessary of belief, "since the authority of [this] Scripture is greater than the power of all human skill" (On Gen. ii. 5, 9; Works, iii. pp. 133–135 [Ben. edit.]; "City of God," xi. 34).

his master; and we need not be surprised to find in Theodore of Mopsuestia expressions on all these points which
the "Christian Topography" merely amplifies. The great
Nestorian teacher [1] dogmatises with vigour on the useful
work of the angels in looking after the stars; on the proportions of the world, with its length double of its breadth; and
on the great mountains in the North.

Even the famous comparison of the world with a tent or
tabernacle, so laboriously worked out by the monk of Alexandria, is suggested by Diodorus of Tarsus,[2] and supported
by similar arguments and texts. Once again, the foundation of the earth on the "stability" of God, rather than
on the equilibrium of a sphere, is a commonplace of
Christian theology from the third to the thirteenth century.[3]
Those divines who inclined towards a compromise with
science, generally found it advisable to use language to
disguise their meaning; sometimes they were obliged to
retract and apologise. Thus Eusebius, in his Commentary
on Isaiah, carefully unsays what he had admitted in an
earlier treatise on the Psalms; and Photius, though one
of the most enlightened of Christian thinkers, is studiously
vague when touching upon cosmographical writers in his
great Encyclopædia.

Compromisers like Origen, and freethinkers like John
Philoponus, were commonly branded with the name of
heretics—a fitting reward for their disgraceful indifference to the right number of heavens, or their insolent

[1] *I.e.* in his lost work, "On the
Creation," as quoted and attacked
by John Philoponus, "De Creatione
Mundi," i. 16, p. 31; 17, p. 32; iii.
10, pp. 119, 124, 125.

[2] Cf. Photius, "Bibliotheca," cod.
223 (Hœsch.)

[3] Cf. the anonymous "Quaestiones
et Responsiones ad Orthodoxos," 130,
p. 481A; Vincent of Beauvais, vi. 4,
372c; and a fragment in the Bibl.
Nat. (Paris), § 54, fo. 193.

contempt for such cherished beliefs as the stellar occupations of the angels.[1]

As time went on, and theology proceeded further and further in systematising knowledge under its own terms and concepts, its language on the principles of geography and astronomy became, of course, more definite. Thus, what St. Hilary thought presumptuous, St. Augustine approved, and Bede improved.[2] The various strata of the atmosphere were all named and described in fourfold, fivefold, and sevenfold divisions, elaborated from the wildest and most fanciful of the Neo-platonists.[3]

The primitive Greek legends of the sun passing behind a wall at night, and so going to his own place,[4] reappear with the added strength of Hebrew hyperbole in Severianus of Gabala and other traditionalists, of whom John the Toiler makes an easy prey. In the same way, the early Oriental conceptions of the earthly paradise recur in the poem of St. Avitus, "On the Creation" (A.D. 523), which, almost in the language of Cosmas, but under the license of poetry, describes how, beyond India, where meet the confines of earth and heaven, lies that asylum from which the first of sinners was driven forth, placed among lofty mountains, inaccessible to mortals, behind eternal barriers—the flaming swords with which the Lord God shut off all access to the tree of life.

And these were only typical examples of early Christian

---

[1] Cf. John Philoponus, i. 12, p. 25; Origen against Celsus, vi. p. 289 (Spenc.); Photius, cod. 36, p. 9; cod. 223, p. 362 (Hœsch).

[2] Like Raban Maur, of Mainz, in the ninth century.

[3] E.g. air, ether, Olympus, the heavenly fire, the firmament, the angelic and divine heavens: cf. St.

Augustine on Gen. xii.; "City of God," vii. 6, p. 630; Basil, Hex. Hom. i. 2, p. 10E, and the excellent summary of all these vagaries in Letronne's article, in the Révue des Deux Mondes for March 15, 1834; and in Marinelli, Erdkunde.

[4] Ecclesiastes, i. 5.

theorizing in the region of geography and cosmography. The position of the Garden of Eden; the habitat of the people of Gog Magog and other monstrous races; and the existence of a literal centre for the earth-circle—were problems which exercised the patristic mind only less than the great controversy upon the "Spherical," "Tabernacular," or other shape of the world itself.

I. As to the earthly Paradise, the plain word of Scripture [1] compelled most theologians to place it in the Furthest East, though a minority inclined to give a symbolic meaning to the crucial words, "The Lord God planted a garden *eastward* in Eden, . . . and placed cherubim at the east of the garden, to keep the way of the tree of life." Augustine here, as elsewhere, shows himself inclined to compromise, as well became one who attempted such a task as the re-statement of the whole Catholic Faith. His knowledge was too many-sided, and his intelligence was too keen, for him not to perceive the importance of a certain liberality of temper in a creed which aspired to conquer the world; and his treatment of the question of the terrestrial Paradise is a good example of his method. For himself, he holds fast to the real existence of Eden, and the literal sense of Scripture on its position; but he allows any one who will, to give the texts at issue a symbolical meaning.[2] To the same effect, though more doubtfully, speaks St. Isidore of Seville, who in so many ways reproduces, at the end of the sixth century, the spirit and method of the Bishop of Hippo in the fifth. In one place the Spanish Doctor repeats the traditional language about Eden, placed in the East, blessed with perpetual summer, but shut off from the approach of man

[1] Gen. ii. 4; iii. 24.

[2] De Civ. Dei, xiii. ch. 21; see also Eucherius, Comm. on Genesis (Max. Bibl. Vet. Pat. vi. 874), and

A. Graf's interesting essay on the "Legends of the Terrestrial Paradise" (Turin, 1878).

by the fiery wall which reached almost to the Heaven; yet elsewhere he seems to countenance a purely figurative sense.[1]

The ordinary conclusion of the more philosophic school of Churchmen is perhaps expressed by Moses Bar-Cepha, " Bishop of Bethraman and Guardian of sacred things in Mozal " near Bagdad, about A.D. 900.[2]   In his "Commentary on Paradise," the ingenious prelate solves past difficulties in the spirit of Hegel himself.   The terrestrial Eden had one existence under two conditions, visible and invisible, corporeal and incorporeal, sensual and intellectual.   As pertaining to this world, it existed, he considers, in a land which was on, but not of, the earth that we inhabit.   For it lay on higher ground; it breathed a purer air; and though many of the saints had fixed it in the East, it was really beyond our ken.

From Augustine onwards, through the writings of Eucherius of Lyons,[3] of St. Basil the Great, and many others, something of this tendency to compromise between the literal meaning of Scripture and the tacit opposition of geography, may be traced in the attempt to give reality to the earthly Paradise ; and the same comes out in the conjecture of Severian of Gabala, adopted by Cosmas and by many of the traditionalists, that the rivers of Eden dived under the earth for a long space before reappearing in our world as Nile, Euphrates, Tigris and Pison.[4]

[1] His scepticism is expressed in "De Differentiis," i. 10 ; his traditionalism in "Origins," xiv. 3 (De Asia).

[2] Migne's editor of "Moses" in Pat. Græc. cxi. cc. 482–608 (1863) places him later, about A.D. 950; but Marinelli, Erdkunde 20, 21, dates him about A.D. 700, doubtless with the assent of S. Günther and L. Neumann, who are responsible for the enlarged German edition of Marinelli's admirable essay. The most interesting passages of Moses' geography are in part i. chs. 1, 2, 7–9, 11–14.

[3] "Commentary on Genesis."

[4] Severian of Gabala, "Oration," v. 6. According to Severian, this subterranean course was to prevent men from tracking their way up to Paradise. Cf. Philostorgius, iii. 7–12.

Homeric and other pre-Christian fancies led many in the early Christian period still to look for Paradise in the North among the Hyperboreans; in the South among the blameless Ethiopians; or in the West in the Isles of the Blessed, of the Hesperides, or of Fortune. Thus Capella, who was probably a pagan survival at the beginning of the most brilliant age of patristic literature, naturally enough looks for his Elysium, "where the axis of the world is ever turning" at the Northern pole,[1] but when we find Archbishop Basil of Novgorod speculating about a Paradise in the White Sea,[2] we have a better illustration of the undying vigour of the oldest and most poetic of physical myths, under almost any changes of politics and religion.

But it was not enough to have decided *where* the earthly Paradise was to be looked for; devout inquiry insisted on a further study of the question. Why was the Garden of Eden placed where Scripture and tradition said? To this query there were various answers. Because spices and incense come from the East, replied the Ravennese geographer; because light has there its origin, said the more ingenious Severian. Man (to his mind) was first placed by God at the extremity of the Orient, that he might recognise in the course of daylight a symbol of his life; and, in the rising again of the heavenly bodies, a suggestion of his resurrection.[3] On the other hand, Raban Maur of Mainz, in later time, reproduces the views of the more liberal thinkers; suggests that the true position of Eden was uncertain; and even implies that the tradition of its Oriental site was founded upon a misconception of the Hebrew text.

[1] Capella, vi. 664.
[2] See Karamsin's "Russian History," as cited by Marinelli, Erdk., p. 22, n. 84; and by Cardinal Zurla, "Vantaggi derivati alla Geografia,"

etc., p. 44.
[3] See the Ravennese, pp. 14, 15, in Pinder and Parthey's edition; Severian, De Mundi Creat.; Raban Maur, "On Genesis," bk. i. ch. 12.

II. Another fruitful topic of speculation was the being and dwelling-place of the monstrous peoples supposed to lie on the outer edge, as it were, of the habitable earth.   Among these, the chief place undoubtedly belongs, both in history and in legend, to the races of Gog Magog.   For on one side they may be said to represent the Huns and other more savage enemies of the Roman world; and from another point of view they are connected with the mythical achievements of Alexander the Great, with the dimly realised fact of the wall of China and other Asiatic barriers of civilisation against barbarism, and with many popular fancies as to the terrors of a Last Day or world-collapse.

To the theologians, the crucial facts about these half-human vampires were recorded in three texts—of Genesis, Ezekiel, and the Apocalypse [1]—which pictured their invasions in times past from the northern parts "as a cloud to cover the land," and foretold their reappearance when Satan should be loosed from prison and go forth to deceive the nations in the four quarters of the earth.   From these it was clear, by the same Biblical interpretation which placed Eden at the end of the East, that Gog Magog was to be put in the extremity of the North.   But where precisely?   Following Jewish tradition, St. Jerome advises us to search "in Scythia beyond the Caucasus, and near the Caspian Sea"—then usually supposed to be an inlet of the Arctic Ocean; [2]—and in this conclusion most writers of the Patristic Age were disposed to agree.   Some, however, attached a symbolical

---

[1] Gen. x. 2; Ezek., chs. xxxviii., xxxix.; Apoc. xx. 8, 9.

[2] Jerome on Ezekiel and Genesis, ad loc. cit.; Augustine, De Civ. Dei, xx. 11; Ambrose, " De Fide ad Gratian," ii. 4. See F. Lenormant, " Magog " in the Museum of the Société des Lettres et des Sciences, Louvain, 1882, vol. i. p. 948, etc.; also Isidore, " Origins," ix. 2, xiv. 3; and the commentaries of Andrew and Aretes of Cæsarea on the Apocalypse—the first apparently written about 400, the second about 540.

meaning to the Gog Magogs, just as to the Eden of Scripture; and the main interest of theological study in this
direction was absorbed in considering who the Gog Magogs
might be, rather than in speculating as to where they lived.
We see this in the "Gothic," "Vandalic," "Hunnic," and
other identifications, not only of Jerome, but also of
Augustine (who on the whole is disposed to take a figurative
view), of Ambrose, of Isidore, and of the successors of
St. Basil, Andrew and Aretes of Cæsarea.

Exact reference to the words of Ezekiel fixed the
"princes of Gog and the land of Magog" within a reasonable distance of Palestine; but the tendency of the legend
was to move the site steadily northwards and eastwards as
the connection grew more close with the Alexander of
Eastern myth; with the wall that he raised against the
savages of Tartary; and with the altars which marked the
furthest point of his advance. The fortifications which
the Sassanid kings of Persia had raised in the passes of
the Caucasus, as when Chosroes Nushirvan strengthened the
defences of Derbend, were naturally connected by a later
time with the wall of Iskander, and the Gog Magogs whom
that wall shut off in their northern darkness; and the Arabs,
as we shall see,[1] gave more definiteness to this popular
fallacy: but not even in Arab literature do we find a more
elaborate treatment of these half true, half fabulous nomades
than in the Christian travel romance of Æthicus of Istria;
nor a happier conjecture of their origin than in the suggestion of Godfrey of Viterbo,[2] who identifies them with the
Lost Ten Tribes.

The Gog Magogs were the chief, but not the only,

---

[1] As in the Koran, chs. 15, 18, etc.,
Massoudy, etc. See pp. 407, 414, 433
of the supplementary chapter in this

volume.

[2] Though falling beyond our period
in this section.

variety of monstrous people whom mediæval fancy adopted and elaborated from earlier mythology. The Giants, the Pigmies, the Cyclops, the Dog-faced men, the Headless, Hermaphrodite, and other tribes of classical legend, received the warm approval and support of many Christian doctors, and the qualified assent even of Augustine, Bede, and Isidore. The latter is at special pains to vindicate the existence of portents, "which are not, as Varro said, things against nature, because they exist by Divine will, but are only against what has been *observed in* nature." Jerome is one of the few theologians who has serious doubts on the reality of Centaurs and similar delightful variations of the common order; but not even he ventures to impugn the Phœnix of Arabia, which held almost the certainty of a revealed truth from Pope Clement to Albert the Great.[1]

In the ninth century, however, a controversy broke out between Ratramm of Corbey and St. Rimbert as to the truth or falsehood of the tale of the dog-headed race, and the alleged descent of some mediæval personages from this people was freely challenged. The "Sciapods," or "shadow-footed" people of the tropics, whose huge feet served them for shade against the sun; the "Antipods" of the disputed southern continent, who grew all awry; the mouthless men of Megasthenes; and the "Indians who lived on the smell of fruit,"—races whom the clearer thinkers and more exact students of the classical period[2] had rejected along with

---

[1] See Isidore, "Origins" (De Portentis), xi. 3, xii. 2; Augustine, De Civ. Dei, xvi. 8; Jerome, Comment. on Isaiah xiv. 4; on Daniel iv. 1; "Life of St. Paul the Hermit," ch. 6; and "Against Vigilantius;" also Bede, on Apoc. xxi. 19; Orosius, ii. 14; "Acta Sanctor," July 25, p. 146.

[2] See, for instance, Strabo, ii. 1. 9, xvii. 2. 2; Lucretius, De Rer. Nat. iv.; Ovid, Trist. iv., Eleg. vii. 11, Metamorph. xii.; Lucan, Pharsal. iii.; Pliny, H. N. x. 2; vii. 48 (in spite of his fabulous tendency); and, more strongly, Xenophon, Lucian, Cicero, Seneca, Galen, and even Plutarch. Cf. Leopardi, "Errori popolari degli antichi," pp. 248, 257–259; and Marinelli, "Erdkunde," pp. 33–35.

Nymphs, Centaurs, and Cyclops, started into fresh life in the writings and the maps of the early mediæval time.

III. Once more, early Christian thought devoted itself with extraordinary zeal to the conception of a Middle Point, navel, or centre of the earth-surface, whether this surface were considered as circular or square in shape. Two texts of Ezekiel and two of the Psalms [1] were supposed to prove that Jerusalem, where God had "worked salvation in the midst of the earth," was this central point. "For thus saith the Lord, This is Jerusalem; I have set her *in the midst* of the nations and countries that are round about." We have already seen how Arculf, on his visit to Jerusalem, soon after the Moslem conquest, was actually shown a column which professed to mark the umbilical spot; tradition had thus, by his time, already taken action, and proved its case by a monument, which itself became a starting-point for new legend; but the tradition was far older than Arculf. It may be found in St. Jerome's "Commentary on Ezekiel" of A.D. 367; in the poem of the Pseudo-Tertullian against Marcion; in the similar verses of St. Victorinus of Poictiers " On the Cross of the Lord;" and in Eutychius of Alexandria, who records an *obiter dictum* of the Caliph Omar, to the effect that the place where Jacob's ladder touched the earth was clearly the central point. At the beginning of Justinian's reign the pilgrim Theodosius (or an editor of his narrative) is content with the more modest view of Jerusalem as only " the navel of all the region" of *Judea;* while the Ravennese geographer seems to prefer a secular middle point in his system; apparently his native place was good enough for him.[2] But the weight of Christian opinion, as time went

[1] Ezek. v. 5, xxxviii. 12; Ps. lxxiv. (lxxiii.) 12; lxxxv. (lxxxiv.) 11.

[2] See Jerome on Ezek. v. 5, etc.,

and other texts as cited above; Pseudo-Tertullian against Marcion, ii. ll. 197, etc. (" Golgotha . . . Hic

on, pronounced more and more decisively in favour of Jerusalem; unlike many other superstitions, this one appeared even to increase in strength as the Middle Ages emerged into a higher culture; and we shall see how it gains an ever stronger hold upon Western map-making till the thirteenth century, and retains some degree of favour far into the fifteenth. Here we can only point out (without reference to crusading and post-crusading instances [1]) that the anti-scientific prejudices of the earlier Church, between Constantine and Charlemagne, were largely responsible for establishing and supporting one of the most persistent of mediæval misconceptions. Not that it was Christian in its origin. The classical idea of Delphi, the Hindu notion of Mount Meru (the Arabic Arim), were both older than the Fathers of the Church, and helpful to them in the way of suggestion; in this case—as in the analogous superstitions of a Double or Manifold Heaven, an Upper or Ethereal Fire, a Northern or other Cupola of the Earth, and a Ministry of Spirits as the controllers, movers, or even essences of the heavenly bodies—the patristic theology was not to blame for begetting false views of the natural world, but only for adopting and strengthening the more fanciful and unscientific part of the tradition that it inherited, while it slighted and cast into forgetfulness so great a part of the solid achievements of the older physical inquiry.[2]

Medium Terræ est, Hic est Victoria signum"); Victorinus, De Cruce Dom. v. 1, etc. ("Est locus ex omni medium quem credimus orbe Golgotha"); Eutychius, cited in Marinelli, "Erdkunde," p. 75, n. 39, and by Leopardi, "Errori," p. 207; also Theodosius the pilgrim (preface), compared with Arculf i. 13. Marinelli, "Erdkunde," p. 74, argues for

Constantinople as the centre of the Ravennese geographer; we have discussed this point on p. 390.

[1] Such as Sæwulf's account of "Compas" in Jerusalem, A.D. 1102.

[2] Cf. the classical and other suggestions for the notions (1) of a manifold heaven—in (? pseudo) Philolaus, who provided for ten æthereal spaces; (2) of an upper fire—also in Philolaus,

From all this, it may be seen whether the more famous names of the early Church add much or little to the geographers we have already examined. But besides these scattered references, there are a few more formal statements, less representative and less important than those of Dicuil, Cosmas, Solinus, and the Ravennese, yet worthy of some closer attention. A few of these are the work of eminent men, such as Isidore; the greater number have a more obscure parentage; but in all, or nearly all, there is evident a blending of those three influences to which we have referred, as governing the science or pseudo-science of the time. The story-teller, the measurement-maker, the physical speculator—these divide the interest of the Christian world.

And among these lesser lights, our first example is Martianus Capella. In the sixth book of his "Nuptials of Philology and Mercury," or Survey of the Seven Liberal Arts, under the title of "Geometry," he discusses the shape and position of the earth, its girth or circuit, its zones or climates, its length and breadth, its main divisions, and other matters belonging to geography.

Our apology for mentioning this at all must be the same as in the case of Solinus. Its writer was probably a pagan of the third or fourth century, but his work became a standard authority in many places and periods of the Middle Ages; it is quoted as a text-book by Gregory of

---

reproduced in Severian of Gabala, De Creat. Mundi, and in Marius Victor's "Poetical Commentary on Genesis," i. 65, etc.

" Æthereis ne desint pabula flammis,
  Et nimium calor ima petens ali-
    menta sequendo," etc. ;

(3) of an earth summit—Aristotle, Meteor. i. 1a; Virgil, "Georgics"

(i. 240–243); Hippocrates, § 10 of "De aere et aquis," reproduced in a number of mediæval writers, especially Cosmas, Æthicus of Istria, chs. 12, 18, 20, etc. ; (4) of spirits as lighting up the heavens, or at least operating as princes of the powers of the air—Varro in Augustine, De Civ. Dei, vii. 6; Appuleius, "De Deo Socratis."

Tours and John of Salisbury, among many others; and its place in the Hereford map, and similar productions of the Dark Age school of map-makers, is of primary importance.

Martianus Minneius Felix Capella may be fairly supposed, from the internal evidence supplied by his own writings, to have been a Latin lawyer, resident at Carthage some time before the Vandal invasion of A.D. 439, or even before the re-foundation of Byzantium by Constantine (c. A.D. 330). It has been conjectured, but without any sufficient proof,[1] that he lived and wrote in the reign of Gordian, in the middle of the third century. In any case, he shows, as we have said, no trace of Christianity, no knowledge of the new name and dignity of Constantinople; on the other hand, he unquestionably resembles Solinus in matter and Appuleius in style: and, without attempting to fix his place more precisely, we may take him as representative of the last half century of the pagan Empire.

He begins his summary of geography by defining the form of the earth. This he considers to be, not flat or concave, but round and globular, as Dicæarchus had long ago laid down. He laughs at the notion of rain coming down "into the lap of the land" in anything more than a popular sense;[2] and he quotes the evidence of astronomers like Eratosthenes, and of travellers like Pytheas, upon the length of the day in different parts as proof of the globular theory. The dimensions of the earth-circle he repeats from Eratosthenes as 25,000 miles.[3]

From this he proceeds to give the customary divisions of five zones, "of which three are intemperate by an excess of contrary qualities." Two are uninhabitable from the cold,

---

[1] Cf. Eyssenhardt's preface (Teubner edit.).

[2] Cap., vi. § 590, etc.

[3] Cap., § 596; 252,000 stades. In all this he possibly utilized the lost work of Varro, on astronomy.

at the poles ; one from the heat, in the centre.   On the extent
of the habitable region known to us in the north temperate
zone—its length and breadth—he refers to the authority
of Ptolemy and of Pythagoras, "most learned of men," but
declares his own knowledge to be quite as good as theirs,[1]
" for I, too, have been over all these (countries), nor does any
part of earth,[2] as I think, remain unknown to me."   " Navigation on every side," satisfactorily attested, to Capella's mind,
the all-encircling ocean.   As to the North, he wanted no
better proof than the voyage of Augustus Cæsar round
Germany to Scythia.   What Rome left undone to the North
East, had been accomplished by the Macedonians of Seleucus
and Antiochus, who had sailed from India into the Caspian,
which, as the belief of his time required, Capella made into
a bay or gulf corresponding to the Red Sea.   Most of the
Southern Ocean between Spain and Arabia had been
" ploughed " by the victorious ships of Great Alexander.
Under Caligula, too, pieces of wrecked vessels had been
drifted from Europe, round Africa, to Asia.   In much earlier
times Hanno had sailed from Carthage to the borders of
Arabia, and this feat had been repeated in later ages, as by
Eudoxus in his flight from Egypt to the Pillars of Hercules,
reported in Cornelius Nepos, and by an unnamed trader
mentioned by Cælius Antipater.[3]

From these interesting guesses at truth in unfounded or
misconceived legends, Capella goes on to copy Pliny and
Solinus upon the boundaries of the three great continents,
upon the Straits of Gades or Gibraltar, and upon the Nile
dividing Asia and Africa, and "intersecting the embrace of
earth by a multitude of streams."   Then describing the

---

[1] Cap., §§ 602, 603, 609.
[2] One or two references to Isidore
are interpolated in the text at this
point—on the length of the inhabited
earth, etc. Cap., §§ 616, 617, 618, 621.
[3] Cap., §§ 619, 620.

various provinces after the same authorities,[1] he repeats, though in a somewhat soberer manner, many of the favourite stories, such as those which touched upon the foundation of Lisbon by Ulysses (at a point which Capella evidently put, like Solinus, in the position of our Finisterre); upon the perpetual motion among the Hyperboreans of the North, "where the axis of the world is ever turning;" upon Mount Atlas, which "rises to the confines of the lunar circle beyond the power of clouds;" upon the "Niger" in the heart of Africa, "having the same nature as the Nile;" upon the "reddening" fountain on the shores of the Red Sea; upon the Iron Beams barring the entrance of the Caspian Gates; upon the "down" which the silk-merchants washed off the trees of the Far East, and of which they make their products; and upon the marvels of India, where men reached fabulous height and age, worshipped Hercules, and never slept by day.[2]

Next to Capella, though of far less importance, we may perhaps take Macrobius, who is also, in all probability, a pagan, and in particular a Neo-Platonist, a figure in the great struggle of the early fifth century, when Christianity finally triumphed and Old Rome finally sank, and when Augustine and Orosius argued against the alleged connection of these two facts. Largely read as he was in the Middle Ages, his Commentary on Cicero's "Dream of Scipio" was an additional support to the vulgar error of an impassable torrid zone[3] to the south of the known world.

---

[1] Cap., from § 627.

[2] Cap., §§ 664, 667, 673, 677, 691, 692, 693, 697. In another of Capella's sections (viii. 857), some have supposed a suggestion of the solar system. "It is here so distinctly maintained that Mercury and Venus revolve round the sun," and their position with regard both to the sun and earth is so correctly defined, that Copernicus, who quotes the "Nuptials," may have gained some encouragement for his theory from this source (cf. W. Ramsay in the Dict. Gk. and Rom. Biog., art. "Capella").

[3] Mac. i. 22.

He repeats the ordinary language about an ocean [1] filling
the equatorial zone; about the five climates; and about a
possible southern world beyond the tropics, inhabited by
beings unknown and inaccessible to us. His system has
been somewhat too positively compared [2] to that of Cosmas,
because of its admitting an outer rim of land surrounding
the ocean, which itself surrounds our earth; but this likeness is merely accidental, arising from his language about
the Antipodean earth. In many respects he is strictly
Ptolemaic, and declares for a round world, immovable in
the centre of the universe; like Ptolemy, again, he inclines
to the view that the external sea, supposed to be of vast
extent, is really small: but, unlike him, he makes the same
terminate in every direction the inhabited earth, forming
it in the shape of a lozenge, narrow at the extremities and
broader in the middle. Finally, he supports the scientific
tradition of terrestrial gravitation, by charmingly circular
arguments of his own. All bodies are drawn to the earth,
he tells us, because it is immovable in the centre; it is
immovable, because it occupies the lowest place in the
Universal Sphere; and it must occupy this place, because
all bodies are drawn towards it.

The treatise of St. Basil the Great of Cæsarea, on the
six days of Creation (the Hexaemeron), has, of course, like
much of Cosmas' "Topography," only occasional reference to
geographical ideas, properly so called; but it is noteworthy,
in spite of its shortcomings, for its comparative caution
and good sense. We have seen how, in several instances,
the Father echoes the traditional absurdities of the
"Scriptural" theorists on the shape of the universe. It is
only fair to repeat more definitely in this place, that Basil's

---

[1] Mac. ii. 9.   [2] By Letronne, *Révue des Deux Mondes*, March 15, 1834.

attitude in general is markedly different from that of the Christian extremists; that he is usually content with a neutral tone towards the Ptolemaic and other doctrines of pagan science; and that the dogmas which he attacks, such as that of the eternity of matter, have rarely been supposed till recent times to be reconcilable with the religious belief of a creation by a personal God. The Hexaemeron is perhaps worthy of some brief treatment as a whole, if only as an antidote to Cosmas; as a proof that the Christian Church of the fourth century [1] contained men who could speak and write upon "cosmography" in a more reasonable spirit; and as evidence of the survival of many parts of the old science in the new theology.

In the course of these nine homilies upon the opening chapters of Genesis, which together compose the instruction delivered by Basil to his co-religionists upon the initial and underlying facts of nature, we have first of all a discussion on the "Heaven and Earth;" then a lengthy explanation of the firmament, the heavenly bodies and their influences; lastly, a discussion of the various forms of life in the sea, in the air, and upon the land. Among other things, natural history is given us in abundant measure, mixed, as in Pliny or Ælian, with plenty of fable,[2] but showing at any rate

[1] The date of the Hexaemeron is uncertain, but it must have been between A.D. 350 and 379. It was translated into Latin by Eustathius Afer (c. A.D. 440), and was imitated both in style and matter by Ambrose, and by the English Ælfric, abbot of St. Albans, A.D. 969. There are many useful notes in the recent edition of the "Nicene and post-Nicene Fathers," vol. viii. (1895). See also Fialon ("Étude sur St. Basile"), who has worked out especially the connection of the Hexaemeron with Aristotle, and above all with the "Meteorologica" and the "De Cælo."

[2] As in the story of the viper and the sea-lamprey in Hom. vii. 5, borrowed from Ælian, Hist. An., ix. 66, but contradicted by Athenæus, vii. p. 312. "The viper, cruelest of reptiles, unites itself to the sea-lamprey, and announcing its presence by a hiss, calls it from the depths to conjugal union." The application of the story is also noteworthy:

a remarkable book-knowledge of birds, beasts, and reptiles. Just in the same way Basil is well acquainted with older inquiries on the shape of the world, and its component parts; and with many details of geography in the strict sense of that word. Thus the Greek conception of an order or law of nature is present to his mind along with his belief in the personal action of a Creator; and by many an instance he shows his knowledge of, and interest in, the past discoveries of physical science. True, he never does more than repeat in these matters; but his profession was theology, and for his purpose it was enough to reproduce the best authorities with discrimination and respect. We do not gather from him, as from some other theologians, that the study of nature in itself was an accursed thing, or that the Greek physicists were only in pursuit of "laborious vanity." He refuses to commit himself for or against the Ptolemaic astronomy; he declines to enter into the difficulties of the world's support in space, of the balance of the four elements, and so forth; and after summarising the opinions of "fine speakers," and especially of Aristotle, he concludes with a natural turn of pulpit oratory,[1] "If anything in this system appears probable to you, keep your admiration for the *source* of such perfect order, for the Wisdom of God." [2]

Dared Basil admit the roundness of the earth and the existence of antipodes? Here, again, his habitual caution makes an answer somewhat doubtful. He refers [3] to the stars

"However hard and fierce a husband may be, the wife should bear with him. . . . He strikes you, but he is your husband. He is a drunkard, but he is united to you by nature. He is brutal, but he is henceforth one of your members, and the most precious of all."

[1] Hex., hom. i. 10.

[2] Again, "Whether we say that the earth rests upon itself or rides upon the waters, we must still recognise that all is sustained by the Creator's power. Let us not disquiet ourselves about essence, but say with Moses, 'God created.'"

[3] Hom. i. 4.

of "the Southern pole, visible to the inhabitants of the
South, though unknown to us;" but Roman traders on the
East African coast had long since come in sight of some of
these, and Basil's language is far from being a definite
acknowledgment of antipodean lands or peoples.

As to the shape of the world, he only quotes the con-
flicting views of the learned without expressing any preference of his own; and ends by contrasting the doubtful
wisdom of the sages with the more sure oracles of the Holy
Spirit.[1] He does this, however, with no little skill and
display of knowledge. "Whether the earth be spherical
or cylindrical, whether it resemble a dish equally rounded
in all parts, or whether it has the form of a winnowing
basket, and is hollow in the middle,—all these conjectures
have been hazarded, each one upsetting the former. Yet
Moses, the servant of God, is silent as to shapes; he has not
said that the earth is 180,000 furlongs in circumference; he
has not measured into what extent of air its shadow projects
itself, while the sun revolves around it; nor stated how this
shadow, when cast upon the moon, is the cause of eclipses.
He has passed over in silence all that is unimportant for us
to learn. Shall we not rather exalt Him who, not wishing to
fill our minds with these vanities, has regulated the economy
of Scripture with a view to the perfection of our souls?"

As to the number of heavens, Basil is unusually literal.
He ridicules the philosophical "pretence" of one all-
including sky, and declares that, far from not believing in a
second, he was anxious to discover "the third, whereon the
blessed Paul was found worthy to gaze."[2] He is equally
firm as to the waters above the firmament, provided expressly
by the Creator, as he conceives, to prevent the dissolution
of the universe by fire. "For the same account was water

---

[1] Hex., hom. ix. 1; see also i. 11.   [2] Hom. iii. 3.

spread over the land, and dispersed in the depths of the earth, in fountains, springs, and rivers"—which last Basil now proceeds to enumerate.[1] "From the winter solstice in the east flows the Indus, greatest of streams, as our geographers teach; from the middle of the east proceed the Bactrus (Oxus) and the Araxes, from which the river Tanais[2] falls into the Mæotid Marsh (Sea of Azov)." From Mount Caucasus came the Phasis; from the north countless other rivers flowed into the Euxine Sea. From the Pyrenees, in the warm countries of the west, rose Tartessus and Ister (Guadalquivir and Danube); the Rhone watered the land of the Gauls; the Nile, and others, flowed through Ethiopia from the higher regions of the south—thanks to Him who ordered all to prevent the victory of fire before its time.[3]

Those who had "travelled round the earth" affirmed that there was only one sea, into which the *Caspian*, the Mediterranean and the Arabian gulfs all discharged themselves, and Basil, after his manner, repeats the established belief[4] without criticism, except to mention the opinion of a minority in the lakelike character of the Caspian. With the same deference, he alludes to the current misbelief in the depression of Egypt below the level of the Red Sea—"for experience has convinced us of this, every time that men have tried to join the sea of Egypt with the Indian Ocean."[5] So complacently did the fourth century acquiesce in the

[1] Mainly from Aristotle, Met. i. 13.

[2] Possibly the Araxes and Tanais are the Volga and Don in this connection.

[3] Hex., hom. iii. 5, 6.

[4] Hom. iv. 4; as in Pliny, H. N. vi. 15; Strabo, xi. 507. Basil (Hex., hom. iv. 6, 7) deals very ably with the subject of the benefits conferred by the ocean on the land, and alludes to a curious anticipation of a modern invention: "Sailors boil even salt water, collecting the vapour in sponges to quench their thirst in pressing need." In Nelson's time the extracting of fresh water from salt was talked of as if quite a new discovery.

[5] Hex., hom. iv. 3. See Arist., Meteor. i. 14; Pliny, H. N. vi. 33; Herod. ii. 158; Strab. xvii. 804.

denial of what the second had seen accomplished, or rather repeated, and which the seventh was again to see performed.

Basil was thoroughly well read in the differences of zones or climates as marked by the course of the sun, the length of daylight, and so forth. "It is winter with us, when the sun sojourns in the south, and lengthens the shades of night in our regions.[1] When, returning from the southern parts, the sun is in mid heaven, and divides day and night in equal parts, a mild temperature returns; thence the sun, proceeding to the north, gives us the longest days, when the shadows are shortest. Thus it is with us in the north of the earth, whose shadow is always on one side [who throw a shadow only one way at noon throughout the year]; but those who live beyond the Land of Spices see their shadows now on one side, now on another, and in one part of the world there is no shadow at all at midday for two days in the year; for the sun is there so directly overhead, that it could through a narrow opening shine to the bottom of a well."

In striking contrast to Cosmas, who conceives the sun as about forty miles across, and little more than four thousand miles from the earth, Basil insists on regarding it, like the moon, as of prodigious size, for "the whole extent of heaven cannot make it appear greater in one place and smaller in another; and all the inhabitants of the earth, from India to Britain, see it of the same size.[2] Judge not according to the appearance," he continues, "nor imagine that because it looks to be but the breadth of a cubit, it is in reality no larger." Could a modern have reproduced more neatly the argument of the early physicists? In the same spirit Basil accepts that influence of the moon upon the tides[3] which, ever since Pytheas of Marseilles, in the

[1] Hex., hom. vi. 8.
[2] Hom. vi. 8, 9.
[3] See Pliny, H. N. ii. 99; Plutarch,

Περὶ ἀρεσκ, iii. 17, who definitely traces the doctrine to Pytheas.

days of Alexander the Great, had been more or less clearly recognized by ancient science. " For as to the Western Sea, it now returns to its bed, and now overflows, as the moon draws it back and urges it forth by its respiration." [1] The result of these and similar instances, skilfully converted by the saint into so many supports of Scripture (though other theologians, both before and after, saw in them only so many suggestions of atheism), is to bring Basil's mind to some perception of the fallibility of unaided and uncorrected sense. Thus " our power of sight is small, and makes all that we see seem small, affecting what it sees by its own condition. But when sight is mistaken,[2] its testimony is also misleading." Yet science has. had no harder struggle than to persuade the world of this very fact; and mankind will more readily credit almost anything against reason, rather than a truth which is so above the ordinary reason as that of the delusive, partial, and surface character of sensuous perception.[3]

Works like the Hexaemeron, commentaries on the Biblical story of Creation, were the staple of Patristic cosmography. It is probable (we have seen) that the chief stimulus of Cosmas, in his anti-spherical and other theories, was a similar treatise of Theodore of Mopsuestia,[4] the Augustine of the Nestorian Church; but as his scientific writings

---

[1] Hex., hom. vi. 11.

[2] Hom. vi. 9.

[3] The zoology with which the Hexaemeron concludes, must not be spoken of here, although it is a fairly good copy of Pliny's, and touches occasionally on geographical notions, as in its excellent account of migratory birds, fish, and animals; but we may perhaps notice Basil's treatment of the silk worm, or "horned worm of India " (Hex., hom. viii. 8), which "turns from a caterpillar into a buzzing insect," and provides the silk sent by the Chinese for the " delicate dresses " of Roman women. It would be unfair to Basil to accuse him of confusing China and India in this passage, but the sentence is a good example of the loose way in which Greek and Latin writers often speak of the Further East.

[4] Probably written c. A.D. 370.

have been lost, we can only conjecture, from the allusions of
Photius and John Philoponus, that such was the case.
Happily, or unhappily, we possess in other writers—who
were possibly disciples of Theodore—some remarkably close
anticipations of the method and the conclusions of the
" Christian Topography ; " and of these the best specimens
are to be found in the Six Orations of Severian of Gabala [1]
(already alluded to), on the creation of the world ; and
in the fragments preserved by Photius from the lost but
contemporary work of Diodore of Tarsus, "Against Fate,"
or Fatalistic Ideas.   As to the former analogy, the likeness is marked.   In several respects Cosmas and Severian
employ almost the same expressions.   In both, the universe
is like a house or box, divided by the floor of the firmament, and arched by the roof of the heaven of heavens ;
in both, the Waters above the Firmament play an important part ; in both, the world is expressly compared to a
tabernacle ; in both, the spherical theory of the earth is
denounced with the same ludicrous vehemence, and refuted
by a misuse of the same texts.[2]   But Severian's treatment
of these matters is merely allusive and occasional, while
Cosmas undertakes an exhaustive exposition of the anti-
spherical view.   The Bishop of Gabala, moreover, indulges
now and then in speculations which the monk of Alexandria
does not always reproduce, as when he points out the true
use of the Upper Waters ; which were not to sail on or to
drink, but to prevent the destruction of the world by the
fiery luminaries of heaven, till that End of all Things, when
they would be serviceable in extinguishing sun, moon, and
stars.   For these last, to his mind, are just so many furnaces ;

---

[1] Of about A.D. 378–380.

[2] E. g. "The sun *came forth* [did
not " rise," as it must over a spherical
earth], and Lot entered into Segor ; "
but of course Cosmas uses many more
texts than Severian.

and, as he naïvely puts it, like other fires, they would in the natural order throw their heat and light *upwards* and away from us, were they not controlled by special Providence so as to cast down their rays for our benefit. A more striking difference is shown in Severian's explanation of the course of the sun, and the varying length of day and night. Unlike Cosmas, he does not make this depend entirely on the northern mountain; although the latter is a part-cause of darkness in his system. On the contrary, he conceives of the sun as really encircling the earth; but in winter it slips out of sight, according to him, at the south-west corner of our world, or of the Oblong which serves him for the earth-surface;[1] and so omitting part of its full day's journey, it has all the more to do in the night, on the west, north, and north-east of the Parallelogram.

Somewhat peculiar in its nature is the attack of Diodore of Tarsus (c. A.D. 394) upon the doctrines of a round world and a spherical universe. In such teaching he discerns the lurking heresy of atheistic fatalism; and one who began by believing in the Ptolemaic system would end, he thinks, by denying God His place as the Creator. As to the rest, it is enough to notice, on the one hand, his assumption, in the manner of Lactantius, that the torrid zone was uninhabitable and impassable; and, on the other hand, his positive language in favour of the Tabernacle theory: "Two heavens there are, one visible, the other invisible; one below, the other above: the latter serves as roof to the universe, the former as covering to our earth—not round or spherical, but in the form of a tent or arch."[2]

---

[1] See Severian, Orat. i. sects. 4, 5; Orat. ii. sects. 3, 4 (firmament, etc.); Orat. iii. sects. 2, 4, 5 (anti-spherical, quoted elsewhere, p. 275); also, on the rivers of Paradise, see Orat. v. 6.

Montfaucon's text and notes are reprinted in Migne, Pat. Græc. lvi. cc. 430–500.

[2] The fragments "Against Fate," as here quoted, are in Photius, "Biblio-

Next, perhaps, among those Christian geographers who gave anything like a formal treatment to the subject as a whole, comes Orosius, whom we have met with already among Latin travellers to the Levant. In his work as a disciple and interpreter of St. Augustine, he wrote his " Universal History " in the way of supplement to the more abstract treatise of his master, " On the City of God." Both works were drawn up within a short time after Alaric's capture of Rome, and both had the same object. They aimed at proving that Christianity was not responsible for recent calamities; that equal and even greater misfortunes had befallen the empire in pagan times ; and that the new religion had not weakened but rather revived the strength of every country where it had been accepted. Orosius' " History against the Pagans " was, therefore, as a controversial tract, radically unhistorical in character, but its treatment was far better than its title ; and in the second chapter of the first book the author inserted a short account of the nations and districts of the earth, which had at least the merits of being lucid, judicious, and fairly well informed. It was also for the most part independent both of Pliny and of Ptolemy ; and was possibly based to a large extent upon earlier sources, such as Strabo, while its definitions were sometimes original. Here, for instance, we find the earliest known use of Asia Minor in our sense; a peculiar account of the rise of the Nile near the mouth of the Red Sea ; and an odd exaggeration of the Isle of Man into a sort of rival of Britain and Ireland.[1] The mouth of the

theca," cod. 223; in Migne, Pat. Græc. ciii., esp. cc. 838, 871. Diodore also wrote on the Creation in the course of a Biblical Commentary (his fragments on Genesis are in Migne, Pat. Græc. xxxiii. cc. 1562-80), but there is nothing geographical in this.

[1] Cf. Mevania in Bede, H. E. ii. 5. Monapia (Men–) in Pliny, H.N. iv. 16, 103. See Bunbury, Anc. Geog. ii. 691, etc.

Ganges he definitely places, after the common prejudice, in the midst of the eastern front of Asia. Africa he terminates, like nearly every one in his day, at about the latitude of the Canaries; and he conceives of the whole continent as long and narrow, squeezed closely between the Mediterranean and the ocean on the north and south.

Orosius, like his teachers, plants *terra firma* in the centre of the ocean, and divides it under the three customary heads. Of these, Asia is first described, in order of its countries, starting from India as next to the sun-rising, and moving steadily west, without anything remarkable in statement; except that happy Arabia is said to "stretch towards the east in a narrow tract" between the Persian and Arabian Gulfs; that the Lesser Asia of the peninsula is now expressly distinguished from the Greater Asia of the continent; and that the Caspian is, as usual, made an inlet of the Northern Ocean, with long winding and barren shores ending at the "roots of Caucasus."[1] In Europe the compiler is even more unimpeachable—although referring to Spain, Italy, and Gaul as if in some way between the Danube and Mediterranean; bringing the British Islands, and especially Ireland, too close to the Spanish coast; and exaggerating the size of Man[2] in the curiously mistaken way to which we have just referred. In his third and last division, Orosius deals with Africa, the chief island of the world, and the proper number of continents. It is in these concluding sentences that we have his famous apology for regarding Africa as a continent to itself,[3] rather than grouping it with Europe to make a set-off against the overshadowing bulk of Asia. For one mistake is balanced by another. If Africa is understated, Europe is over-estimated. Its extent towards the north-east is greatly,

---

[1] Cf. Oro. I. ii. 15 ; I. ii. 21 ; and I. ii. 48.

[2] Oro. I. ii. 55–74

[3] Oro. I. ii. 84.

though vaguely, magnified, but in the same misty language
in which the upper course of the Nile is described,—first in
the manner of the Plinian school from Mount Atlas, then (by
a possible confusion with the Blue Nile of Abyssinia) from
Mossylon [1] harbour, near the straits of Bab-el-Mandeb.

A sketch of universal geography, similar to that of the
Ravennese "Anonymous," is next to be found in the tract of
Julius Æthicus, part of which is almost verbally identical
with another compilation—the "Libel" of Julius Honorius.[2]

With this treatise of one Æthicus has often been confused a very different and probably later treatise, the
cosmography of Æthicus of Istria; which professes to be
translated by a priest named Jerome from a Greek original;
which ha saroused, like the "Catalogue Geography" of Julius
Æthicus, a surprising degree of literary interest; and which,
in its present form, seems to be of the seventh century. It
will, perhaps, be useful to examine it a little more in
detail.

Shadowy as is the alleged existence of this "philosopher;"
and doubtful as is the ascription to this Græco-Scythian
Mandeville of either of the works which pass under his
proper name, and enjoyed so great a popularity in the
Middle Ages—we have at any rate in the production of
Jerome the Priest, an apparently original work of the early
Christian period. As it stands, this Cosmography of
Æthicus of Istria is one of the longest, one of the wildest,
and certainly the most obscure and enigmatical among early
Christian geographical monuments. The *Presbyter* who
undertakes to abridge and elucidate, and who complains so

[1] It has been suggested that
Mossylon is confused with the *Massyli*
and *Massæsyli* of Numidia, tribes
among whom Juba supposed the
Nile to rise. Cf. Pliny, v. 9, 52; and
Solinus, c. lvi., who mentions the
Massylic promontory. Oro. I. ii. 28.

[2] Cf. Cassiodorus, De Inst. Div.
Script., c. 25.

frequently of the difficulties of his text, is himself the worst offender. Incessantly interrupting his original, real or pretended, by tirades and reflections of his own, he rarely fails to make confusion worse confounded; and many sections of the book in its present state are absolutely unintelligible. Obviously anxious to identify himself with St. Jerome, he bears in himself a sufficient refutation. He is really a copyist of Isidore [1] and other encyclopædists. The narrative is occupied with the journeys of Æthicus by sea and land, with his observations on the products of the earth and the men of different nations, and with his trading ventures. Himself a Christian neophyte, the Istrian was moreover so illustrious a philosopher, that his native land had become the seat of the learning that had fled from Athens. Whether his reputation was well-founded, may be seen from the contents of the present treatise. Herein he discourses on the fabric of the world; on unformed matter, Paradise, the earth, sea, and sky; on the fall of Satan, and on the Angels; on the table of the sun, the moon, and the stars; on the portals of the heaven and the hinges of the world; and on all the various lands and seas of the inhabited and habitable earth. In his more detailed descriptions, he evidently prides himself especially upon his treatment of the races which the Old Testament leaves unmentioned, and of certain matters not treated in any other writings; and it is on these points where few had specialised, and where his authority was of all the more weight, that his credit was naturally most firmly established. Thus Roger Bacon, in the thirteenth century, quotes " Æthicus the Astronomer " on some of the

[1] He was well acquainted with Jerome's life and works; and copies from the latter names, allusions, and expressions, such as the famous passage from letter 103 (no. 53 in Migne), about Hiarchas living among the Brahmins, sitting on a golden throne, drinking of the Fount of Tantalus, and instructing his disciples on nature and on the courses of the stars (ch. 17).

more recondite details connected with Alexander, with the
Amazons, and with the Gog-Magogs; and Walter Raleigh,
in the sixteenth, repeats the testimony of "that ancient
Æthicus" on the locality of Eden,[1] backed as it was by
the weighty affirmation of St. Jerome, who, as translator
and editor, had made himself responsible for the statements
of the "Scythian Philosopher." The compiler assures us
that many of the Istrian's narrations had not been repeated
by him lest their marvels should cause the pious to stumble.
Only facts well ascertained could be allowed in this place;
and, among these, we have a record of the conquests of
Romulus[2] in the Balkan and Danube lands, and of his
victories over Lacedæmon and over Francus and Vasus,
ancestors of the Franks who "built Sicambria."

Again, the brave deeds of the giant Phyros among the
Albanians of Central Asia; of Alexander[3] when he threw
down Jason's altars lest they should rival his own; and of
Pompey, whose exploits had been recorded by his faithful
companion Theophanes, add many surprising details to the
ordinary history. Thus, when the Macedonian hero shut up
"Gog-Magog and twenty-two nations of evil men" behind his
Caspian gates and Wall of iron, the prophecy of Micah was

---

[1] Raleigh's confusion is remarkable. This, he tells us, was "not that latter Æthicus, otherwise called 'Istic,' but another of a far higher time . . . made Latin out of the Greek by Saint Hierome" ("History of World," bk. i. ch. 3, § 10). See Bacon, "Opus Majus," ed. of 1733, pp. 168, 190, 225, 228–230, 235.

The Æthicus ("Cosmography") which Count Everard, brother-in-law of Charles the Bald (?), bequeathed along with the Synonyma of Isidore in 837 to his eldest son Unroch, is considered by Avezac ("Éthicus," 36) to be a copy of the Istrian; but it was more probably one of the other Æthicus (cf. Le Mire, Codex Donationum, 1624). Raban Maur is the oldest certain authority who cites Æth. Istric. (c. A.D. 860). The passages which Avezac (cf. p. 37) makes Isidore cite from Æth. Istric. are more probably purloined by the latter's compiler from the Encyclopædist of Seville.

[2] Chs. 63, 103.

[3] Ch. 64.

fulfilled [1]—he " contended before the mountains " and " the
hills heard his voice, even the enduring foundations of
the earth," for with a loud sound they were plucked out
of the ground and piled one upon another.   But far better
than this, Æthicus saw with his own eyes the Amazons to the
north of the Caspian suckling the Centaurs and Minataurs
of that region; and the bituminous lake, mouth of hell,
whence came the cement of Alexander's wall, when he stayed
in the city of Choolisma, built by Magog, son of Japhet.[2]
In Armenia the philosopher searched in vain for Noah's
Ark; but he saw dragons, ostriches, gryphons, and ants
large and voracious as dogs; and he could testify from
personal experience that, when rain descended upon Mount
Ararat, there was a rumbling that could be heard to the
borders of the country.[3]   A different quest—for the Garden
of Eden—though equally fruitless, brought the explorer to
the Ganges; where he was entertained by a hospitable
Indian king, fought with hippopotami, and rivalled or even
surpassed the exploits of Apollonius of Tyana.[4]   From Ceylon
or Taprobane, Æthicus sailed round to the North-West by
the encircling Ocean, passing on his way Syrtinice (island
of the Sirens) the navel of our hemisphere in the Indian
Ocean; Ireland, "full of false doctors;" the Isle of Dogs or
dog-headed men in the Northern Sea; Bridinno, the land of
dwarfs; and the country of the Gryphons, both the gold-
guarding quadrupeds, and also a people distinguished for

[1] Micah vi. 1, 2. For the Alexander myth, see Æthic. Istric. chs.
32, 33, 36, 39, 41, 59, 60, 62–64, 69, 75,
82, 84. This legend is further discussed in the supplementary chapter
(pp. 407, 433, etc.), where the Arab
tradition is noticed.
[2] Chs. 59, 60, 67, 68, 75.

[3] Chs. 70, 105.
[4] Christian mythology, suggests
Lelewel (Géog. Épilogue, p. 7), may
have invented the travels of Æthicus
as a set-off to those of Apollonius,
which are exactly copied by the
Istrian in reference to India.

music, for war, and for navigation.[1] A little nearer to
matter of fact, is our compiler's mention of the Turks—a
people monstrous, abject, idolatrous, with yellow teeth, as
befitted the offspring of Gog and Magog. This inviting
race is apparently located by Æthicus in Modern Russia,
touching the Northern Ocean on one side and the Black Sea
on another.[2] Among the pirates of the Northern Ocean
Alexander the Great had once lived, to learn from them
"the depth of ocean and of the abyss," and his *submarine*
navigation in those parts is faithfully chronicled by the
Istrian traveller.[3]

But besides practical exploration, Æthicus gives us a
system of the universe. His sun is a disc which enters by
the gate of the East to enlighten the earth, and retires by
that of the West in order to return during the night to its
starting-point, hidden by thick mists or a great mountain [4]
which screens it from human sight, but allows it to impart a
fraction of its radiance to the moon and stars. The poles, or
hinges of the world, are connected by a mighty line from the
extreme of icy cold in the North to the rich, salubrious, and
vitalising centre in the South, whence blow [5] the winds that
propagate serenity. Æthicus will not allow of any rotation
of the earth, which reposes upon the Abyss. Scarcely any one
is more prodigal of earth-navels, or centres, than our Istrian
or his abbreviator—the isle of the Sirens, Nineveh, Jerusalem, and the southern extreme of earth, all serve for this in
turn,—but we can hardly be surprised at any extravagance

[1] Chs. 18, 19, 22, 28, 31, 33, 36, 41,
53, 56, 63.

[2] Chs. 31, 32, 63, 64; cf. Pliny, H.N.
vi. 7, Mela. i. 21.

[3] Chs. 36, 40, 67. This story is
copied by Roger Bacon, "De Mirabili
Potestate Artis."

[4] "Astrixis," ch. 21. The name
occurs in Orosius, i. 2, as a mountain
of Western Africa. See also Æth.
Istric. chs. 16, 18, 20. Isidore,
Etym. iii. 40; xiv. 5.

[5] Chs. 20, 21.

here. No ordinary limitations seem to bind the illustrious neophyte, or rather the forger who in all probability first invented this wild original, and then sheltered himself behind the name of the great Latin doctor. Yet the success of his manœuvre gives more reasonable ground for surprise. We have been asked to see the hand of Saint Jerome in a work which separates Tullius and Cicero, which refers to the *sixth*-century poems of Bishop Alcimus Avitus of Vienne;[1] which in its mention of the Turks and other inadvertences clearly belies its pretended fourth-century origin; which bears evidence on every page of a Greek struggling to write impossible Latin; and which—apart from all these inconsistencies—is a libel on the intelligence, the style, and the vocabulary of the author of the Vulgate.[2] Even this was not enough for credulity. Not only was St. Jerome the translator, but Æthicus was a real traveller. His disputes with Aurilius and Arbocrates in Spain, his conversations with Fabius in Athens, his voyages in the Northern Sea were genuine. It was unfortunate he sometimes strayed into fable, but so did many excellent writers; and if he described Babylon in full splendour, Thebes as Pausanias saw it, and Greece in the sense of the Byzantine Empire after the Saracen conquests, these anachronisms were due to the vividness of his historical imagination. After this, it needed little or no assurance to add that Orosius, Solinus, and Isidore copied *him*—although the copyists rarely failed to give a clearer and simpler account than their supposed original. So have eminent scholars[3] of the nineteenth

---

[1] See Æthic. ch. 11.

[2] So long ago as 1658, Will. Burton, in his commentary on "Antonine's Itinerary," said all that was needed about the then unpublished Istrian, "a book containing many things fabulous and foolish, and unworthy St. Jerome's pains in translating, if he ever did it."

[3] On the various " Æthican " and "pseudo-Æthican" works, see Gronovius, appendix to his Pompon. Mela

century bowed before claims which appeared grotesque to Pico della Mirandola in the fifteenth, securing another victory for the time-honoured device of Ctesias and Mandeville, and once more accepting as sufficient evidence of itself the word of one whom we cannot but suspect both of plagiarism and imposture.

The so-called Æthicus of Istria is probably, as we have seen, a compilation not earlier than the seventh century; the other Æthicus may be fairly supposed to have written his "Cosmography" at a date a little subsequent to the opening of the sixth.

Two kinds of geographical description were common in these times. One was fourfold, dealing with the earth in reference to the cardinal points of North, South, East and West. The other was threefold, answering to three Continents, and resting upon a Biblical analogy with the three sons of Noah; just as the former method looked for support to the four Gospels and the four Major Prophets. Julius Honorius, like Cosmas,[1] employed the quadripartite division; Paulus Orosius the tripartite; our present Æthicus— " Æthicus the cosmographer"—copied and combined the two.

But at the beginning, he repeated with fuller detail than is elsewhere to be found, the tradition of Cæsar's measurement of the earth. Julius Cæsar, he declares, the inventor of the bissextile year, that man so profoundly learned in Divine and human law, induced the senate (when he was consul) to decree that all the Roman world should be

of 1722; Avezac, "Éthicus et les Ouvrages Cosmographiques intitulés de ce Nom " (Paris, 1852); Lelewel, " Géographie du Moyen Age," epilogue, §. " Les Éthicus ; " Wuttke, " Cosmographia Æthici Istrici " (Leipsic, 1854); (" Die Aechtheit des Auszugs . . . des Æthicus "); K. A. F. Pertz, De Cosm. Æth. (Berlin, 1853); Walckenaer, in " Biographie Universelle," and Ch. Müller, in " Nouvelle Biographie Générale" (Paris, 1856).

[1] In book ii. of the "Christian Topography."

measured by prudent men; and within thirty-two years the
whole work was accomplished by Zenodoxus in the East, by
Theodotus in the north, by Polyclitus in the South, and
(as the Honorian text supplies) by Didymus in the West.
In this curious passage, Æthicus probably gives a genuine
tradition, with some errors of his own. A survey of the
imperial roads, such as he refers to, was indeed almost certainly the origin of the map of Agrippa at Rome (set up in
the reign of Augustus), of the map preserved at Autun in
the third century, and of other "painted worlds," of which
we have at least one survival, in the Peutinger table.

The rest of the "Cosmography" is practically (though not
always verbally) identical[1] with those excerpts of Julius
Honorius which are first named by Cassiodorus (about A.D.
500) as a useful book for the monks of his time; and with
the second chapter of Orosius's history, which, in the
Æthican collection, follows the excerpts aforesaid.

Æthicus indeed writes as a patriotic Italian, and lays
greater emphasis on the glory of Rome than do his models,
but, as a rule, his servility is close enough. Thus his list of
Northern peoples is reproduced verbatim with the unlucky
addition of a few Oriental nations, who have slipped in by
mistake from another part of the original Catalogue.
Like the Istrian, his imagination sometimes runs together
different ages and events, as when he refers to the gates[2] of
what he evidently conceives as Christian Rome animated by
a commerce worthy only of the pagan Empire; or witnessing the pageants of the old civilisation in a time which
had heard the name of the Huns by the Western Sea.

[1] The amount of difference is only
about one-seventh (see Riese's edition
of the Minor Latin Geographers).
It seems probable that Julius the
Orator (whom Cassiodorus quotes)
lived pretty near to the latter's own
time (see Cassiodorus, De Inst.
Div. Script. ch. 25).

[2] *E.g.* "The gates of Felix," who
died A.D. 274.

But in both cases this jumble is natural enough.   Just as an air of spurious antiquity has been given to the Istrian by the legend of St. Jerome's version, and all the details which are meant to bear out the same; so the other Æthicus struggles to gain a like advantage for himself by his allusions to Ancient Rome; and in both cases the pretence was highly successful.   For just as the Istrian's travels were accepted as real and their translation by St. Jerome as genuine; so his namesake has been treated as the source and not the copyist of Orosius' geography, as the author of the Antonine itinerary, and even of the Peutinger Table, and the Notitia Dignitatum; while John of Salisbury [1] pays him the final compliment of quoting as from *his* pen some undoubted lines of Horace and of Juvenal.

Like the other catalogue-geographies of his age, this " Cosmography " is, for the most part, made up of lists of place-names, marked, as we might expect, by peculiar con-fusedness.   No regard is paid to distinctions of country, race, or religion; the only attempt at regular and orderly treatment is in the case of certain rivers; and of these there is only one which really interests the compiler, and that is the " beautiful Tiber, king of streams."

And with the enumeration of Julius Æthicus we may group the similar though earlier work of Vibius Sequester, probably of the fourth century, which may have been used by the later Honorius and his copyist, and which gives a brief register of the Rivers, Fountains, Lakes, Forests, Marshes, Mountains and Peoples " of which the poets make mention." [2]

---

[1] Metalog. ii. 4, 7; Polycrat. i. 8, 13; ii. 2; iii. 1, 2, 4, 8, 9, 14; viii. 15, 24.   For the best treatment of this (as well as of the Istrian) Æthicus, see the essays of Avezac and Lelewel as cited above (especially Avezac, pp. 64–120).

[2] See Riese, Geographi Latini Mi-nores; Notices in B.U.; and N.B.G.; Brunet, Manuel (1864), v. 1171, 1172; Engelmann, Bibl. Class (1847), 467; Graesse (1867), VI. ii. 296.   Vossius, Hist. Lat. (1651), 727.   The tract is dedicated by Sequester to his son's use.

It was either contemporary with Æthicus, or a little later, that there appeared a more important work of Christian science than that of Vibius, at least as far as its mediæval influence was concerned. Few books ever illustrated the value of translation more than the version now made by the grammarian Priscian[1] of the old Greek Coast Survey of Dionysius "Periegetes." But for this and the similar performance of Avienus, one of the most popular of geographical tracts would have remained closed to the West, and our "Anglo-Saxon" map in the Cotton Library,[2] for instance, would have been drawn to illustrate some other text. The transcribers both treated their model pretty freely, paraphrasing, abridging, and inserting at will (as where Avienus supplies an improved description of the sources of the Rhine and Danube[3]). But neither added much to the current misconceptions, except a welcome confirmation. It is true Priscian uses rather peculiar phrases about the shape of the earth, which he insists on likening to a sling; but this is a commonplace with a certain school of classical geographers, though it becomes quite unconventional later. Like Orosius and the rest, but more precisely, he compares both Europe and Africa to oblong tables in form; and his stories of voyages round from the Northern Ocean[4] to Ceylon, of the columns of Bacchus in the extreme East corresponding to the columns of Hercules in the West, and of the Red Sea's title from the burning south wind that desolated it, are only too well known to us already.

Passing by various other works of the early Christian time, which merely allude to things geographical, or have a

---

[1] Of Cæsarea, 468–475 (according to Chevalier); Avienus (Rufus Festus) is probably of the earlier fifth century. Of the two versions, Priscian's was much the closer.

[2] Tiberius, B. v. folio 59.

[3] Descriptio Orbis Terræ, ll. 433, etc.; partly from Pliny, iv. 12, and from Strabo and Ptolemy.

[4] Cf. Strabo, bks. ii. and xi.

strictly local interest, such as the poems [1] of Ausonius, or the history of Ammianus Marcellinus (who, like Ptolemy himself, has been too confidently credited with the "earliest mention" of the sea of Aral), we now come to the sixth century.

And here we have, first of all, the interesting piece of advice which Cassiodorus, the minister of the great Theodoric in the Ostro-Gothic kingdom of Italy, gave to the monks of his time. He urges them to study cosmography with especial care, and in their reading to refer, above all, to Scripture, and the writings of Julius Honorius, Ptolemy, Dionysius, and one Marcellinus, who had composed an account of Constantinople and Jerusalem.[2]

Probably no writer of this time had juster or more enlightened geographical notions than Procopius; but he only takes account of their subject-matter in the course of the history of Justinian's wars. From his allusions, however, we may gather that he did not altogether share the ordinary view of the encircling ocean as the limit of the habitable world. In the same critical spirit he apparently ignored the traditional division of three continents, as he believed, like his age, that the mass of Asia was fully equal to all the land of Europe and of Africa; and as to the Nile, though elsewhere he repeats the fable of its flowing from the Indies, his ignorance of its sources is plainly avowed.[3]

Far more singular is the language of Procopius about Britain, which has now evidently relapsed into the haze on the horizon of knowledge, first penetrated by Pytheas; and has become to the Byzantine historian, after the lapse of

[1] The *Mosella* (A.D. 368) and the *Ordo Nobilium Urbium* (cf. Bunbury, Anc. Geog. c. xxxi.).

[2] De Inst. Div. Litt., as cited before.

[3] In the same way as he disclaims any precise knowledge of the extremities of Africa (Hist. of the Vandal and Gothic Wars, esp. De Bell. Goth. ii. 14, 15; iv. 20). Procop.'s Thule is clearly Norway.

eight hundred years, a dim and ghostly country on the out-
skirts of the inhabited world, in the Western parts of which
no men were to be found, but only the spirits of the dead.

Another sixth-century historian—largely used, as we
have seen, by the Ravennese geographer—devoted a good
deal of space to the description of countries. Jornandes, in
his " Rise and Deeds of the Goths " [1] (c. A.D. 551), gives many
local details of northern lands, especially of the modern
Russia, Prussia, and Scandinavia,[2] and refers with awe to the
impassable ocean, whose outer boundaries no one had ever
ventured to approach or to describe.

The geographical notices in Gregory of Tours are chiefly
of interest to practical travel ; but he is also careful to let
us have his judgment on the torrid zone as uninhabitable,
and on the Nile as flowing from the East, or, in other words,
from Paradise.

Last of the pre-Moslem geographers of Christendom is
St. Isidore of Seville. In the thirteenth and fourteenth books
of his "Etymologies," or "Origins," the Spanish bishop
follows the example of the Spanish presbyter Orosius in an
attempted survey of the world, which is brief, definitive, and
educational. For although Solinus is quoted two hundred
times, the work of Isidore is not the compilation of a
bestiary, nor are his objects those of the fabulist in any
shape. The natural history he gives us is meant to instruct,
not to amuse.

Thus, in his thirteenth book, he tenderly deals with the
world as a whole, with the ocean and the Mediterranean
(which he is the first to define clearly by that "proper
name"), with the inlets of the sea, and with the tides,
lakes, pools, and rivers of our earth. Coming to Continental
geography, in his next section he enumerates [3] the various

---

[1] Chs. i.–iv.

[2] On which he cites Ptolemy.

[3] Isid. xiv. 3–5.

countries from east to west; the Mæotid Marshes, or Sea of
Azov, he considers, in rather unauthorised language, to
form, along with the Tanais, or Don, the northern boundary
of Asia; in Africa he evidently knows of nothing south
of Abyssinia but inaccessible wastes, and nothing south of
Fezzan but the ocean.[1]   In Europe, again, he makes Ireland
the land of "Scots," and Ireland the antidote to serpents,
into two separate countries; on the other hand, he shows,
for a professed theologian, a quite noteworthy breadth of
general ideas,—admitting the possible existence of Antipodean lands, or a "fourth part of earth to the south of the
Interior Ocean," unknown to us from the heat of the sun,
as he unhappily hastens to add.   The "Fabled Antipods,"
or Antipodean people, who were said to live in the extremity
of this land, is probably St. Isidore's compromise between
religion and science.   For whatever might be said of
worlds beyond our ken, it was plainly heresy to assert, as
Virgil did a little later, the existence of a race of men who
could not be descended from Adam, and for whom, therefore, Christ had not died.[2]

The geography commonly ascribed to the famous
Armenian historian, Moses of Khorene, in the fifth century,
has been also assigned to Ananias of Schirag in the seventh.
In any case, it is simply a version of certain parts of Ptolemy,
with a few additions and remarks,—a version which seems
itself to have been founded upon an earlier work of one
Pappus of Alexandria,[3] author of a "Christian Topography,"
which some have conjectured, in the face of all evidence, to

[1] Isid. xiv. 5.

[2] An early imitator of Isidore is
probably another geographical writer
of this time, the anonymous author of
the "Versus de Provinciis Partium
Mundi," in a manuscript of the later
seventh or earlier eighth century
(Paris Bibl. Nat. Lat. 5092), in 129
lines, which need not be further
noticed.

[3] Known to Suidas, and cited by
him.

be the same as the work of Cosmas under that title.   Beside
Pappus, the Armenian redactor quotes Constantine of
Antioch, who had written upon the same subject ; Denis,
who is possibly the classical Dionysius Periegetes ; and one
Apollon, who is still more difficult to identify. He appears,
moreover, to have borrowed somewhat from a "History of
Alexander" of the Oriental pattern.

Following Ptolemy,[1] he expresses his belief in unlimited
land beyond the inhabited earth, rather than ocean, and in
the truth of alleged journeys far into the torrid South, to
Agysimba and the Mountains of the Moon.   Once more, he
repeats his teacher on the land-locked character of the
Caspian as of the Indian Ocean ; on the overwhelming size of
Asia, and especially of Ceylon ; and on the fish-eating Ethiopians, the chariot of the Gods,[2] and other features of Western
and Eastern Africa: just as he reproduces him in nearly all
the more prosaic details of various countries. From Christian
authorities he derives, it is true, some more imaginative
touches—"the earth built on nothing," in the words of Job
and St. Gregory the Illuminator; "the arch of heaven
passing from the east towards us in the middle of the earth,"
as Constantine of Antioch had said; the "water in the
foundations of the land," of which St. Basil had spoken in his
Hexaemeron. From the same teachers, he refutes Ptolemy's
suggestion that Yemen,[3] or happy Arabia, was in the centre

---

[1] See M. J. St. Martin, "Mémoire
sur l'Arménie, 1819 ; " the edition of
(the doubtful) Moses at the Armenian
convent in Venice, 1881 (" Moses de
Khorene "); the Latin translation
of the Whiston brothers (London,
1736), and St. Croix, in *Journal des
Savants*, for 1789, p. 217. Mr. F. C.
Conybeare has kindly shown me
his manuscript translation of some
sections of the genuine Ananias.

[2] Teneriffe ?

[3] Yemen, or the Sabean Land,
where the Queen of Sheba came from,
was obviously an impossible earth-
centre. Did not the Old and New
Testaments say plainly that she came
from the *ends of the earth* to hear the
wisdom of Solomon ?

of the inhabited world; for this place was clearly due to Jerusalem, where God had " worked salvation in the midst of the earth." Yet on the whole the Armenian geographer is Ptolemaic and classical in spirit, and very much the reverse of credulous. He rejects the griffins of Arabia; he refuses to dogmatize about the resting-place of the Ark; and as to the double-faced, dragon-footed, six-handed, and other exceptionally endowed races on the borders of China, he refuses to believe in any of them. When he says that no ship has ever sailed north of Scandinavia and the Shetlands,[1] he does nothing worse than repeat the ordinary tradition of the Old Empire; as to monsters, he is satisfied with a moderate selection of such as contented Pliny; his account of the long walls of the Caucasus is markedly in contrast with the mediæval fables about the rampart of Gog Magog, in the same region of the world; and he expressly parts company with those who took the Bible as an exclusive guide to the science of geography.

Very different from the mild reasonableness of his spirit is the true Ananias of Shirag. In his chapters about the " Earth," the Sea, "the Heavenly Orders" and " Luminaries," he does scarcely anything but echo the strictly Patristic views with considerable violence of expression. He " abhors " to quote the speculations of wicked philosophers on the suspension of the world in space; he denounces the idea of antipodean peoples, surrounding the globe " as flies surround an apple; " and in general he seems to consider almost anything as self-condemned which had once been broached by the " insane heathen." As against their delusions, he affirms, for instance, that the Ocean[2] has in it no living creatures, is without boundary, and is carefully avoided by

---

[1] Scandia and Thule.　　　[2] " The sea which envelopes the earth."

the light of the sun; that the Caspian communicates with the outer sea, if not on the surface of the land, at any rate by subterranean channels; that the earth's foundations are literally laid upon the waters, as it is said in the Psalms; and that evaporation is not caused by the heat of the sun, but by the ordinance of God. Because pagans had supposed the moon to derive her light from the sun, Ananias leans to the belief of "two church writers," who regarded it as independent and original. But chief among the "church writers" that he uses, must have been St. Basil, and when following the arguments and illustrations of the Hexaemeron,[1] Ananias greatly improves the character of his polemic.

The Venerable Bede has already been noticed as an historian of practical travel in his account of Arculf; but he has also a certain place in geographical science, and one of considerable importance. For among the lesser Christian doctors who directed and instructed the Church between Gregory the Great and Gregory the Seventh, between the later Fathers and the earlier schoolmen, no one left a more famous name than the monk of Jarrow; and his *obiter dicta* were quoted on matters cosmographical as they were on matters grammatical, rhetorical, or theological.

In three separate treatises [2] he delivered himself upon the "Constitution of Heaven and Earth," in language which

---

[1] As upon the uniform size of the sun, from every terrestrial point of view, as proving its real greatness and distance, we may notice that he quotes from *the heathen* the comparison of the universe to an egg, and of the earth to an iron mass held fast in mid air by the attraction of a magnetic vault or roof. Against the possibility of antipodes, he claims to have had a special revelation in a private interview with the sun ("a youth, beardless and golden-haired, with gold-anointed lips"), who expressly told him that he did *not* give light at night to any beings beneath the earth.

[2] *I.e.* (1) "De Mundi Cœlestis terræque Constitutione;" (2) "De Elementis Philosophiæ;" (3) "De Natura Rerum."

(on many points) kept carefully within time-honoured misconceptions, but with a certain vigour and freshness of style.
The earth,[1] to his mind, was an element placed in the midst
of the universe, as the yelk in an egg; around it was the
water, like the white of egg about the yellow; around the
water was the air, like the membrane within the shell; and
this again was encircled by the fire—itself the shell or
cover of all. From the action of these elements upon the
earth in the centre, this last received diverse qualities—heat
in the middle, and cold at the extremities,—whence came
the uninhabitable regions of the tropics and the poles.[2] For
it is plain that he conceived the external fire, not as a real
shell, but only as a belt, like Saturn's rings. If his words
mean what they say, it is equally plain that he conceived
the earth as absolutely spherical; but this was now so unusual an opinion, that it is likely he would have preferred
the comparison to a cylinder cut in half along its length—
in other words, to a disc, or the form of a Roman shield, a
half-curve. Of the two temperate zones Bede declares his
belief that both were habitable, but only one actually inhabited, probably from the theological difficulties of fitting
Antipodean man into the Jewish tradition and the Christian
scheme of salvation.

It was the ocean,[3] encircling all the inhabited region
known to us, which filled the torrid zone, and divided the
northern from the southern earth; and, from its position, this
ocean was, of course, not to be traversed—so that between
the "upper" and "lower" regions of the world (as he calls
them) there was a great gulf fixed, so that they which would

---

[1] De El. Phil., iv., p. 225, Col. edit.
of 1612. This was a pagan speculation.

[2] So Theodore of Mopsuestia, in
John Philoponus, "On Creation," iii.
10, 119.

[3] De Mundi Cœlestis terræque
Constitutione.

pass from hence could not, neither they (if any there be)
that would come from thence.

As to the continents (whose traditional threefold division he did not challenge, though he evidently held the
orthodox view of Africa as a long and narrow strip along
the south of the Mediterranean), Bede[1] simply copies the
well-worn phrases, about Asia as the half of *terra firma*
equal in size to both its rivals together; about the Nile and
Paradise as forming the eastern and southern boundaries
of the same Asia; and about the Sea of Azov[2] as limiting
Europe on the north.

Virgil, the Hibernian bishop of Salzburg, was the most
original,[3] as he was the most fanciful geographer of the
eighth century. In A.D. 748, St. Boniface, as the head of
the Roman missions in Germany, wrote to Pope Zacharias
to complain that this Irish intruder (who died in 784, in the
odour of sanctity, as the apostle of Carinthia) was then
teaching various perverse and wicked doctrines against
God and his own soul. In particular, he had declared his
faith in another world and other men, another sun and
another moon beneath the earth.

Zacharias answered by condemning these errors, and
ordering Virgil to come and clear his doctrine at Rome.
But the pope (like men at the present day) seems to
have been very doubtful as to what the accused really
meant. If Boniface had understood aright, Virgil must
retract, or be driven out of the Church. But the language
of Boniface was itself ambiguous; and not less so are all

---

[1] De Nat. Rerum, c. ix.

[2] Enormously exaggerated, as by
nearly every early geographer. Even
Ptolemy makes it much greater than
the Black Sea; and the ordinary
language (cf. Isidore) spoke of the
Euxine as *flowing into* it, like the
Propontis into the Mediterranean.

[3] A.D. 745–784. He was patronized
and advanced by King Pepin le
Bref, who was impressed by his
learning.

other references to the new theory.   Either Virgil was speaking of the Antipodes, or he was not.   If he was, he had the companionship (at least, as to the possibility of such "opposite countries") of St. Isidore,[1] and a respectable minority of educated opinion.   It is not probable that the court of Rome would then have cared to close the gates on an opinion which Basil and Ambrose, among others, had declared an open question.   On the other hand, the assertion of a separate human race was distinctly heretical. If, again, Virgil was suggesting another world, placed like a layer below the present, and as it were enclosed within it, he was broaching a novelty too audacious for the Church of his time to tolerate.[2]   All accounts are agreed as to his learning, especially in Greek; but he may not have understood all that he read.   Overmuch study, a fertile imagination, slender reasoning powers, and a tendency to confusedness of thought, may together have been responsible for some vagaries.

Raban Maur, the famous ninth-century bishop of Mainz, was another man of position and reputation who dabbled in geography.   We know him best as an opponent of early papalism, a defender of the liberties of the German Church against Roman aggression, and an enemy of the extreme predestinarian school of his time.   But he was also an Encyclopædist.   In his book, "De Universo," he gives us a summary of knowledge as then conceived, and in the

[1] Possibly of Bede as well.

[2] Cf. Jaffé, Mon. Mog., 167, 190, 191; Mabillon, AA. SS. O. S. B., iii. 2, pp. 308–318; Pertz, Mon. Germ. Hist. SS., xi. 84–86 (1854); Ussher, Works (Elrington), iv. 324, 461–465. In any case, the Benedictine editors of the Histoire Littéraire de la France are a little too enthusiastic and incautious in speaking of St. Virgil, "who was the first to discover the Antipodes," among the glories of the eighth-century Church (iv. pp. 19, 26).   We may notice that Virgil's theory requires not only a new heavens and a new earth, but *another sun and moon.*

eleventh, twelfth, and thirteenth sections of this treatise
he attempts a description of the world. Like Isidore, he
begins with the waters, great and small, from the ocean to
the pools left by rain; secondly, he passes in review the
various regions of the land; lastly, he discusses in detail
the natural features of the earth, and the mysteries of phenomena—earthquakes, "the depths of Erebus," and so forth.

He appears to accept, like the more liberal thinkers of
the early Christian time, the circular, or at least semi-
circular, form of the earth, but on nearly all other points
he only transcribes the ordinary stories, principally from
Solinus, Orosius, and Isidore, and many of his ideas are
barely on a par with those of Hesiod. Thus in reference
to the inhabited earth, he clings to the notion of its being
a quadrilateral; for this right-angled shape seems to him
the only satisfactory explanation of the text which declared
that the elect should be "gathered from the four winds,
from one end of heaven to the other." [1]

The last work that need be mentioned here is the compilation of Guido.[2] The author, a priest of Ravenna, seems
to have written, about A.D. 850,[3] this sketch of Mediterranean
coast-lands. Like his original, the anonymous geographer
of the same city, he stops at the mention of Ravenna to

---

[1] Matt. xxiv. 31. Cf. on the
encircling ocean, "De Universo," xi.
3; the three continents with Asia
equal to the other two, xii. 2; the
walls and rivers of Paradise, xi. 10,
xii. 3; the Caspian communicating
with the Northern Ocean; Jerusalem
in the centre of the world; the ocean
coming up to the south of Fezzan,
etc.

[2] Cf. J. A. Fabricius, Biblioth.
Lat., iii., art. "Guido."

[3] Though some critics have traced

his origin to Pisa ("Guido the
Pisan"), and brought down his date
to the twelfth century. See Bock's
"Lettre sur . . . Liber Guidónis,"
in *Annuaire de la Bibl. Roy. de
Belgique*, xii., 1851, pp. 145–157.
But these contentions seem very
doubtful. See Avezac, "Le Ravennate;" the edition of Guido by
Pinder and Parthey, 1860; Tira-
boschi, Stor. Lett. Ital. III. ii. 255,
256; arts. in Biog. Univ., and Nouv.
Biog. Gén.

give us some details about himself and his time; "for here I, all unlearned, and least of the servants of Christ, was brought up, which town was once distinguished as the seat of the court, and is now illustrious from its hierarchical dignity."[1]

Guido begins with some words of praise for the social instinct in man,[2] which shows him his duty to the world at large—like Cato in Lucan, "Nec sibi sed toti genitum se credere mundo."[3]　It is this feeling, he continues, which has led him to dedicate some part of his labour to the general use, and to describe the regions of the coast.　Here and there he adds a few notes to his model.　Brundusium, lately destroyed by Romoald of Beneventum; Beneventum, the famous ducal city; Cassino, celebrated as the seat of the mother-house of the Order of St. Benedict;—these are instances of the commentary which Guido supplies to the catalogues of the text-book he so closely follows.[4]　But throughout his register he is chiefly interested in the martyrs who to his mind had raised the transient glory of great cities[5] into an eternal one, and his attention is but seldom arrested by anything of secular concern.

VI. Maps.

The popular idea of the habitable world among the subjects of Augustus, of Trajan, and even of Aurelian and Diocletian, was naturally much more confined, simple, and

---

[1] Cap. 20 (Pinder and Parthey).

[2] Caps. 1, 2.

[3] Lucan, Pharsal. ii. 383.

[4] Caps. 27–52.　"Salerno, where now rests the body of St. Matthew;" refers to the translation of the Apostle's relics to Salerno in 954; so this entry must be of subsequent date.　The Romoald of text is prob.

Duke Romoald II. 703–730.

[5] E.g. Constantinople, that "wore the purple and diadem of the world's empire;" Athens, once the "nurse of philosophers and orators;" and "renowned" Aquileia, which "most cruel Attila" destroyed (caps. 106, 110-117).

symmetrical than that of Strabo or of Ptolemy. According to the former, the master of Rome was literally master of the earth; every part of it that was worth inhabiting was either a province of the Empire, or paid tribute to the same; Rome and the ancient world were one and the same thing. It was the ambition of the earlier Cæsars to realise this in literal fact, and their poets and courtiers spoke of it as if already done. Of the extent of Asia and Africa, even in the sense of a rough notion that these continents were of considerable size, few indeed had any idea; most, even of the educated class, firmly believed that Europe was greater than either of its rivals; and only with Marinus and Ptolemy was a different theory adopted by a powerful school. However much the Alexandrian geographer was deceived and dazzled by the new light that broke on him,—however we may wonder at his notion of unlimited land to south and east (making of the Indian Ocean an inland sea, and filling up the Southern Hemisphere with his extension of Asia and of Africa), we cannot forget that he was the first to recognise something of the true bulk (though not the true shape) of the land surface of our globe.

Very different was the earlier and generally more popular system of Eratosthenes, dating from the time of the second Punic war, which was really adopted by Strabo, while he reviled its author; by the men of letters, whose patriotism it suited; and by the populace who, with a blissful ignorance of their real teacher, took their geography from the poets,[1]

[1] See Reinaud's masterly treatise, "Rélations de l'Empire Romain avec l'Asie Orientale" (Paris, 1863), especially pp. 28, 36–39, 41–43, 51–55, 61–75, 80–82, 140–158, etc. Reinaud devotes himself in this work especially to illustrating the Augustan conception of the (literally) world-wide empire, as expounded by Virgil, Horace, Propertius, Tibullus, and others. This is, of course, strictly speaking, anterior to our subject, but it is essentially connected with mediæval theories.

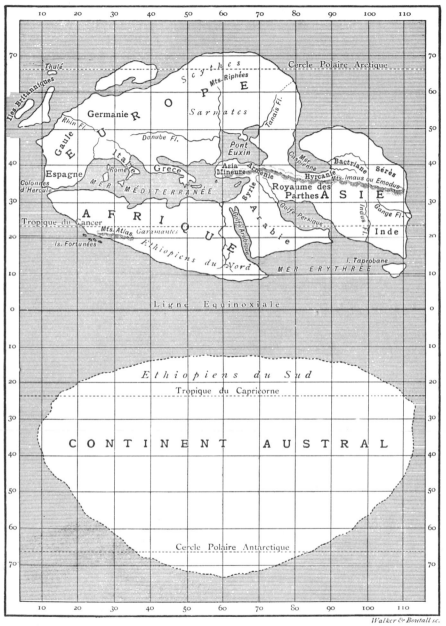

THE WORLD OF ORDINARY CLASSICAL GEOGRAPHY (AFTER REINAUD).

the orators, and the flatterers of the court and people of
Rome.   The vulgar belief, in the days of Cæsar and Cicero,
had its scientific basis in two theories.   For one it had the
simple doctrines of Eratosthenes—of a world divided in five
zones, of which one was torrid, two temperate, and two Arctic;
and of a habitable earth, which was entirely confined to the
north temperate zone, and in which each of the three continents was conveniently cut short,—Europe losing much of
its north and east, Asia far more in the same quarters, and
Africa the whole of its central and southern portion.[1]   But,
besides this, imagination might revel in the fancies of Crates
(about 160 B.C.), who, not content with the charge of the
great library at Pergamum, added to the known world one
or more additional continents in the midst of the untraversed
ocean, and especially an Australian or Antipodean world,
peopled by the Ethiopians of the South.   The possibility,
and even the likelihood, of such had indeed been already
indicated by Aristotle;[2] Crates popularised the old conjecture; and it seems to have been generally admitted by the
writers, from Virgil to Pliny, who governed the ideas of
the educated and half-educated multitude.

Ptolemy was the luxury of the select few; the geography
of the men who governed the Roman Empire, who fought in
its armies, or taught in its schools, was, beyond doubt, represented in the Peutinger Table far better than in the maps
of the Alexandrian geographer; and the Peutinger Table
is but a convenient exaggeration of the world-scheme of

[1] In this system Europe was made
equal to two-thirds of the bulk of Asia
and Africa together, and greater than
either of them separately; it thus
covered three-eighths of the entire
land surface of the world; being in
the proportion of *thirteen* against
the *eleven* of Asia, and the *eight* of
Africa.

[2] Meteorologica, ii. 5, §§ 10, 11.
See the dissertation of M. Charles
Jourdain, "De l'Influence d'Aristote
. . . sur la Découverte du Nouveau
Monde" (1861).

Eratosthenes; where the Ganges marks the Furthest East, and the Sahara Desert the Furthest South; and where the provinces of the Empire cover the greater part of *terra firma*. It is this system, either with or without the additions of Aristotle and Crates, which is the true basis of the higher mediæval geography from the time of its revival in the crusading period. Neither Ptolemy, nor Cosmas, nor the Arab geographers (so far as they professed any distinctive scheme or chart), ever quite displaced the system we have outlined among the deeper students of the Middle Ages. Not that they always followed it; still less that they always understood it: but dim or clear, it was the centre of their truer theories, the life of all in their geography that was not simply mythical.

No one can take up any of the works which fairly represent the scientific element in the geography even of the earlier Christian centuries, without seeing the truth of this; without tracing back, as already suggested, the common original of the more enlightened Christian geographers (through the Peutinger Table, and the other "Painted Worlds" now lost to us),[1] to the work of Eratosthenes in the third century before our era. In the speculations of Virgil upon another world beneath our own, we have an exact revival of the "Australian theory," which had sprung from the older Greek speculation; and there are few indeed of the "Latin" geographers, truly deserving of that name, whether in the Roman Empire or in the Roman Church, who do not follow the definitions of the school of Eratosthenes in the main features of their descriptions or designs. Teacher and disciples alike place India and the African Desert at the extremes of East and South; in both, the habitable earth lies like an island in the midst

---

[1] Pliny, H. N. iii. 3.

of an encircling ocean; in both, the Caspian is an inlet of the Northern Sea, and Scandinavia an island to the north of Germany.   Only two survivals, as we have said, actually remain to us from the map-science of the Old Empire—the Peutinger Table, and the plans which illustrate the geography of Ptolemy;[1] but there are at least ten classical references to other works of a similar kind, mostly in the nature of pictorial descriptions of the Roman world, or of particular provinces of the same, authorised by the Government, and set up for the instruction of the citizens in public places of the capital or other great cities.[2]   Every one of these has perished, so far as they are not embodied in the two relics that time has spared; and scarcely a trace of their influence is to be seen in the cartography of the earlier Middle Ages.   Reasoning from what we possess to what we have lost, we may assume that these classical maps, whatever their faults in delineation of outline, possessed at least one redeeming quality — fulness, and even vastness, of information; and this is precisely what is wanting in the sketches of the Christian period before the crusades.

Miserable indeed was the state of map-science in the centuries whose geography has occupied our attention so far; if we judge it, as we must, from the examples that have survived.   In all, these examples (of the sixth, seventh,

---

[1] Ascribed to a draughtsman named Agatlïodæmon, whom some (e.g. Lelewel and Marinelli) conjecture to have lived in the Byzantine period, say about A.D. 450; but who more probably executed these plans under the Pagan Empire, if he was not an *alias* for Ptolemy himself.

[2] The ten references in question are: (1) In Varro, "De Re Rustica," i. 2. (2, 3) Propertius, "Elegies,"
iv. 11 ; v. 3.   (4) Vitruvius, Architect. viii. 2, 6, etc.   (5) Eumenius of Autun, "Oratio pro instaurandis scholis," chs. 20, 21.   (6) Suetonius, "Domitian," ch. 10.   (7, 8) Pliny, "Natural History," iii. 3, 17; vi. 139. (9) Ovid, "Pontic Epistles," II. i. 37, etc.   (10) Lampridius, "Life of Alexander Severus," ch. 45. All these are non-Christian and pre-Constantinian; the similar references

eighth, and ninth centuries) cannot be estimated as more
than nine in number: the plans of Cosmas (reckoned as
one, and only one, mappe-monde, as his sketches merely
represent this single world-conception from various points of
view); the map of Albi; the " Image of the World," in the
(?) ninth-century Sallust at Leipzig; the similar " Imago
Mundi rotunda," at Strassburg; the three sketches of the
world-circles, or climates, in the Paris manuscript of St.
Isidore's " Book of Wheels," of about A.D. 900; the plani-
sphere, in a ninth-century manuscript at Leyden; and the
plan inserted by Santarem in his Atlas,[1] from a Madrid
manuscript of the same century. With this our meagre
list must come to an end. For not even the earliest
surviving specimen of the " Beatus Maps "—that in the
possession of Lord Ashburnham at Battle—can really be
assigned to so early a date.[2]

Some hasty theorists have imagined that other maps
of this time must have existed; supposing the peripli, or
coasting records, of Roman traders and navigators, to have
been accompanied by coast charts. But these peripli, so
far as known, were simply sailing directions and nothing
more, not drawn but written; and whatever designs of a
cartographical nature the Old World may have had for the
help of its mariners, we have no warrant for assuming the
existence of such coast charts, as we have for believing in
the reality of many lost road-maps, such as the magnificent
specimen that Conrad Peutinger brought to light in 1507.

We have pointed out already that the plans inserted
in the Florentine manuscript of Cosmas are probably of the

---

of Vegetius, in his " Epitoma Rei
Militaris" (iii. 6), addressed to Valen-
tinian II. about A.D. 380; and of
Cassiodorus in his " Letter to the

Monks" (De Inst. Div. Script.), fall
within the Christian period.

[1] Sheet IV., No. II.

[2] *I.e.* earlier than the tenth century.

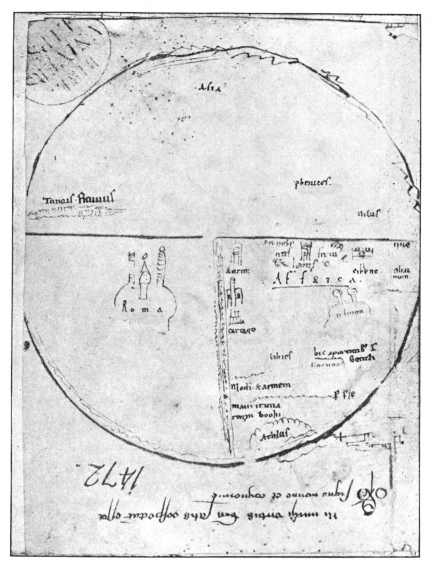

THE WORLD ACCORDING TO THE NINTH [OR TENTH?] CENTURY MAP-SKETCH IN SALLUST
MS. AT LEIPSIC.

[To face p. 380.

author's own designing in the sixth century, and have been considered by many as the oldest of Christian maps.   There is, however, one of still earlier date requiring notice in this place,—that famous example which, although in the main of the Augustan period, was probably revised and reissued several times, in the second, third, fourth, and fifth centuries—under Theodosius, according to one tradition; under the Antonines, or under Valens, according to recent surmise,—and which may be claimed, in a secondary sense, as belonging to our subject.   This claim is made a little more specious by the fact that the Peutinger Table (for it is this which is here in question) was undoubtedly put into its present shape by a monk of Colmar in 1265, and is thus, as we have it, mediæval, or at least mediævalised. Yet there can be no question that the table is essentially a map of the pagan world—a touchstone, as it has been called, of ancient geography; that the Christian and mediæval accretions are trifling and superficial; and that even in our present copy we have a pretty faithful repro- duction of a road-map, designed to give a view of the Roman Empire and the outside world, about the time of Augustus.

This being so, we shall not attempt to describe it at any length.   Like the maps of Ptolemy, it is in spirit, if not in letter, almost entirely pre-Christian, and therefore beyond the scope of this inquiry; but, without taking an unfair advantage of the interpolations which connect it with the fifth or the thirteenth century—such as the desert where the children of Israel wandered forty years, the mountain where they received the Law, or Mount Olivet—we may briefly indicate the main features of the table.   It gives a view of the world under twelve divisions,[1] from Britain

---

[1] Of which the first (the most westerly, including Spain and Bri- tain) is much mutilated and almost destroyed. Cf. edit. of Desjardins,

to the mouths of the Ganges in the Eastern Ocean, drawn out in a greatly elongated and distorted form, which form is obviously adopted as a convenient way of displaying the principal lines of route. On this plan (somewhat similar in shape to the Bayeux tapestry) are laid down, not only the roads of the Empire with their stations, but also three classes of illustrations. The smaller towns are depicted by little houses, the greater—Rome, Constantinople, Antioch, and Alexandria—by vignettes or medallions; three forest districts, two in Germany and one in Syria, are represented by sketches of trees. The general appearance of the map is probably due to its original—one of those "painted worlds" which we know to have been set up in Rome under Augustus, as by Vipsanius Agrippa in the Portico of Octavia,[1] and which may have resulted from the survey of the provinces ascribed by tradition to Julius Cæsar.[2] Such public tables were corrected from time to time as high official authorities, and even used for the instruction or confusion of youth; on the other hand, private mapmaking was discouraged.[3]

1869-1874 (unfinished); of Konrad Miller, 1888; and the Studies of Ruelens (Brussels Institute of Geography, 1884) and of Bryan Walker (Cambridge Antiq. Soc. Communics., vol. v. pp. 237-264—1881-1884). Also cf. Avezac, Le Ravennate.

[1] Pliny, H. N., iii. 2, s. 3, sect. 17; iv. 12, s. 25, sect. 81.

[2] Æthicus, Cosmography, pref.

[3] Cf. Propertius (v. 3, 37), who was himself a sufferer from this kind of instruction; and Eumenius, the orator ("Oratio pro Instaurandis Scholis," cc. 20, 21), who advises (A.D. 298) that boys should be made to study geography from the Portico pictures, and refers especially to one at Autun. The same Eumenius, in addressing Constantius Chlorus, the father of the great Constantine, expatiates on the delight with which a Roman ought to look upon such a mappe-monde, as he would see thereon nothing but regions subject to him, or in alliance with him (nihil alienum): "Panegyrici Veteres," i. 254; Reinaud, "Relations de l'Empire Romain avec l'Asie Orientale," pp. 254, 255. On the other side, Suetonius (Domitian, 10) tells us how Metianus Pomposianus was charged with having in his own possession a map of the world depicted on parchment—a capital offence in the time of Domitian.

Except for a very few instances, where the interpolation may be easily traced, there is nothing in the Peutinger map which has any reference to a time later than Diocletian; and the greater number of the names it contains may be referred to an era earlier than the death of Augustus in A.D. 14.[1] The arrangement of the barbarian tribes on the frontiers of the Empire seems to agree pretty nearly with what we know of them in the reign of Marcus Aurelius; and the importance of the name of Persia, for instance, in the far East, perhaps points to a revision of this part of the table as late as the third century, at some time subsequent to the great Persian revival of A.D. 226: but these details leave the essential character of the plan strictly classical. Recent conjectures have assigned the final arrangement of the table to the mysterious Castorius, whom we only know as the alleged source of most of the facts and figures in the anonymous geographer of Ravenna.[2] The references of various authors of the fourth century—Vegetius, Lampridius,[3] St. Ambrose, and St. Hilary of Poictiers—to pictorial itineraries of their time, have been pressed into the service of this theory, which, however, stops short of assigning a Christian authorship to the table, though bringing its composition down to the middle of the fourth century.

A work which contains nearly six hundred notices of heathen temples and worship could hardly come as a whole from a Christian hand, though, as we have pointed out, some notes have undoubtedly been added by a Christian reviser, just as certain others (for example, the mention of

[1] So concludes Desjardins (p. 79), speaking more narrowly of Gaul.

[2] Cf. Miller, Die Weltkarte des Castorius (1888), which strives to discredit the connection between the Augustan maps and the table (p. 67), and to fix the date of Castorius to A.D. 365–6, in the reigns of Valentinian and Valens, whom Miller thinks the three chief medallions commemorate.

[3] Life of Alex. Severus, ch. 45.

" Jerusalem, which is now Elia ") prove the workmanship of a redactor in the latter days of the pagan empire, between Hadrian and Constantine.

It is obvious that the plans inserted in the Florentine [1] manuscript of Cosmas are, if genuinely drawn by the author of the topography himself, the oldest known examples of Christian maps—of those, at least, which are not mere re-issues of pagan originals. On the whole, it is probable that these sketches were really drawn by the "learned writer" when he "set down his excommunication;" but even as they stand in manuscript, they are certainly older than anything of their kind,[2] except the mappe-monde of Albi.

They consist, as will be seen by a reference to their reproductions in this volume, firstly, of five sketches of the universe, drawn especially to illustrate the great mountain in the north of the world, the heavens above and below the firmament, and the course of sun and moon ; and, secondly, of two delineations of the earth's surface, the encircling ocean and the patriarchal world beyond. One of these is a mere outline of general features ; but the other forms, though roughly, a true mappe-monde. In this the Mediterranean is drawn with much greater fidelity than we find in any Christian work before true surveying began with the Portolani of the thirteenth century. The Black Sea and Propontis are both recognisable, though less successful than the main part of the inland or " Roman " water ; the Caspian, Red Sea, and Persian Gulf are depicted as three inlets from the ocean, running due north and south ; and the three rivers of Nile, Euphrates, and Tigris all appear as coming through from the outer earth, into Babylonia and Egypt, by passages beneath the ocean. The earth, like the ocean and

[1] Ninth century. [2] *I.e.* Christian maps.

THE WORLD-MAP OF COSMAS.

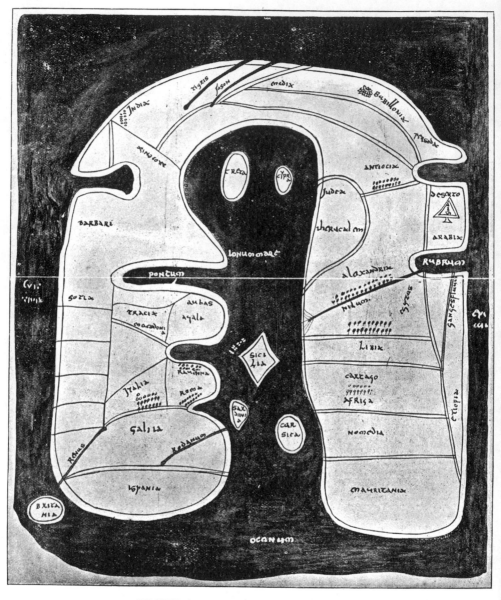

THE WORLD ACCORDING TO THE MAPPE MONDE OF ALBI.

[To face p. 385.

the antediluvian land, is absolutely right-angled; and in Paradise, beyond the east wind (which is portrayed blowing its trumpet towards the Euphrates), are depicted ten great lakes or fountains of waters, from which spring the rivers of our world.

The other plans in the " Christian Topography " have not much bearing on geography. Most of them are occupied with Old Testament subjects, or with the animals of India.[1] But two are devoted to the problems of the Zodiac, the Heavenly bodies and the Antipodes. In the last example, four men are drawn standing feet to feet, in scorn of a doctrine so repugnant to common sense as that of a round world.

In the library of Albi, in Languedoc, exists the earliest mappe-monde which has actually come down to us from this period. It occurs in a manuscript of the eighth century, and is designed to illustrate the cosmography of Julius Honorius and of Orosius; but it is a mere sketch, very poorly executed, with many bad mistakes.[2] The connection

[1] In this connection we may notice that while the giraffe, or camelopard, the lion, the elephant, the tortoise, and the dolphin are fairly well represented, the rhinoceros, hippopotamus, and seal (phoca) are grotesque.

[2] Thus Judea appears on the south of the Mediterranean, Antioch to the south-east of Jerusalem, Crete to the North of Cyprus, Sardinia to the north of Corsica, the Ganges in the south of Africa. The west wind (zephyr) is turned into a south wind; the Caspian is an inlet from the Northern Ocean. Sicily is sharply four-cornered; and Britain, about the size of Corsica, lies close off the north-west of Spain. Spain and France together form a single peninsula. The Red Sea, Persian Gulf, Black Sea, and Caspian (all coloured green like the Rhine, Rhone, Nile, etc.) are made parallel, with a general direction from north to south; the Red Sea and Persian Gulf are exactly opposite to the Euxine and Caspian. The habitable world is pictured as an oblong, rounded at the corners, and surrounded by the ocean; but it is really confined to the Mediterranean lands, or the area of the old Empire, and Asia is reduced to a fringe of land on the east of the Mediterranean. Yet though so strictly Roman in plan, Italy is very barbarously drawn. India, Media and Babylonia appear all together along

which some have imagined between this and the map of Cosmas will not bear investigation. Yet, poor though it is, the Albi map as it stands is the unaltered work of the time of Bede and Charles Martel (c. A.D. 730), and, accordingly, venerable as the oldest geographical monument of Latin or Western Europe in the Middle Ages.

Six other map sketches, of small importance, and all apparently of the ninth century, were long ago unearthed from the recesses of great libraries by the diligence of Santarem. Three of these, two of them planispheres, one, after the Arab fashion, showing the south at the top, occur in a single manuscript at Paris; one, from the library of Roda, in Aragon, is now at Madrid; the last two are to be found at Strassburg and Leyden respectively.[1] None of these present any features of interest; except perhaps that, in the Spanish example, Asia appears as greater than all the rest of the world together; while, in the Strassburg map, the encircling ocean is drawn in Homeric and "Cosmic" fashion as a sort of river between inner and outer belts of land.[2]

Once more, some notice must be taken of maps which have now perished, but which we know to have been executed before the close of the ninth century. And about one of these lost representations of an incredibly contracted world there is an especial interest.

the eastern boundary of the map, where the Tigris and Phison (? Ganges, see p. 391, n.) suggest an Oriental Paradise which is not expressly indicated. The Nile, we may notice, joins the Red Sea and the Mediterranean; Mount Sinai is designated by a huge triangle, and all the people of Northern Europe are included in Gothia. Perhaps the closest parallel to the Albi example (though far superior) is the Anglo-Saxon map of the tenth century, in the British Museum (Cotton, Tib. B. v.). The manuscript is numbered 29, and entitled "Miscellanea, scilicet Dictionarium Glosæ in Evangelia." The map is on folio 487.

[1] We have reproduced all these from Santarem's atlas.

[2] See Bibl. Nat. (Paris) MSS. Lat. 4860; Strassburg MSS. civ. (15); Leyden Lat. MSS. Voss. Q. 29.

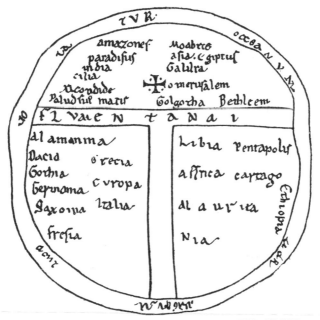

MAPPE MONDE FROM A MS. OF THE NINTH CENTURY, IN THE
LIBRARY AT STRASSBURG.

The sketches of Cosmas and of Albi are isolated works; it is in Spain, in the early days of Moslem rule and in the heat of the Adoptionist controversy, that the original is probably to be found of the first important *group* or school of Christian maps. The priest Beatus, who in the year 798 died in the Benedictine convent of Vallecava or Valcovado in the Asturias, and who opposed Felix of Urgel and his followers on the question of the "adoption"[1] of Christ in the Godhead, has been identified with much plausibility as the draughtsman of that plan which is the common source of the maps of St. Sever, Turin, Ashburnham, and seven others of the earlier Middle Ages, executed at various times between the tenth and thirteenth centuries, but all depending on a Spanish-Arabic prototype of the eighth. This prototype, however, appeared anonymously in a commentary on the Apocalypse, which has been fixed by internal and external criticism to a date in or near the year 776. The friends and enemies of Beatus in the Adoptionist quarrel, Fidelis[2] his abbot,[3] Queen Adosinda[4] his penitent and patroness, Etherius his ally, Elipandus[5] his opponent in the theological strife, are all well-known figures in the Spanish history of the time. He is connected by one tradition with the more famous Alcuin, as master with scholar; and at any rate he shares with his celebrated pupil the episcopal abuse of Elipandus, as an obscure "hill-man" and cave-dweller, a "babbling denizen of the woods," an "instructor

---

[1] As contrasted with his eternal and inalienable right therein.

[2] A curious coincidence with the (? Irish) traveller Fidelis, who must have lived at this very time. But the name is common enough, like that of Deusdedit, or Beatus himself. Six instances are pointed out by Letronne in the Acta Sanctorum (Feb. iii. 147; March iii. 907; June i. 264, 376, 633;

June ii. 666).

[3] Of St. John of Pravia, near Oviedo.

[4] Wife of King Silo (774–783).

[5] Archbishop of Toledo. Beatus by one account was a deaf-mute. (See J. Maria de Eguren, Descriptive Memorial of Spanish MSS., Madrid, 1859; and Cortambert in Bulletin Soc. Géog., Paris, 1877, pp. 337–363.)

of brutish beasts," a "forest donkey," and the like. His
friends, on the other hand, though declaring that his life
bore out to the full his title of Saint, are less explicit than
could be wished about his scientific attainments; and the
possibility still remains open that another hand may have
supplied the map to that commentary, which is in all
likelihood the work of Beatus.[1]   All this, however, is but of
small importance; as the original has not survived, and we
only possess derivatives belonging to a period subsequent
to the ninth century. Of these we intend to give an account
in the second section of this history, under the period which
we may call that of the Vikings and the Crusaders, from
the tenth century of our era.

Two other notices of lost maps, both of the Karling
period and of the eighth century, have a certain interest.
For one, Bishop Theodulf of Orleans (788–821) speaks of
himself as having painted a picture of the world upon a
wall of his house; and in obscure verses describes this map.
Like Alcuin,[2] he seems to have divided the habitable earth
into the three parts of Europe, Africa, and the Indies.
Like Ptolemy, he declares himself in some of his expressions
in favour of a fixed and immovable world; but in other
places he uses language very inconsistent with this belief.

Once more, the celebrated "librarian" Anastasius tells
us how Pope Zacharias—the same pontiff who helped the
Karling Dynasty to the Frankish Throne, and stamped out
the geographical heresies of Virgil—had had a mappe-
monde designed for his own use. In one of the chambers
of the Lateran Palace, this great churchman caused to be
painted a representation of the world, ornamented with

[1] Cf. its dedication to Etherius;
and see Miller, "Weltkarte des
Beatus," pp. 1–9; Cortambert (as
above).

[2] See Bishop Theodulf, "Carmina,"
iii.; Alcuin, "Carmina," xiii.

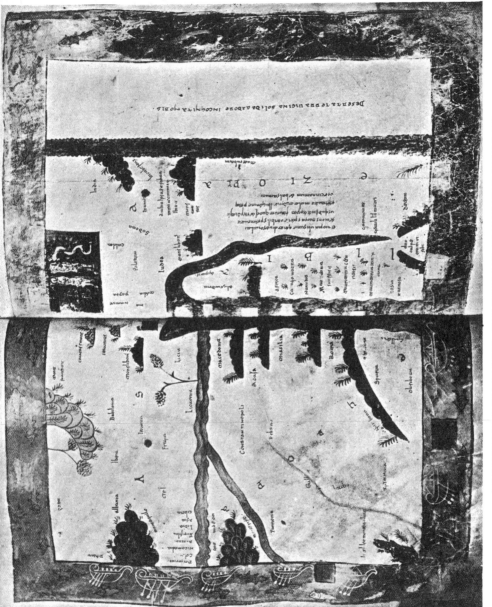

THE ASHBURNHAM MAP OF THE TENTH CENTURY. OLDEST DERIVATIVE SURVIVING OF THE ORIGINAL PLAN OF BEATUS.

descriptive verses or titles : the reputation of Zacharias
stood high for scholarly attainments, as for ecclesiastical
policy; of Greek origin himself, he was well acquainted
with a language that was now almost forgotten, but still
reverenced in the West ; and in spite (or even because) of
his strong objections to Antipodes, he may have found
pleasure in having before his eyes a world-picture of an
orthodox pattern.[1]

We have also to regret the loss of a map of this period
even more interesting than that of the Beatus commentary.
Einhardt, in his " Life of Charles the Great," tells us about
certain wonders of the emperor's library.　Among these
were three tables of silver and one of gold.　On one of the
former there was portrayed the "entire circuit of the
earth," divided into the three continents ; on the other two
were planned out the cities of Rome and Constantinople.

In that time it was hazardous to make the precious
metals a vehicle for art or science; and in the war of 842,
the precious silver table was broken up and divided among
the soldiers.[2]

A similar design, but of a ruder kind, was prepared, " with
subtle labour," at the monastery of St. Gall, about 870 ;[3]
but nothing can be heard of it in after-days, and we do not
know (though we may suspect) that this and the last-
named plan were in any way connected with the Peutinger
Table, or some of the other ancient designs which fed the
expiring flame of geographical science in Christendom.

There remain a few yet more obscure allusions to lost
maps of these ages.　Thus Vegetius, in his epitome of

[1] " Orbis Terrarum descriptionem
depinxit atque versiculis ornavit."
See Santarem, " Essai sur Cosmographie," ii. 23, 24; Andres, " Dell'
origine . . . d'ogni litteratura," vol.
iii. ch. 2.

[2] Einhardt, ch. 33; Col. edit. of
1521, p. 41.　See Lelewel, Géog., i. 9.

[3] Ratpert, De Casis Monasterii S.
Galli, c. 10.　See Miller, " Die Weltkarte des Castorius."

Matters Military,[1] addressed to Valentinian II. about A.D. 380, refers to a plan then in existence, which is probably different from the Peutinger Table, though a work of much the same kind; Cassiodorus, under Theodoric the Great, the barbarian restorer of Italian civilisation, expressly mentions one Dionysius[2] as the author of a table which seems to have contained, like that of "Peutinger," a map of the Empire and the known world of that time; similar language is used by St. Ambrose and St. Hilary of Poictiers; and the Ravennese geographer himself claims to have designed "with wondrous skill" a picture of all the lands that he described. On this last in particular, much ingenious conjecture has been spent. Granted that Vegetius and Cassiodorus are thinking of plans more or less closely resembling the lengthened oblong of the Peutinger Table, yet the map of the Ravennese, if it was ever really executed, must have been very different from these, answering to the anonymous geographer's written descriptions. Was it, then, round, square, oval, or of what other shape? Was it planned from a centre at Jerusalem, Constantinople, or Ravenna itself? Or was it, after all, only the work of the Castorius whom the Ravennese so constantly quotes, and who was probably the compiler of a pictorial itinerary of the classical pattern? It does not seem worth while to enter upon a long discussion of a design which may never have existed at all, and we shall content ourselves with indicating a preference for the oval and Ravenna-centred reconstruction of Avezac.[3]

---

[1] iii. 6.

[2] ? Periegetes.

[3] Which is here reproduced with some modifications. (See Rav. i. 18.) Kiepert has given, in Pinder and Parthey's edition of the Ravennese, a circular restoration, with Jerusalem in the centre; Marinelli ("Erdkunde," 71–74) has argued very skilfully for a middle point at Constantinople; while Lelewel believes (Géog. i. 6, 86) that the map of the Ravennese was right-angled.

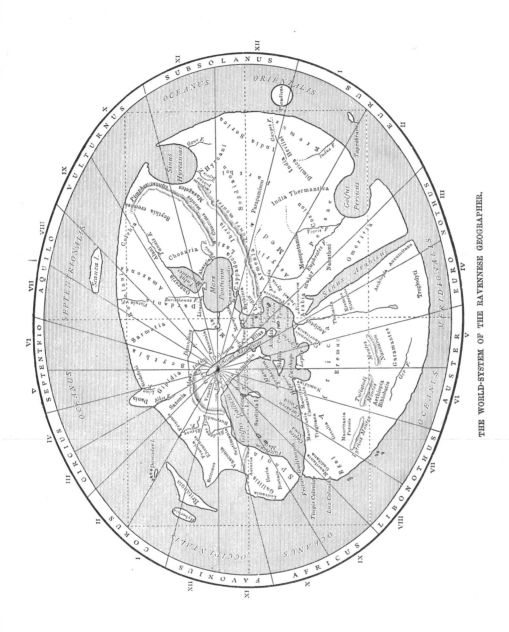

THE WORLD-SYSTEM OF THE RAVENNESE GEOGRAPHER.

Lastly, we may notice an attempt, apparent from the map-sketches of this time, to reconcile the contradictory language of Scripture on the *circuit of the earth* and the *four corners of the same*, by the device of a T within an O ; which also indicated in a convenient manner the division of continents. This is to be seen in the Madrid sketch-map, and in the Strassburg example within our period, as well as on innumerable plans of later date ; for, as Dati said—

> " Un T dentro a un O mostra il disegno
> Come in *tre* parte fu diviso il mondo." [1]

It may seem that an exaggerated attention has been given, in this review of geographical science within the early mediæval world, to the Europe of the first six centuries after the triumph of Christianity ; but it is of no little consequence to us whether the theories in question were right or wrong, sensible or senseless, profound or ridiculous. In any case, they had an immense and a long-continued influence upon human thought ; men suffered and even died for daring to oppose the beliefs that now were being consolidated ; and it is not of small importance whether man's views of the world that he inhabits were such as to cramp his energies and terrorise his mind, or the reverse.

ADDITIONAL NOTE TO PAGE 386.

The Phison is identified with the Ganges by Augustine De Gen. ad litt. viii. 7 ; by Jerome, Epistle iv. ; by Ambrose, De Paradis. c. 3 ; as by Josephus, Ant. I. i. § 3. So apparently most of the Fathers. But Philostorgius thinks it the Hydaspes ; Severian of Gabala, the Danube ; Epiphanius concludes it is Ganges and Indus *together* (Ancor. c. 58).

---

[1] Dati, " Sphera," iii. 11.

CHAPTER VII.

NON-CHRISTIAN GEOGRAPHY OF THE EARLY MIDDLE AGES.

THE Christian geography, whose development — or degradation—we have been watching, often appears as if it were an outcome of a dying world; yet the time was not without some clear signs of a new and living one. Any careful study of the earlier Middle Ages reveals the fact that, behind the apparent barbarism and comparative backwardness of Christian society, the foundations of modern civilization were being laid under healthier conditions than the old Empire, with all its magnificence, had ever realized. And now, in the eighth and ninth centuries of our era, two new forces of penetrating character began to act upon the seemingly inert mass of the Western nations. The Arabs in the South, and the Vikings in the North, appearing as the mortal enemies of the Christian world, in the end awakened it to fresh activity, and inspired it with the new energy, the new blood, the new knowledge, which found so profound and so universal an expression in the Crusading age. Of these new forces, the Arabic or Southern was the earlier and the more intellectual; the Viking or Northern was the later, but the more racial or vital in its action upon Christendom. Both begin as non-Christian powers—the one heretical, the other heathen; both are well worthy of a separate and detailed treatment: but as our subject is properly limited to the geographical expansion of *Christendom* alone,[1] it is.

[1] And, except for purposes of illustration, of Latin Christendom.

impossible for us to consider either of these movements with the same minuteness as the story of Christian enterprise itself. We can only attempt to sketch the main features of their history, to trace the chief ways in which they affected the development of Europe, and to form some idea of their respective positions in the general drama of the discovery of the world. Here we shall content ourselves with adding to the account already given of Christian geography to the close of the ninth century, a short review of non-Christian enterprise in the Eastern world for the same period; and for this purpose we shall select from two classes of material —one Arabic, the other Chinese,—treating both with especial reference to their bearing upon the Christian world of the West. The Norse or Viking movement we shall leave to the second part of our subject—to the Crusading age and the central period of the Middle Ages, with which it is essentially connected.

I.

And, first, we may try to estimate the Arabic share in the earlier geographical advance. Controlling, as they did from the seventh century, most of the centres of ancient learning in Africa and Asia,[1] the Arabs were able to take advantage of older knowledge, if they cared to do so. And this they did, to an extraordinary degree. No race has ever shown a greater keenness for the acquisition of knowledge, or more favour to the growth of science. Leaving on one side their achievements in chemistry, in physics, or in mathematics, and looking only to their geography, we shall find the contrast between Islam and Christendom more and more sharply defined in this age, if judged not by faith but by works, by contemporary monuments rather than by the

[1] Above all, Ptolemy's own Alexandria.

prejudice of later times.   But let us first of all admit to the
full what may be said to disparage Arab thought in general,
and its geographical labours in particular.   For it has left us
many works, but few masterpieces ; and its geography, in
especial, lacks concise and orderly treatment, is constantly
vitiated by tendencies both to rambling and to story-telling,
and has an altogether inadequate conception of the sea.

Thus it was wanting in those great discoveries that
rewarded the daring of European sailors in the fifteenth and
sixteenth centuries.   No Arabs, so far as we are aware, ever
ventured across a great ocean in the manner of Columbus ;
or carried out such a coasting of unknown lands as the
Portuguese in their progress round Africa ; or tried to realize
that doctrine of the roundness of the earth, which was so
clearly taught by the ablest of the Mussulman geographers.

Instead of this, they rather helped to intensify old
superstitions about the ocean and its dangers.   Thus some
theologians declared that a man mad enough to embark
upon the *Sea of Darkness* (or Encircling Ocean) should be
deprived of civil rights, as manifestly irresponsible for his
actions.   And so, at the very time when Christian exploration was beginning in the Atlantic, one light of Moslem
science declared such exploration to be impossible, for
"whirlpools always destroyed any adventurer : " while
another decreed the ocean to be "boundless, so that ships
dared not venture out of sight of land ; for even if the sailors
knew the direction of the winds, they would not know
whither those winds would carry them; and, as there was no
inhabited country beyond, they would run a risk of being
lost in mists and fogs."

Again, though the Arabic knowledge of the earth was
wider than Ptolemy's, and far sounder than his for many
regions in the east and south, the Moslem scientists showed

a wonderful docility in repeating the Greek traditions in geography; and in some cases they added to old mistakes wilder inventions or confusions of their own.   Thus the symmetrical divisions of the earth's surface into three parts water and one part *terra firma ;* of the habitable earth into four chief empires; of the circuit of the globe into equal lengths of land and sea,[1] all reappeared (with many other ancient axioms) in Arabic geographers.

In Greek language they talked of the five (or seven) zones or *climates,* and of the length of the inhabited earth as just twice the breadth.   From India they derived their doctrine of a Cupola or Summit of the world, in which were curiously combined two of the superstitions which appear in Christian thought; namely, the notions of Jerusalem as the navel of the earth, and of the northern mountain round which sun and moon revolved, and on which therefore day and night depended.   From a mingling of Eastern fancy with Western history, the Arabs formed many of their stories; for instance, their favourite legend of the tribes of Gog-Magog, and the wall of brass and iron behind which they had been prisoned by Alexander of Macedon or by one of the Cæsars.

Once more the over-refined state of their language was a hindrance to the progress both of true art and true science among the Arab race.   The love of rhyme, of antithesis, of rhetorical repetition, so highly developed in their literature, ended in degrading cleverness to artificiality and style to mechanical contrivance.   Though they sat at the feet of the Greeks, they never learnt an important part of their lesson : their surprising and sometimes intolerable diffuseness is in sharp contrast to the precision, the concentration, and the epigrammatic power of their great models; and so, among

[1] 180° in each.

the twenty thousand writers of standard Arabic, there are few indeed who have reached a catholic reputation. Yet, with all its faults, the Arab mind accomplished much. In geography it preserved perhaps the main part of the Greek tradition. In certain fields, both of practical and theoretical activity, it greatly improved upon the Greek results; and in the face of the backwardness, the barbarism, and the credulity of contemporary Europe, its work is still more remarkable. The almost Arctic night of the one seemed to leave to the other an almost equally unbroken daylight. Men like Massoudy, Albyrouny, or Edrisi had a better and more adequate conception of the old world in general than was possessed by any Christian before the thirteenth century. The use of the magnet was naturalized in the Caliphate, though in a very limited way, generations before it had passed westwards to Christendom; the construction of maps and globes had reached a considerable proficiency in Islam, while our own draughtsmanship was rudimentary and, by comparison, almost ridiculous.

In three directions Arabic explorers more especially widened the horizon of what we may call the concrete, as opposed to the abstract or scientific, world. First in the far East they improved the connections between China, India, Tartary, and Persia to such an extent that, in a sense, they may be said to have realized, for the first time in history, the true bulk of Asia. The lands beyond the Ganges, the Jaxartes, and the Bolor Mountains had never before been so thoroughly and so permanently brought within the ken of the Levantine countries. Again, it was the Arabs who first of civilized races made any lasting impression on Soudanese Africa beyond the Sahara, or upon the Zanzibar coast of the Indian Ocean—from Magadoxo to Sofala. Lastly, the earliest attempts to penetrate the steppes of European Russia

were due to the trade enterprise of Saracen merchants. And,
as usual, these movements, like all great advances of the
human race, were the outcome of favourable circumstance.
The subjects of the undivided Caliphate had a wider outlook,
and better opportunities for a still greater enlargement of
the field of vision, than had been possessed by any people
or any country since the Antonines ; and they were, almost
beyond conception, more fortunately placed than the Christian nations of the pre-Crusading time. The last of the
Ommiads[1] (c. A.D. 750) reigned over three-fourths of the
empire of Alexander, together with, perhaps, one-quarter of
the dominion of Trajan. From the burning heat of the
Sahara to the pleasantly temperate lands of Gascony and of
Bactria,—in Cordova and in Samarcand, in Scinde and
Cyprus,—the same sovereign was acknowledged a hundred
years after Mohammed had sent his embassies to Heraclius
and to Chosroes, and called on them to join with him in
acknowledging the Unity of God.

It may be useful for the better understanding not merely
of Arab, but also of mediæval geography in general, if we
examine a little more closely the commercial connections of
Islam with non-Moslem nations, and the mercantile highways under the more or less direct control of the successors
of Mohammed.

The principal trade-routes[2] within the Caliphate were,
after all, the courses of the two river-valleys of Mesopotamia
and their continuation in the Persian Gulf. The commerce,
like the politics of the Empire, centred in Bagdad and
Bassora. It was from this source that the main current of

---

[1] And the earlier Abbassides controlled nearly the whole of this great
dominion. Spain was the only important loss resulting from the revolution of A.D. 750.

[2] On this especially, see Heyd,
"Commerce du Levant," i. 24–51, etc.

their trade started for India and for China, just as the lesser
stream of East African commerce took its rise in the
harbours of the Red Sea. Very early in the history of Islam,
the Arabs established their factories in the "lands of the
sun-rising;" and their merchants were probably among the
strangers to whom the port of Canton was thrown open in
A.D. 700. Half a century later (in 758) this town was
actually pillaged and burnt by the subjects of the Caliph,
in alliance with native rebels; but until 795 they continued
to frequent this harbour; and, even after they had abandoned
it, they found a second home in Khanfu for another hundred
years. Arab markets existed also in Cochin China and
Ceylon. After the domestic revolution which convulsed
China in 878, their trade in the far East seems to have been
more and more concentrated at Kalah, in the Malay Peninsula—a point expressly named in the Voyages of Sinbad
the Sailor. The Chinese merchants therefore, so far as
they still desired to retain the Arab trade, were now compelled to resort to the aforesaid Kalah, which took the place
that Ceylon had formerly held, for instance, in the sixth
century. The Malay emporium was doubtless the source
of Malayan Islamism. From the days of Massoudy to
those of Aboulfeda, Kalah was the "chief harbour"
for all the regions between Oman and China; and
from this commerce came the improved knowledge of
Java which the mariners of Siraf gained in the tenth
century.

There is reason to believe that before A.D. 700 (and perhaps
even before Mohammed) Arab merchants were already
established in Ceylon; and their trading colonies were
thickly scattered at a very early date along the Malabar
coast, where the Zamorin Kerman Permal, at the beginning
of the ninth century, embraced Islam and opened his

dominions to Moslem commerce.   Thus, in 916, Massoudy,[1] in the course of his Indian journeys, came upon a settlement of ten thousand Mussulmans at Saimour, near the present Bombay ; many of them born in that country, of Arab parents, and enjoying, like the Moslem colony at Khanfu, the privilege of self-government.

While the Arabs sprinkled the Malabar coast with their trading colonies, their armies had already reached the Indus. At the same time[2] that Kutaiba received orders to advance upon Kashgar, and threaten China by way of the Gobi Desert and the Great Wall, his colleague, Mohammed Ibn Kassim, commanding the armies of the Caliph in Scinde, was urged to attack the Celestial Empire on the side of India, conquering Hindostan on the way, and thus completing the triumph of Islam in the Eastern world.   The general who should first reach the Land of Silk should have the government of the same—to this the Commander of the Faithful had pledged himself ; and the ruler, who already from his palace at Damascus held sway over more than half the diameter of our hemisphere, from the Atlantic to the Hindu Kush, might well hope to hear of the submission of Benares and Canton.   All on fire with the prospect of such a victory and such rewards, the northern army spread over the land of Bokhara and Samarcand to the banks of the Jaxartes, and poured through the hill-country of Ferghanah upon Kashgar.   No less eager to be first in the race to the China Sea, the southern or " Indian " host started for the Ganges Valley, and entered Moultan, where their leader hung a piece of beef round the neck of the great Hindu idol of that

---

[1] Massoudy, "Meadows of Gold," ii. 85 (Barbier de Meynard and Pavet de Courteille); Reinaud, "Mémoire sur l'Inde," p. 242, and his edition of the "Two Mussulman Travellers " ("Relations des voyages dans l'Inde et à la Chine,") p. xlviii. Ibn-Haukal, Albyrouny, and Kazwini speak to the same effect.

[2] At the opening of the eighth century.

holy city.   But the sudden death of the Caliph, "the glorious and inactive " Walid, abruptly ended these gigantic schemes, though not before the Son of Heaven, terrified by the coming storm, had bowed before the power of Kutaiba, and sought to make his peace with presents and fair words.[1]

Within a hundred years from this time, the conquering age of the Caliphate had begun to pass away ; and till the time of the Sultans of Ghazni, three centuries after Kutaiba, the movement that he had led was in abeyance, and Islam only advanced in India and Central Asia by the more peaceful means of commerce and social intercourse.   Thus the interior of Hindostan remained almost unknown to Arab enterprise, although the coasts were familiar enough. Towards the east, the Moslem geographers, like the Moslem merchants, usually stopped about Moultan in their progress through the upland of Northern India.

One constant danger of the *coast* routes, towards Ceylon on the one side and Zanzibar on the other, was the nest of pirates in Socotra ; but, in spite of this, a regular trade in the merchandise of Further Asia[2] was maintained in the Red Sea ports, in those of the Persian Gulf, and even in some of the harbours of the east coast of Africa beyond Guardafui.   Daybal, near the mouth of the Indus ; Muscat, Sohar, and Siraf to the east ; Aden, Djeddah, Suez, and Magadoxo to the west and south of Arabia, seem to have been the chief centres of this southern trade in the first three centuries of the Hegira.   It was by this maritime route, in one or other of its branches, that most of the

---

[1] See Edrisi (Jaubert), i. 167; Reinaud, in Mém. de l'Acad., xvii. 185, 186; Rémusat, "Mélanges Asiatiques," i. 441, 442; de Sacy, in Not. et Extraits, ii. 374, 375.   Yule, Cathay Prelim. Essay, lxxx., lxxxi.

[2] See Massoudy, i. 303, 308; ii. 52; iii. 7, etc., 12, 37, 43–48.   Also in the "Two Mussulman Travellers," p. clviii. of Reinaud's Preface, and pp. 93, 142, and 153 of the text.

products of the Indian Ocean and of South-Eastern Asia, as well as of the Soudan countries, arrived in the Levant.

By comparison, the overland routes were unimportant, at least in reference to the value of the traffic that passed over them. Even from Samarcand, Balkh, or Bokhara,[1] men usually preferred the ocean way to China, rather than face the terrors of mountain and desert along the caravan track. Between India and the Caliphate, merchants, if they did not go by sea, usually followed one of two distinct paths, either north-west from the mouth of the Indus through Beluchistan, or from the Punjab to Cabul and Ghazni. From the great marts of the modern Afghanistan, both the Oxus valley on one side and Mesopotamia on the other were directly supplied. But *within* the lands of Islam, as they stood in the eighth and following centuries, many of the rarest treasures which the Mediterranean world had always been forced to seek in distant countries were to be found without further trouble. It was hardly needful to go to China for silk, when the culture was naturalized in Merv and Bokhara; ambergris, pearls, and precious stones were to be found off the coasts of

---

[1] But of course a certain commerce was maintained, though liable to interruption from the Turks; and setting aside occasional and extraordinary journeys, such as those of the great Chinese pilgrims (Fa-Hien, and Hiouen-Thsang, etc.) and some Arab travellers (such as Misar Abou Dolaf, son of Mohalhal), we have, as evidence of a regular commerce in the time of the early Caliphate, certain facts recorded by the Arab historians. Thus, at the capture of Samarcand and Bokhara by the Arabs, one of the chief merchants of the country offered 5000 pieces of Chinese silk to save his life. In the time of Massoudy, two routes were principally followed from the Sogd to China (Mas. i. 347–349). The former apparently passed by Lake Issyk-Kul, and Tengri Khan along much the same way that Hiouen-Thsang followed on his outward journey, and occupied two months (according to Abou Zeyd Hassan in the "Two Mussulman Travellers," p. 114, Reinaud),—an extremely short journey for that time. The other route possibly took Hiouen-Thsang's *homeward* course by Khotan. There was also a route to China through Thibet, but this was extremely difficult, and almost exclusively used for the musk trade.

Arabia and in the mountains of Persia, as well as in Ceylon and the further East; cotton and the sugar-cane, myrrh and incense, woven and embroidered stuffs, rare and sweet-smelling woods, ivory, and metals of almost every kind, could be obtained without once crossing the borders of the kingdom of Walid, or even of the shrunken realm of Haroun al Raschid.

Along the northern frontier of Islam, as we see from various Mussulman travellers, there was an amount of trade and a variety of trade-routes which may well surprise us for that age. By comparison with the great southern water-ways, this commerce was of course inconsiderable; but, like Ibn Fozlan's account of the Russians, it has an interest of its own in the light of later history. From the marts of Bokhara and Samarcand on the North-East, an active trade flowed by the Sea of Aral and the Caspian to Derbend and the lower valley of the Volga on the west. The southern coasts of both the great inland seas of Central Asia were completely under Moslem control from the early years of the eighth century; and besides the traffic thus opened between the Oxus Valley and the Black Sea, Arab traders pursued their way from Astrabad on the Caspian, and Djordjan(ieh) on the Sea of Aral, to the land of the tolerant Khazars of Southern Russia, who welcomed Moslem, Christian, Jew, and Pagan alike,[1] and whose king in the tenth century corresponded both with Constantinople and Cordova.

Let us now turn for a moment from commercial to intellectual influences. One point of especial importance to us

[1] See the letter of the Spanish Jew Chasdai to the king of the Khazars in Carmoly ("Itinéraires de la Terre Sainte," Brussels, 1847, p. 38). It was largely by this way that those vast numbers of Arab coins passed into Northern Europe which have been found in modern times in the Scandinavian, German, and other hoards, of which one example near Mainz yielded 15,000 pieces of money.

in this part of the subject is the connection between Arab and Christian thought which is the key to so much of the history of the later Middle Ages. In dealing with the period of the Crusades we shall have to notice this more fully; but it may not be out of place to quote one or two illustrations of the way in which Moslem influence prolonged the life and malevolent activity of certain superstitious ideas. For such illustration we have only to look at expressions of European scholars of the twelfth and thirteenth centuries, who were living in countries far distant from Islam, at a time long after the intellectual glory of the Arabs had begun to decay, and when Christian scholastic philosophy had reached an independent position—yet who, on many points, were content to reflect the mind, and even the words, of Mohammedan writers of this early time, of the eighth, ninth, and tenth centuries.

First of all let us take Adelard of Bath (our own English translator of the Astronomical Tables of the famous "Kharizmian," Mohammed), who in 1110–14 undertook a journey in Egypt, Arabia, and other parts of the Levant, seeking out "the causes of all things and the mysteries of nature;" and who at last returned successfully to the West with a "rich spoil of letters," and especially of Greek and Arab manuscripts. He had had in Paris the best education his time could offer, and he writes commonly with good sense and a fair amount of enlightenment and knowledge. But he seems to have swallowed all the Arab formulas about the World-Summit,[1] and the symmetrical divisions of the earth, and he

---

[1] This "cupola," known to the Arabs as Arim, seems to have been derived immediately from the Hindoo myth of such a world-summit; the name, Reinaud suggests, is from the great Indian kingdom of Odjein or Oudyana, which the Buddhist pilgrim-travellers found in so flourishing a state in the fifth, sixth, and seventh centuries A.D. (See the accounts of Fa-Hien, Hoei-Sing, and Hiouen-Thsang.)

reproduces them exactly.   "Arim, or the terrestrial cupola,"
he tells us, " is under the Equator, at the point where there
is no latitude ; " the chief places of every country, he continues, might be fixed from the meridian of Arim ; and
among the Saracen geographers this valuable task had been
already accomplished.   Their examination of the stars and
of the earth's surface started from this centre, and proceeded
in due course to the four ends of the earth.   Each of these
termini was at the same distance from the central height—
a fourth part of the world's girth, or ninety degrees of
geographical measurement.

To the same purpose, again, writes Gerard of Cremona
(1114–1187), who had imbibed a certain amount of Mohammedan lore during a residence at Toledo.   The middle point
of the world, he had learnt, was called Arim ; it was said to
be in India ; it was in the centre between east and west, and
between the two poles,—each one of these points being 90
degrees distant from it ; it was a mathematical centre known
to Hermes Trismegistus and to Ptolemy, as well as to the
Arabs, and it had been used by all of them ; it was unques-
tionable that Alexander of Macedon marched just so far to
the east of Arim as Hercules to the west ; and at both
extremities one reached the encircling ocean: these were
the chief facts as known to Gerard, and expressed in his
"Theory of the Planets." [1]

Once more, in the thirteenth century two of the greatest
of mediæval thinkers, Albert and Roger Bacon (to say
nothing of Alfonso the Wise of Castile, in his famous
" Tables "), reproduced the essential points of this doctrine,
its false symmetry and its compromise between the true and
the traditional, sometimes with variations of their own.

[1] Plato of Tivoli (about 1150) is not so explicit, but appears to take
substantially the same view.

Albertus Magnus, whose position among the schoolmen was generally reckoned as second only to Aquinas, in his "View of Astronomy" repeats Adelard upon the question of Arim, "where there is no latitude;" while Bacon, the first Christian worker of any real power or insight in the exact sciences, allows himself a long digression,[1] not only upon the real and the legendary East and West, but even upon the question of a twofold Arim or World-Summit. One of these, he suggests, may be placed "under the solstice, the other under the equinoctial zone." His perception, however, is clear enough to prevent him from attaching any practical value to Arim. It was, he expressly tells us, a traditional expression, useful for calculation; rather than a real fact which must be taken account of. It was only serviceable for the men of theory, in speaking of the habitable world as known to them, according to the "true understanding" of latitude and longitude; and this "true understanding," or theoretical assumption, was not adequate to what had been accomplished in travel "by Pliny and others." It was the Arim theory, as reproduced in the "Imago Mundi" of Cardinal Peter Ailly (written, or at least published, in 1410), which was responsible for the doctrines of Columbus [2] on the pear-like shape of the world; forming, as he conceived, a sort of second earth-summit in the Western Hemisphere.

But to return. The expansive action of the Arab race did not begin with Mohammed. Many centuries before, a colony of their people seems to have crossed the Red Sea

[1] Opus Majus.

[2] The Old Hemisphere, he writes to Queen Isabella in 1498, which has for its centre the isle of Arim, is spherical, but the other Hemisphere (the New or Western one) has the form of the lower half of a pear. Just a hundred leagues west of the Azores the earth rises at the equator, and the temperature grows keener. The summit is over against the mouth of the Orinoco.

and founded the Abyssinian nation in the highlands where the
Blue Nile takes its rise.   At a date scarcely less remote, the
sun-worshippers of Southern Arabia have been credited with
the building of the ruined cities of Mashonaland, and with
the first working of the gold mines of the Sofala coast, to
say nothing of their asserted trade-connections in Persia, in
India, and even in China.   But all these developments fall
into a period anterior to that of the Christian Empire; and
in themselves rest upon somewhat vague and doubtful
inferences.   For a long time before the proclamation of
Islam, Arabia seemed more likely, in spite of its fine natural
defences, to become the spoil of other nations rather than
the conqueror of half the world.   Thus the dominion exercised by the Abyssinian kings over Yemen, and the suzerainty
claimed by the Persian monarchs over a large part of the
peninsula in the sixth century, gave little promise of the
activity that would burst forth like a volcano within that
same peninsula in the seventh.

Our concern here is with the Arabic geographers in that
time when, after the temporary collapse of scientific interest
in Christendom, they filled the place of schoolmasters to
Europe, to bring it to a knowledge of its own powers.   To
some extent they accomplished this result by the terrible
discipline of their attacks; but they also performed their
task by preserving and transmitting the older knowledge so
much lost sight of by Christendom.   It is not till after
the Crusading period has fairly begun that Christian Europe
really begins to take advantage of Arab labours; but as
much of the best Arab work was done before the middle
of the tenth century, it is necessary to pass it briefly in
review as a supplementary chapter to that religious geography which fills all the earlier Middle Ages.

The science of the Koran is not very promising, as

we may see from its language about the seven heavens and
seven earths, the signs of the Zodiac, or the mythical achievements of Doul-Karnain [1] (Alexander the Great?); but it is
interesting to see how in this case the earlier and purely
religious conceptions are left behind, though never repu-
diated, by that scientific naturalism which Islam developed
before the Crusades.

The poetic language of the prophet upon the constella-
tions offered no particular difficulties;—" We have set forth
the Towers of heaven [2] and decked them for the beholders,
and we guard them from every cursed Satan;" [3] but the
elaborate recital of the legend of the wall of Gog-Magog
might have caused more trouble if Moslems had ever set
themselves to construct a strictly theological geography;
based, after the Christian model, upon the language of their
sacred books. When the Lord of the two horns (declares
Mohammed, in a phrase which has been variously applied to
Alexander, to Julius Cæsar, and to Augustus),—when Doul-
Karnain went forth with his army, he first marched "to the
going down of the sun, and found it set in a miry fount." [4]
Then, having arrived at the end of the West, he turned and
followed a route to the extremity of the East, where he found
a people unsheltered from the heat. And at last (seemingly
in the far North) he came upon a race, dwelling between
two mountains, "who scarce understood a language."

"And they said, O Doul-Karnain, verily Gog and Magog [5] lay waste
this land; build us a rampart between us and them. And he said, Bring
me blocks of iron; and when he had filled the space between the
mountains, he caused them to blow upon it with bellows, and heated it
fiery hot, and poured molten brass upon it. And Gog and Magog were
not able to scale it, neither were they able to dig through it."

---

[1] "He of the Two Horns." [4] Koran, ch. 18.
[2] Lit., "Towers in the heavens." [5] Yadjoudj and Madjoudj.
[3] Koran, ch. 15.

But the world of Mohammed was limited to the Levant, or nearer East; Damascus was probably the furthest point outside Arabia ever reached by him; he knew roughly the extent and power of the Persian and Roman dominions, as well as of his own country; of all else he shows little knowledge. But the first generation of his followers was in a very different position—in a hundred years the fullest extent of the Caliphate had been reached; and in the cooler time that followed the heat of conquest, science had opportunity to assert itself. Under the influence of two classes of teachers, and by means both of indirect example and of direct teaching, the Arabs began to work for civilisation as they had worked for political empire. They recollected the tradition that " the ink of science was of more value than the blood of the martyrs," and they turned to obey the behest of Mohammed to " seek knowledge, even in China." It was in this spirit they took lessons of the Nestorians and the Jews.

We have seen something already of the extent, persistence, and frequency of Nestorian missionary travel; we must here take some notice of their men of learning, whose work in transmitting to the Moslem world so much of ancient knowledge deserves some gratitude. In the great college at Edessa, before its suppression by the orthodox Emperor Zeno, in 479, were translated into Syriac many of the Greek and Latin classics. The Nestorians were conspicuously successful in medicine. Their efforts were countenanced by the Abbasside Caliphs; and Haroun al Raschid put the direction of his schools in the hands of the famous Nestorian, John Masué; just as several of the leading Moslem families had already entrusted the education of their children to Nestorian teachers.

Not less important was the position of the Jews, especially of Alexandria, under the rule of Islam. Their physicians

were even more celebrated than the Nestorian, and the
Caliph Moawiyah was attended by a Jewish doctor, just as
his successor Haroun al Raschid employed a Hebrew envoy
in his transactions with Charlemagne. Through these two
classes of instructors, the Arabs became gradually aroused to
the interests of astronomy and geography.

It was in the eighth century that the sleepers were
really awakened; in other words, it was under the Caliph
Almansor (A.D. 753–775) that geographical science began to
take shape among the Arabs. Material of two sorts was
chiefly useful to and used by them. On the one hand, the
practical travel of Arab generals, governors,[1] merchants, and
pilgrims; the itineraries drawn up for the use of armies; the
maps or representations draughted by provincial adminis-
trators, were put under contribution. On the other hand,
the Moslem geographers made free use of the methods and
results of previous students,—Indian, Persian, and Greek.
Their geography from the first was thus bound up with
mathematical calculation; and formal work in theory
preceded by a good many years any formal or literary
treatment of practical travel.

About A.D. 772 Almansor ordered an Arabic version to
be made of the Sanscrit astronomy, known by the name of
" Absolute Truth," [2] which had just been brought to Bagdad
by an Indian "philosopher." This was the beginning of
great things. In the earlier years of the ninth century, the
Caliph Almamoun, successor of Haroun "the just," created
the first true school of geographical science which had been
seen since the days of the Antonines. A not inadequate
collection of Greek works was formed; the Almagest and

---

[1] Thus Sallam Ibn Melik, as the
governor of Spain in 721, sent the
Caliph Yezid II. a description of that
province.

[2] The Sindhind.

Geography of Claudius Ptolemy were turned into Arabic, along with a considerable portion of Euclid, Archimedes, and Aristotle;[1] and an observatory was founded at Bagdad (in A.D. 820), where, as well as at Damascus, attempts were soon after made (in 830 and 833) to determine the obliquity of the ecliptic. Once again, Almamoun caused a simultaneous measurement to be taken, in Syria and in Mesopotamia, of a space of two degrees of the terrestrial meridian. For the translations of Greek books, made, as they usually were at this time, from Syriac versions by Syrian Christians, did not satisfy the Caliph. He wished to institute a fresh examination of the facts and theories set forth in these books; and especially he was anxious to gain some independent assurance upon the size of the earth.

The ambition of the prince was felt by his subjects. Thus Mohammed the Kharizmian, whom Almamoun had chosen to direct the Bagdad Library, compiled a " System of the Earth " after the Ptolemaic pattern—a sort of index of place-names, each accompanied by its latitude and longitude. In the same reign, various astronomical tables were composed,[2] which aimed at giving the position on the earth's surface of the principal Mussulman towns. An abridgment was also compiled of the Sanscrit astronomy already noticed —an abridgment, however, which added to its original a quantity of material derived from Greek and Persian investigations, and which has been preserved to us in the Latin version of Adelard of Bath. Nor was this all. Mohammed of Ferganah from the Upper Oxus country (" Alfergany "), in his book of " Celestial Movements," which afterwards

---

[1] The now lost work of Marinus of Tyre was also translated.

[2] See the tables, for instance, of Yahya, the son of an astronomer famous under Almansor; and of Ahmed Ibn Abdallah, author of the earliest of the great Mohammedan " Canons " of astronomy.

passed into Latin through a Hebrew channel, gave a picture of the world and of all its principal countries and towns under the seven *Climates* of Greek geography. He also wrote upon the astrolabe and the other instruments most used by the astronomers of the time.

So far nearly all Moslem geography had been mathematical, concerned with astronomy in the first place, and only referring here and there to descriptive earth-knowledge. One of the earliest treatises that attempted to fill this want was the " Collection of Peculiar Species " made by Nadhar, son of Schomayl, about A.D. 800, in which the qualities of terrestrial objects are discussed, from " mountains and defiles " to " milk and truffles." The reports of distant countries which, as we have pointed out, had been steadily furnished to the central Moslem Government by generals, viceroys, and spies [1] ever since the great expansion of the Arab race in the seventh century, were of course in the nature of State secrets, and only a very small proportion ever gained publicity. But a much more important advance (than that of Nadhar) was made at this very time towards geography in its more exact and ordinary sense. First of all, under Almamoun himself (c. A.D. 830), we have the work of Amrou, son of Bahr, surnamed Aljahedh from his staring eyes, who took advantage of his residence in the port of Bassora to collect facts and fancies from the merchants and travellers he met there. Bassora, the harbour of Bagdad, was then perhaps the chief centre of Moslem commerce; even the ships of China came up to its quays; and with such a concourse of traders and trade-news from the ends of the world, Aljahedh was inspired to compose the earliest of Arabic geographies,

[1] See the account in Frähn's "Ibn Fozlan," p. xxv., of Abdallah Sidi Ghazi's Twenty Years' Stay in the Byzantine Empire as a Spy of Haroun al Raschid.

properly so called. His "Book of the Cities and Marvels of Countries" has not come down to us; according to Massoudy, it was both inaccurate and credulous; but if the title may be supposed to indicate the contents, it laid down the method usually followed by the main school of Arabic writers, who limited their work to a description of the earth itself. For it was at the same time a "book of cities" or a gazetteer, and a "book of marvels" or a collection of natural history, folk-lore, and fairy stories; and almost every Oriental geographer or historian, however scientific in aim, tends in practice to confuse these varieties. To speak more generally, Arabic scholars of every class are constantly neglecting to keep fact and fancy strictly apart. Thus even Albyrouny scatters, in the midst of his most severe inquiries on the "Categories of Indian Thought" and the "Chronology of Ancient Nations," stories and narratives which, though never merely fabulous, are often trivial, and simply illustrate the underlying fancy or poetic spirit of the writer. But Albyrouny is in the main an exception to this common failing of Asiatics; few clearer, stronger, and more subtle minds than his ever illuminated the course of Moslem thought. It is in the work of such as Massoudy that we see a more fair and full example of this characteristic of Oriental treatment. Into a treatise like the "Meadows of Gold and Mines of Precious Stones" the author pours every fact that he has collected, every story that he has heard, every fancy that has impressed his imagination. The result is a medley of history, geography, astronomy, chemistry, poetry, mathematics, metaphysics, and a hundred other things—so many pearls, as the author would have said, all strung together on a single thread,—the story of the rise and triumphs of Islam. Selection, concentration, judicious and typical illustration, a dramatic limitation of subject, a critical use of material—these and other faculties, so highly prized in classical and modern literature, are here not wholly absent, but largely overruled by other feelings.   Above all things, the Oriental wished to be interesting, to tell all that he had to say, to give in one view his interpretation of the world, to present in one collection every tradition that he had received. He poured the whole contents of his note-books or of his memory into the finished work; and order, arrangement, the pursuit of a definite line of thought, were to him but secondary matters.   For in him the ruling faculty was imagination, and to his imagination the infinite complexity of life and nature most strongly appealed.

Aljahedh was not a practical traveller, and his imperfect book knowledge, or the misleading tales of voyagers, led him to imitate the old Greek superstition and connect the Nile and Indus as one river.   But extensive journeys by land and sea beyond the limits of the Caliphate were now beginning; and elementary mistakes like the aforesaid were fast being made impossible, by such men as Soleyman the merchant, who in the middle of the ninth century, at the time of closest intercourse between China and the Moslem world, travelled to the farthest East by sea.   To the voyages of this Sindbad we shall soon have to refer again.   But before we leave the time of Almamoun we must notice at least one other name.   Abou Yousouf Yakoub, surnamed " Alkendy," from his connection with the noble house of Kenda, was entrusted by the Caliph (c. A.D. 830) with a supervision of the translations then being made from Greek, Indian, and Persian sources.   He was the reputed author of more than two hundred volumes, a number which probably includes the work of some of his disciples.   To one of the latter was due the " Book of Routes and Principalities," so warmly praised by Massoudy; while a combination of savants

was probably responsible for the Alkendian version of
Ptolemy, and for the well-known treatise on the Tides,
referred to by writers of this epoch.

The impulse given by Almamoun did not die with him.
The ninth century of the Christian era, the third of the
Hegira, was crowded with Moslem scientists and travellers.
About A.D. 840 Sallam, surnamed the Interpreter from the
many languages with which he was acquainted, was entrusted
by the Caliph Wathek-Billah with the exploration of various
regions to the north of the Mussulman Empire. He was
especially charged with the search for the monstrous peoples
of Gog-Magog, and for Alexander's wall. Sallam passed
through Armenia and Georgia, crossed the Caucasus, and
visited the Khazars of the Volga River, then at the height of
their prosperity. Proceeding onwards, he made the circuit
of the Caspian, explored a large part of the Ural and Altai
ranges, and returned to Mesopotamia by Bokhara and
Khorasan. A few years later the famous Djafar, surnamed
Abou Maschar (the Albumazar of the Latin Middle Ages),
commenced his work as an astronomer—work, however,
which only in a very secondary sense bore any reference to
geographical knowledge. A late tradition makes him
journey to the banks of the Ganges to initiate himself into
Brahmin science; Massoudy, at any rate, copies from him a
description of the monsoon in the Indian Ocean; but he
clearly belonged to the more abstract and mathematical
school.

The later years of the ninth century were remarkable (as
we know) from the fact that they marked the zenith of Arab
and Moslem intercourse with China, on the eve of the
revolution of 878. How extensive this intercourse had
become is witnessed by Abou Zeyd Hassan of Siraf and the
anonymous traveller who has been identified with Soleyman

the merchant.[1]   These accounts not only give us a description of the various coasts and seas to the south and southeast of Asia, but tell of the meeting of Chinese and foreign merchants along the whole extent of a great line of trade which stretched from the Persian Gulf and Bassora in the west, to the Yellow Sea and Khanfu City—a Hongkong of the ninth century [2]—in the east.   Abou Zeyd moreover narrates the journey of his friend Ibn Vahab to the Court of China, and his memorable interview with the Emperor, wherein that potentate owns the superior majesty of the Caliphate; cross-examines his visitor upon the history of the Prophets; shows him the portraits of Christ and of Mohammed; and dismisses him with a lecture for equivocating.

The anonymous author who reproduces the narrative of Soleyman, takes us by sea from the Persian Gulf to China. From the Maldives to Ceylon, from Ceylon to the Andamans, from the Andamans to Khanfu, he records the natural features, the marvels, and certain characteristics of the natives in each place he touches at.   Thus, as to the four stopping-points just named, ambergris, cocoa-nuts, and female sovereignty he considers especially noteworthy in the first; Adam's Peak, the giant footstep of the Patriarch (or of Buddha), and the ruby mines, in the second; cannibalism in the third; the foreign merchants in the last.   The course of navigation from Bassora also passed by Siraf,

---

[1] The two were translated and edited together by Renaudot in 1718 (English Version 1733); later works on the same subject were composed by Reinaud in his "Relations des Voyages dans l'Inde et à la Chine . . . dans le ix\u1d49 siècle," 1845 (which gives the best version of the "Two Travellers"), and in his "Mémoire . . . sur l'Inde," 1846.   See also Walckenaer in "Nouvelles Annales des Voyages," 1832 (1), and Bretschneider on the other side of the question, "Knowledge possessed by the . . . Chinese of the Arabs," London, 1871.

[2] The Quinsaÿ of Marco Polo; the Hang-cheu-[fu] of the modern Chinese.

Muscat, the Malabar coast, and "the gates of China" (the straits of Malacca?); and so to the Sea of Pitchy Darkness on the east coast of Asia. The description has all the charm of freshness and originality—the flavour that pervades the early writings of the men of any leading race in a subject or a field of action lately discovered or opened up by them, and offering worthy material. This is obvious enough in some of the stories which are every now and then added to the main narrative. Near the Andamans Soleyman describes an island with mines of silver :—

"And here once a boat-load of men came off from a ship and kindled a fire on the shore, and they saw silver run from beneath it; wherefore they shipped as much of the earth or ore as they thought good. But as they went on their voyage the sea was stirred by so furious a gust, that to lighten the ship they threw overboard all their ore."

Since that time, concludes the story with a touch of mystery, "the mountain has been searched for with care, but it has never since been seen." Again, the waterspout was watched with wonder, and described with faithfulness, by these early Moslem seamen.

"In this sea there is often beheld a white cloud which at once spreads over a ship and lets down a long thin tongue or spout to the surface of the water, which it disturbs after the manner of a whirlwind; and if a vessel happen to be in the way, she is immediately swallowed up. But at length this cloud mounts again and discharges itself in a prodigious rain."

But the greater part of both these records is taken up with a description of the habits, government, religion, social customs, and national or tribal characteristics of the Chinese and the Indians; and we hear at length about the silken dress, the poll-tax, the terrible punishments, the paintings and bells, tea[1] and rice-drinks, drums and porcelain of the

[1] "A certain herb, which they drink with hot water, and of which great quantities are sold in all the cities; it grows on a shrub more

one ; and the Suttee, self-torture, and caste-system of the other.   An interesting picture of the state of the foreign (and especially of the Arab) merchants in Khanfu comes from the original relation of Soleyman.   The Moslems of China, according to him, were under a kadi or judge, appointed by the Emperor himself, and invested with more than the authority of a modern consul-general.[1]   The administration of the Custom-house was strict, but not unfair or illiberal.   When merchants at this time entered China by sea, their cargo was seized, and conveyed to warehouses for six months.   Then a tax of three-and-thirty per cent. was taken on each commodity, and the rest returned to the owner.   The Emperor had the right of pre-emption ; but he paid to the " utmost fraction of the value," and so " dispatched his business immediately and without the least injustice." Foreign merchants, like the natives, were taxed " in proportion to their substance ; " and if they wished to travel—for even this was not forbidden them—they were obliged to take a passport from the Governor of the district and another from his lieutenant; giving also, as they passed from one place to another, a full account of themselves, their family, position, and business.[2]

This early Arab study of the Far East recorded its impression that India was greater in extent " by one-half " than China, but not so populous; for in the Indies were

bushy than the pomegranate, and of a more taking smell, but with a kind of bitterness.   The Chinese boil water, which they pour upon this leaf, and this drink cures all sorts of diseases."

[1] For China till the end of the ninth century was, to some extent, a commercial State ; its exclusiveness was the creation of circumstances.

[2] This is all confirmed from other sources, and sufficiently credible ; but the Anonymous had got hold of an odd story about Chinese punishment of bad governors, that they were *eaten;* and his generalization can hardly be accepted, " that the Chinese usually eat all those that are put to death."

"many desert tracks," but China "was peopled throughout its whole extent." The India of these descriptions was pretty certainly the whole vast tract between the Indus and the Gulf of Tonquin; their China is much the same as ours, and does not of course include Thibet, Mongolia, or any part of Turkestan.

Abou Zeyd originally undertook the simple task of reading, revising, and re-issuing the anonymous relation of A.D. 851; but living as he did after the revolution of 878, he is naturally led into the composition of a supplementary account, in which he corrects some mistakes of the older narratives, records the travels of Ibn Vahab, and describes the sack of Khanfu and the consequent collapse of foreign trade with the Celestials. An officer of rank, he tells us, revolted in the year of the Hegira 264 (A.D. 877–8); got together a multitude of vagabonds and abandoned people; and marching on Khanfu, took the city after a long siege. He put all the inhabitants to the sword; and, besides Chinese, there perished in this massacre 120,000 Moslems, Jews, Christians, and Parsees, "who were there on business of traffic." The rebel cut down all the mulberries and other trees of the district, ruined for a season the silk trade, and drove the Emperor from his capital. At last the "plague" was stamped out by Tartar armies; but the Empire of China continued in a miserable state, torn by civil war, plundered by brigand Mandarins, and disgraced by cannibalism.

"From all this," concludes the Arab, "arose unjust dealings with the merchants who traded thither, so that there was no outrage, no treatment so bad but they exercised it upon the foreign traders and the masters of ships. And for these things has God punished them by withdrawing His blessing, and especially by causing that navigation to be forsaken, so that the merchants returned in crowds to Siraf and Oman, according to the infallible orders of the Almighty Lord, whose name be blessed."

Abou Zeyd moreover had, from the lips of Ibn Vahab

himself, when "already advanced in years, but having all his senses perfectly about him," a description of the Chinese Court and country at a date subsequent to the journey of Soleyman, but apparently earlier than the sack of Khanfu; and the whole of his narrative is remarkable for its bearing on Arab intercourse with the most distant parts, and for its illustration of the Arab spirit. It is Sindbad the Sailor under other names.

"There was a man of the tribe of Koreish (Mohammed's own)," says Abou Zeyd, "who was named Ibn Vahab, and he dwelt at Bassora. And once, when that city was sacked [by a band of pirates from the Zanzibar coast, in A.D. 870],[1] he left Bassora and came to Siraf, where he saw a ship ready to sail to China. And the mind took him to go on board of this ship, and in her he went to China, where he had the curiosity to visit the Emperor's Court. He came to Khanfu, and so travelled to Kumdam [or Singanfu, one of the Imperial residences at that time], after a journey of two months. And here he stayed a long time, and presented several petitions, signifying that he was of the family of the Prophet of the Arabs. And when he had his audience, the Emperor asked him many questions about the Arabs, and particularly how they had destroyed the kingdom of the Persians. Ibn Vahab made answer that they did it by the assistance of God, and because the Persians were involved in idolatry, adoring the stars, the sun, and moon, instead of worshipping the true God. To this the Emperor replied that the Arabs had conquered the most illustrious kingdom of the whole earth, the best cultivated, the most opulent, the most pregnant of fine wits, and of the most extensive fame. Then said he, What account do the people in your parts make of the other kings of the earth? To which the Arab replied that he knew not. Then said the Emperor to the interpreter, Tell him we esteem but five kings; and that he whose kingdom is of widest extent is the same who is master of Irak [Babylonia]; for he is in the midst of the world, and surrounded by the territories of other kings; and we find he is called the King of Kings. After him we reckon our Emperor, here present, and we find that he is styled the King of Mankind; for no other king is invested with a more absolute power and authority over his subjects; nor is there a people under the sun more dutiful and submissive to their sovereign than the people of this

---

[1] Aboulfeda, ii. pp. 228, 238, etc. (Reinaud); also see Reinaud's edi-   tion of the "Two Travellers," p. cxix.

country; we, therefore, in this respect, are the Kings of Men. After us is the King of the Turks, whose kingdom borders upon us, and him we call the King of Lions. Next, the King of Elephants; the same is the King of the Indies, whom we also call the King of Wisdom, because he derives his origin from the Indians. And, last of all, the King of Greece, whom we style the King of Men; for upon the face of the whole earth there are no men of better manners, nor of comelier presence, than his subjects. These, he added, are the most illustrious of all kings, nor are the others to be compared with them. Then, says Ibn Vahab, he ordered the interpreter to ask me if I knew my Master and my Lord, meaning the Prophet, and if I had seen him? I made answer, How should I have seen him, who is with God? He replied, This is not what I mean; I ask you what sort of a man he was in his person. I replied that he was very handsome. Then he called for a great box, and, opening it, he took out another contained therein, which he set before him, and said to the interpreter, Show him his Master and his Lord; and I saw in the box the images of the Prophets, whereat I moved my lips, praying to myself in honour of their memory. The Emperor did not imagine I should know them again, and said to the interpreter, Ask him why he moves his lips? I answered, I was praying in memory of the Prophets. How do you know them? said the Emperor. I replied that I knew them by the representation of their histories. There, said I, is Noah in the Ark, who was saved when God sent down the waters of the Flood; and I made the usual salute to Noah and his company. Then the Emperor laughed, and said, You are not mistaken in the name of Noah, and you have named him right; but as for the universal Deluge, it is what we know not. It is true, indeed, that a Flood covered a part of the earth; but it reached not to our country, nor even to the Indies. I made my answer to this; and then said I again to him, There is Moses with his rod and the children of Israel, and there is Jesus upon an ass, and here are His Apostles with him. Ah, said the Emperor, He was not long upon the earth, for all He did was transacted within the space of little more than thirty months. After this Ibn Vahab saw the histories of the other Prophets, represented in the same manner we have briefly declared.

"Then, says the same Ibn Vahab, I saw the image of Mohammed riding upon a camel, and his companions about him on their camels, with shoes of the Arab mode on their feet, and leathern girdles about their loins. At this I wept, and the Emperor commanded the interpreter to ask me why I wept? I answered, There is our Prophet and our Lord, who is also my cousin. He said I was right, and added that he and his people had subdued the finest of all kingdoms; but that he had not the satisfaction of enjoying his conquests, though his successors had. I afterwards saw a great number of other Prophets, whom the interpreter took to be those of their land (of China) and of India.

"The Emperor then asked me many questions concerning the Caliphs, and their mode of dress, and concerning many precepts of the Mohammedan religion, and I answered him the best I could. After this he said, What is your opinion concerning the age of the world? I made answer that opinions varied upon that head; that some were for six thousand years, and that some others reckoned more and some less. At this the Emperor and his first minister, who was near him, broke out into a laughter, and the Emperor made many objections to what I had advanced. At last said he, What does your Prophet teach upon this subject? Does he say as you do? My memory failed me, and I assured him that he did. Hereupon I observed I had displeased him, and his displeasure appeared upon his countenance. Then he ordered the interpreter to speak to me in the following strain: Take heed of what you say, for kings never speak but to be informed of the truth of what they would know. How can there be among you various opinions concerning the age of the world? If so it be, you are also divided upon the things your Prophet has said, at the same time that no diversity of opinion is to be admitted on what the Prophets have pronounced, all which must be revered as sure and infallible. Take heed, then, how you talk after such a manner any more. At last he asked me, How is it that you have forsaken your king, to whom you are nearer, not only by the place of your abode, but by blood also, than you are to us? In return to which I informed him of the revolutions which had happened at Bassora, and how I came to Siraf, where I saw a ship ready to spread sail for China; and that, having heard of the glory of his empire and its great abundance of necessaries, curiosity excited me to a desire of coming into his country, that I might behold it with mine own eyes. And I said that I should soon depart for my country and the kingdom of my cousin, and that I would make a faithful report of what I had seen of the magnificence of the empire of China and of the vast extent of the provinces it contained, and that I would make a grateful declaration of the kind usage and the benefactions I there met with,—which seemed to please him much. He then made me rich gifts, and ordered that I should be conducted to Khanfu upon post-horses. He wrote also to the governor of the city, commanding him to treat me with much honour, and to furnish me with like recommendations to the other governors of the provinces. Thus was I treated everywhere, being plentifully supplied with all the necessaries of life, and honoured with many presents till my departure from China."

Abou Zeyd then adds, in the course of his remarks upon

the original narrative of Soleyman the merchant, a wildly
distorted story of the wreck of a Siraf vessel being carried by
wind and tide round Eastern and Northern Asia into the
Caspian (which he supposed [1] to flow into the Northern
Ocean), round Northern Europe into the Mediterranean, and
round the coasts of the Mediterranean on to the shore of
Syria, where it was at last stranded and recognised by its
peculiar make, "the boards not being nailed, but, as it were,
sewn together." He gives no hint of the old freshwater
canal from the Nile to the Red Sea, which had now been
closed for a century and a quarter or more; on the contrary,
he speaks of the separation between the "Sea of Aden" and
the "Sea of Syria" as the work of God, and so eternal and
unchangeable.

The narrative of another Arab merchant, from the
province of Khorasan (who, like Ibn Vahab, had travelled to
China and brought back an account of his success in obtaining justice from the Emperor against a fraudulent official),
leads Abou Zeyd to a description of Khorasan, "almost
conterminous with China," since "from China to the Sogd"
of Samarcand [2] it was only two months' journey. Yet an
almost impassable desert (the great plain of Gobi or Shamo)

[1] Yet Abou Zeyd was a contemporary and friend of Massoudy, who
knew far better. Reinaud ("Relations," pp. xvi.–xxiii.) has pointed
out several highly probable parallels
between the "Meadows of Gold" and
the "Two Travellers." Abou Zeyd
does not appear to have journeyed
much himself, and hence probably
his Caspian and other blunders; but
he tried to follow the best written
authorities, and his friendship with
Massoudy was of service to both of
them.

[2] The Siraf ships, says Abou

Zeyd, dare not attempt to navigate
the Red Sea higher than Djeddah,
the port of Mecca. This sea is "not
like that of India and China, whose
bottom is rich with pearls and
ambergris; whose mountains are
stored with gold and precious stones;
whose gulfs yield ivory; and among
whose plants are ebony, red wood,
brazil, aloes, camphor, nutmegs,
cloves, sandal-wood, and all other
aromatics; among whose birds parrots
and peacocks; among whose rarities
musk and civet."

prevented much trade or even war on the north-east. Only towards the border of Thibet was overland intercourse to be had with the Flowery Land, and by this route most probably travelled the Arab traders mentioned by Abou Zeyd, and notably " one who had a vessel of musk on his back," and tramped on foot from Samarcand to Khanfu, traversing " all the cities of China " on the way.

The wealth, the fanatic and ferocious self-devotion, the intricate idolatry, and the moral baseness of the Indians are successively touched on by the Moslem writer, who saw in their case the fulfilment of the Koranic text, " The wicked have a mighty pride." " We praise the Almighty and glorious God," he exclaims, as he comes to speak of the famous idol of Moultan, " we praise Him who hath chosen us to be free from the sins that defile the men involved in infidelity."

Lastly, we hear a little about the semi-barbarous southern shore of Arabia ; about the troublesome and dangerous navigation of the Red Sea ; and about the Zanzibar or East African coast, now being rapidly colonised by Arab adventurers. This land of the negroes was of vast extent ; but its inhabitants were a natural prey to the nobler races of the earth. " In their heart they venerate the Arabs, and, when they see one of them, fall down and cry, Here comes one from the land of Date Palms—for they are very fond of dates."

Christianity still survived in Socotra at this time, and most of its inhabitants were Christians—Christians of the Nestorian faith, no doubt ; for the island had long been a bishopric and a mission centre of the great schismatic communion ; just as in still earlier time it had been an outpost of Roman commerce.

The commotions which shattered Chinese trade and

closed the country for a time to foreign influence diverted, but did not depress, the exploring spirit of the Arabs. Their activity was never higher than in the seventy or eighty years which lay between the riots of 878 and the death of Massoudy in 956. This same time was to Europe and Christendom perhaps the most dismal and lifeless of epochs—the interregnum between the extinction of the Frankish Empire of Charlemagne (A.D. 888) and the restoration of the same as a purely German kingdom by Otto the Great (962). We have seen already how this time, and indeed the whole century and a quarter which closed the first Christian Millennium (c. 875-1000), is almost wholly barren of Latin exploration or geographical study; and we may think that the political troubles of the time are a sufficient reason for this lifelessness; yet in the Bagdad Caliphate practical and scientific activity prospers and increases throughout this period side by side with governmental anarchy. Al Radi, who died in 940, was the last Caliph who was truly Emperor as well as Pope; and his reign saw the end of the domestic revolution which transferred the military power of the Abbassides to their Turkish mercenaries and the Emir Al Omra. For although the political coherence and persistence of the Arab race had been steadily waning since the days of Almamoun, its intellectual vigour was far from being exhausted, and not even a temporary slackening is apparent till the eleventh century. It will be convenient for us, however, to close this summary view of the earlier Moslem geography about A.D. 950, for various reasons. First of all, with Massoudy and certain others, his contemporaries, closes the direct succession of what may be called the school of Almamoun. And secondly, from this time the leadership of scientific (in particular of geographical) interests now falls more and more to strangers and foreign courts; to men who were not Arabs by blood, and who were indeed religious, but not political, subjects of the Caliph. Albyrouny, the greatest geographer of the next age, is a client of Sultan Mahmoud of Ghazni, a Persian by race, with an inborn hatred of the dominant Arabs.[1] Thus, although the armies of the Caliphs no longer conquered, the Arab and Mussulman descriptions of past conquests were steadily becoming more and more scientific and exhaustive. Thus about A.D. 880, a Bagdad Imam, Aboul Abbas Ahmed, surnamed Albeladory, who was tutor to one of the princes of the Royal House, compiled a "Book of the Conquests of the Countries," in which an historical narrative was combined with a geographical description. At the same era, Ibn Khordadbeh drew up his official notices of the principal trade-routes,[2] which, as Director of Posts and Police in Media, he had been ordered to furnish to the Caliph.

As his name proves, this "son of the Magian" was descendant (and, in fact, grandson) of a Persian fire-worshipper, who, like most of his faith and nation, embraced Islam, and so made the best of both worlds. His grandson, who enjoyed the favour of the Caliph Motamed, was employed, about the year 880, with the task of ascertaining the proper taxation and the actual payments of each of the provinces of the Bagdad Empire, and especially of Mesopotamia and Irak.

Ibn Khordadbeh had great opportunities. He might have composed a work of first-class historical and geographical value, if he had been anything more than a tabulator.

---

[1] Similarly the tenth-century writers, Mukadassi and Hamza of Ispahan, though to a far less degree, may be thought to illustrate the decline of political allegiance within the Caliphate. Neither of them, interesting as they are, call for notice in an account like this, which only deals with representative persons and events.

[2] Between 880–884. He died in 912.

Unhappily his mental outlook was strictly limited by his
professional calling, and so his book, for the most part, is
thrown into the form of a ledger, or of a business circular,
rather than of a literary treatise. If he ever enters into
details, they are usually those of some romantic legend.

The Caliph's postmaster begins by stating the aim of
the treatise required of him, in a sort of dedication to his
sovereign; and then follows his " description of routes, and
enumeration of distances and imposts." From one place to
another is so many miles; the distance traversed amounts
to such and such a land valuation; so much is cultivated,
and so much is waste; the ancient land-tax was so much,
and the present so much, more or less;—this is the almost
invariable form of entry, and about a work of this kind
there is more political than geographical interest.

But, besides the famous summary of the great trade-routes
quoted below, we have here and there passages of more
general value. Thus at the commencement of the treatise
Ibn Khordadbeh gives a summary of his scientific views,
which are those of a well-educated disciple of Ptolemy, and
contrast very strikingly with contemporary expressions from
the Christian and European world. Though scientific in the
main, they reproduce, however, some of the " vain imagin-
ings," among the more solid results, of Greek and Latin
thought; and in one of his comparisons, that of the universe
to an egg, the Arab assessor of taxes exactly reproduces the
classical language, of which we have already had an echo in
Bede.

The earth, he concludes, is round like a sphere, and is
placed in the midst of the celestial area "like the yellow in
an egg." All bodies are stable on the surface of the globe,
because the air attracts the lighter principles of these bodies,
while the earth attracts towards its centre their weighty

parts, in the same way that the magnet acts upon iron. The earth is divided into two parts by the equator, stretching from west to east. This answers to the extent of the earth in length, and is the greatest line of the terrestrial globe, just as the zodiacal line is the greatest of the celestial sphere. Again, the earth extends in breadth from pole to pole, 90° on each side of the equator; but it is only inhabited for the space of 24° of this latitude; the rest is covered by the great sea. The north part of the world which we inhabit is alone habitable; for the southern part is desert from excessive heat, and the antipodean land placed below ours contains no inhabitants.

So much and more in the same strain does Ibn Khordadbeh give us of general theory before he begins his catalogues. In the arrangement of these he pursues the following plan: Starting from the neighbourhood of Bagdad, he first treats of the inland countries to the frontier of China; then he describes the coast route to the Yellow Sea, from Aden and the Persian Gulf; then he details the western routes from the Tigris to the Atlantic; lastly he treats of the northern and southern extremities of the earth. The most interesting part in the treatment of Central Asia is the description of the Turks, then still outside the pale of Islam, and classed as either Manicheans or fire-worshippers. Ibn Khordadbeh dwells at some length on the state of the Turkish Khan, his golden tent, and the iron gates of his chief town; [1] and he enumerates among the Turkish tribes dwelling between China, Thibet, and the Caspian, Petchinegs, Kipchaks, and Kirghiz, whose land produced the musk of commerce.

Passing to the southern sea-route, we hear in succession of the various ports of the Indian Ocean—and first of Aden,

---

[1] Page 22, in Goeje's edition.

where no corn or cattle could be had, but plenty of amber, aloes, and all the spices of the East. In Ceylon, we are told of Adam's Peak (whose "summit is lost in the clouds, though visible at times to navigators some days' journey distant "), as well as of the jewels, the wild beasts, and the native dwarfs of the island. Ibn Khordadbeh, who is very credulous and uncritical on matters which did not come within his own sphere of observation, gives some marvellous narrations about the phenomena of the Indian Sea ; many of the facts to which he alludes are treated with just that touch of legend which renders the account useless, or even pernicious, rather than helpful, to science. Thus his whales two hundred fathoms long, his serpents that devour elephants, or his sea-horses—"just like those of the land," only that their manes reach to their feet—are instances of the fabulist spirit in a professed historian.[1]

Yet with the thread of legend is constantly interwoven that of observation. In a confused way he describes the unique appearance of the flying-fish, the habits of the turtle, the horn of the rhinoceros, the double leaf of the pepper plant. Almost everywhere he contributes a fable to enhance the fact. Thus the rhino's horn, if cut open, displays, according to him, the image of a man, a beast, a bird, and a fish, all in white, on a dark ground ; but he also describes with fair accuracy the leading features of the southern Asiatic coast, down to the lesser known Godavery and Brahmapoutra rivers, the Nicobar and Andaman Islands, and the kingdoms of Assam, Orissa, Malaya, and Java,— where the ruler worshipped Buddha ; where was one of the famous volcanoes of the world ; and where men took ship for the Spice Islands. We seem to hear an echo of Solinus in the story of the Indian island which rings nightly with the

[1] Pages 41, 45, 48, etc.

sound of music, a tolerably clear proof that it was the residence of an infernal spirit; as well as in the story of a
marvel to be seen in a neighbouring island, such as Sancho
Panza might have wished to govern, where the inhabitants
were all apes in the shape of asses.[1]

Ibn Khordadbeh is less mythical when he comes in due
course to China itself. He describes the great port of
Khanfu and the products of the celestial kingdom soberly
enough; likewise the rivers, whose mighty estuaries then,
as in the time of Marco Polo, were the highways of a traffic
astonishing to a European, and respectable even to an Arab,
of that age.

Beyond China, Ibn Khordadbeh has pretty sound information about Japan and Corea, both [2] rich in gold, so that
in "Wak-Wak" the very dog-chains and ape-collars were
made of the precious metal.

And now, having followed out the Eastern route to the
furthest point known, the compiler gives us a series of
similar catalogues and notes on the countries, revenues, and
roads of the West, North, and South.

First, on the track from Bagdad to the Atlantic, he
repeats, as he has done in his Eastern survey, a certain
number of stories which show how, in the midst of his
statistics, he still preserved the spirit of a romanticist. The
Jordan he has heard does not disappear for good in the Dead
Sea or Fœtid Lake ; some great authorities have traced it
again in India, and their views deserve respect. In Spain,
bordering as it did on the far distant land of the Western
Christians ("enemies of the Unity of God," as the Arab

---

[1] Page 48.

[2] The islands of Wak-Wak in Ibn
Khordadbeh undoubtedly seem to be
Japan, though in so many other
Arab writers they are spoken of as

if off the Zanzibar coast. With a
Ptolemaic Africa there would be no
great inconsistency in this, as we
may see from Edrisi's map. See
Goeje, Arabische Berichte over Japon

politely terms them), there were many wonders, such as a
volcano in the north, and all sorts of magic things in the
old royal city of Toledo, where King Roderick and his
Goths discovered them. Once more, as to the Northern
and Western Ocean, Ibn Khordadbeh reproduces the more
traditional and superstitious view, natural to a man whose
horizon was strictly " Levantine " or even " Persian." " The
sea that stretches beyond the land of the Slavs (on
the shore of which is the *town* of Thule), and the sea of
the Fortunate Islands (Canaries), are not frequented by
any ships, and yield nothing to commerce." Lastly, his
elaborate and fairly creditable *précis* of the resources and
organization of the Byzantine Empire, and of the buildings
of Old Rome, is accompanied by some wonderful tales, such
as that of the Mirror in the Pharos at Alexandria, which
reflected all that happened at Constantinople ; while the
whole of his Western section is pervaded by the fancies
that the earth was divided into three exactly equal parts of
cultivated land, of desert, and of sea ; that the land of the
blacks covered one-sixtieth part of the surface of the globe,
and that Egypt was just one-sixtieth part of Negroland.

Although he devotes a separate section of his compilation
to the countries of the North, Ibn Khordadbeh contents
himself here with a few very imperfect notes on Armenia,
the Caucasus, and the country of the Khazars in the lower
valley of the Volga ; and his chief contribution to science
in this section is a tale of intricate fancifulness about the
Divine punishment of the Romans for their sack of Jerusalem, and the final accomplishment of the heavenly vengeance
after 500 years by the coming of Mohammed.

On the lands and trade-routes of the South, we have for
the most part catalogues of Arabian districts, ports, caravan stages, and land values ; but in this connection Ibn

Khordadbeh gives us his famous summary of the course of trade from West to East in the hands of Jewish and Russian merchants. The Jews, according to him, were the chief middlemen between Europe and Asia. They spoke Greek and Latin, Persian and Arabic, the Frankish dialects, Spanish and Slav. By one route they sailed from the ports of France and Italy to the Isthmus of Suez, and thence down the Red Sea to India and Farther Asia. By another course, they transported the goods of the West to the Syrian coast; up the Orontes to Antioch; down the Euphrates to Bassora; and so along the Persian Gulf to Oman and the Southern Ocean. A distinct commerce was maintained by the Russians. From the most distant parts of the Slav countries they came down to the Mediterranean to sell their fox and beaver skins. On another side they descended the stream of Volga, crossed the Caspian,[1] and transported their wares on camels to Bagdad. Two other overland ways from the most distant West are noticed by the observant post-master. On the one side merchants may leave Spain, traverse the straits of Gibraltar, and go from Tangier along the northern fringe of the desert, to Egypt, Syria, and Persia. This is the Southern route. One may also take the Northern, through Germany, across the country of the Slavs to the Lower Volga; thence descending the river and sailing over the Caspian, the trader may proceed along the Oxus Valley to Balkh; turning north-east, and traversing the country of the Tagazgaz Turks, the traveller finds himself at last upon the frontier of China.

Having now finished his fourfold survey, Ibn Khordadbeh

---

[1] The town of Rey or Rai, to the south of the Caspian, near the present Teheran, was the point where these merchants met with those of the Levant, of the Danube Valley, and of Persia. Reinaud refers (Aboulféda, lix.) to the account of this great mart "in the tenth-century Arab MS. entitled 'Book of the Countries,' now possessed by the British Museum."

proceeds to close his work with some notices of a
general kind. First among these comes his division of the
habitable earth. In Europe he includes Tangier and all
the northern coast of Africa to the frontier of Egypt; of
the rest of the Old World, he makes a triple partition.
Asia he divides between "Ethiopia" (which includes in his
mind Yemenite Arabia, India, and even China), and
" Scythia," or the country of the Turks and of the Russians,[1]
with Armenia and Khorasan. That portion of Africa which
he does not reckon with Europe,—in other words, the Sahara
and the Soudan,—he calls Libya, but in this again he insists
on comprehending Egypt. A more perverse assignment
has been rarely made: for although Ethiopia was sometimes
understood to cover a good deal of the shore-land of South-
Western Asia,[2] it would not be easy to find an extension of
the term to China in any mediæval writer; while the treatment of Europe almost seems to defy explanation. No part
of Africa had more steadily obeyed the great European
power of Rome than Egypt. Yet Egypt is the single one
of the North African provinces to be excepted from the
apocryphal Europe of this description.

Ibn Khordadbeh ends, like some of the Christian
geographers of this time, with some casual remarks upon
"various notable things"—buildings, rivers, mountains,
valleys, and climatic effects of certain countries; and from
these we may select a few instances which illustrate more or
less happily the knowledge and spirit of the writer, who is
again representative of a thoroughly second-class intelligence
in the Moslem world of his day; an intelligence, however,

---

[1] At least the part of it inhabited
by the Khazars. Possibly his odd
arrangement of Europe may be due
to a confused reminiscence of the
Roman Empire, which of course
dominated the African side of the
Mediterranean.

[2] Just as "India" was often
extended to include "Ethiopia" or
Tropical Africa.

which was precisely that of the mass of fairly educated Mussulmans.

1. The true builder of the Pyramids " was known only unto God," but some said that his name was King Ptolemy the Claudian,—a delightful confusion, which we have already met with in the Ravennese geographer, between the great scientist of Alexandria and the Hellenist dynasty of Egyptian kings.

2. The wall of Gog-Magog Ibn Khordadbeh describes minutely from the relation of Sallam to the Caliph Wathek-Billah. In this account, the real and the legendary were inseparably confused; but, as we have remarked before, the Moslem envoy clearly accomplished a good deal of travel and exploration in the lands around the Caspian. It is, however, upon the more legendary side of his narrative that Ibn Khordadbeh especially dwells. Thus we are told he travelled twenty-seven days " till the sun became black above him, and emitted a noisome odour." From the famous rampart of Alexander he extracted an iron powder by scraping one of the bricks, whose dimensions he ascertained to a nicety; though by an unlucky oversight he makes the height of the gate surpass that of the wall itself. Ibn Khordadbeh learnt from his informant all sorts of interesting facts about the great barrier, its appearance, its gigantic key, and the dwarfish Gog-Magogs beyond; but the whole narrative contains no reality except so far as it preserves a confused tradition of the Wall of China; and Ibn Khordadbeh is careful not to locate this portent too closely.

3. Among the "particularities of divers countries," Thibet produced in its inhabitants, and even in a visitor, an extraordinary sprightliness of temper. No one ever felt dull or melancholy there. If one went to Corea, the climate

had so subtle a charm that, like the comrades of Ulysses among the Lotus-eaters, he wished to stay there for ever. Whoever resided a year in Mosul (Nineveh) felt fresh strength rising within him. On the other hand, there were places such as Ahwaz, where one was never free from fever, and where madness was only a question of time; just as in the lands at the mouth of the Persian Gulf, no abstinence could save one from excessive fatness.

Among the latest Arab geographers of the ninth century were Alkateb and Kodama, surnamed Aboulfaraj (Abulfaragius).[1] Both these flourished about A.D. 890, and wrote upon the different commercial tracks, markets, frontiers, and physical features of the lands of Islam; but works of this type were now common enough, and added little or nothing of original value. Results of a higher kind were aimed at by a group of travellers and authors, who form a fitting close to this earlier period of Moslem enterprise. Albateny, Aldjayhany, Ibn Fozlan, Alestakhry, Ibn Haukal, and Massoudy are all to be found in the first half of the tenth century; and together they carried out the geographical mission of the Arab race with a completeness not hitherto attained.

In purely scientific inquiry, scarcely any Moslem astronomer threw more light upon the relations of the earth with the heavenly bodies than Mohammed the son of Djaber, known as Albateny, from his birthplace at Batan in Chaldea. His whole life was passed in the study of the stars; but he was not content, like many others, with commenting upon the Almagest of Ptolemy: he examined things afresh for himself, and succeeded in determining,

[1] The earliest of three famous writers of this name, not the author of the Kitab al Fihrist (who flourished A.D. 980) or the Historian of the Dynasties, who lived and wrote in the thirteenth century.

more exactly than ever before, the obliquity of the ecliptic, the eccentricity and mean movement of the sun, and the precession of the equinoxes. In the twelfth century the introductory portion of his Astronomical Tables was translated into Latin by Plato of Tivoli—not much to the satisfaction of Arabic scholars.

In Aldjayhany, the "man of Djayhan," who appears about A.D. 913 as Vizier of a practically independent dynasty [1] in Khorasan, we have another proof of the survival and even heightening of intellectual interest at the time of the Caliphate's disruption. This zealous patron of discovery made use of his high position to gather travellers about him, to question them on the lands they had visited, to procure fresh reports of neighbouring countries, and to compare these new lights with the more accredited of older accounts. From all this was gradually produced under his orders a "Book of the Ways by which to know the Kingdoms;" ampler in detail, and more scholarly in construction, than any earlier work of the same kind. In particular, it described the peoples and districts of Hindostan with such fulness that it seems to have formed the basis of Edrisi's chapter on the same region. Aldjayhany probably intended to use his geographical collections for political ends; he was aiming at the conquest of Northern India and much of Central Asia; and only death prevented his attempting what Mahmoud of Ghazni achieved nearly a century later.

In A.D. 921 the Caliph Moktader-Billah sent an embassy to the Bulgarians of the Volga,[2] who had just embraced Islam. In the train of this mission went Ahmed Ibn Fozlan, who has given us the first reliable picture of mediæval

[1] The Samanides.

[2] Possibly prompted by a remembrance of the early mission of Sallam about A.D. 840 to the Caucasus, the wall of Gog-Magog, and the country of Samarcand, etc.

Russia. He describes with admirable clearness, accuracy, and good sense, the vast steppes over which he travelled, and their inhabitants, "the most unwashen of men whom God has created."

Unlike their Bulgarian neighbours, they retained their pagan faith and manners, which were as rude and blood-thirsty as those of any people. Private war, blood-feud, robbery, and murder were normal incidents of their life; even in their justice the final appeal was to the trial by battle. For "if their king have judged between two, and they are not content, he biddeth them decide their quarrel with their swords." [1] From their birth the Russians were trained to fight. "When a son is born to any, the father putteth a sword into the hand of the child, saying, 'That only is yours which you can win for yourself with this.'"

Ibn Fozlan first saw the Russians as they came down the Volga to trade, and their stature was the thing that most surprised him. They were "tall as palm trees" in the eyes of the Arab, and their complexion, "ruddy and flesh-coloured," seemed remarkable enough to the bronzed and swarthy Southerner. Every one, he noticed, carried an axe, a knife, and a sword; the last-named were of Frankish work, broad in the blade, and wavy in the moulding. The greatest ornaments in their esteem were beads of greenish glass.

When they descended the Volga for merchandise,[2] their habit was to leave their boats at anchor in the river, and build themselves great wooden booths upon the banks. Till the traffic was over they lived in these; after their business was done, a business which lay especially in slaves, they took to their boats, and returned to their own land.

Ibn Fozlan was, above all, interested in their funeral

[1] Frähn, "Ibn Fozlan," p. 3.   [2] Frähn, "Ibn Fozlan," p. 5.

customs, which included a variety of Suttee.   The Russian
dead, rich and poor alike, were burned, not buried; and
wives were expected, though not compelled, to die with
their husbands.[1] Should the woman, however, after agreeing to so reasonable a request, show any wish to withhold
this trifling favour, force was used; and she was not allowed
to disgrace herself by turning back.   But this was not
often necessary; the victims as a rule died "drunken and
happy." [2]

On one occasion, the traveller was present at a great
funeral, where the corpse, richly dressed in gold-embroidered
garments "from the land of the Greeks," lay in a boat upon
the river while a tremendous butchery took place to appease
the spirit.   A dog, two horses, a yoke of oxen, a pair of
fowls, a wife, and six attendants of the departed chief, were
slaughtered in succession, and all consumed together on
one pyre.

We can hardly be certain whether Ibn Fozlan actually
visited the Russian court and saw the king, whose body-
guard of "four hundred brave young men," under a
"general who is their Vizier," is briefly noticed by him.
All he tells us about their polity might have been gained
by his intercourse with the traders whom he saw among the
Bulgarians of the Volga, and the same applies both to their
social customs and to their religion.

They worshipped, he tells us, wooden idols, which were
nothing more than beams planted in the earth, and rudely
shaped in their upper part into the figure of a man.   They
had a firm belief in visions, especially in reappearances of
their departed friends and relatives; but their faith, which
in all emergencies was strictly fatalist, regarded as impious
any attempt to prolong the life of the sick.   When a Russian

---

[1] Frähn, "Ibn Fozlan," p. 11.   [2] Frähn, "Ibn Fozlan," p. 13.

fell ill, he was left alone with some bread and water to take his chance. If he recovered, his friends were glad to welcome his return; if not, they made haste to conciliate his ghost, not only with a holocaust such as Ibn Fozlan has already described, but also with offerings of food which might have prevented death if it had not been wicked to "fight against God."

Let us now turn one moment from land to sea. It was from the journeys of real explorers in this time, explorers such as Soleyman the merchant, or Ibn Vahab, that the Sindbad Saga began to take shape. It is obviously based upon the narratives of the "Two Mussulman Travellers" and similar records, such as those of Misar Abou Dolaf, son of Mohalhal; who in A.D. 942 accompanied certain Chinese envoys on their return from Bokhara to the Celestial kingdom. Misar described the regions of Tartary, China, and India which he had visited; but of his account, only a few fragments have survived in later compilations.[1] Once more, the narratives of Sindbad have something in common with a "Book of Marvels" attributed to Massoudy; and still more is borrowed by the Arab compiler from Greek poetry

[1] Such as the Geographical Dictionary of Yakout. Misar's account (in fragments) has been edited and translated by Schlözer, Berlin, 1845, and an English abstract of the same is given by Yule, "Cathay," prelim. essay, pp. cxi., clxxxvi.–cxciii. The narrative of Misar is extremely confused. On the way from Bokhara to China he seems to have visited all the Turkish tribes from the Black Sea to the Amoor, including the Baj-Nak or Pechinegs, the Khirghiz, and the Tagazgaz. He passed through Khotan and Thibet, if we may trust his place-names, and returned to the Caliphate by the Southern Sea and the coasts of India, by way of Kalah (in the Malay Peninsula), Malabar, Moultan, and Cabul.

The chief value of this lies in the rarity of recorded overland journeys through Turkistan to China; and the *substance* of Misar's narrative may be considered genuine, but the different portions have been hopelessly jumbled together, and the remarks on "objects of interest" are often in the most legendary style of Oriental history.

and myth, from the Indian tales of " The Seven Sages," and from Persian traditions of the later Sassanid time. But when all this has been admitted, we must still recognise in the story of Sindbad a true history, in a romantic setting, of Moslem travels in the ninth and tenth centuries. The exploits of many voyagers are here ascribed to one man ; he is delivered with incredible frequency of good fortune from every kind of danger ; but there are few of the incidents, even the most surprising, that cannot be shown to be at least founded on fact.

The essential truthfulness of the Sindbad Tales was perceived in the last century by some European critics, and notably by our own Richard Hole, whose " Remarks " of 1797 appear to have been made with the help of nothing better than Galland's imperfect and Frenchified version of the " Arabian Nights " and a good acquaintance with general literature, especially of the Greek and Latin classics. But an excellent critical judgment such as his may often produce surprising results with old-fashioned and even inferior tools ; and something of the spirit and method of Gibbon himself may be traced in this essay ; which Reinaud has not disdained to use and to commend ; and which undoubtedly, whatever its mistakes, pointed out the true way of dealing with that perplexing kind of literature where prose has been reset as poetry, or a series of narratives recast as a series of novels.[1]

[1] See Richard Hole's " Remarks on the Arabian Nights Entertainments, in which the origin of Sindbad's Voyages . . . is particularly considered," London, 1797 ; also Reinaud's " Abulféda," preface, pp. 77, 78, etc., and his " Mémoire sur l'Inde " (1849). Some help may be found in Renaudot's " Anciens Rélations de l'Inde et de la Chine," otherwise " The Two Mussulman Travellers," noticed already ; in Reinaud's edition of the same (1845) ; in Langlès' " Voyages de Sindbad " (1814) ; and in Walckenaer's commentary in the " Nouvelles Annales des Voyages," 1832 (1). There are a few useful notes in Lane's translation of the " Arabian Nights." Reinaud has prefixed to his edition of the " Two Travellers " an admirable *Discours préliminaire*.

In dealing with the Arabian Odyssey, we are, of course, at a loss, from the very few definite indications of place which are vouchsafed to us. Naturally it is not the business of the writer to localize his marvels; his only aim is to interest the public of the bazaars and the coffee-houses, who would care nothing about the reality of the stories told them so long as they were wonderful, and certainly would not be on the watch for anything like proofs of the actual occurrence of the incidents related. Precisely opposite is the interest of the modern inquirer. To him the story of Sindbad is valuable, not on account of its extravagances, but in spite of them; not because it transports him into an ideal world, but because, with the best intentions to do so, it is rarely if ever successful in its attempt to hide the present from his view. In the guise of fable, he recognises everywhere an account of places known to and visited by men of the present day; and he strives to restore the names and the positions which are hinted at but not expressed.

In all, seven voyages are recorded; but only in two of these, the first and the last, do we hear of any destination or goal of the journey. It is equally certain, however, that each of the seven expeditions had a like definite object, and that each brings us in its course to various definite parts of the Indian Ocean.

In the first voyage Sindbad, being desirous of improving his fortune by trade, realised his property, left Bagdad, and embarked at Bassora for the Isles of Wak-Wak,[1] probably

---

[1] Very high authorities (*e.g.*, Reinaud) have supposed these to be the Zanzibar Islands, but on the evidence for Japan see a monograph of M. de Goeje (" Arabische Berichte over Japon ") and his " Ibn Khordadbeh," pp. 49, 50. Langlès believes hem to be the Sunda Islands; Lane (see " Arabian Nights," iii. 480, 481) again takes Wak-Wak to be a general name for all the islands with which the Arabs were acquainted to the east of Borneo; but Kazwini, whom he quotes in support of his view, hardly seems doubtful in his identification of Wak-Wak with Japan

Japan. He passed by an infinite number of small islands, which from his description may be identified with the Laccadives, off the south-western coast of India. At last he landed on one like a " garden of Paradise ; " but it proved to be only a whale's back. The whale was roused by a fire being kindled on its dorsal fin, and dived. Sindbad was thrown into the sea, which at last carried him to the Island of the Mares, possibly the *Ilhas de Cavallos*, near Ceylon. An exactly similar story of a whale island occurs in the

As to this, notice his three statements : 1, it is in the sea of China ; 2, it produces gold for bricks, dog-chains, and ape-collars,—in other words, for necessaries and luxuries alike ; 3, no one knows what is beyond it save God. On the other islands mentioned by Sindbad on his first voyage : 1. Rahmi or Ramni is clearly identified with Sumatra, the Lesser Java of Marco Polo, by a comparison of the notices in the " Two Mussulman Travellers," and in the "Sindbad Voyages" with those of Polo, Edrisi, Kazwini, and the later geographers. 2. The island of Sanf, one month and ten days from Khanfu, according to the "Two Travellers," has been plausibly conjectured by Marsden to be Tsiampa in Cochin China, lat. 13° N. ; and Edrisi supports this by calling it a Chinese island. 3. Kalah is in the Malay Peninsula, and not Coulam in Malabar, as Lane tries to prove. In Heyd's view, it is the furthest point of Sindbad's travels eastwards. 4. Kamar, famous for the Kamari aloes of Sindbad's narrative, is stated by Edrisi to be only three miles from Sanf, but, in spite of this, some have identified it with Cape Comorin. 5. Lane, apparently influenced by Sir William Jones, who

is followed by R. Hole, identifies Zapage or Mihraj with Borneo absolutely ; but this seems rather uncertain (see Purchas, "Pilgrims," V. i. 2 ; Ramusio, i.). True, Pigafetta and Maximilian of Transylvania give a description of the King of Borneo in Magellan's time (A.D. 1520), rather similar to Sindbad's ; and the latter mentions precisely the same want of a good breed of native horses in his kingdom. In all this we are at a loss, from the vague language of the Arab geographers and the entire change of place-names since their day ; and are often thrown back upon inference from local products, which, of course, are frequently found in many lands, and thus are a very hazardous and uncertain form of proof. May not the true explanation of Sindbad's Mihraj be found in the empire of Java, which at this time (ninth and tenth centuries A.D.) included most of the Malay peoples and some part of the continent of India ; which as a whole was often called the kingdom of Zabedj (= Zapage) ; and whose sovereign enjoyed the title of Maharaja (? Mihraj). See Reinaud's edition of the "Two Travellers," p. lxxiv., and Massoudy as cited by Reinaud in that place.

Christian romance of St. Brandan; but the saint's comrades, unlike the Arab merchant, have time to get back to their ship from the quaking and deceptive soil. The Eastern tale also asks us to believe that the whale had slumbered on the surface long enough for a fine soil to accumulate, for lofty trees to grow, and for rivers to form themselves. But in both cases it is the same imprudence of the sailors that brings about the catastrophe.

From the Island of the Mares [1] Sindbad is taken by the friendly grooms of King Mihraj to a country abounding in camphor and pepper, which is probably one of the Spice Islands beyond the Malay Peninsula, and which seems to be intended in a mention by the "Two Mussulman Travellers" of a country near Sumatra. Sindbad only gives us the name of the sovereign, Mihraj, possibly the "Maharaja" of the then powerful Java, who reappears in the sixth voyage as the "Solomon of the Indians;" the "Two Travellers" add the place-name of Zapage "under a King Mihraj and not far from Rahmi," a common Arab designation of Sumatra.

In the kingdom of Mihraj, Sindbad meets his old captain, recovers his property,[2] and sets out on his return to Bassora; but before this he records various wonders of that distant sea—an island called Kasil, "where is heard nightly the beating of drums;" fish three hundred feet in length, but so fearful that they could be scared away by the beating of two sticks; and other birdlike creatures that swam in the ocean, but had heads like owls.

The first of these portents was a cherished belief of the

[1] With this legend, cf. Homer, "Iliad," books xix., xx. (lines 264, etc.), and a somewhat similar story in Ibn Khordadbeh.

[2] Which he had left on shipboard when he landed on the whale-island with the exploring party.

mediæval world, which we have had already in Solinus, of a mountain in West Africa; which Ibn Khordadbeh puts in the Southern Ocean; and which Argensola in the sixteenth century actually locates according to native tradition in Banda, possibly the very spot now pointed out to Sindbad. " Cries, whistles, and roarings " were reported by the Christian narrator as having issued from that island for many ages, and Argensola is irresistibly driven to the same conclusion as the Arab sailor : " Long experience has shown that the spot is inhabited by devils." [1]

Sindbad's description of the whales and flying fish of this sea is almost exactly in the words of Ibn Khordadbeh; and with the Moslem device for scaring away the great Cetaceans, we may compare the Greek story of Nearchus on his voyage from the Indus to the Persian Gulf, sounding his trumpets with terrifying effect against a whole school of sea-monsters.[2]

In his second voyage, Sindbad is marooned on an unnamed island by his treacherous companions, who, from the adventure that follows, may be supposed to have sailed for the Zanzibar coast. In his desolation, the castaway finds a roc's egg. With his customary *savoir faire,* he infers that the roc itself will soon return to hatch the " great white dome " before him. Very soon the sun is darkened by the flight of the giant bird, that could take up an elephant with a single claw. It descends upon its egg, broods over it, and sleeps—" extolled be the perfections of Him that sleepeth not." Sindbad promptly ties himself

[1] Argensola, " History of the Moluccas." Sindbad is even more explicit; he tells us the name of the chief devil. It was El Dejjal, head of the Genii in rebellion against Allah.

[2] For the Arab language about the owl-headed fish, we may compare Father Martini's similar language about the parrot-beaked variety in the sea near Canton.

to a leg of the monster, and is carried by it when it awakes to the Valley of Diamonds; in modern language, from Madagascar to India. The roc alights to pick up a serpent, and Sindbad at once unties himself, rather dizzy with his flight, and with an unpleasant consciousness that he has only fallen from bad to worse; for the Valley of Diamonds swarms with gigantic snakes, and its sides are of inaccessible height and steepness. Suddenly he is roused by a piece of meat plumping down in front of him. It flashes across his mind that the old story of the Diamond Valley was true after all, though hitherto he had supposed it to be fable. At once he took advantage of the deliverance thus offered. He tied himself to the meat, and everything happened in the orthodox manner. An eagle came down for the flesh, and carried him up with it. When it reached its nest, the diamond merchants rushed out to see if any jewels had stuck to the carcase they had just thrown down. They drove away the bird, and found their meat without jewels, but with Sindbad adhering to it instead. They expressed some natural disappointment, until that crafty adventurer, who had taken care to line his clothes with diamonds before his last flight, produced enough to reward their trouble. After his escape, Sindbad traded with great profit in the Camphor Islands; where he describes with perfect accuracy the native method of obtaining the drug by boring in a tree and catching the sap as it ran out in a standing vessel, like the caoutchouc or indiarubber of South America. He adds the favourite and highly fabulous story of the rhinoceros spitting the elephant on its horn, and so carrying it about without any inconvenience from the extra weight.

No one of the voyages has excited more derision than this, but something may be said even for the roc and the

Valley of Diamonds. And first as to the roc. " In form," wrote Marco Polo, " it is said to resemble the eagle, and those who have seen this bird assert that its wings when spread measure sixteen paces in length ; " [1] and he tells us that a feather was brought to Kublai Khan of the size of ninety spans, and that all his informants were agreed that the bird was no griffin or creature of fable, half bird and half beast, but a gigantic eagle. Modern zoologists [2] have reconstructed for us the æpiornis of Madagascar, a bird six times the size of the ostrich, one of whose eggs is now pre- served at Paris ; and the moa (or dinornis) of New Zealand, which reached a height of eighteen feet as it stood upright, is described in old Maori hunting songs. Once again, both the vulture of South Africa and the albatross of the far Southern Ocean, whose wings have been known to spread to fifteen feet and upwards, have been quoted as possible sources of the roc legend. [3]

Secondly, on the Valley of Diamonds, and the method of obtaining them by birds of prey, a precisely similar account is given by Marco Polo of " certain deep valleys " in the kingdom of Murfili or Golconda ; and much the same is said by St. Epiphanius of Cyprus (about A.D. 400) of a valley " in the desert of great Scythia." [4]   Benjamin of

[1] If, as we may suppose, this " pace " was the ordinary one of 2½ feet, the spread of the roc's wings would be 40 feet.

[2] Especially Owen and Geoffrey St. Hilaire.

[3] Kippis, in his " Life of Cook," p. 146, records the finding of a gigantic bird's nest in an island off New Holland (Australia), twenty-six feet round and two feet eight inches in height. On the size of the roc, cf. also Pigafetta's account in his narra- tive of Magellan's voyage (Ramusio,

i. 369). The existence has also been conjectured of birds of the eagle tribe, who *preyed on the Moa.*

[4] In his treatise on the twelve stones on the High Priest's breast- plate (" De XII. Lapidibus Rationali Sacerdotis infixis "). Epiphanius was bishop of Salamis in Cyprus, and died A.D. 403. In his account, the diamond hunters skin lambs and throw down their carcases, which are brought up by eagles with diamonds sticking to them.

Tudela in the twelfth century repeats the story, and some trick of the sort seems to have been really practised at some time or other, though perhaps only as a makeshift on a particular occasion, and not as a custom.

Sindbad's third voyage seems to have been intended for China, but his ship is thrown away on the coast of the Mountain of Apes,[1] possibly in Sumatra, and the crew next falls into the power of a negro cannibal, one-eyed, most terrible, with projecting lips and tusk-like teeth—an Arabic Polyphemus. Escaping from his clutches, like Ulysses from the Cyclops, by grinding out the monster's only eye, Sindbad makes his way to a place he calls Selakit, where sandal-wood was abundant, probably Timor. Here and in the neighbouring Moluccas he got great store of spices, and noticed various wonders of the deep—gigantic turtles, sea-cows, and sea-camels (dugong or manatee ?). From the Clove Islands he again returned to Bagdad, " the abode of peace."

Three such voyages might have contented him, but a wicked desire of prying into what the Creator had kept hidden drove him once more to sea; when of course he was soon wrecked on a cannibal island, producing pepper and cocoa-nuts (the Andamans?), where the "ghouls" and " magi " who inhabited it offered their captives a food which destroyed their reason, and then fattened them for eating.[2]

[1] These apes he describes as filthy little dwarfish men, covered with hair like black felt, and measuring two feet in height. For these, cf. Marco Polo's account of the Pigmies of Sumatra, which Polo, with his usual acuteness, perceives to be monkeys (ourang-outangs), bk. iii. ch. xii. William de Rubruquis tells of similar dwarfs in Cathay, and his account was noticed with special interest by Roger Bacon (see Purchas, iii. 32, 58). The classical references to the Pigmies, as Homer, Iliad, iii. 5; Pliny, H. N. vii. 2, are mainly based, no doubt, upon the dwarf tribes of central Africa, but Ptolemy puts certain Satyr islands ($N\hat{\eta}\sigma o\iota\ \tau\hat{\omega}\nu\ \Sigma\alpha\tau\nu\rho\hat{\omega}\nu$) off the coast of India, beyond the Ganges, just where required by the Sindbad story. The adventure with the negro is of course pure myth, copied in every detail from Odyssey ix.

[2] Cf. Ptolemy's islands off Further India, inhabited by men-eaters called

Sindbad alone avoided the "insane root," and so escaped after a time to the sea-shore, where he was rescued by some white men gathering pepper. They took him to their own country, where he married and settled. Then follows the marvellous tale of his being buried alive, according to the custom of the land, with his dead wife; and of his deliverance by following the track of an animal that came into the cavern of the dead from the sea by a little hole. This adventure, which in some ways recalls the escape of Aristomenes of Messina in the Spartan war (by his clutching hold of a fox's tail), is very difficult to locate. One must be content with remarking that soon after leaving the country, whose uncomfortable funeral ceremonies[1] he had just experienced, Sindbad passes the island and city of the Bell, which he places at ten days' sail from Ceylon, on the western side of the Bay of Bengal.

On his fifth voyage, the traveller is cursed with sacrilegious companions. Finding a roc's egg on an island unnamed, they break it up, pull out the young bird, kill and eat it. Their fate was like the crew of Ulysses,[2] when they killed the oxen sacred to Apollo. The parent rocs pursued the ship and shattered it with huge stones, which they dropped from above. Sindbad alone escaped, upon a plank, to an "island like a delicious garden;" where he met the Old Man of the Sea, who has generally been identified

---

Maniolæ (bk. vii.). The maddening herb given by the cannibals to the sailors may be compared with the lotus - eating episode in the Odyssey; with Plutarch's story of a similar report of Mark Antony's soldiers; and with Davis's account of Sumatra in 1599. (Purchas's "Pilgrims," i. 120.) Hole, pp. 99, 100, refers as a parallel to the Bhang-

eating so frequently mentioned in the "Arabian Nights" themselves; but the effect of this was deep sleep, and not madness.

[1] Cf. Mandeville's story of a Far Eastern custom of male as well as the usual female suttee; but this he says was voluntary, and so probably exceptional.

[2] Odyssey, xii.

with one of the huge apes of Borneo or Sumatra.[1] With this agree all the notes that are given us by Sindbad about his appearance and habits. He never spoke, we are told; he lived on fruits; his skin was like a buffalo's for roughness; the strength and clinging power of his legs were immense. Finally, he had all the imitative folly of the monkey race. Once he saw Sindbad merry with wine, he wished to be so too; as Sindbad drained his calabash at a draught, so did he; and drunkenness caught him off his guard.

We next find Sindbad trading in pepper and aloes-wood off the Camaree coast, in which we may recognise the Komar of the "Two Mussulman Travellers," and the Coromandel of modern India; and near this part of the world the adventurer employs divers with great success in pearl fishery, doubtless in the always famous oyster-beds off Cape Comorin and Ceylon.

The sixth voyage (after the usual shipwreck and Sindbad's escape by the subterranean river) deals only with sober fact. In the description of Ceylon, which forms the chief interest of this narrative, we are told rightly enough of its position "under the Equator and the Equinox," of its dimensions (250 miles by 100 miles),[2] of its famous mountain of Adam's Peak, of its rubies and other jewels.

But, besides repeating the ordinary facts as they might be found in Ibn Khordadbeh, or the classical descriptions of Taprobane,[3] Sindbad gives a particularly graphic and full account of the presents sent by the Island King to Haroun al Raschid. The yellow skin on which the letter of greeting

---

[1] We may notice that in Banda, as Hole points out, p. 155, all the essentials of the story are found, even to vines, which are not too common in the Spice Islands.

[2] Eighty leagues by thirty.

[3] As in Diodorus Siculus, ii. 4; Pliny, Nat. Hist., vi. 22.

was written may be supposed to have been prepared from the hide of the hog-deer; and all the presents—the ruby cup, the aloes, the camphor, and so forth—are equally characteristic of Ceylon.

The seventh and last voyage differs from all the others in some respects. First, the destination, Ceylon, is distinctly stated, and, what is still more remarkable, it is actually attained; again, with this change of the general plan, the treatment of details is also changed. The customary shipwreck is omitted, and the dramatic disaster needful to the story is only introduced in the shape of pirates on the return. Once more Sindbad now goes in a new capacity. He is a private adventurer no longer; no longer merely the owner of a ship. He now sails from Bassora as the Envoy of the Caliph to Ceylon. Lastly, this journey is a direct consequent of the gifts and compliments with which Sindbad was charged by the Indian Prince at the close of his last voyage. But in the interval he has become a changed man. He now hates the sea, and all thought of further wandering, as much as he once thirsted for it. To him now—

> " Hateful was the dark blue sky,
>   Vaulted o'er the dark blue sea,
>   Sore task to heart worn out by many wars,
>   And eyes grown dim with gazing on the pilot stars."

Submissive to the will of the Commander of the Faithful, Sindbad goes out once more, and such trifling misadventures as a capture by pirates scarcely make much difference to his persistent good fortune. True, he is for a time a slave; true, he falls into the power of a herd of furious elephants; but this is only the device of the story-teller, to add one more to the respectable and ancient legends of animal sagacity.

Pliny and Ælian [1] have told of elephants adoring the moon, writing; or at least understanding, Greek; performing difficult exercises in arithmetic, and so forth; but the Arab has a finishing touch of his own to give. It was explained to Sindbad why the elephants, when they had him in their power, not only spared his life, but showed him a secret hoard of ivory. They knew that, if they killed him, plenty of other men would come and hunt them for their tusks; what their enemies wanted was not their bodies but their ivory, and the best way to quiet those same enemies was to keep them supplied with a sufficient stock of the precious article.

Therefore, Sindbad gravely informed the Caliph, was his life spared once again, and his fortune afresh increased; and Haroun, adds the narrative, with beautiful irony, though he might have disbelieved such a tale from another man, could not doubt *his* sincerity.

Massoudy, though slightly earlier in time than his contemporaries Alestakhry and Ibn Haukal, closes his work within a year or two of theirs, and it will be an advantage to keep our notice of him to the last. As the encyclopædist of Oriental geography in this age, he affords a more fitting conclusion than any other to this inquiry; the leading figure must come, if possible, first or last on the programme; and there is no serious distortion of time-order in doing so here.

The Sheikh Abou Ishak, called Alestakhry, from his birthplace in Estakhar, or Persepolis, travelled about A.D. 950--1 in most of the countries of Islam, from India to the Atlantic, and from the Persian Gulf to the Caspian Sea. Of these journeys he composed an account under the title of a "Book of Climates," beginning with Arabia as the

[1] See Pliny, Hist. Nat., viii. 44; Ælian, Hist. Animal., xi., xiii.

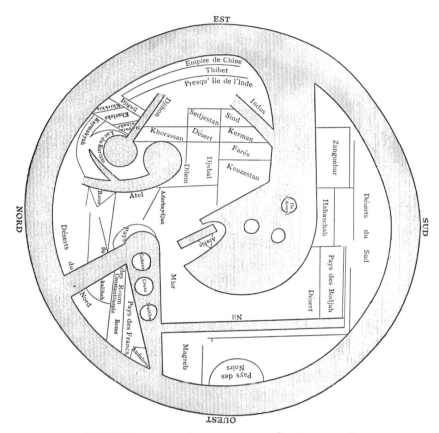

THE WORLD ACCORDING TO IBN HAUKAL (AFTER REINAUD).

central Moslem country, and devoting a chapter to each
province of the Caliphate, with a coloured plan to illustrate
each chapter. Ibn Haukal, whose real name was Mohammed
Aboul Kassem, performed a similar journey, and left a book
so nearly identical with that of Alestakhry that it has
caused great confusion to modern research. In the valley
of the Indus the two travellers met and exchanged notes ;
at the request of Alestakhry, Ibn Haukal took the former's
manuscript into his own charge, corrected it in certain
places, and finally composed a fuller record of his own upon
the basis of the other. For both works, we have the same
divisions of subject-matter, and the same number of chapters ;
the very expressions are often identical. But the account
of Ibn Haukal is more literary and more developed ; as
might be expected from a native of Bagdad, who from 943
to 969 seems to have been travelling incessantly, though
always, we may suppose, within the limits of Islam.

In the opening of his " Book of Ways and Provinces,"
the author, first begging the pardon of God for so profane
a task as travel, fortifies himself by the examples of Ibn
Khordadbeh, Kodama, and Aldjayhany (whose writings he
had always used), and indicates the plan of his work :—

"I have described the earth in its length and breadth ; I have given
a view of the Moslem provinces ; but I have taken no account of the
division by climates, in order to avoid confusion. I have illustrated every
region by a map. I have indicated the position of each, relative to other
countries. The boundaries of all these lands, their cities and cantons, the
rivers that water them, the lakes and pools that vary their surface, the
routes that traverse them, the trades that flourish in them,—all these I
have enumerated : in a word, I have collected all that has ever made
geography of interest either to princes or to people."

There are certain exceptions, Ibn Haukal tells us later,
which he felt it necessary to make.

" I have not described the country of the African blacks and the other peoples of the torrid zone; because, naturally loving wisdom, ingenuity, religion, justice, and regular government, how could I notice such people as these, or magnify them by inserting an account of their countries ? "

Coming to details, the region of Islam is defined as superior to others in that it is more extensive. Bordering alike upon the northern and southern ocean is pathless desert, but inhabited and cultivated ground stretches along the diameter of the world, from China to Morocco. Of the great inland seas, the Persian Gulf and the Mediterranean communicate with the outer ocean, but not the Caspian. Ibn Haukal avoids the trap into which stumbled so many Latin geographers, and describes how one may make the circuit of this great salt lake without ever quitting *terra firma* except for the crossing of rivers. The extent and number of the tribes of Gog-Magog (in Turkestan) were known " only unto God." Wherever he leaves the Caliphate, Ibn Haukal is vague and uncertain. Sometimes he is downright fabulous, or rather Koranic, as in his story of the tribe of Russian Jews who were turned into monkeys for hunting on the Sabbath. Here and there, however, he preserves interesting and trustworthy notices of the outside world, as in his account of the gold mines and (still surviving) Christianity of Nubia ; of the white race scattered among the blacks of the Zanzibar coast ; [1] of the idol of Moultan in Scinde, and of the habits of the Tartars of the Volga. When he tells us that the Nile flows from the *east* to Fostat (Cairo), he repeats the language of earlier writers who were thinking of the freshwater canal from Suez to " Babylon." In a similar way, his language on the Nile sources is suspiciously like certain of the Greek and Latin expressions, as to the mysterious river springing out of

[1] These were doubtless the Arabs of the Emosaid migration.

a cavern near the land of Zanzibar, in a place that could
be approached, but never quite arrived at.

Of all the countries of Islam, but especially of Mesopotamia and the region of Samarcand, Ibn Haukal has clear
and fairly accurate ideas.   When he says, in his account of
Syria, that all the Greek philosophers came from Tyre, or,
in his account of Kurdistan, that Saul, the King of Israel,
came from the Kurdish village of Shehr Werd, he is going
out of his depth, for he has few weaker points than ancient
history.   In matters of his own day, race, and religion, he
was far better equipped.   Very curious and valuable are his
notices of the contemporary travels of the men of Tarsus, and
of the inns or caravanserais reserved for them in every great
city of Islam, as well as of the fire-temples still existing in
Persia ; of the trade and manufactures of the Levantine
Moslems, and of the wealth of ports like Siraf, where " some
traders were possessed of four millions of dinars, and some
of more ; and yet their clothes were like the clothes of hired
labourers."   To Ibn Haukal, the pearl of the earth was
Samarcand ; although he draws a picture of peace and prosperity in almost every region from the Nile to the Oxus,
and from the Taurus to the Pamir.   But in " Sogd " there is
something better than the best.   " In all the world there is
no place more delightful or more health-giving than these
three—the Plain of Samarcand, the Oasis of Damascus, the
Valley of the Aileh."   But the last two do not satisfy Ibn
Haukal.   " A fine prospect ought to fill the view completely,
and nothing should be visible but sky and verdure."   Now
Damascus and the Aileh, though beautiful, are of small
extent, and encircled by desert ;—

"but the Sogd, for eight days' journey, is all full of gardens and orchards
and villages, corn-fields and villas, running streams, reservoirs, and
fountains both on the right-hand and on the left; and if one stood on the

old castle at Bokhara, one could not see anything but rich country as far as the eye could reach, even to the horizon, where the green of the earth and the azure of the heavens were united."

The people were suited to the land. They spent their money in improving the roads, in building caravanserais, in repairing bridges. "Such was the hospitality of the inhabitants, that one would imagine all the families of the land were but one house." In some dwellings the doors were nailed back against the walls, and had been so for a hundred years and more, so that no stranger should ever be denied admittance. Food and lodgment were to be had for money in above two thousand inns, without recourse to the generosity of private citizens; yet every peasant allotted a portion of his cottage for the reception of a guest, and the greatest pleasure of the owner was in persuading a stranger to accept his liberality.[1]

By contrast with this, we may notice how on another frontier of Islam—at Derbend under the Caucasus—life was less tranquil; for the savage Tartar enemies of the city, living all around it, were "as numerous as the waves of the sea that come up to its walls." Happily at "Atel on the Volga," the townsmen had some allies—a Jew king, a tribe of Christian Bulgarians, and a number of Mussulman merchants. But, taken altogether, Ibn Haukal's description portrays Islam at a time of singular prosperity. Even in Ferghanah, where Moslems were obliged incessantly to watch the motions of the Turkish hordes beyond Khokand, were groves and gardens and orchards, and flourishing towns with rich bazaars, many acres of land sown with corn,

[1] Ibn Haukal tells of a Christian church in Herat, but makes only slight mention of Christianity in Samarcand; yet we know, both from Albyrouny's language ("Chron. of Ancient Nations," p. 282 in Sachau's E. tr.), as well as from the Nestorian funeral inscriptions lately discovered in the Semiretchi, or district of the seven rivers, that Christianity had many followers in Central Asia beyond the Oxus at this very time.

and furnished with windmills and watermills, that were not known in Europe till the first Crusade.

Two works of mathematical geography were produced at the eastern and western extremities of the Mohammedan world while Ibn Haukal was still on his travels.

From the banks of the Syr Daria, Mohammed, surnamed Alfaraby, born of a Turkish family at Farab, the modern Otrar in Ferghanah, came to Bagdad about A.D. 920. He studied logic and philosophy under two Christian or Nestorian teachers, and his "Book of Latitudes and Longitudes," in which the principal places of the earth were not only fixed but described, must have been completed before his death at Damascus in 950.

Eleven years later (in A.D. 961), Bishop Harib presented to the Caliph Hakem of Cordova his Latin version of the Arab Almanac, in which, under astronomical and astrological headings, some reference was made to matters geographical.[1]

Several of the writers and travellers we have noticed enjoyed in their time no small fame, and are referred to with respect by the later compilers and summarists—Yakout, Aboulfeda, and the rest. But they have nearly all come down to us in so fragmentary a state that we can form little or no idea of their real merits; while those works which we possess in full, such as the "Route Guide" of Ibn Khordadbeh, or the "Provinces" of Ibn Haukal, are for the most part too dry and tabular in their form, and too brief in their matter, to sustain a comparison with the encyclopædic work of Massoudy.

Aboul Hassan Ali, a native of Bagdad, was called Al Massoudy, because he counted among his ancestors a Meccan named Massoud, whose eldest son accompanied the Prophet

---

[1] This, like the work of Albateny and Alfaraby, will be more fully considered in the next volume.

on the Hegira, or flight to Medina. We do not know the year of Massoudy's birth, but only that he left his home at an early age, and died in A.D. 956. In the course of his wanderings he passed through every country of the Moslem belt or climate, from Further India to Spain. But he also penetrated regions that few Arab writers had described before, and even China and Madagascar seem to have been within the compass of his later travels. In one place he compares himself to the sun, whom nothing can escape, and applies to his own case the verses of the poet :—

> "I have gone so far towards the setting sun
> That I have lost all remembrance of the East,
> And my course has taken me so far towards the rising sun
> That I have forgotten the very name of the West."

Massoudy visited successively Persia, India, Ceylon, the lands of Central Asia from Ferghanah to the Caspian, the countries of Northern Africa, Spain, and various parts of the Greek or Eastern Empire. In A.D. 915, we find him at Bassora and Persepolis; next year in India, in Palestine, and in the Isle of Kambalou (Madagascar ?), off the eastern coast of Africa. Soon after this he appears in Oman and Southern Arabia ;—and he especially commemorates another visit to Bassora and his native Tigris Valley, after an absence of nearly thirty years, in A.D. 943. Massoudy was not a specialist in any particular branch of knowledge; although his writings are a storehouse of geographical fact, he never composed a formal treatise on the subject; and he has no independent position as a mathematician, an astronomer, or a professor of the exact sciences in any form. More than that, he does not seem to have possessed that thorough acquaintance with other languages, such as Greek and Sanscrit, which was acquired by a man like Albyrouny. As we have suggested before, there is a lack of order, of symmetry, and of selection in his productions; the central historical thread is sometimes almost lost in the digressions, and the number of the subjects treated of causes a bewildering variety of colour. For it was his aim that there should be "no branch of science or tradition" which he had "not dealt with, either at length or in brief;" and in this comprehensive ambition it is easy to recognise not only the cause of his defects in form, but the secret of the charm and value of his matter. He is not an original thinker, but he is an excellent observer and a first-class collector and transmitter of curious lore; and in him, as in so many Orientals, was combined the antiquarian and the poet. Thus to him there was a special force and meaning in the thought of the impermanence and changefulness, not merely of man, but of the earth which seemed so firm beneath him; and the vision of the old Arab seer of El Hirah, in the ninth chapter of the "Meadows of Gold," is not altogether unworthy of comparison with the opening paragraphs of the "Timæus" of Plato, or even with the sixty-fourth sonnet of Shakespeare, as a comment on the thought :—

> " When I have seen by Time's fell hand defaced
>   The rich proud cost of outworn buried age;
> When sometimes lofty towers I see down-rased,
>   And brass eternal slave to mortal rage;
> When I have seen the hungry ocean gain
>   Advantage on the kingdom of the shore,
> And the firm soil win of the watery main
>   Increasing store with loss, and loss with store—
> When I have seen such interchange of state,
>   Or state itself confounded to decay,
> Ruin hath taught me thus to ruminate :
>   That Time will come and take " all things " away." [1]

---

[1] When Khaled conquered Babylonia, relates Massoudy, the man of El Hirah, who was sent to make terms with the conqueror, at first seemed "a fool," who, "when one thing was asked, answered another," but in the end of the dialogue he turned the tables. "What is the

The "Meadows of Gold" Massoudy describes as his offering to "the most illustrious kings and to the learned;" and in this work he declares that he has compressed together everything that an educated man should know, whether elsewhere described or not. He considers herein the histories of famous peoples, and especially of the Arabs. He indicates the regions occupied by various nations; he distinguishes the different seas, canals, rivers and islands of the world, and all its physical features. He quotes the opinions of sages on the form and stability of the globe, on the extent of the habitable world, on the size of the seven zones or climates, on the age and duration of the earth, on the cardinal points and the stellar influences.

The whole book is divided into one hundred and thirty-two chapters, containing in mere length somewhat more than Hallam's "Middle Ages" and much about the same as Mommsen's "History of Rome." The first two sections are prefatory. The third, fourth, fifth, and sixth are devoted to pre-Mohammedan history, especially of the Jews; from the seventh to the seventieth, we have a blend of history, geography, and discussion on questions of national manners, chronology, belief, architecture, and so forth. The last sixty-three chapters are mainly occupied with the story of Mohammed and the Caliphate, with occasional digressions.

Only a few of these divisions are purely geographical,

meaning of these fortresses?" asked Khaled. "They are built for mad people, who are shut up in them till they come to their senses" (*i.e.* till they learn the truth of the flux of all things, and see the folly of building for eternity, or even for a moderately distant future). "And how many years have come over thee?" "Three hundred and fifty." "And what hast thou seen?" "I have seen the ships of the sea coming up over this firm land with the goods of Scinde and of India. The ground that is now under thy feet was then covered with the waves; where is now the sand of the desert was once full of villages, trees and crops, canals and streams. So God visits His servants and His country."

such as the eighth, " On the Globe, the Seas, the Beginning
of Rivers, the Mountains, the Climates, the Stars that pre-
side over them." As a rule, a particular country or kingdom
is only described as to its position, extent, and natural
wonders, after its history has been sketched.   Thus, in
chapter thirty-six, we have the list of Lombard kings and
a summary of their deeds, before we are supplied with an
account of the country they inhabit. As Massoudy proceeds
in his survey, the subject tends to narrow itself down to
a simple record of Islam ; but a brave attempt is made in
the earlier chapters to realise the universal ambition of the
author.   Thus, among nations, the Jews, the Hindoos, the
Chinese, the ancient Assyrians and Persians, the Pagan
Greeks and Romans, the Christian Byzantines, the Egyptians,
the Negroes of the Soudan, the Slavs of Russia and Eastern
Europe, the Franks, Spaniards, Lombards, and finally the
Arabs in all their divisions and dispersions, pass in succession
before us.   Again, in chapter eleven, " all the different
opinions " on the ebb and flow of the tides are recorded : in
chapter sixteen we have " a comprehensive view of the
wonders of the sea : " and in other places elaborate discussions " on the soul, intellect, and animal life ; "[1] on ghosts,
witchcraft, demons, and ominous sounds and signs; on
visions, dreams, and the differences between the rational and
irrational soul; on the calendars of the Copts, Syrians,
Greeks, Persians and Arabs, as well as on the revolutions
of the sun and moon, and on the influences of the heavenly
bodies upon this world.

Massoudy's treatment of some of the vexed questions of
geography is especially interesting. He concludes that the
Caspian was land-locked, and that it did not connect with the

---

[1] See chaps. xlviii.–lxii.

Black Sea or with the Northern Ocean.[1] On the other hand, he believes in a channel from the Sea of Azov to the Arctic Sea, as in a similar canal dividing Africa on the south from an Antarctic continent. On his scheme the Indian Ocean, or Sea of Habasch (Abyssinia), contains most of the water surface of the world; and the Sea of Aral appears for the first time in Moslem geography. The girth of the world he cut down even more than Ptolemy. The latter had left an ocean to the west of Africa; the former made the Canaries or Fortunate Islands, the limit of the known Western world, abut upon India, the limit of the Eastern.

Lastly, it may be well to illustrate what we have said in general as to Massoudy's method and subject-matter, by a few more detailed examples of his merits or defects.

1. In his eighth chapter the size, shape, motion, and main divisions of the earth are expounded in a way that even modern science must recognise as not wholly inadequate.

"Mathematicians have divided the earth into four quarters—east, west, north, and south—and into inhabited and uninhabited worlds. They say it is round, that its centre falls in the midst of the universe, and that the air surrounds it on all sides. The cultivated or inhabited land begins from the Fortunate Islands in the Western Ocean and goes to the extremity of China,—a space of twelve hours (in the daily revolution of the sun), which amounts to half the circumference of the earth, or 13,500 of those miles which are in use in such a measurement. The breadth of the habitable land extends from the equator northward to the Isle of Thule, which belongs to Britain, and where the longest day has twenty hours— a distance of sixty degrees, or one-sixth of the circumference of the

[1] In the Christian geography of the earlier Middle Ages, as we have seen, perhaps to weariness, such an idea was almost unknown, nearly everybody repeating the old classical mistake of the Caspian as an arm of the Northern Ocean. The misconception referred to was prevalent enough among the Arabs, and is repeated by Abou Zeyd Hassan and many others; but not so unanimously as in Christendom. European ideas were first properly corrected on the subject by the missionary travellers of the thirteenth century, John de Plano Carpini, and the rest.

THE WORLD ACCORDING TO MASSOUDY (AFTER REINAUD).

earth.   The extent of the cultivated world is thus one-twelfth of the whole surface of the globe." [1]

Then from the observations of Ptolemy and Almamoun's astronomers, Massoudy proceeds to give the length of a degree as equal to 56 miles, the girth of the world as 20,160 miles (27,000, according to previous computation), and its diameter as 6,414 miles.[2]   Passing to the spheres, he considers with Ptolemy, that the revolution of the Zodiac is the cause of day and night,—"for it carries the sun and moon and stars with itself from east to west round the two poles, the pole of the Bear and the pole of Canopus, once in the space of a day and a night."   In the same way, Massoudy reproduces the Alexandrian astronomer on the questions of latitude and longitude, the equinoctial line, the poles and the axis of the world.

"The line which cuts the sphere of the Zodiac in two from east to west is called the equinoctial line, because when the sun is upon it day and night are equal in all countries of the world.   Both poles are at the same distance from this line.   The direction in the sphere from north to south is called Latitude, and the direction from east to west Longitude.   The spheres are round; they include the earth, and turn round it as a circumference round the centre of the circle; and the sphere which makes the daily revolution turns round the axes and the poles just like the wheel of the carpenter or turner.   Those who live on the Equator have day and night always of equal length, and see both poles, whereas those who live in the North never see Canopus, and those who live in the South never catch sight of the Bear."

As to the curvature of the earth, Massoudy urges the well-known argument of the disappearance of objects at sea, and makes use of Mount Damavand as an instance.

"This is about twenty parasangs from the Caspian.   If ships sail on this sea and are very distant they first perceive the north side of the

---

[1] One-half by one-sixth.
[2] A mile has 4,000 black cubits; these are the cubits of Almamoun for measuring cloth, buildings, and ground; one cubit has 24 inches.

mountain towards the summit, and the nearer they come to the shore the more is seen of it. This is an evident proof of the spherical form of the water of the sea, which has the shape of a segment of a ball."

Along with this clear and scientific exposition, Massoudy repeats the pet story of his race about an earth-summit, the Arim of tradition—

"a point of the Equator on an island between India and Abyssinia, which is known as the dome of the earth; and is in the middle between north and south as it is in the middle between east and west, between the Fortunate Islands and the furthest regions of China, at the point where there is no latitude, as Mohammed Alkharizmy has said." [1]

2. Massoudy's discussion " of seas and rivers " is not less philosophic :—

" The author of the Logic (Aristotle) says that the seas change their places in the lapse of centuries and the length of ages. And, indeed, all seas are in a constant motion; but if this motion is compared with the volume of water, the extent of the surface, and the depth of the abysses, it is as if they were quiet. There is no place on earth that is always covered with water, nor one that is always land, but a constant revolution takes place effected by the rivers, which are always shifting, for places watered by rivers have a time of youth and of decrepitude, like animals and plants, with this difference, that growth and decay in plants and animals manifest themselves in all parts at once, so that they flourish and wither at the same time. But the earth grows and declines part by part."

Water, he thinks, is often produced by "air that is in the bowels of the earth," for in itself it is no element, but only the product of the rottenness of the land and its exhalations.

3. In his account of the Nile, Massoudy introduces a detail of peculiar interest. The great river (which he refuses, unlike so many other geographers, to identify with

---

[1] Coming to comparisons, Massoudy estimates the earth as 37 times greater than the moon, 32,000 times greater than Mercury, and 24,000 times greater than Venus, but only equal to 164th part of the sun, one 63rd part of Mars, one 82nd part of Jupiter, one 99th part of Saturn, etc.

the Indus, merely because crocodiles are found in both [1]) comes from the mountains of the Zanj, or the highlands that front the Zanzibar coast; it flows through the Negroland, or Soudan, and sends off a branch to the Black Men's Sea, or Indian Ocean.   And this, he proceeds, is the sea of the island Kambalou,[2] which is well cultivated, and the people are Moslems, but speak the Negro language.   The Moslems had conquered this island, just as they had taken the isle of Crete in the Mediterranean.   Now this happened at the end of the Ommeyad dynasty, and "from it to Oman, according to sailors, is about five hundred parasangs."   The island in question has been conjectured to be Madagascar, though it may possibly be Zanzibar or Pemba; and the Arab incursions referred to are almost certainly those of the Emosaid family and their followers, which arose out of an abortive domestic revolution, a few years before the Abbassides supplanted the House of Ommeyah, and which resulted in some of the most important contributions of the Arab race to geographical knowledge.   It was about A.D. 742, less than a decade before the change of masters in the Caliphate, that the Emosaid family, presuming on their descent from Ali, tried to make Said, their clan-chieftain, Commander of the Faithful.   The attempt failed; and the whole tribe fled, sailed down the Red Sea and African coast, and established themselves as conquerors, colonists, and traders in the Sea of India.   At first, Socotra seems to have been their mart and capital, but before the end of the tenth century they had founded merchant settlements at Melinda, Mombasa, and Mozambique; which in their turn may have led to acquisitions in the islands off

[1] Just as a little later he rejects the delusion of some that the Oxus flowed into the Indus—because the head-waters of the two were in places not so very far apart.

[2] Sea of the Zanj.

the coast.[1] Massoudy expressly tells us of Sofala, the most distant of these colonies "at the extremity of the country of the Zanj;" and to men who had reached the coast of Mashonaland an attack on Madagascar was no great matter.

4. On the Kharizmian Lake, or Sea of Aral, Massoudy is very explicit, as becomes one who has personally visited what he describes. It was, he says, the greatest lake of all that region, and many believed it to be the greatest of the habitable earth; in length and breadth it was about one month's journey. It was not without traffic and port towns, mainly inhabited by Turks; both the great rivers of Balkh and Ferghanah, the Oxus and the Jaxartes, flowed into it, and boats plied upon the river and the lake. Near here was one frontier of Islam, beyond which dwelt the unbelieving Turks.

5. The difference between the small, choppy waves of inland seas and gulfs, and the huge rollers of the ocean, was well known to so extensive a traveller, and is vividly described by him, not without some fanciful embellishment. "In the Sea of India are blind waves, as high as mountains, between which abysses open like the deepest valleys; but they do not break, and hence no foam is generated by collision as in other seas, and many think these waves enchanted. Often," adds Massoudy, "have I been in peril at sea, in that of China, in the Mediterranean, in the Caspian, in the Red Sea, and off the coast of Arabia, but never I found danger like that of the Sea of the Blacks" (or of India).

---

[1] Massoudy adds a confused tradition: "The water which falls from the Nile into the sea of the Zanj forms an estuary, which comes to the upper part of this river through the country of the Zanj, and separates this country from the remotest provinces of Abyssinia." Not less involved is his reference to the Persian Gulf "beginning at the Sofala (lowlands) of the Negroes" (Zanj).

The length of the Indian Ocean, he tells us again, is from east to west along the Equator, beneath the line of the revolutions of the heavenly bodies; and the influence of these upon its waters is felt in proportion to their nearness to the Equator.

According to some of the sailors of Siraf, ebb and flow took place only twice a year over most of the Indian Ocean, but a few years before (in A.D. 925, A.H. 303) Massoudy himself saw a wonderful flood-tide coming in from the sea, like a mountain, in the Gulf of Guzerat or Cambay.

"The ebb is so marked in this gulf that the sand lies quite bare at times, and only a little water trickles in the midst of the expanse. I saw a dog on this sand, which was left dry by the water like the sand of a desert; the incoming tide caught him and drowned him, though he ran as fast as he could." [1]

6. In sharp contrast to Massoudy's treatment of the Eastern and Southern Ocean is his language as regards the Western, the Green Sea of Darkness, or the Atlantic. Like most of his race, he considered it " impossible to navigate beyond the Strait of the Idols of Copper " (of the Pillars of Hercules, or of Gibraltar).[2] The Idols themselves bear inscriptions to that effect, placed there by " King Herakles the giant." " For no vessel sails on that sea : it is without cultivation or inhabitant, and its end, like its depth, is unknown." It is true, however, that some adventurers have tried to penetrate its mysteries; and such an one was Khoshkhash, the "young man of Cordova," who once collected a crew and sailed off upon the ocean, and for a great space of time was never heard of, till he returned with a rich cargo. The story of his exploits, Massoudy declares, was well known

[1] This, of course, was a bore, or tidal wave.

[2] In c. 14, however, he repeats the statement of some sailors, that in certain directions the Sea of India was *endless*. On the young man of Cordova, see "Meadows of Gold," c. 12.

in Spain, and in all likelihood the later "Wanderers" of Lisbon, who, in the eleventh (or twelfth) century, reached Madeira, according to the narrative of Edrisi, were endeavouring to imitate his example.

7. One of Massoudy's weakest points is naturally the geography of Central Europe, which he had never examined for himself.[1] He is content with repeating from others that the Danube rises in a great lake, and flows through the Sea of Azov into the Black Sea; even on the much more accessible neighbourhood of Constantinople his information is curiously distorted. A river channel, he says, branches off from the Sea of Azov, connecting it with the Mediterranean; the length of this is three hundred miles, and the average breadth is fifty miles. On its western bank is Constantinople, and along it runs an unbroken line of cultivation. There is little more precision in all this than there is in another tradition he gives us, from Alkendy, of the vast lake in the North of the habitable world, extending almost to the pole.

8. On China and the Chinese trade, Massoudy reproduces the accounts of Soleyman, of Ibn Vahab, and of Abou Zeyd Hassan of Siraf;[2] but he adds that Kolah[3] had now become the centre of commercial exchange on this side, as a convenient half-way house at a time when the junks of the Yellow Sea no longer came up to the "Stakes" off Bassora, and the Arab merchants had been driven out of Khanfu.

---

[1] In the Mediterranean, Massoudy applies the title of Adriatic to the sea *west* of Italy. A little later (in c. 14) he mentions the tradition of the prophet about the four rivers of Nile, Euphrates, Jaïhun, and Saïhun, springing from four columns of ruby, sapphire, emerald, and chrysolite, planted in the midst of the Atlantic. As to this and similar stories, as of tides being regulated by the toe of an angel in the Sea of China, or of the personality of waterspouts as living dragons, Massoudy declares them to be in no sense necessary of belief.

[2] Whom he knew personally.

[3] ? Kolaba, near Bombay.

Similarly on Russia, our encyclopædia abridges Ibn Khordadbeh and Ibn Fozlan, supplementing those writers by some points of more recent history, but omitting nothing of importance that had been noticed by earlier travellers —such as the use of the Volga River for trade between Bulgarians, Russians, and Khazars; the silver mines of those parts; the different hordes and tribes which made up the Russian people, but all "without king or revelation;" and the extensive commerce of the central mart of "Bulghar" or "Volgaria," whose merchants journeyed to Spain, France, Rome, and the Byzantine Empire. Not even the "fiery craters" of the Naphtha springs at Baku are omitted, or those "islands of the falcons" in the Caspian which Europeans mostly learnt of from Marco Polo, four centuries later.[1]

Among the Khazars of the Lower Volga, Massoudy adds with emphasis, the majority are Moslems, and the army of the king consists of Mussulmans from Kharizmia, who had emigrated at an early period, after the spread of Islam, from east to west of the Caspian Sea. Before entering their new country, they made good terms for themselves—the right to profess Islam publicly, to build mosques, and to call to prayers, the privilege of being judged in all religious and civil matters by their own kadis, and the permission to remain neutral in any war between the Khazars and a Moslem army.

"And besides the soldiers," there were many other Mussulmans in this kingdom in Massoudy's day,—artisans, tradespeople, and merchants, who had a "great public mosque" to themselves, with a minaret which towered above the royal palaces, and several private mosques, where

---

[1] Massoudy's allusions to Turkish history (invasions of Europe, etc.) are not so satisfactory as his geography of these parts. On a sixth century Christianity among Turks, see Theophyl. Simoc. v. 10; Theophanes, Chronog. A.M. 6081.

their children could be instructed. This was the result of wholesale emigration. For on the decline of the Caliphate, justice and security were easier found in the border king-doms of non-Arab races and of newly converted Moslems than in the Central Kingdom, where the highways were now "unsafe and badly kept," [1] where every local chief was making himself independent as a satrap of old, and where the "pillars" of Islam seemed to be giving way, and the foundations sinking beneath the feet of the believers.

II. Chinese Geography.

In this supplementary sketch of the non-Christian geography of the earlier Middle Ages, there remains one important field, and one only, for our notice. The practical enterprise and scientific research of Christendom, of the Cali-phate, and of China, together comprise everything of value in this period for the story of geographical advance. Accord-ing to the plan we have set before ourselves, the two former of these three divisions have been already treated, the one in detail (at least in comparative detail), the other in outline; something, however slight, must be said about the last, the Chinese, or Far-Eastern, branch of the subject. In attempt-ing this, we shall be content perforce with an even less full selection of typical material than in the case of Arab or Moslem geography; for, as our aim is properly to describe in the first place the progress of Christendom along one particular line, and only in the second place to touch upon the parallel progress of non-Christian races (with especial reference to the bearing of this upon Christian Europe), we shall find but little to study in the Chinese records of this time. Only at long intervals does the furthest stretch of Celestial exploration even come within sight of the

[1] Massoudy, c. 17.

Mediterranean world; yet it is during this very period, before the Crusades led to the great expansion of Mediæval Europe, that China least resembled its modern self, and showed itself least inclined to live its life apart from the rest of the world. During these centuries, between the age of Constantine and that of our English Alfred (A.D. 300–900), several embassies are exchanged between the Cæsars and the "Middle Kingdom;" and several Buddhist Monks travel from the "Flowery Land" to Central Asia, to India, and possibly to America, in striking likeness to the contemporary journeys of Christian missionaries and pilgrims. For in both Faiths there was much the same emphasis upon the duties of Worshipping in the scenes of the Founder's life and death; and of going out into the world and preaching His Gospel to every creature. In the same period Christianity itself, in a Nestorian form, passes, as we have already seen, from the Levant to the Yellow Sea, while Chinese junks ply regularly, during a great part of this time, between the dominions of the Son of heaven and those of the Persian sovereign whether Chosroes or Caliph. Never, therefore, shall we discover a greater activity, a wider foreign intercourse, or a more universal ambition among the Celestials; never did their kings strike more boldly for the conquest of Asia; never did their travellers go further afield for the objects of religion, learning, or commerce.

Yet in spite of these interludes of comparative accessibility to, and intercourse with, the outside world, China has always remained the land of a peculiar people, and this distinctive character is very prominent in their geographical writings and allusions. Take, for example, the record of the greatest of their pilgrim travellers. Hiouen-Thsang performed journeys of extraordinary reach, difficulty, and importance, yet in his lengthy memoirs there is surprisingly little geography. The bulk of his work is taken up with religious meditations, and with disquisitions upon points of philosophy, morality, and even grammar. He has many descriptive passages, it is true, but they usually relate to religious processions and other spectacles, to the scenes of the miracles of Buddha, to the relics of the same, and to the shrines and other sacred buildings of India. He gives us the impression of a man chiefly devoted to abstruse speculation and reflection; his interest in the present-day world—the world of the effective traveller or explorer—is but slight. He cares little about facts, as weighed against ideas.

And the same may be said in general of the other narratives of Chinese travel. Their geography, like all their observations on material fact, is incidental, is generally overlaid by a great amount of what we may call talk about abstractions, especially of ethics and metaphysics, and is also hampered by the form of their language, and their half-contemptuous indifference to the customs and nomenclature of most other countries.[1] Thus their equivalents for Western place-names are often exceedingly difficult to explain: in the case of the Roman Empire itself, they never attempt a more accurate designation than the nicknames of Tathsin, Antu, or Fulin;[2] the Parthians are always "Ansi," the Arabs "Tashi," in their annals. And if this is the measure they deal out to the leading nations of the earth, is it likely that they will take more trouble to learn the proper names of little states and towns in Central Asia? The whole of their records of foreign lands is mystified, as it were, by this

---

[1] India, as the sacred Buddhist land, is usually an exception. But see Sung-Yun's sarcastic language about some of the Punjaub kings, as quoted below.

[2] Respectively seeming to mean;

(1) Great China, a nickname usually, but not exclusively, applied to the Roman Orient; (2) Antioch, Antony, or Antonine; (3) The City (= Polin, or Constantinople?).

perverse system, which only on rare occasions condescends to give us a native name in native dress, and so leaves many, if not most, of the identifications which have been attempted scarcely more than probable at the best.

It was under the Han Dynasty, and in the years immediately before and after the birth of Christ, that the two great Empires of the extreme East and West first came in sight of one another. It is possible, indeed, that the land of Likan, or Likian, referred to in Chinese annals of the second century B.C., may be a corruption of the name of the Seleucidæ,[1] who at one time inherited all the central part of Alexander's Empire from Syria to the Oxus, but the earliest definite intercourse with Rome, as such, appears to be about the time of the Christian era, when, as Florus[2] tells us, envoys came from the silk country, a journey of four years, to seek the friendship of Augustus. The dominion of the Cæsars as a whole was known to the Celestials as Great China,[3] till some time after the seat of power had been removed to Constantinople; but the name of Rome does not occur in their annals. With obstinate perversity they clung to a mistake of their earliest Western travellers, or envoys, who identified the capital of the West ("Antu") either with Antioch or with Antony, at a time when the triumvir was living in Egypt, governing the Levant, and intriguing in Persia, India, and Bactria.[4]

[1] See Pauthier, "De l'Authenticité de l'Inscription de Singanfu," pp. 34–55, etc.

[2] iv. 12.

[3] Tathsin.

[4] See Reinaud, "Rélations de l'Empire Romain avec l'Asie Orientale," pp. 39–55, etc. Coins of Julius Cæsar and of Mark Antony have been found in Northern India, near Lahore, in a Buddhist tope, supposed to have been built by Kanichka, King of Bactria, who then or a little later (A.D. 10–40, according to Lassen) ruled the Punjaub. Virgil, Propertius, and Plutarch (" Life of Antony ") have all alluded to the alliances of Antony in the Far East; and Propertius (bk. iv., Eleg. 3) has even led M. Reinaud to believe that

The embassy of the Chinese to Augustus is more
clearly mentioned on the Latin side; but it is only in
the records of the Han and the Tsin that we hear of the
Roman missions of the second and third centuries to the
Far East, from emperors whom we may identify with
Marcus Aurelius Antoninus (the Antun of the Chinese),
with Alexander Severus, and with Carus, all famous for their
Persian victories or conquests, and all, therefore, possessing
special advantages for closer intercourse with China.   The
Antonine embassy of 166 seems to have reached China by
sea; those which arrived in the early part of the third
century and in the year ¡284 probably[1] took the overland
route, by the "Stone Tower," or Tashkend,[2] like the
merchants[3] whom Ptolemy mentions.   In the earlier
centuries of the Christian Empire, we lose sight for a long
time of any intercourse, even the faintest, between China
and the Mediterranean world; but in the time of Justinian,

a Roman envoy, poetically named
Lycotas, not only visited Balkh, the
capital of the Bactrian kings, but
helped Kanichka, or his predecessor,
in some campaigns against the
Chinese at this very time.   See
Lassen, Ind. Alt., ii. 766, 768, 806,
etc.   The uncommon knowledge
shown by Pausanias on the true
nature of silk, Reinaud ingeniously
suggests, may have been derived
from the Antonine embassy of
A.D. 166.

[1] Lacouperie thinks they too
came by sea.   "Western Origin of
Chinese Civilisation."

[2] The name *Tashkend* is simply
translated by Ptolemy's Λίθινος-
Πύργος, or Turris Lapidea.

[3] Ptolemy even gives us the name
of a trader, Maes Titianus, whose
agents had made this journey across

Asia several times about A.D. 100.
On their side, the Chinese record
jugglers from "Great China," arriving in their country by way of the
Shan States in Ptolemy's lifetime
(about A.D. 120).   This, however,
may not refer to Rome, but to
another country with a similar
Chinese nickname.   It is also open
to question whether the Celestial
mission to Augustus, recorded by
Florus, (which has been fixed to
20 B.C. for its arrival on the Mediterranean), or the return missions
from Rome to China of A.D. 166,
236 (?), 284, etc., had anything of an
official character.   The "envoys"
may have been merely traders.   See
Terrien de Lacouperie, "Western
Origin of Chinese Civilisation;"
Reinaud's "Relations de l'Empire
. . . avec l'Asie Orient.," pp.217–304.

Cosmas, as we have seen, gives us a vague description of a Far Eastern land, which might be either Assam or China itself.

A little later, in the early years of the seventh century,[1] Theophylact seems to have heard something of the Celestials, their wars, and the "heavenly" title of their sovereign.

On their side, the Chinese, about this time (A.D. 620–650), refer in a pointed manner to the changes in the Mediterranean world, when they say that the land formerly called Great China, was now termed "Fulin" (Polin), or, in other words, the empire of the Greek-speaking city of Byzantium. This critical period, answering to the lifetime of the Emperor Heraclius, was one of great activity in China; when the great conqueror Yangti tried in vain to re-open intercourse with Rome; when he and his successors of the "Thang" overran Tonquin, Siam, and much of Central Asia; when Hiouen-Thsang travelled to India, Tartary, and Afghanistan; and when envoys arrived at Singanfu from many a kingdom trembling before the Saracen advance, from Nepaul and Magadha (or Behar), in India; from the last king of the "fire worshippers" in Persia, and from the Christian sovereign of Constantinople.

The Chinese annals describe the capital of Fulin (Constantinople) very vividly, as if from the account of an eye-witness. The compass of the walls, as given by them—at twenty miles—is nearly the same as in the estimate of Benjamin of Tudela in the twelfth century, and an excellent picture is drawn of the new Queen of the West. It stood upon the shore of the sea. The houses, built of stone, rose to a great height. The people of the city numbered a hundred thousand fires, or families. Outside the walls were immense suburbs, forming a second town, well-nigh as

---

[1] Theoph. Simocatta, ch. vii. 7, 9 on the Taugas.

unbroken as the first. The mansions of the city were adorned with colonnades and enclosed in parks. The sovereign had twelve principal ministers. The eastern gate of Fulin was two hundred feet high, and covered with gold-leaf;[1] another of the city ports had over it a golden steel-yard, and a marvellous clock, with a golden image which marked the hours by the dropping of a golden ball. Over the flat roofs of the houses cooling streams of water were poured in the heat of summer from conduit pipes. And if the subjects were so luxurious, the magnificence of the prince must needs be answerable thereto. His jewelled cap, his flower-embroidered robe of silk, the regal wings of his head-dress, all these the Chinese record in the annals of the " Middle Kingdom."

Nor is this all. The story of the siege of Constantinople by the Caliph Moawiyah (A.D. 671–678), of his failure, and of his presents of gold and silk to purchase peace, is to be found, mutilated indeed, but still recognisable, in the same annals.

A generation earlier (in A.D. 643), during the reign of Taitsung, the Trajan of Chinese history, the long-interrupted intercourse of diplomacy seems to have been renewed, and an embassy arrived from Fulin with gifts of emeralds and rubies, which we may suppose were sent by Heraclius to win the help of China against the Arabs.

Similar missions from Constantinople, in 711 and 719, sent by Justinian II. and Leo the Isaurian,[2] with presents

---

[1] Exactly as Massoudy describes the Golden Gate, with its "doors of bronze," on the *west* side of the city ("Meadows of Gold," ii. 319). It was really at the south end of the western wall. Cf. also the "Saga of King Sigurd," in Snorro Sturleson's "Sagas of the Norse Kings."

[2] The head of this embassy (of 719) is called Yenthuholo by the Chinese, and the name has been supposed to be their rendering of Leonto-Isauro (Λέοντος Ἰσαύρου).

of lions and great sheep with spiral horns, may have had a like object. The time when Leo's envoy must have been despatched from the Bosphorus coincides exactly with that terrible moment when the Mussulmans put forth all their strength for the capture of Byzantium, and when, on the other side of Europe, they had overrun Spain, and were entering France by the passes of the Pyrenees.

Lastly, in 742, the arrival from Fulin of certain *priests of great virtue*, who may or may not have been the same as the band of Nestorian missionaries under Kiho, who, according to the inscription of Singanfu, arrived in 744 from the Roman Empire, is duly chronicled. Here ends the list of the more important notices for our period of Chinese intercourse with the Western world of pagan and Christian Rome,[1] and till near the close of the eleventh century the Caliphate seems to have barred the way against any recurrence of the same.

The narratives of the Buddhist pilgrims which we shall have to notice are mainly concerned with India; but the Chinese annals are strangely imperfect and fragmentary in their notices of the sacred country. Their first mention of it does not go back before B.C. 122; and within the scope of our period,[2] most of the references are to Cinghalese embassies, reaching back to the early years of the fifth century (A.D. 405). During the next age (for instance, in 515) the kings of Ceylon declared themselves vassals of China. Following the journey of Hiouen-Thsang and the conquests of Yang-Ti[3] (605–617), several of the kings of Central India, and especially of Behar, opened relations with

---

[1] See Pauthier, "De l'Authenticité de l'Inscription de Singanfu;" De Guignes, in Mem. de l'Acad., xxxii., xlvi.

[2] A.D. 300–900.

[3] In the valleys of the Red River and the Mekong.

China, from about A.D. 640; in the eighth century the
rulers of Kashmir paid tribute, as a protection both against
the Arabs on the West and the Thibetan marauders on the
East; and repeated missions arrived from various states of
Hindostan, most of them probably eager for any assistance
they could procure against the all-conquering Moslems.
On one occasion (about A.D. 730) a Hindu prince begged the
Emperor of China for an especial favour—he did not want
merely men and money; he craved, above all, a title of
honour for his troops. This difficult problem produced
great agitation in the court of the Son of Heaven, but at
last all claims were satisfied. The emperor conferred on the
army of his ally a glorious diploma. Henceforth it was " the
army which cherishes virtue," or "which makes the pursuit
of virtue its chief care."

In the middle of the eighth century China lost control
of many of its vassals in Central Asia, and the last mention
we have of intercourse with India in the limits of this period
is no later than the Singanfu Inscription, or, in other words,
the attempt of the Emperor Tetsung, in 787, to form a
league against the marauders of Thibet.

The dealings of China with Persia in the days before
Islam appeared, and with the Caliphate after that great
upheaval,[1] were of course considerable; and Arab writers and

---

[1] See Bretschneider's "Chinese
Knowledge of the Arabs," etc., 1871;
Yule's "Cathay" (preliminary essay, §§ iv., v.); Reinaud's "Relations
de l'Empire Romain avec l'Asie
Orientale," his "Mémoire sur l'Inde,"
and his editions of Aboulfeda (introd.), and of the "Relations" of the
Two Mussulman travellers (*discours
prélim.*); Gaubil, "Histoire de la
dynastie Thang;" Abel Rémusat, in
Mém. de l'Acad. des Inscr., VIII. (new
series); and De Lacouperie, "Western Origin of Chinese Civilization,"
1894; also Pauthier, "De l'Authenticité de l'Inscription Nestorienne de
Singanfu;" Klaproth, "Mémoires
relatifs à l'Asie" (1824–28), and
"Tableaux Historiques de l'Asie"
(1826).

statesmen certainly possessed a clearer and fuller knowledge of the Silk Land than any other of our informants.

But here we must content ourselves with a reference to the accounts of Mohammedan travellers, whom we have already followed to Khanfu,[1] and other parts of the Yellow Sea, adding in this place only a notice of one or two entries in the annals of China.

In the reign of Chosroes Nushirvan, embassies were exchanged between that great prince and the Emperor Wuti,[2] probably for the purpose of a league against the Turks; but the last successor of Chosroes appealed in vain to the ruler of China, in 638, for aid against the Arabs. The wretched exile, flying before the horsemen of the Saracen Caliph like another Darius before a Semitic Alexander, and doomed to a similar fate in the same region of the world, had appealed as a last hope to the great Emperor Taitsung, who claimed to rule over several vassals to the west of Tengri Khan. But beyond the Oxus, he received only the chilling answer that the Son of Heaven regarded his friendship as most sacred; but with people of such superior virtue as the Arabs, it was clear that resistance would be impious, and he could only recommend his ally to make the best terms in his power.[3]

As a matter of fact, the Chinese were greatly terrified by the progress of Islam, which soon stripped them of their vague suzerainty in Western Turkestan; in A.D. 679 and 709, as again in 751, their attempted action against the Caliphate proved miserably abortive, and in the early years of the eighth century [4] the Arab General Kutaiba forced something very like tribute from the Celestials by his advance

---

[1] Or Hangcheufu, the Quinsay of Marco Polo.

[2] About A.D. 560–67.

[3] It is only fair to say this comes from the Arabs.

[4] A.D. 710–13.

upon Kashgar. But for the death of the Caliph Walid, it was said, the Moslems would have marched right on to the Eastern Sea.

Of especial interest to us is the description in the Chinese annals of the sea-voyage from Canton and their other harbours to the Persian Gulf. After the domestic troubles of 878 and subsequent years, their junks seem, as a rule, to have been afraid to go beyond Ceylon; but from the fifth to the ninth centuries, for five hundred years, the ships of China, as Massoudy tells us, might often be seen lying moored in the mouth of the Euphrates, or at various points on the shore of the Persian Gulf. In Massoudy's [1] lifetime, China had already begun to abandon anything of a progressive or commercial policy. How different a spirit moved among her people in earlier times we have tried to show; but our best evidence has yet to come in the travels of the Buddhist monks and saints, with which we shall conclude this bird's-eye view of Eastern geography.

The earliest [2] of the great Chinese travellers that come within our period is Fa-Hien, who started from the valley of the Ho-ang-ho in the last year of the fourth century (A.D. 400) in search of the Buddhist books of discipline, and returned to Nanking on the Yangtse Kiang in 414, after fifteen

---

[1] "Meadows of Gold," i. 216, etc. (in Meynard's edition).

[2] Before his day three pilgrims, at least, had gone to the "West" (India, Khotan, etc.), in the third and fourth centuries A.D., especially one Fa-ling in about 320, but their journals have not survived. See Stanislas Julien's "Vie et Voyages de Hiouen-Thsang," and "Voyages des Pèlerins Bouddhistes" (1853), etc.; Beal's "Buddhist Records of the Western World," in Trübner's Oriental Series (1884), a translation of the Records of Fa-Hien, Hoei-Sing, etc., and Hiouen-Thsang, in 2 vols.; also his version of H. T.'s life, in 1 vol., of the same series (1888); and Legge's "Fa-Hien" (1886); Bretschneider's "Notes on Chinese Travellers to the West" deals only with thirteenth-century narratives. Klaproth claimed to have discovered Fa-Hien's work in 1816, and assisted Rémusat in the editio princeps of 1836 (Paris).

years of wandering.   He seems first to have gone north by
west, almost to Tengri Khan, and the range of the Thian-
Shan, to somewhere near the site of the present Kharashar.
Thence he made his way southward to Khotan; south-west
to Peshawur, and the neighbourhood of Kabul; south-east
to the Jumna at Muttra, and the Ganges at Kananj; finally,
down the Ganges Valley to Patna, Benares, and the sea,
where he took ship for China, by the straits of Sunda, visiting the sacred isle of Ceylon on the way, or rather by a long
detour from the way.

His tone throughout is of the devout, but sensible, and
not often hysterical pilgrim-traveller. His record is truthful,
clear, and straightforward, and most of his positions can be
identified; what is more surprising (in a Chinese) is the
humility with which he writes.   To him, as a Buddhist first,
and a Celestial afterwards, China was outside the inner circle
of blessing, in which only Indians could sun themselves;
the relation between the two was, to his mind, that of a
province to the capital; and over and over again he records
the aspiration of himself or his friends, "From this time
forth, let me never be born in a frontier land; may I ever
live in a central kingdom, not in a border kingdom."

The earlier part of Fa-Hien's narrative is strictly geographical: then, as he comes to India, narratives of the life
and wonders of Buddha more and more fill his pages, and
the record of his own adventures is more and more coloured
by the supernatural.

Starting from the great city which was then the capital
of the Empire, Chang-an, or Singanfu, near the north-west
frontier of China, and passing the Great Wall, the first
obstacle to be traversed was the River of Sand, or Desert of
Gobi, the home of "evil demons and hot winds," where the
only way-marks were the dry bones of the dead, and where

no bird was to be seen in the air above, no animal on the
ground below. " For there," says Marco Polo of the same
region, " dwell many spirits which cause marvellous illusions
to travellers, and make them to perish; for if any stay
behind and cannot see his company, he shall be called by
his name, and, so going out of the road, is lost. By night,
too, they hear the noise of a company which, taking to be
their own, they likewise perish. And oft are to be heard
there playing upon divers instruments of music, the beating
of drums, and the noise of armies marching." Fa-Hien, by
painful experience, discovered that diabolical agency was
not confined to the deserts of Turkestan. There, legend
said, a sand-storm had once covered as many cities as the
days of the year in one space of four and twenty hours; this
was bad enough, but in the mighty mountains to the north
of India,[1] where our pilgrim endured sufferings " unequalled
in man's experience," he learnt also what dangers were to be
feared from the hill-dragons, who could " spit forth poisonous
winds, and cause showers of snow, and storms of sand and
gravel."

Arriving at last in safety at Khotan, where in later times
the mass of the people have embraced Islam, Fa-Hien found
enthusiastic Buddhists,[2] " with monks in myriads," and was
spectator of a festival where the king went out with bare
feet to meet the image (of Buddha): " carrying in his hands
flowers and incense, and with head and face bowed to the
ground, he did homage, scattering the flowers and burning
the incense."[3]

Similarly,[4] in Yarkand, in the Karakorum Mountains,
and in Afghanistan,[5] where Islam now almost exclusively

[1] Chs. ii., vi.
[2] Chs. ii., iii.
[3] The same prince had built, or
rather completed, a monastery, which

had been in progress for eighty years.
[4] Chs. iii., iv.
[5] Fa-Hien's Kipin = Kabul; his
Lo-i, or Ro-hi, = Afghanistan.

prevails, were then "earnest followers of the Law" of Buddha.

From the "wall-like hills" of the Hindu-Kush,[1] Fa-Hien descended suddenly into the gorge of the Indus, a drop of 10,000 cubits, as he regarded it. The Chinese monk is well abreast of modern travellers in his appreciation of this famous defile. "When one approached the edge of it, one's eyes trembled; if one wished to go forward, there was no place on which to plant the foot, save that in old times men had chiselled paths along the rocks, and hung ladders on the face of the same, and bridged the water at the bottom of the gorge with ropes. Seven hundred were the ladders they had put up, and the breadth of the stream was eighty paces."[2] Some Chinese travellers of earlier time had described this place; but not even the most famous of them, Fa-Hien notes with quiet exultation, had actually reached so far.

It was apparently in A.D. 402 that our pilgrim entered India, and he passed the next ten years in the "central" Buddhist kingdom. But here, as we have pointed out before, meditations upon Buddhist moralities almost entirely replace descriptions of travel. We only get bare notices of journeys to Peshawur, to Afghanistan, and back into the Punjaub, and down the valleys of the Ganges and Jumna.[3] Thus various places are visited for the sake of the shadow, the alms-bowl, or the skull of Buddha, and scarcely anything is dwelt upon in connection with them, except the relics they contain. Yet here and there we find passages of more general interest. For an example of this we may turn to the scene on the "little snowy mountains" between the Punjaub and Afghanistan, where one of Fa-Hien's company sinks down beneath the

---

[1] Ch. vii.

[2] The modern Beal, Watters, and Cunningham (see the latter's "Ladah," pp. 88, 89, quoted by the two former), confirm the picturesque truth of this description.

[3] Chs. xii., xiv., xvi., etc.

cold. " A white froth came from his mouth, and he cried out,
' I cannot live any longer ; leave me, and save yourselves.
Let us not all die here.' " But Fa-Hien's courage was not to
be shaken. " Our purpose was not to win good fortune," he
exclaimed, as he embraced his dying friend. " Submitting to
fate," he pressed on, and crossed the range ; beyond this he
came to the Afghan[1] country. Thence he returned to the
low and level lands of the Indus Valley, where thousands of
monks welcomed the visitor from the Border Land of China.

Further to the south and east, on the banks of the
Jumna, he reckoned three thousand of these religious men ;
for Buddhism had not yet been driven out of India ; and all
along the course of his journey, from the Sandy Desert to
Muttra, the kings and rulers of the various countries he had
visited were everywhere of his faith.

But his travels had now brought him to the plains where
the older religion of Brahma was soon to break out in fierce
revolt against the heresy which undermined its caste-system.
The difference of the countries impressed itself forcibly upon
Fa-Hien, and he tells us that from the Indus to the Southern
Sea all was level ; there were no more great mountains with
rushing torrents, only the lowland with its deep, calm, slow-
moving rivers. The traveller now lingered among the holy
scenes of Buddha's life ; for each one called up to him some
fresh tale of his sacred books, some fresh reminder of the
object of his search. Thus at the Jetvana monastery in Oude,
where Buddha had once lived for five and twenty years,
crowds of monks came out and asked him his name and
country. " From the land of Han " (China), he replied.
" Strange," said the monks, " that the men of a border
country should travel so far in search of our law. Not in
all the time that we have lived here, not in all the

---

[1] Lo-i, or Ro-hi.

generations that have followed one another in this place has it ever been known that men of our Law came hither from the land of China." [1]

The birthplace of Buddha, on the modern Kohana, some hundred miles north-west of Benares, Fa-Hien found in ruins as it had lain since the lifetime of the sage, and the whole country round about was a scene of desolation, abandoned to elephants and lions, who attacked travellers.[2] On the other hand, in Patna, one of the earliest centres of Buddhism,[3] were monasteries and hospitals, dispensaries and schools of the pilgrim's faith, and many monuments of King Asoka's princely devotion. In the true spirit of the pilgrim, Fa-Hien one night ascended the Vulture Peak, near Patna, that he might more perfectly imitate his master, who had spent many days upon that very summit. At the foot of the hill he bought incense-sticks, flowers, oil and lamps, and hired two attendants to carry his offerings before him. Arrived at the sacred spot, he burnt his incense, and strewed his flowers; then as the night came on, he lighted the lamps and chanted certain portions[4] of the Law of Buddha. With the morning light he returned to the plain. A later story tried to enhance this simple narrative by the legend of two black lions[5] which appeared to " try " him, " licking their lips and waving their tails" as if ready to attack; but the picture needed no aid from fable. Fa-Hien, on the lonely height, so many hundred miles from his home, watching through the night with the intense eagerness of the devotee, if only he could, by place and time and circumstance, work himself back into the life and spirit of his

---

[1] Ch. xx.

[2] Ch. xxii. Perhaps the " lions " were really leopards.

[3] After it had won the State to itself with Asoka's conversion.

[4] The Surangama Sutra.

[5] Leopards probably. See what Sung-Yun says later about the Chinese ignorance of lions.

Teacher, this is the real and sufficient interest of the scene.[1]

In Patna, and at other places[2] along the lower Ganges Valley, Fa Hien spent the next five years copying out the "Books of Discipline" he had come so far to see, and finding everywhere multitudes of Buddhists.

The last of the kingdoms in the Central Land which our pilgrim thought worthy of a visit was Ceylon, reached by him in fourteen days from the Ganges Delta, as he "went floating over the sea to the south-west, embarked in a merchant vessel." And here his own land was brought to his remembrance by a trivial incident. As he stood one day by the great jade image of Buddha in the shrine on the "Fearless Hill,"[3] he saw a merchant offering a native Chinese present, a white silk fan, and a sudden weariness of his long exile seized upon the traveller.

"For years past he had only conversed with men of strange countries; his eyes had never rested on a familiar object; his fellow travellers had all been parted from him; no face or shadow was now with him but his own." But before he would think of return he transcribed all the sacred texts, as yet unknown in China, which he could find in Ceylon, witnessed the festival of the exhibition of Buddha's tooth; and remarked the trade of "Sabean" or Arab merchants to the island, two hundred years before Mohammed.[4] Not unnaturally Fa-Hien preferred the straighter though more dreaded sea voyage to the interminable length and already experienced perils of the land

---

[1] Ch. xxix.

[2] Notably in Tam-look, near the mouth of the Hoogly, then the principal centre for trade with China and Ceylon.

[3] Ch. xxxviii. This is famous as being marked by the highest tope in Ceylon, the Abhayagiri, said to be 250 feet high, which was built about 90 B.C., and is still standing.

[4] Ch. xxxviii. May we suspect the text here?

transit, but danger still pursued him, and a storm burst upon the ship after three days' sail. The vessel sprang a leak, and Fa-Hien came near to seeing the loss of all the books and images he had collected. Day and night the tempest continued, till on the thirteenth morning land was sighted, the leak discovered, and the danger averted. The chief fear now was from pirates. Yet, with a return of dark and rainy weather, the ship might again be driven out of its course; as the mariners had no compass or any guide but the signs of heaven. "The ocean spread out, a boundless expanse. In the darkness of the night only the great waves were to be seen, breaking one upon another and giving forth a brightness like the light of fire." Passing by Java,[1] where "various forms of error flourished," a second storm brought Fa-Hien within measurable distance of the fate of Jonah. The crew's one anxiety was to get rid of the holy man at any cost. It was his presence, they declared, that brought all misfortune upon them. But he was saved by the interference of a "patron," and fifteen years after his departure from the upper valley of the Ho-ang-ho he landed near the mouth of the same river with all his painfully won spoils. He had visited, in his own judgment, nearly thirty kingdoms, from the desert of Gobi to the farthest limits of India; he had traversed countries of which his ancestors had no complete account;[2] and in the true spirit of discovery he had gone on "without regarding his own poor life," recording diligently all that he had met with, that others "might share with him in what he had heard" and seen.

Of the later journeys of Chinese travellers before the

[1] Here he seems to have changed vessels, as if it was impossible to sail straight from Ceylon to China in one ship at that time.

[2] Ch. xl.

Revolution of 878, we shall select three, the most interesting, important, and typical of their class. First comes
the expedition of 518 to India and other lands " over
against the sun-setting ; " secondly, we have the disputed
missionary journeys of the fifth and sixth centuries to
Eastern countries, which have been interpreted by some as
a Chinese discovery of North America ; lastly, there is the
voluminous record of Hiouen-Thsang's famous pilgrimage
in Turkestan and India during the early years of the seventh
century.

Many records of early Chinese travel still probably
remain unknown to Western scholars ; others, though
known, have never been edited or translated ;[1] and such as
have been offered to the European student contain scarcely
anything but repetitions of the words, the thoughts, and the
experiences of the travellers we have instanced.   Thus in
the " Memoir " of I-tsing upon the " eminent men of religion
who went to seek for the law in the Western regions," at
various times in the latter half of the seventh century, we
have notices of no fewer than fifty-six travellers, mostly
native Chinese, who followed in the steps of Fa-Hien and
Hiouen Thsang between A.D. 650 and 700, but none of
these add anything equal in value to their great predecessors.
This is true even of I-tsing himself, who is the leading figure
in this later series of pilgrims ; who sailed from Canton in a
Persian vessel for India at the age of thirty-six (A.D. 671) ;
who visited Java, Sumatra, and the Nicobars on his way
to and from the sacred land ; and who did not finally return
to China till his sixty-second year (A.D. 695).   It is not a
little remarkable, however, that none of these travellers are

---

[1] Cf. the list given by Stanislas
Julien in his introd. to the " Vie et
Voyages d'Hiouen - Thsang," and

Beal's opinion, " Buddhist Records,"
i. 21.

mentioned anywhere else; apart from I-tsing's record, we
should know nothing of their movements; and yet in one
short space of forty or fifty years, a Chinese Plutarch is able
to collect three-score such notices of religious travel. It is
probable that the triumphant return of Hiouen-Thsang in
645 was in part the cause of this amazing activity in the
next two generations; but may we not suppose that dozens,
perhaps hundreds, of similar journeys have passed unrecorded
in those ages of China's missionary and political expansion
which here come within our view?[1] Among the fifty-six
worthies whom I-tsing commemorates, about half seem to
have taken the southern or ocean route, from the China Sea
to the Bay of Bengal; the rest followed one of the overland
tracks to the north or south of the Kuen-lun; and a surprising
number of the latter made their way through the highlands
of Thibet and Nepaul, usually described as so dangerous for
passengers.[2] I-tsing's biographies, viewed as a whole, are
almost startling in their interest; the evidence they present
of a philosophic nation on the move is so surprising: but,
taken singly, these records are, as we have said, not distinctive or representative enough for further notice in this
place; and in the same way, though chiefly for another
reason, we must stop short of any discussion of the Chinese
cartography of this time.   It is noteworthy that in A.D. 721
the Priest Y-hang was commissioned to make a survey of
the Empire by " triangulation," and that observers were

---

[1] A.D. 300–900.

[2] See, for I-tsing's records, the
French translation and commentary
of Ed. Chavannes' "Mémoire composé
à l'Époque de la Grande Dynastie
T'ang, sur les Réligieux Eminents
qui allèrent . . . dans les Pays d'Occident" (Paris, 1894); also S. Beal's
translation of the " Life of Hiouen
Thsang " (1888), the preface of which
contains a good summary (pp. xvii.–
xxxvii.) of I-tsing's biographies.
Among the travellers mentioned,
twenty-one are expressly recorded to
have gone by sea to India, twenty by
land, some nine of these passing
through Thibet, e.g. the first-recorded
Hiouen-Chiou, c. A.D. 650.

also sent at the same period into Cochin-China, Tonquin, the south of India, and the north of Tartary, to observe the respective length of days and nights, and the motions of those stars which were not visible on the horizon of Singanfu. It is also memorable, especially in the light of contemporary Christian and Moslem movements in geographical theory, that at the beginning of the ninth century a Chinese official, named Kiatan, constructed a map thirty-three feet long by thirty broad, planned out in squares of fixed size, in which the Celestial Empire, India, the Caliphate, and the Dominion of Constantinople were all inserted.[1] But it is not worth our while to enter any further into a subject which has so little relation with Western and Christian thought. We need only refer to such a picture of the world as is given in the " authorised " preface to Hiouen Thsang's " Records " to see how different is the atmosphere of Chinese cosmography from anything in the ordinary run of European thought, though it reminds us sometimes of Arabic and Indian conceptions. In the middle of the world, and surrounded by the great sea, stood Mount Sumeru (like the Arim of the Moslems), fixed on a circle of gold, and with sun and moon revolving round it. On various sides of this are seven sacred mountains, and seven seas, as well as the four continents where men have made their dwelling. In the midst of the southern continent (Asia, as known to the Chinese) lay the Cool Lake[2] to the south of the Fragrant Mountains and to the north of the Snowy Mountains. From the eastern side of the lake, through the mouth of a

[1] See Reinaud's edition of the Two Mussulman Travellers (discours préliminaire, cxxx.–cxxxiii.); Abel Rémusat, " Sur l'Extension d'Empire Chinois du Coté d'Occident," in the " Recueil de l'Académie des Inscriptions," viii. 80, etc.; Gaubil, " Astronomie Chinoise," ii. 74, and his " Histoire de la Dynastie T'ang," in vol. xvi. of the "Mémoires de la Chine."

[2] The Syr-i-kul, source of the Oxus.

A CHINESE MAGNET·FIGURE, AS USED
IN SHIPS OF EIGHTH AND NINTH
CENTURIES A.D.

silver ox, flowed the Ganges to the south-eastern sea; from the south of the lake, through the mouth of a golden elephant, the Indus poured forth to the south-western sea; from the west of the lake through the mouth of a horse of lapis lazuli, issued the Oxus to the north-western sea; and from the north of the lake, through the mouth of a crystal lion, proceeded the River of China to the north-eastern sea.[1]

After this specimen, we may, perhaps, be excused from examining more closely into Chinese theory, and may turn with fresh satisfaction to the practical side of their geography.

And here we have first to notice their claim to a very important discovery. The invention of the compass has sometimes been assigned to the Chinese at this early period; but apparently from a confusion between the use of the compass proper and that of magnetized iron. Even at the lowest estimate, however, Chinese knowledge on this point was much farther advanced than that of the Greek and Roman world. Claudian has a poem on the magnet,[2] but he only describes, like Pliny, its attraction for iron, and does not hint at its power of indicating the poles; whereas the Celestials were certainly aware, in the first place, of the communication of magnetic fluid to iron; and in the second place of the mysterious power of iron so magnetized, as early as A.D. 121.

One of the earliest methods of employing this magnetized iron, was to place a bar of the same in the arms of a wooden figure on a pivot; and beyond this the invention does not seem to have gone before the tenth century. In other words, the needle had not yet been brought into use, either floating on a straw in water, or mounted on a pivot; and

[1] See Julien, "Pèlerins Bouddhistes;" the same in Beal's version, "Buddhist Records," i. 10–17, with some excellent notes in both.

[2] Idyl v.

the South (which, in China, took the place of the North as
the primary quarter of the heaven) was indicated merely by
the outstretched hand of the little magnetized man upon
the prow of a vessel, or by the bar of polarized iron, which
the image held like a spear in its hands. It was with such
magnetic indications that the Chinese, from the third
century A.D., must have ventured on their long voyages
from Canton to Malabar and the Persian gulf; and it was
no doubt through their reliance in a great measure on this
safeguard that they braved the seas of the Southern Ocean
with the largest build of ships in existence during the
earlier Middle Ages—junks able to carry six or seven
hundred men, whose towering bulk was still remembered at
Siraf in the days of Massoudy.[1]

Next, in the department of travel, the journey of
Fa-Hien was followed a century later (A.D. 518) by the
mission of Hoei-Sing and Sung-Yun, to collect sacred texts
and relics from "western countries," a mission in every way
similar to that of Fa-Hien, except that it was not, like his,
self-imposed. In this case the Government, and especially
the Empress-Mother, commissioned two envoys with definite
orders.

Like their more famous predecessor and successor, they
first of all crossed the *drifting sands* or Gobi Desert on
the way to Khotan, suffering sorely from the cold and the

---

[1] See Klaproth, "Lettre sur la
Boussole" (addressed to Alexander
Humboldt); and Reinaud's *Discours
préliminaire*, in his edition of the
"Two Mussulman Travellers." The
earliest use of the water compass in
China is fixed by Klaproth at A.D.
1111–17, nearly a century earlier than
its first mention in Europe (1180–90).
The magnetized objects must have
been exceptional in the fifth century,
for when Wu-Ti, afterwards emperor,
stormed Singanfu in 417, he seized
upon one of these as a great curiosity.
Things must have changed before
the eleventh century, when it was so
common that Chinese fortune-tellers
rubbed the "point of a needle with
a magnet stone, so as to make it
point to the South."

wind. From Khotan they turned south-west, and struggled through the gorges of the Kuen-Lun, compared with which the most famous passes and mountains of China were as nothing, and where men reached the "middle point of heaven and earth."

Each of our Chinese travellers does full justice to the mountain scenery of the Roof of the World,—the "continuous ascent, the precipitous and overhanging crags, towering up to the very heavens;"—and Hoei-Sing has all the enthusiasm of a modern traveller as he describes the view "from the summit of the range." [1] "From this point, as a centre looking downwards, it seemed as though one were poised in mid air." No trees or shrubs grew on these highlands; the air was icy cold, and the north wind swept along the drifting snow. To west and east flowed the rivers on their separate course from this, the central watershed of Asia; while to the south, in the "clear vapours" of dawn and sunset, rose up "like gem-spires the great snowy mountains" of the Himalaya.

The envoys seem next to have entered a land then ruled by the White Huns, so celebrated in Byzantine and Persian history, and including the modern Cashmere. Thence they made their way into Northern India, sometimes crossing mountain chasms on chains of iron, whose slippery height none but a mountaineer could safely traverse, "for there is nothing to grasp at in case of slipping, but in a moment the body is hurled down 10,000 fathoms." [2]

In the Punjaub, they visited, like Fa-Hien, various holy sites of the Buddhist faith—the place of the Shadow, of the Staff, of the Robe and so forth, of Sakya-Mouni.

---

[1] See Beal's "Buddhist Pilgrims" (1869), a translation of Fa-Hien, Hoei-Sing, etc., pp. 182–184; reprinted in "Buddhist Records of the Western World."

[2] Beal, p. 188.

During their stay, which lasted till 521, a fierce war was in progress between the kings of Peshawur[1] and Kabul, and the Chinese ambassadors received but scanty reverence. Disgusted to find that the Indian princes[2] paid little respect to the letters of the Son of Heaven, they "perceived that these remote barbarians were unfit for exercising public duties, and that their arrogancy was not to be bridled." To Sung-Yun, unlike Fa-Hien, China was the true and only Central Kingdom; and he had no "desire to be born" in any other. The loveliness of the Punjaub, "the gentle breeze, the songs of the birds, the trees in their spring-time beauty, the butterflies that fluttered over the flowers"[3] simply caused him "to revert to home thoughts;" and he took his departure from the disobedient and "self reliant" Hindu courts "without formal salutation."[4]

Among all the ventures of Chinese explorers in this period, the most romantic and the most doubtful is the traditional voyage of certain Buddhist priests to Eastern lands, the Land of the Fu-sang Tree, the Land of Women, the Land of Marked Bodies, and the Great Han country; which have been identified with various points of North-Eastern Asia and North-West America, and even with California and Mexico.[5]

[1] Ghandara.

[2] Especially the King of Ghandara (Peshawur).

[3] Beal, p. 194.

[4] Page 199. A curious notice is given us (pp. 199-200) of two young lions being sent to the King of Ghandara (Peshawur) about A.D. 520, and seen by Sung-Yun; he noticed their "fiery temper and courageous mien," and also that the common pictures of such animals in China were not truthful.

[5] See (1.) the elaborate monograph of Vining, "An inglorious Columbus; evidence that . . . Buddhist monks . . . discovered America in the fifth century A.D." (1885).

2. Neumann and Leland, "Fusang, etc.," (1875.)

3. Bretschneider's article in *Chinese Recorder*, 1870 (October).

4. Theo. Simpson in "Notes and Queries on China and Japan" (1869). And for the initial discussion of the whole question—

The narrative records how the kingdom of Fu-Sang was made known to the Chinese, at a time which answers to the year of Christ 499, by one Hoei-Sin, who seems to have lived in that country for some time past. It was situated, he declared, to the east of the Middle or Celestial Kingdom, 20,000 furlongs (li) east of the Great Han Country. It took its name from its fusang trees, which served the inhabitants for food, fibre, cloth, paper, and timber. The people of this country waged no war and had no armour ; they possessed horses, deer, and cattle with horns of wonderful length, that could bear an immense weight ;[1] and they

5. De Guignes' "Investigation of the Navigation of the Chinese to the Coast of America"; in the "Proceedings of the (Paris) Academy of Inscriptions and Belles Lettres," vol. xxviii. A.D. 1761. As early as August 28, 1752, this opinion of De Guignes was known to Père Gaubil, who writes from Pekin under that date, to express his disbelief in the Chinese account.

6. Similar incredulity was expressed by Philippe Buache, in his "Considerations on New Discoveries to the North of the Great Sea" (1753); and by Humboldt, in his "Views of the Cordilleras" (1814); as well as by Père Hyacinthe, in his "People of Central Asia ; " and, above all, by Klaproth, in vol. li. of the "Nouvelles Annales des Voyages " (1831). But, on the other hand,—

7. The Chevalier de Paravey supported De Guignes (1844), as did Neumann in vol. xvi. of the *Zeitschrift für Allgemeine Erdkunde*, whose article was incorporated by Leland in his "Fusang," as noticed above.

8. In 1865 M. Vivien de Saint Martin, in the *Geographical Annual* for that year, combated the whole theory of an American discovery, in a paper " An Old Story set afloat again ; " and his arguments were repeated in 1875, at the Nancy Congress of Americanists, by M. Lucien Adam.

9. De Guignes' view, however, was again championed in 1876, by the Marquis D'Hervey de St. Denys, in his " Mémoire sur . . . Fousang " (Acad. Inscr. and Belles Lettres) and in his translation of the thirteenth-century Chinese classic, called "The Ethnography of Foreign Peoples."

10. Lastly, Professor Wells Williams, in the American Oriental Society's publications, Oct. 25, 1880, expressed his disbelief in the terms of Klaproth, to which he adds some new points; while on the positive side Eichthal severely criticized Klaproth and the other sceptics.

11. Vining, in the earlier part of his treatise, reprints all the more important passages of the Fusang literature.

[1] One hundred and twenty bushels.

used these animals, and especially their tamed stags, to draw their carts (like the reindeer of the Lapps to-day).

Among fruits they enjoyed pears and grapes; among metals, gold, silver, and copper—but they set no value on any of these except the last.

They were ruled by a king who changed the colour of his garments (green, red, yellow, white, and black), like some of the Tartars, according to a cycle of years, but who took no part in government for the first three years of his reign. Their nobles were divided into three classes, and the crimes of these exalted personages were punished with peculiar solemnity: "They were put under ground with food and drink;" a ceremonial leave was taken of them by their friends and all the people; and they were left "surrounded with ashes."

The men of Fusang punished nearly all crimes with imprisonment; for smaller offences they employed a dungeon in the south of their country; but the greater criminals were immured for life in a northern prison, and their children were enslaved. The marriage ceremonies of this country were much the same as in China, except that the intending husband had to serve the girl's family for a year; like the Celestials, they paid extreme reverence to parents, and made offerings to the images of ancestors.

Till lately they had known nothing of the law of Buddha; but some forty years before Hoei-Sin returned to China, five devotees from Central Asia[1] came by sea to Fusang and taught their faith. By them the "holy images" were dispersed throughout the country.

The Kingdom of Women was next described as a

---

[1] From Kipin, says the narrative; that is, apparently, from Cophene or Afghanistan, a very holy land of Buddhists at this time, before Islam overflowed it, as we see from the pilgrim records of Fa-Hien, etc.

thousand furlongs east of Fusang. The people were erect
in stature, and very white in colour, but covered with an
immense growth of hair that reached to the ground. Their
children could walk when little more than three months old,
and within four years they were fully grown. They fed
upon a salt plant like wormwood, and fled in terror at the
approach of a human being.

The Land of Marked Bodies, like that of the Dog-headed
Men, and of Great Han, was discovered and described, accord-
ing to the Chinese annals, some time after the return of
Hoei-Sin, and between the years A.D. 502–556.

The first-named country, of the tattooed race who " marked
their bodies like wild beasts," was seven thousand furlongs
to the north-east of Japan. Like the Brahmins of India,
the nobles bore upon their foreheads certain lines which
showed their rank. As a people they were merry, hospitable, and peaceful—easily pleased with things of small
value. The house of their king was adorned with gold,
silver,[1] and precious articles, and in traffic they used gems
as the standard of value.

Another entry in the records of the Liang dynasty tells
how some Chinese mariners were driven by the winds to an
island where they found men of unintelligible language,
who had dogs' heads, and barked for speech. Among other
things they used small beans [2] for food; their clothing
resembled " linen cloth ; " from loose earth they constructed
round dwellings, with doors or openings like the mouths of
burrows. Lastly, the Great Han Country was described in
the early part of the sixth century A.D., as five thousand

---

[1] The Chinese account appears to
hint at their use of quicksilver—
" water-silver,"—but the expression
is of doubtful meaning.

[2] In this some have tried to recognize a description of the Mexican
centli, or maize.

furlongs east of the Land of Marked Bodies, to which the customs of the former were very similar in their rude simplicity. Only the language was different.

In this account it is evident that Fusang is the central point. No one who regards this as apocryphal is likely to attach any importance or reality to the other countries named; and some of the staunchest defenders of the American theory, like Neumann, have limited their apology entirely to Fusang, treating the Land of Women, the Great Han Country, and the rest, as a sort of legendary appendix to the true story, which it has discredited by association. Fusang, it is said in effect, can be shown to be some part of North America, but the rest of the narrative is stuffed with fables, and beyond all hope of identification. On the other hand, some[1] have boldly maintained that every point can be fixed; that the whole hangs together; and that fatal injury is done by the surrender of any part—for if Fusang is Mexico, it is no less clear that the Land of Women is Panama, that the Marked Bodies are to be found in the Aleutian Islands, and that the Great Han Country corresponds to the southern shore of Alaska.

With a more modest assurance, the great scholar[2] who first made known to Europe the entire Fusang record, was content with California as his equivalent for Fusang itself, placing Great Han in Kamskatka; and, after all that has been said on both sides of the question since the time of De Guignes, his conclusion (with some modification) remains, perhaps, the most probable. That is to say, while it seems unreasonable to reject altogether the Chinese tradition of the discovery of a Far Eastern land answering to some part of Western North America; and while it is impossible to doubt that in the past, as in the present, men could pass

---

[1] *E.g.* Leland and Vining.   [2] De Guignes.

from one continent to the other by the stepping-stones [1] of the Aleutian Islands, or the narrow passage of Behring's Straits [2]—yet it is hazardous to attempt anything like a series of positive and unqualified " locations," and both unhistorical and extravagant to bring down the places named into the tropical belt of the New World. Unhistorical, because in the first place there can be little doubt that the climate of regions such as Alaska, like the climate of Iceland and Greenland,[3] was then far milder than at present; and because, in the second place, it is not only unnecessary, but inaccurate, to overlook the perpetual movements of migration in the American continent before the European discovery of 1492. For if from Aztec, or pre-Aztec parallels in modern Mexico, we can establish anything like a resemblance with the people of Fusang as described by the Chinese, we remain face to face with the certainty that all its races once came into Central America from the Far North (according to the native tradition), and so with the probability that in such an early period as the fifth century A.D., the race which has left the Fusang characteristics in our Mexico must then have

[1] Captain Barclay Kennon, who superintended a recent survey of North Pacific waters for the United States Government, in a letter to Leland, testifies that a sailor in an open boat could cross from Kamskatka to the peninsula of Alaska by the Aleutian Islands during the summer months, and hardly ever be out of sight of land. Add to this, that the sea there abounds in fish, and that the warm Japanese current takes the very direction of Hoei Sin's suggested voyage.

[2] Where Captain Cook, for instance, on August 12, 1778, was in sight of Asia and America at the same moment.

[3] Thus the Vikings of the eleventh to fifteenth centuries possessed twenty churches on a single one of the Greenland Bays, with cornfields and pasturage, and enjoyed a climate sufficiently mild for a literature to flourish, and for constant commercial intercourse to go on with Norway, Iceland, and " Vinland." The increased severity of the sub-Arctic zone has, of course, affected Greenland far more than Alaska, which is still described as a country of " pineapples and polar bears, icebergs and strawberries."

been inhabiting a region at least as distant as the latitude of Lake Superior.

Extravagant also, because a journey from the Yellow Sea to the Mexican Coast, and still more to Panama, could not possibly have been described as one of thirty-two or thirty-three thousand furlongs.[1] Every Chinese traveller to India tends to over-estimate his distances, sometimes at nearly double their actual extent; and if this was the case by land, where constant opportunities presented themselves for checking and correcting calculations, and where men passed through many towns whose intervals one from another were pretty accurately known, how much more would this occur in a coasting voyage[2] of so vast a sweep, amounting, even in hard modern figures, to over 8000 miles.[3] Need we, then, look any further than the Peninsula, Strait, and southern coast of Alaska, or, at furthest, the islands which fringe the western coast of British Columbia, for the places of this narrative?

It is only fair to notice that powerful objections have been raised to the whole theory of an American Fusang. As Klaproth pointed out long ago, the mention of vines and horses is a serious stumbling-block, for both these objects were absolutely new to the American soil when the Spaniards introduced them—so, at least, it was believed both by Europeans and by natives.

Again, as we have already hinted, the Chinese had no satisfactory means of determining the length of their journeys at sea, and their statements of so many thousand furlongs are simply guess-work.

---

[1] Li.

[2] No mention is made of a direct passage across the ocean, which, of course, is in itself unlikely, and would have been a good deal longer than the great venture of Columbus.

[3] i.e. A coasting from the modern Shanghai by E. Coast of Japan, and across Ocean by Aleutian Islands.

Once more, the name of Fusang raises one or two special difficulties.   First of all, those who identify the fusang tree with the Mexican aloe seem to overlook the clear statement of the original record, that the country was named from the tree or shrub " Useful Mulberry," familiar to the Chinese long before Hoei-Sin; as well as the fact that the Mexican aloe, so far as known, was purely indigenous to the New World, and only imported into Asia from the Philippines in the sixteenth century under the name of Spanish Hemp.   As a matter of fact, the fusang tree of the narrative answers better to the paper-mulberry of Japan than to the Mexican aloe; and from many, if not most of the details given, Japan would seem to be the best alternative to North-West America.   Japanese writers claim that Fusang was an ancient title of their country, " on account of its beauty." [1]   The copper which the original story mentions as so useful in Fusang, has long been a celebrated product, both in Japan itself and in the Loo-Choo Islands adjoining; here, too, the vine and the horse have been known from remote antiquity; while iron is even now almost as rare in the kingdom of the Mikado as in Fusang.

The whole description of Hoei-Sin has accordingly been conjectured,[2] with some plausibility, to refer to an early attempt of Buddhist missionaries upon the south-west region of Japan, near Nagasaki; for although the annals of Japan are said to fix the first incoming of the Law of Buddha at A.D. 552, this may well refer to the formal conversion of the Islands, and need not at all exclude a pioneer venture half a century earlier.

Korea had received the " Three Precious Ones [3] " between

---

[1] According to Klaproth.

[2] As by Klaproth, Bretschneider, and Theo. Simson.

[3] " Buddha," " The Law," and " The Congregation."

A.D. 372 and 384, and it would be strange if the Faith, which had already travelled from India, should have made no attempt, in its most zealous and proselytising age, to cross the Strait of Korea, about the width of St. George's Channel, in the next hundred years (c. 380–480).

The hairy people of the "Land of Women" have naturally suggested to many the Ainos of Northern Japan; but the "Marked Bodies" certainly point rather to the American Indians than to any people of North-Eastern Asia; and having now reviewed the evidence for an Asiatic, and against an American Fusang, we must glance at the arguments which, as we have hinted already, make possible and defensible the main lines of De Guignes' position.

The inquirer may of course, like Bretschneider, reject the whole tradition as the invention of "a lying Buddhist," and a "consummate humbug," but any one not prepared for such drastic measures will be inclined to weigh carefully the analogy repeatedly advanced by modern anatomists and physiologists between some of the Tartar tribes and some of the American aboriginals. The same cautious person will also give some attention to the argument of a striking likeness between certain architectural monuments of Central America and those of Asiatic Buddhism;[1] to the discovery

---

[1] Thus Vining brings forward eight curious instances :—

1. An image found in Campeachy looking like a Buddhist monk (p. 571 of "An inglorious Columbus," and on cover of volume).

2. A sculptured table at Palenque resembling a seated Buddha with a worshipper offering to it (pp. 591–592).

3. A seated figure on a lion (?) throne, in stucco, also at Palenque (p. 593); both in posture and in attributes, this recalls one type of Buddha statue, but with serious differences; and the face, we may observe, is exactly that of an American Indian chief.

4. The façade of a building at Uxmal, with a seated figure like a Buddha.

5. A Mexican image somewhat Buddhistic, and said to represent Quetzalcoatl (p. 595).

6. A temple at Palenque, bearing some resemblance to the Boer-Buddha in Java.

in North America of fossil remains of the horse, some so recent [1] "that they must be regarded as coeval with man;" to the antecedent possibility and even probability of at least occasional transit from Asia to America, and *vice versâ*, in the latitude of the Behring Sea; to the undoubted achievement of the Vikings in the face of much greater difficulties on the eastern side; and to the likelihood of an original migration of the human race into the New World from Northern Asia rather than from any other quarter.

The Chinese record, if it is to be treated fairly, must not be minimised any more than it must be exaggerated; and if its words and measurements forbid us to identify Fusang with Mexico or Panama, they also surely require something more extensive than a journey to Japan, which the Chinese of Marco Polo's day reckoned as only fifteen hundred miles from their southern provinces, and which is distinctly named in our present narrative as a starting-point for the Land of Marked Bodies. Nothing has yet been found in Japan to answer to Hoei-Sin's account of the prison customs of Fusang, the assembly of the people to judge guilty noblemen, the peculiar punishment of the same, the sequence of colours in the royal garments, the use of deer as beasts of burden, and other particulars.

The tin, hammer-shaped coins of the Aztecs have been compared with the shoe-shaped ingots of "Sycee" silver,

7. Some (doubtful) elephant sculptures at Palenque.

8. "Elephant pipes," in carved stone, from Iowa, U.S.A. These last bear a most striking resemblance to a *tuskless* elephant, and have suggested to some the conventional symbol of Buddha; but the latter is always tusked in Asia, and the American finds point rather to a native variety of the great beast.

We must remember, moreover, that anthropologists have brought together apparently strong evidence of the *simultaneous* occurrence of forms of worship, and social customs, etc., among savage tribes in utterly different parts of the world, and quite independently of one another (Lubbock).

[1] Neumann and Leland, ch. iv.

current in China; the copper used so largely in Central America (instead of gold and silver) before the European invasion, seems once to have been worked as far north as Lake Superior; and traces of "Mexican" art and influence have been found as far as Tennessee along the course of that migration which, as we may surmise, had crossed from Asia into Alaska many ages before Hoei-Sin, which Buddhist travellers of the fifth century A.D. may have discovered on its slow progress southwards, and which may have left in its final tropical home some memorials of an intercourse with the Old World.

Both in China and in Japan the tradition of an ancient discovery of countries far to the East is said to be very old, very widespread, and very obstinate;[1] and a modern instance gives some colour to it. In 1833, before the introduction of Western appliances and enterprise into Nippon, a Japanese junk was wrecked near Queen Charlotte's Island off British Columbia; just as in 1832 a fishing smack from the same country, with only nine men on board, driven out of its course between Formosa and Tokio, arrived safely at the Sandwich Islands. Such undoubted facts may well encourage those who believe in the substantial truth of this Chinese claim in the way of American discovery, and a negative argument from an equally undoubted fact may be added. No one now disputes that the Norsemen reached the eastern coast of America about A.D. 1000, and repeatedly revisited the same; yet no one can point to a single proof of their presence, or relic of their occupation. All the evidence comes from the written traditions of the Vikings themselves. Why, then, should we ask for so much more in confirmation of the word of Hoei-Sin and his Buddhist

[1] Contrast with this the distinct opinion of the Arabs, *e.g.* of Aboulfeda, that beyond Japan was no inhabited land.

friends than we expect in support of the pretensions of Red
Eric and his house ?   Grant that the "internal" witness
(from consistency and clearness of statement, absence of
fable, and so forth) is far weaker in the case of the Chinese
than in that of the Norsemen ; but this is surely balanced
to some degree by the greater "monumental," and other
present-day evidence, of the former claim.

Last of our examples of Chinese travel comes the journey
of Hiouen-Thsang [1] (A.D. 629–646), undertaken at the very
time which saw the first overflow of Islam, the collapse of
Persia, and the conquest of Egypt and Syria by the Arabs,
who, as they advanced with hardly a pause from the far
south-west of Asia, missed only by a short interval a meeting
with the Chinese pilgrim on the banks of the Oxus.

It is equally noteworthy that this age was also one of
revived Chinese activity and rule in Further India and
Central Asia, resulting from the fresh vigour imparted to
the Empire by the great rulers of the seventh century,
Yang-Ti and Taitsung.   As usual, a fresh start of exploring
energy accompanies a fresh lease of national life ; extensive
and daring travellers are not often to be found among the
men of effete races and disordered commonwealths.

Like Fa-Hien, the new "Master of the Law" (so his

---

[1] The memorials of Hiouen-Thsang
are preserved in two works : 1. The
"Records of the Western World
(Si-yu-ki) ;" 2. "History of the Life
and Journeys of H. T." (by Hwuy-
Le and Yen-tsung, two of his disciples).   The whole of these writings
were edited and translated by Stanislas Julien (1853, etc.) in his "Voyages des Pèlerins Bouddhistes"
(3 vols.), which is the text here referred to (especially of vol. i., "The
Life and Journeys"); also by S. Beal,
in Trubner's Oriental Series, 1888
(the "Life"), and 1884 (the "Records ").   The "Records" are more
in the form of a gazetteer or geographical dictionary than of a continuous narrative, concerning themselves with a description of all the
countries known to Hiouen-Thsang,
but passing over in silence many
parts of his journey.   Refs. to pages
without book-title are to the "Life"
in Julien's edition.

disciples style him) travelled into the West, "into the Land of the Brahmins, to seek for the Law," for copies of Buddhist Scriptures wanting in China; like his predecessor, once more, he set out from Singanfu, "the divine city of Chang-An," in the north-west corner of the Empire; like him, he crossed the Gobi Desert, and suffered from all the illusions of the demons in that terrible waste.[1]   Here guides and attendants all forsook him, and to his excited and fearful imagination there appeared visions of brilliant armies, brigand troops, squadrons of horses and of camels, each moment changing form before his eyes.   As any Christian might have done, he routed the phantoms with a few words of Scripture or devotion; but in the night, the torches of wicked spirits blazed around him, and by day sandstorms almost blinded him with their dust.   For five days he tasted nothing, but at last he reached an oasis, and soon after emerged into the pasture-land of the Oigour country in Eastern Turkestan,[2] the modern Khamil, near the Southern Altai Range.   Thence he passed through Kao-Chang or Turfan, Karashar, and the Aksu District, on the north-east of Kashgar, purposing to cross the Icy Range of the Bolor or Tengri Khan.   But on the hither side of these mountains Hiouen-Thsang was detained two months by heavy snows upon that gigantic barrier, where "the endless sheets of snow and ice that had collected from the beginning of the world stretched up to mingle with the clouds," and where avalanche and ice block fell ever and anon from the mountain sides upon the narrow pass.[3]   His crossing was probably made by the Muzart

---

[1] "Life," p. 22 (Julien).

[2] Pages 28, 29.

[3] Pages 53, 54. A curious detail is added in the "Records of Western Countries" (Beal, i. p. 25): "Those who travel this road should not wear red garments, nor carry calabashes." Red clothes would doubtless irritate the demons of the mountain, and calabashes might burst, when the water in them had frozen, with so loud a report as to cause some of the quaking masses of snow and ice to fall upon the traveller.

defile under Tengri Khan, where all the warmth of fur-lined garments could not save some of his new companions from the piercing cold. On the western side, the pilgrim descended to the Lake of Issyk-Kul, " a vast sheet of water with high-swelling waves," to the south of the district of the Seven Rivers, where he met the Khan of the Turks out hunting. In the light of recent discoveries, we may be pretty sure that Nestorian Christianity was then active in this very region, but Hiouen-Thsang tells us nothing about it; although he notices the Buddhism of some of these Turks, the fire-worship of others, and the silken garments of their chief and his court—evidence of a trade connection with China, or at least with Khotan.

From Issyk-Kul he made his way to Talas,[1] the modern Turkestan, on the northern bank of the Jaxartes. Here the Turks had ruled for the last half century around the " thousand springs " from the Bolor to the Sea of Aral, and from Lake Balkash to the Hindu-Kush. It is not without interest to compare the reception of Hiouen-Thsang by the Turkish khan with that which his ancestor Dizabul gave in A.D. 571 to Zemarchus and the embassy of the Byzantine Justin II.[2]

To the Eastern, these Tartars appeared chiefly interesting as Buddhists; to the Western, as good fighting material useful in an alliance against Persia. From Talas to the Indian frontier the course of Hiouen-Thsang is extremely hard to follow. He seems, however, to have passed through Tashkend and Nujkend, and so across the Jaxartes to Samarcand. To the north-west of this he describes a desert as

[1] The chief emporium of the country beyond the Jaxartes, frequently mentioned in Arab writers —where the Chinese suffered a severe defeat from a Moslem army in or about A.D. 751 (De Guignes, i. 58).

[2] Julien, 55–59.

barren though not as vast as Gobi, the great waste of the
Kizil-Kum to the south-east of the Aral Sea. But there is
no reason to believe that he traversed this; [1] for his route
lay to the east by way of Samarcand, Kashania,[2] and possibly
Bokhara; and he finally crosses the Oxus in its upper course
near Balkh, making his way through the Iron Gates that lie
some ninety miles south-south-east from Samarcand. Thence
he arrived in Bactria; passed from Balkh to Bamian, where
the rock-hewn figures of Buddha that he describes may still
be seen; [3] and so reached at last the land of Kapisa on the
upper valley of the Kabul River, whose chief town, "at the
foot of a mountain in the north," may perhaps be the modern
Afghan city of Ghorband.[4]

He had now entered within the more ordinary limits of
Levantine trade and travel; in Samarcand he found himself
outside the frontiers of Buddhistic kingdoms, and among a
people of fire-worshipping apostates; he claims to have converted the king to the ancient faith, [5] and to have refilled the
empty convents, which in Fa-Hien's day seem to have been
prosperous enough. May we not conjecture that Buddhism
had receded—for it had certainly not advanced—on this its
south-west border, in the interval? [6] South of the Oxus,
however, and especially in Bamian, the traveller's faith was
in no need of revival; relics of Buddha were still honoured

[1] Any more than Kharizmia, which
he also describes, and which is perhaps the most westerly region noticed
in the "Records of Western Countries"
(Beal, i. 35).   The two texts of
Hiouen-Thsang, the " Life " and the
" Records, " are inconsistent here.

[2] Half-way between Samarcand
and Bokhara.

[3] One of these, the Life of H. T.
credits with a length of 1000 feet.

It was recumbent, and within the
precincts of a monastery. This sounds
far-fetched, and sixty yards appear to
be the greatest length discovered by
modern explorers in the Bamian
Statues. See Beal's edition of the
"Records," i. 51, 52.

[4] A short distance north-north-
west of Kabul itself.

[5] " Life," pp. 59, 60 (Julien).

[6] A.D. 400–600.

there, and the monks greeted their visitor with the respect
that befitted a doctor of the law.

Hiouen-Thsang describes with the natural interest of
personal experience the Iron Gates [1] of the Oxus (often compared by others with those of Derbend on the Caspian); the
fertility of Balkh, so often celebrated by the Arabs; and the
snowy mountains that surrounded Bamian and Kabul, re-
calling the glaciers of Tengri Khan.

It was apparently through the Khyber Pass that the
traveller now entered India, on his way to the kingdom of
Ghandara, whose capital, as in the days of Sung-Yun, was
then fixed in the modern Peshawur, at the eastern end of
the Khyber Gorge.[2] Just beyond Peshawur, he crossed the
Indus, close to its junction with the Kabul River; then,
turning north-east into Cashmere, he visited various holy
sites in a tract that no European, till lately, has ever traversed—between Attock and Skardo, under the shadow of
Dapsang. In this remote land both Brahmins and Buddhists
located some of their earliest traditions; and, among the
thousands of topes that studded the country, some were
already old and ruinous in the time of Hiouen-Thsang.

After a stay of two years in the Punjaub and Cashmere,
varied by a journey into Thibet, the Master of the Law, who
had refuted every Indian pundit that had ventured to dispute
with him, moved on to the Ganges Valley [3] by way of
Canoge. Here he traversed and described the little states
which then covered the land of the modern Oude, Allahabad
and Benares, famous for the scenes of Buddha's life and

---

[1] " This pass, traversed by a narrow
road, is bordered on the right and left
by mountains of prodigious height.
On both sides is a rocky wall of an
iron colour. Here are set up double
wooden doors, strengthened with iron
and furnished with many bells " (pp.
61–68).

[2] Pages 76, 77.

[3] " Life," pp. 85, etc.

death,[1] and surveyed with exhaustive care by the devout and learned pilgrim.

Several times he narrowly escaped death from roving brigands and Thugs;[2] once he was on the point of being offered as a sacrifice by some "pirates," who were, perhaps, scarcely prepared for the contemptuous indifference of a Buddhist saint. With angry cries and gestures they told him of their purpose. "If this vile body," exclaimed the pilgrim, "can give you any satisfaction, it is yours." He advanced to the altar with the utmost calmness, ready, as he said, to enter Nirvana with an untroubled soul. Suddenly a furious wind raised the river in flood, broke down the trees, and whirled the dust around. The pirates fell on their faces in terror at the evident wrath of heaven. Hiouen-Thsang was saved.[3] But in death or deliverance his composure was the same. "How could men dare," he exclaimed, "for the sake of a passing satisfaction to their miserable bodies, which pass away in a moment like the brightness of the dawn, to bring upon themselves the tortures of an infinite cycle of ages?" The pirates with humble contrition received his instructions, accepted his blessing, and saw in the calming of the tempest proof of the Divine mission of their teacher.

In the face of simple robbery and ill usage, the "Master" preserved an equally unruffled countenance. He seemed even to rejoice. With beaming face he asked his companions why they should be troubled at the loss of their paltry goods. Was "not the life more than the meat, and the body than the raiment?"

[1] He especially deals, like Fa-Hien with Prayaga (our Allahabad) and with Magadha, our Behar, south of the Ganges, near Patna. Near here was the Palibothra of the Greeks, the capital of Sandracottus (Chaudragupta).

[2] *E.g.* "Life," pp. 97–100, 116–19. I-tsing, a little later, suffered from the same scourge in his Indian travels.

[3] "Life," pp. 116–119.

After visiting divers places on the lower Ganges Valley—
Champa [1] in the north-west corner of modern Bengal;
Burdwan, near the present Calcutta; and Tamlook [2] at the
mouth of the river (where Fa-Hien in his day took ship for
Ceylon)—Hiouen-Thsang made his way into Southern India,
crossing the Godavery, and apparently reaching as far as
Madras and the Pala River in the centre of the Carnatic, as
if intending, like his predecessor, a journey to Adam's Peak.
Yet he did not visit Ceylon in person, though he describes
it, and relates the lion-stories of the Cinghalese race, and
various tales of the priceless jewels of the island. Fearless
of earthly danger, the pilgrim may have shrunk from any
voyage, however short, on the treacherous and uncertain
element, which, as men knew well, was governed only by the
demons.[3] Perhaps he would not risk his life for any such
impious folly, even though it were to see the sacred jewel
that flashed upon the top of the Buddha Tooth-Temple [4] of
Ceylon, "visible for two hundred leagues on a cloudless
night, like a planet in mid air." [5]

Denying himself the spectacle of this wonder, like that
of the dwarfs to be seen in the Southern Ocean, "with men's

[1] Kadjinga.

[2] Tamralipti. It has been noticed
how Tamlook, though well known to
the Chinese travellers, seems to have
been entirely unvisited by the Arabs,
who were singularly long in reaching
many districts of Central and Eastern Hindostan.

[3] Page 183. See Tennent's " Ceylon," i. 543, 544.

[4] This famous gem, variously described as a diamond, a pearl, an
amethyst, a ruby, and a jacinth or
"hyacinth," is noticed by Fa-Hien,
by Marco Polo, by Cosmas the Indian
traveller, and by several of the Arab
geographers—"the very finest ruby,"
says Polo, "that was ever seen, as long
as one's hand and as thick as a man's
arm, without spot, shining like a fire,
not to be bought for money. Kublai
Khan offered the value of a city for
it, but the King (of Ceylon) answered
he would not give it for the treasure
of the world." Possibly the "Car-
buncle" purchased in Ceylon for the
Chinese emperor early in the fourteenth century may have been the
same jewel.

[5] Page 184.

bodies and bird's beaks, who lived on the fruit of cocoa-trees," [1] Hiouen-Thsang now struck off to the north-west till he arrived at the Malabar coast. Thence he made his way to Baroche in Guzerat (the Barygaza of the early Mediterranean traders),[2] and so to Scinde, the Indus, and Moultan, where he completed his circuit of Indian kingdoms, and found himself again in the Punjaub, with " Persia to the north-west." In a confused way he repeats, at this point, the time-honoured story of the Island of Women; which he seems to place off the south-west of Persia, and makes a dependency of the Kingdom of " Fo-lin," or the Byzantine Empire.[3]

His reverence for the sanctity of Buddha's native country drew him back to the Upper Ganges, where he presided at a great Council, refuted the errors of the Brahmins, and exposed the folly of the local saints, of men " who rubbed themselves with cinders till they looked like a cat in the chimney, or ate tainted and rotten meat as if they were pigs feeding upon garbage, and yet for such acts, the crown of madness, were considered holy." [4] There was not much love lost now between the old religion with its caste system and the new with its levelling doctrines, and the Brahmin reaction against the faith which, at the opening of the fifth century (when Fa-Hien travelled to India), seemed in a fair way to universal victory, was now gathering all its strength for the counter revolution. Within two hundred years [5] of Hiouen-Thsang's departure, a follower of his might have sought in vain within the Peninsula for the hospitable con-vents, the applauding crowds, the generous monarchs who were still found to welcome the Master of the Law.

---

[1] Page 201.
[2] As in the Periplus of the Eryth-rean Sea.
[3] See " Life," p. 208 (Jul.).
[4] Pages 217–225.
[5] Circ. A.D. 640 to 840.

With perhaps ominous bitterness, the pilgrim rejects [1] the common tradition of the sanctity and healing virtues of the Ganges, as a fable invented by the "heretics;" and with something of the same spirit, he answers the Indian Buddhists, who would fain have had him settle among them and forget his old home in the "Border Land." China was no outer country of barbarians, he replied, but a land of grave magistrates and law-abiding people, of virtuous princes and loyal subjects, of loving fathers and dutiful sons, of men who paid a due respect to age and wisdom. There, too, all the depths of science had been explored; there the movements of sun, moon, and planets were truly calculated; there all kinds of instruments had been invented, the seasons of the year divided, and the properties of the six tones of music ascertained. Nowhere had the Law of Buddha more faithful followers.[2]

We may gather, from some other incidents recorded on this second Ganges journey, how strong was now the rivalry between the orthodox of the two camps. At the Buddhist Council [3] above referred to, where Hiouen-Thsang complains of the presence of no fewer than two thousand Brahmins and "naked heretics," or fakirs, the civil power had to enforce agreement by a proclamation, which assigned loss of the tongue to any backbiter, and loss of life to all who should assault the "Master of the Law." Again, we have a curious history [4] of how the Buddhist doctrine had been restored in Cashmere.[5] The heretic king had been killed on his throne, and the impious race of the apostates had been rooted out. So true is it that Buddhism has never been propagated by force.

[1] "Life," page 105.
[2] Pages 230, 231.
[3] This was held, under the patronage of King Siladitya of Prayaga, at Kanya Koubdja, in Magadha (see

"Life," pp. 235, 243, etc.).
[4] Pages 248, 249.
[5] By a prince ruling in the Upper Oxus Valley (in Tokharistan).

And now Hiouen-Thsang set out on his return. Unlike
Fa-Hien, he declined the most tempting offers for the ocean
transit, and declared that nothing should hinder him from
revisiting his old friends in Central Asia. Refusing all the
presents offered him on his departure except a garment of
fine wool and a rich spoil of sacred books and images,[1] he
journeyed from Oude to Attock without mischance—for
though woods and hills alike swarmed with brigands, they
did him no harm. But in the passage of the Indus some
fifty of his precious manuscripts were lost, through a sudden
gust of wind in mid-channel. This, of course, was due, as
the pilgrim learnt afterwards, to Divine wrath. He was
trying to leave India with some native flowers and fruits ;[2]
and no one had ever yet attempted such impiety without
loss.

After a short stay in Cashmere, Hiouen-Thsang plunged
again into the gorges of the Hindu Kush—" a mass of dangerous summits and terrible peaks, rising into forms the
most strange and varied—at one time a plateau, at another an
arrow-like point ;—the scene changed at each step." [3] After
more than a week's steady climbing, the travellers, apparently still accompanied by the elephant on whose back
Hiouen-Thsang had crossed the Indus, stood upon the Roof
of the World. Here—the snow and ice all around them, the
clouds beneath them—they saw on every side the stony
summits of the mountains stretching as far as the eye could
reach, " like a forest of trees stripped of their foliage." So
high was this land, and so stormy were the winds that swept
it, that the birds could not cross it in their flight.

Hiouen-Thsang was now [4] on the Pamir ; and no traveller,
from his day to the present century, visited, or at any rate

[1] Pages 260, 261.
[2] Page 264.
[3] Pages 266, 267.
[4] A.D. 645.

described, Lake Syrikul, the true source of the Oxus, which
the Chinese pilgrim makes into a vast lake, " greater than
the range of eyesight," and which Lieut. John Wood, when
he rediscovered it in 1830, reduced to the more moderate
dimensions of fourteen miles by one, though establishing
more firmly than ever its claim as the loftiest sheet of fresh
water in the world. The hideous ugliness of the Pamir mountain tribes; their savage manners, and brutal character; [1]
the blue eyes which distinguished them from all surrounding
nations, the shrines of Buddha that dotted their country,
were alike noticed by the pilgrim, as he struggled back on
his homeward route from the Kabul Valley to Khotan; [2] and
in most of what he says, his record has a striking agreement
with modern accounts of Central Asia. He is not the equal
of Marco Polo as a discoverer; but in some places he explored
further, and saw more clearly than the great Venetian.
Thus, on his outward way, he anticipated the present-day
discovery of the depression which separates the mountain
masses of Pamir and Altai; as on his return he lighted upon
the sources of the Oxus.

Well might he reckon up the difficulties he had surmounted,—" the vast plains of moving sand, the gigantic
heights of snowy mountains, the scarped rocks and iron
gates of passes, the impetuous waves of torrents, lakes, and
rivers,"—for his seventeen years of travel had not been without result. He had done something to revive the failing
energies of Western Buddhism; he had recovered many

---

[1] Pages 270, etc.

[2] We may notice that Hiouen-
Thsang's homeward journey between
these points kept to a more southern
and eastern route than his outward
way. The latter went by Karashar,
Lake Lob, Tengrikhan, and Issyk-
Kul to Talas and Bokhara; the former
crossed Badakshan and the Pamir to
Syrikul, and so to Kashgar, Yarkand,
and Khotan. The last named, from
a legend of its first king, was known,
he tells us, by the title of " Teat of
the World."

sacred texts; he had exalted the honour of Chinese learning. What is of more importance to us, he had been a patient and daring traveller, a faithful observer, a true citizen of the world, a not unimportant member of that noble band of pioneers who, by their journeys and their writings, first breached the barriers of ignorance and fear between distant nations.

Here we must leave for the present the first part of our subject. As far as it relates to Christendom, this is also the most barren, unpleasing, and apparently hopeless of periods. Like those Asiatic rivers, which, after flowing through a lovely country full of inhabitants, finally lose themselves in a dreary marsh or sandy desert, so the expansive energy, the external interests, the geographical knowledge of the Roman world, seem gradually to pass, between the fourth and the tenth centuries, from abounding life into an almost absolute torpor. Fragments of the older learning, more and more perversely misunderstood; occasional displays of the older spirit of enterprise, more and more spasmodic and ineffective,—these are all, or nearly all, that remain to us as we reach the darkest epoch of the Christian Middle Ages.

But we have already remarked enough upon this apparent down-grade movement, and the real, racial recuperation which underlies the more obvious stagnation and failure of the time. We have now to look forward to brighter days, to the evidence which later ages would offer of the unrivalled strength, determination, and daring of the Christian peoples. Despised, ignorant, and uncouth as they are on the eve of the crusades, it is only the uncouthness of an awkward boyhood that keeps them back; their latent power of mind and body will yet, in the long run, prove itself the master of every rival: and in the explorations of the Norsemen, with which our next period begins, we are already on the way to the great discoveries, conquests, and colonies of modern Europe.   The spread of Arab enterprise and the versatility of its energy has been indeed surprising ; but it did not possess the deep and stern perseverance of the European : it was in the Viking, in the Crusader, in the Christian navigator of the fifteenth and sixteenth centuries, that the invincible persistence of old Rome was more truly born again ; and in its old age Europe would still realise the hope of its youth, that world-wide dominion which the Cæsars had dreamed of, aimed at, but left unfinished.

There was no disgrace to the Western world in its long time of disorderly struggling from a pagan into a Christian civilization or organized life ; great things were yet in store for it :—

> " And it might thereupon
>   Take rest ere it be gone
>   Once more on its adventure brave and new,
>   Fearless and unperplexed
>   When it wage battle next,
>   What weapons to select, what armour to indue."

ADDITIONAL NOTE.—I.

ON THE MANUSCRIPTS OF THE PRINCIPAL TEXTS.

[Those personally examined are marked thus *.]

BORDEAUX PILGRIM. (1) At Verona, No. 52 in the Chapter Library, probably of the 8th cent.; the oldest text, but imperfect; wanting, according to Tobler, all the central part, from Cæsarea on the way out, to Terracina on the way home. (2) At St. Gall, No. 732* contains a fragment of the Itinerary under the title "De Virtutibus Hierusalem," wedged in between two parts of a manuscript of Theodosius the Pilgrim. It omits all the text descriptive of the journey to and from Syria. This copy is of A.D. 811, very plain, without illustration, rubrication, marginal notes, or other special features. It is single-columned, contains 16 lines to the page, and occupies fols. 104–113 of the volume. (3) At Paris, in the Bibliothèque Nationale, MSS. Lat. 4808,* fols. 66–72 bis, is a very complete and valuable (10th cent.) copy of the Bordeaux Itinerary. From this Pierre Pithou (in 1589) published his Editio Princeps; a transcript made by him of the MS. is now in the Municipal Library at Orleans, No. 265. Here the gaps in the St. Gall and Verona MSS. are supplied, and this copy is more exactly and carefully written than either of the others. Like the copy at St. Gall, this is a perfectly plain text. Montfaucon found two other MSS. of this Itinerary in the Vatican (Montf. Bibl. Biblioth. i. 81, 83), but no one since his day has been able to discover them.

PAULA, Peregrinatio. As written by St. Jerome, there is naturally no lack of manuscript authority, in copies of the latter's works; Tobler refers especially to two MSS. at Munich, in the Royal Library there. (1) No. 12,104 (Lat.) of the 11th cent. (2) No. 14,031 (Lat.) of the same period. The same applies to the letter of Paula and Eustochium to Marcella.

MELANIA, Peregrination; one MS. at Paris, Bibl. Nat. Lat. Nouv. acq. 2178*, fols. 241–257. Double-columned; 37 lines; Spanish Visigothic hand of 11th cent., very large script.

EUCHERIUS. On certain of the Holy Places (De aliquibus locis sanctis) two MSS. (1) In Paris, Bibl. Nat. Lat. 13,348* of the 8th cent. (fols. 64–69 bis), with some lacunæ, but fairly complete and very important. A single-columned text, plain, without special features, in large handwriting. (2) In Rome, Vatican, 636ᴀ of 13th cent., transcribed by Philip Labbé in 1657.

Breviary of Jerusalem, one MS. In the Ambrosian Library at Milan, No. M 79 Sup.* Discovered by Bethmann, in 1854, at end of a MS. of Bede De Locis Sanctis. It occupies fols. 44 to 44 bis of the volume; and is in 9th cent. hand.

Theodosius, De situ terræ sanctæ, three MSS. (1) At St. Gall, No. 732*; of A.D. 811; cut into two portions by the fragment already noticed of the Bordeaux Pilgrim, and occupying fols. 98–104, and 113–114 bis. In character, size, etc., it is identical with the interpolated MS. of the B. P. (see above). Tobler's highly fanciful reconstruction of the text has more reference to the next MSS. (2) London, B. Mus. Titus D. iii.,* fols. 68, sqq., of 13th–14th cents. (3) Louvain University Library, No. 10 of 16th cent., bound up with the book of Gervase of Tilbury, De Otiis imperialibus, and agreeing very closely with (2), at London.

Antoninus Martyr, 14 MSS. (1) At St. Gall, No. 133* of 8th–9th cents.; fols. 602–657. This is a MS. without title, initial letter, rubrication, marginal notation, or any ornamental features; but complete, and the oldest existing. It is bound up with a MS. of Æthicus of Istria, and eight other texts; the page is single-columned, and contains 19 lines. (2) At Berne, Municipal Library, No. 582* (fols. 76–96 bis) of 9th–10th cents. A MS. like that just noticed in its lack of ornament, etc., but wanting some chapters, e.g. fols. 76, 85, 89, 90, 91, 94, are a good deal damaged. It is bound up with the famous Berne MS. of Arculf, is written in same hand, and contains same amount to the page (19 lines). Tobler's collation is imperfect. (3) At Brussels, Biblioth. Publique, No. 2922 of the 9th cent. (4) At Paris, Biblio. Nat., No. 12,277* (Lat.), an excellent MS. of the 11th–12th cents., once belonging to St. Germain des Prés, and bound up with Bede De Locis Sanctis. The Antonine MS. occupies fols. 44–52. (5) At Munich, Royal Library, No. 19,149 of 10th cent., containing only cc. 38–43 of the Soc. de L'Orient Lat.'s text. (6) At Paris, Bibl. Nat. Lat., No. 2335* of 12th cent., fols. 21–26, unornamented MS. much abbreviated; single-columned, 46 lines to page; few marginal notes, no rubrication except at initial heading. (7) At London, B. Mus. Add., 15,219* of 12th cent., fols. 3–11, single-columned, 29 lines; difficult script, much abbreviated. No special features. (8) At Rome (Vatican), 636ᴀ of 13th cent. (9) At Vienna, Biblioth. Cæsar. Palat., 2432 of 12th–13th cents. Much abridged. (10) At Périgord, Episcopal Library, of 12th–13th cents. ["Olim Caduinensis"]. (11) At Paris, Bibl.

Nat., 4847* (Lat.) of 14th cent., fols. 1–7, single-columned. No special features. ["Olim Colbertinus."] (12) At Piacenza, Archiv. S. Anton., c. A.D. 1360. (13) Ibid., Bibl. Commun. Palastrelli, No. 139 of 16th cent. (14) At Berlin, No. 32 (Lat.) of 15th cent.

ARCULF, thirteen MSS. (1) At London, B. Mus., Cotton, Tiberius D. v.* of 8th–9th cents. Fols. 78 bis–93 bis. Double-columned. 38 lines to page. End much damaged by fire. Does not contain the plans. This MS. has not been adequately collated for the text of Tobler and Molinier (Soc. de L'Or. Lat.). (2) At Brussels, 2921 of 9th cent., without the plans. (3) At Berne, 582* of 9th cent. Contains the plans, at fols. 8, 17, 21, 29 (in red). Whole MS. on fols. 1–48; 19 lines. Well collated by T. M. (4) At Paris, B. N. 13,048* (Lat.) of 9th cent. Contains the plans. (5) At Laon, Bibl. Municip., 92 of 9th cent., a fragment. (6) At Vienna, Lat. 458 of 10th cent. (7) At Munich, Royal Libr., Lat. 19,150 of 10th cent., a fragment, but with plans. (8) At Paris, B. N. 12,943,* of 11th cent. Double-columned: 41 lines; fols. 90–97 [is wrongly catalogued as MS. of Bede, De Locis Sanctis]; without the plans. (9) At St. Gall, 320* of 12th cent., without the plans, folios 254–284. Single-columned, 34 lines. No special features. (10) At Cadouin, Abbey Libr., (Périgord diocese) of 12th cent., with plans. (11) At Rome, Vatican, 636A, of 13th cent. (12) At Vienna, Bibl. Cæs. Palat. Lat., 609 of 13th cent., with plans. (13) At Rome, Regin., 618 of 15th cent.

BEDE (De Locis Sanctis): six chief MSS. (1) At Munich, Roy. Libr., 6,489 of 9th cent. (2) At Brussels, Libr. of Duke of Burgundy, 8,658 of 9th cent. (3) At Wurzburg, Univ. Libr., MS. Th., f. 74, etc., of 9th cent. (4) At Laon, Bibl. Municip., 92 of 9th cent. (5) At Milan, Ambros. Libr. M., 79 sup.* of 10th cent., fols. 38·bis–44. · Some of Arculf's plans (of holy places in Sion) on fol. 40. Double-columned, 41 lines. (6) Paris, B. N. 2,321* (Lat.) of 10th cent. Fols. 135–151. Contains plans of Arculf. Also, among perhaps 100 other MSS. of this popular text, are to be noticed:— (7) At Paris, B. N. Lat. 14,797* of 12th cent. (8) At London, B. Mus. Add., 15,219* of 12th cent. Fols. 12–19; single-columned; 29 lines. Sketch of Cenaculum. (9) At Cambridge, Caius College MSS., No. 225*, fols. 171–173, single-columned, 35 lines. (10) At London, B. Mus., Faustina A. vii.* of 12th–13th cents., fols. 156–162 bis. Double-columned, 27 lines, no plans. (11) At Oxford, Lincoln Coll. 96*, of 13th cent. (12) At Dublin, Trin. Coll. E., 62 of 13th cent. (13) At London, B. Mus. Add., 22,635*, double-columned, 65 lines, fols. 44–46 bis. With plans on fols. 44, 44 bis, 45, 45 bis, presenting some peculiarities. (14) At Paris, B. N. 12,277* of 15th cent. fols. 52–58 bis. To these we must add a Bede MS. of 8th–9th cents. at London B. Mus., Cotton, Faustina B. i.,* fols. 196–203 bis. Single-columned, 28 lines. On fol. 197 a sketch in green of Holy Sepulchre.

WILLIBALD, six MSS. (Hodœporicon). (1) At Munich, Royal Libr. Lat., 6,890 of 8th–9th cents. (2) In same Libr. 4,535 of 9th–11th cents. (fragment). (3) At Rome, Vallicellan., C. 73, of 11th cent. (fragment). (4) At Munich, Royal Libr. Lat., 14,396 of 12th cent. (5) At Carlsruhe, Grand Ducal Libr., 84 of 13th cent. (the Codex Augiensis, fragmentary). (6) At Paris, B. N. Lat., 9744* of 15th cent., fols. 1–10. A MS. of Willibald's Itinerary (Codex Oxenhusianus) was edited by Canisius in Lect. Antiq. iv., 705–718.

COMMEMORATORIUM de Casis Dei, etc.; one MS. at Basel, University Libr., in vol. ii.* of Bruchstücke von Handschriften, pp. 12–13. This is of 9th–10th cents., much damaged at beginning and end.

BERNARD (the Wise). ¡Four MSS. (3 surviving). (1) At London, B. Mus., Cotton Faustina B. i.* Single-columned, 28 lines, fols. 192–196 of 8th–9th cents., like the Bede that follows it, with which it has been repeatedly confused. A MS. of primary value, not sufficiently collated, and wrongly ascribed to 13th cent., by Tobler and Molinier. (2) At Oxford, Lincoln Coll., 96 * of 13th cent. (3) At Vienna, Bibl. Cæs. Palat., 2,432 of 14th cent. (4) At Rheims, once seen by Mabillon in Monast. Libr., and said to contain correct date, unlike (1) and (2), now lost (in French Revol.?).

DESCRIPTIO Parrochiæ Hierusalem, six MSS. (1) At Rome, Regin. 196 of 12th cent. (2) At Brussels, Libr. Duke of Burgundy, 9,827 of 12th cent. (3) At Paris, B. N. Lat., 5129* of 12th cent. Double-columned (afterwards 3 and 4 columns), fols. 56–67 [54–71, "Descriptio Locorum circa Hierusalem"]. (4) At Rheims, City Libr., 821 of 12th cent. (5) At Douay, Public Libr., 838 of 12th cent., fols. 49, 50 in close agreement with (1) and (4); (6) At Paris B. N. Lat., 6,189,* fragment, of 13th cent. (of c. A.D. 1270), seems to agree mainly with (1). A 7th MS., at Brussels, of 17th cent., in Libr. of Duke of Burgundy, was probably based on a lost 12th cent. one.

NOTITIA Antiochiæ ac Hierosolymæ Patriarchatuum, 5 MSS. (1) At Paris, B. N. Lat., 17,801,* close of 12th cent., double-columned, 37 lines, fols. 271, 272, embedded in a MS. of William of Tyre. (2) At Rome, Regin., 690 of 13th cent. (3) At Rome, Vatican, 2002 of 13th–14th cents. (4) At Cambridge, C.C.C. Lib., Lat. 95 of 14th cent. (5) At Dol, College of St. Jerome, now lost.

QUALITER Sita est Civitas Hierusalem, one MS. In Library of the Arsenal at Paris, No. 1161 of early 12th cent.

SOLINUS, 153 MSS. (i.) Arras, No. 870 of 13th cent.; (ii.) Autun. No. 39 of 11th cent.; (iii.) Basle, No. F. ii. 33 * of 14th cent.; (iv.) Berne No. 170*, of 12th cent.; (v., vi.) Bonn, Univ., 73 and 2543, both of 15th cent.; (vii., viii., ix., x.) Brussels, Nos. 10,066 of 12th cent., 10,862 of 13th cent., 17,881 of 15th cent., 18,679 of 14th cent.; (xi., xii., xiii.) Cambridge, Univ.

Libr., Nos. *DD. xi. 79 of 12th cent., *KK. ii. 22 of 14th cent. ; *Mm. ii. 18 of 14th cent. ; (xiv.) Darmstadt, No. 737 of 13th cent. ; (xv.) Dresden J.n. 43 of 13th cent., with a spurious preface; (xvi.) Engelberg, n. I., 4, 15 of 10th cent. Two leaves wanting. Preface and conclusion the same as in the St. Gall MS. (xvii.–xxiii.) Florence; Laurentian. Plut. 29 Cod. 35 of 15th cent. ; Laurentian. Plut. 66 Cod. 19 of 14th cent. ; Laurentian S. Crucis Plut. 20 Sin. Cod. 2 of 11th–12th cents. ; Laurentian. Conv. Soppr. n. 56 of 15th cent. ; Laurentian Conv. Soppr. n. 359 of 15th cent. ; Laurentian S. Mark. n. 209 of 11th cent. ; Laurentian Ashburnham n. 1030 of 11th cent. ; (xxiv.) Frankfort. Westermann MS., now in Library of the Gymnasium, of 12th cent., a MS. "sui generis ; " (xxv.) Heidelberg Palatine, No. 1568 of 11th cent. [and another of 13th cent.]; (xxvi., xxvii.) Copenhagen, Nos. 443, 444 of 14th and 11th cents. ; (xxviii.–xxxvii.) Leyden, Publ. 13 of 14th cent., Publ. 67 C. of 15th cent., Publ. 68 of 13th cent., Publ. 113 of 11th cent., Publ. 124 of 13th cent., Publ. 130ᴀ of 1432, Voss. Q. 11 of 15th cent., Voss. Q. 29 of 10th cent., Voss. Q. 56 of 12th cent., Voss. Q. 87 of 9th cent. (xxxviii.–lviii.) London, viz. :—B. Mus., *Arundel 5 of 15th cent. ; *Burney No. 213 of 15th cent. ; *Burney No. 256 of 12th cent. ; *Cotton Vesp. B. xxv. of 12th cent. ; *Cotton Cleop. D. 1 of 12th cent. ; *Harleian, 2569 of 15th cent. ; *Harleian, 2583 of 16th cent. ; *Harl. 2584 of 14th cent. ; *Harl. 2604 of 15th cent. ; *Harl. 2,645 of 13th cent. ; *Harl. 3859 of 12th cent. ; *Harl. 5373 of 13th cent. ; *B. Mus. Regius 13 C. vi. of 14th cent. ; *Regius 15 A. xxii. of 12th cent. ; *Regius 15 A. xxxii. of 12th–13th cents. ; *Regius 15 B. ii. of 12th–13th cents. ; *Regius 15 B. xi. of 12th–13th cents. ; *Additional 12,014 of 15th cent. ; Add. 17,409* of A.D. 1416 ; *Add. 18,315 of 13th cent. ; *Add. 30,898 of 13th cent. ; also a MS. of 15th cent. in poss. of Quaritch. (lix.–lxiv.) Milanese MSS., viz. :—Ambros. A. 226 inf. of cent. 14th ; Ambr. C. 99 inf. of 10th cent. ; *Ambr. C. 246 inf. of 13th cent., profusely illustrated ; Ambros. D. 36 inf. of 15th cent. ; Ambr. E. 151 sup. of 14th cent.; *Ambr. I. 118 sup. of A.D. 1469. (lxv.) Montecassino MS., viz. :—No. 391 of 11th cent.; (lxvi.–lxviii.) Montpellier MSS., viz. :—No. 121 of 12th cent. ; No. 131 of 12th cent. ; No. 132 of 12th cent. ; (lxix.–lxxvi.) Munich MSS., viz. :—No. 327 of 15th cent. ; No. 4611 of 12th cent. ; No. 5339 of 15th cent. ; No. 6384 of 10th cent. ; No. 14,632 of 12th cent. ; No. 17,207 of 12th cent. ; No. 17,208 of 10th (?) cent. ; No. 23,746 of 10th cent. ; (lxxvii.–lxxx.) Naples MSS., viz. :—No. iv. D. 16 of 1472 ; iv. D. 17 of 15th cent. ; iv. D. 18 of 16th cent. ; iv. D. 19 of 14th cent. (lxxxi.–lxxxvii.) Oxford MSS., viz. :—Bodleian *Canon. Lat. 147, of 1377; *Bodl. Canon. Lat. 161, of 1457; *Bodl. Laud. Lat. 4, of 1406 ; *Bodl. Rawlin. Auct. F. iii. 7 of 12th cent. ; *Bodl. Rawl. Auct. G. 45 of 12th cent. ; Magd. Coll., No. 50 of 11th cent. ; All Souls Coll., 97* of early 14th cent. (lxxxviii.–cxvii.) Paris MSS., viz. :

B.N. Lat.* 1702, of 1396, written at Toledo; Ibid. *Lat. 4873 of 12th–13th cent.; *Lat. 5719 of 14th cent.; *Lat. 6810 of 10th cent. V. important and basis of Salmasius' edition; *Lat. 6811, of 13th cent.; L[at]. *6812, '3,* '4,* '5,* '6,* '7* of 12th, 13th, 14th, 15th cents.; *L. 6831 of 10th cent. *L. 6832, '3,* '4,* '5,* '6,* of 12th, 13th, 15th cents.; *L. 6843 of 15th cent. (end); L. *7,230 of 10th cent., important, highly valued by Salmasius; L. *7230 A. of 10th cent.; L. *7231 of 10th cent.; *L. 7594 of 12th cent.; L. 11,206 of 15th cent.; *L. 11,382 of 13th cent.; L. 13,698 of 15th cent.; *L. 17,543 of 12th cent.; *L. 17,569 of 11th cent.; L. 18,245 of 15th cent.; L. 18,246 of A.D. 1467 written at Viterbo; Maza-rine Library, No. 1526, written in 1406. (cxviii.) Padua MS., viz., Univ., No. 1234; (cxix.) Perugia MS., viz., No. 32. (cxx.–cxliv.) Roman MSS. viz.:—Vatican, No. 1699 of 14th cent.; No. 1860 of 14th cent.; No. 1933 of 15th cent.; No. 1934 of 15th cent.; No. 3342 of 10th cent., important; No. 3343 of 10th cent., important; No. 7646 of 15th cent.; Ottobon, No. 1140 of 1444; Ottobon, 1387 of 14th cent.; Ott., 1952 of 15th cent.; Ott., 2072 of 14th cent.; Palatine, 876 of 14th cent.; Pal., 1357 of 13th cent.; Pal., 1569 of 16th cent.; Pal., 1570 of 15th cent.; Regin., 1478 of 15th cent.; Reg., 1534 of 15th cent.; Reg., 1643 of 13th cent.; Reg., 1658 of 13th–14th cents.; Reg., 1752; Reg., 1875 of 14th cent.; Urbinas, 999 of 15th cent.; Barberini, viii. 63 of 15th cent. (before 1494); " Casanatensis " B. iii. 1 of 15th cent.; Libr. of Victor Emmanuel, No. 17 of 10th–11th cents. (cxlv.) Rouen MS., viz.:—1421 of 12th cent.; (cxlvi.) St. Mihiel, viz.:—42 of 11th cent.; (cxlvii.) St. Gall, viz.:—187* of 10th cent., important; (cxlviii.–cl*) Venice MSS., viz. :—Marcian, Lat. cl. x. No. 29 of 14th cent.; Marc. cl. x. No. 102 of 15th cent.; Marc. cl. x. No. 115 of 12th cent.; Marc. Zanet. Lat. 389 of 15th cent. (cli.–clii.) Vienna MSS., viz :—No. 215 (Endl. Cat. ccxlix.) of 15th cent.; No. 3184 (Endl. Cat. ccl.) of 15th cent.; Wolfenbüttel, (clii.), viz.:—Gud., No. 163 of 10th cent.

COSMAS. Two chief MSS. (1) Vatican of 9th cent. (2) The Florentine MS., Laurentian Libr. Plut. ix., n. 28 of 10th cent., containing all but the last sheets of book xii., on fols. 279, with the plans as given in Montfaucon, Marinelli, and this volume.

RAVENNESE. Five MSS. (1) At Rome, Vatican, Urbinas, 961 of 13th cent. (2) At Paris, B. N., 4794* (Lat.) of 13th–14th cents. (3) At Basel, F. V., 6* of 14th–15th cents., fols. 85–108 bis, single-columned, 31 lines. In this the text of books, iii., iv., v., is fuller than in any other. (4) At Leyden, Voss. 208, a copy of (2). (5) At Munich, now lost, mentioned by Schmeller in the catalogue of the Royal Library at Munich.

DICUIL. Seven chief MSS. (1) At Paris, B. N., 4806* (Lat.) of 10th cent., fols. 25–40, single-columned. This was basis of Chas. Athan.

Walckenaer's edition of 1807. (2) At Paris, B. N., Suppl. Lat., 671.* (3) At Dresden, Regius D. 182, of about A.D. 1000. (4) At Oxford, of 15th cent., among the Canonici MSS. in the Bodleian, quoted by Parthey without further reference. (5) At Venice, class x. cod. 88 (97, 2.) of 15th cent. (6) At Vienna, Endlicher Suppl. 14 of 15th cent. (7) At Munich, Royal Libr., "Victorianus" 99, of 1436. No other of date earlier than 1500.

ÆTHICUS. Among the numerous Æthicus MSS. we may mention :— (1) At Paris, B. N., 4871* of 11th cent., fols. 112, etc. (2) Ibid., 4808 of 11th–12th cents., fols. 1–19 bis. (3) Ibid., 8501A of 13th cent. (4) Ibid., 7561, fragment, of 11th cent. (5) At London, B. Mus., Cotton, *Vespasian B. x. of 8th cent., the oldest MS. (6) Ibid., Harleian, 3859 of 11th–12th cent. (7) Ibid., MSS. Reg. 15 B. ii. of 12th cent. (8) Ibid., Reg. 15 C. iv. of 12th–13th cents. (9) At Leyden, Nos. 69, 77 (Voss. 104). Three other MSS. at Rome, in Vatican Libr., are mentioned by Montfaucon, Bibliotheca Bibliothecarum, pp. 25 b, 57 c, 88 c.

CAPELLA. (1) At Bamberg, M. L. V. 16, 8 Jæckii, n. 391 of early 10th cent. (2) At Carlsruhe, n. 73 (Reichenau) of 10th–11th cents. (3) At Darmstadt, n. 193 of 10th–11th cents. (4) At Berne, n. 56 b. of 10th cent. A list of more than twenty others is given by Eyssenhardt, pref. to Capella, 14–28; among which we may especially mention (5), at Cambridge, Libr. of C. C. C.

BASIL, Hexaemeron. (1) At Paris, Regius, 1824. (2) Ibid., 2286, from collection of Henry II. at Fontainebleau. (3) Ibid., 2287, (1) & (2). (5) Ibid., 2349. (6) Ibid., 2892. (7) Ibid., 2896. (8) Ibid., 2989. (9) Paris, Colbertinus, 3069. (10) Ibid., 4721. (11) Paris, Coistiniani, 229, very early and valuable of 9th cent. (12) Ibid., 235. The above twelve were used by the Benedictine editors, and are given after their (now old-fashioned) enumeration, which is followed in Migne. There is also to be noticed in British Museum (13), Harleian 5576, and (14) Arundel, 532 of 10th century.

GUIDO. Five MSS. (1) At Brussels, 3899–3918 of 13th cent. (2) At Florence, Riccard. 881 of 13th–14th cents., profusely illustrated. (3) At Rome, Vatican, Sessorian. 286 of 15th cent., from the Libr. of the Holy Cross Monastery at Jerusalem. (4) At Vienna, Cæsar. C. C. C. xxxiii., Endlicher, No. 3190 of 15th cent. (5) At Milan, Ambros., R. 104* of c. A.D. 1500, fols. 245–251 bis, single columned, 29 lines. Without ornament. Marginal notes by Biraghi, who dates Guido after A.D. 954, because of mention of St. Matthew's body at Salerno (translated in that year).

MAPS. Of MSS. which contain maps noticed in this volume, we may mention :—(1) For Cosmas' plans, Florence, Laurentian Library, Plut.

ix., n. 28. (2) For Albi map, No. 29 in Albi Library. (3) For Sallust map, Leipsic, in fragment containing commencement of the Catilina. (4) For the 9th cent. "climate"-sketches at Paris, B. N. (Lat.) 4860. (5) For the Strassburg map, Strassburg MSS. civ. (15). (6) For the Leyden map, Leyden MSS. (Lat.), Voss Q. 29. (7) For the Ashburnham (Beatus) map, Ashburnham MSS. 15. The Peutinger Table is in the Imperial Library at Vienna. No notice is taken of the MSS. of Arab and Chinese geographers referred to in Supplementary chapter.

ADDITIONAL NOTE.—II.

ON THE EDITIONS OF THE PRINCIPAL TEXTS.

THE principal edition of nearly all the texts of pilgrim-travel herein referred to is the collection of Tobler, Molinier, and Kohler, in 3 vols., published in the Geographical Series of the Société de L'Orient Latin: "Itinera Hierosolymitana et Descriptiones Terræ Sanctæ," etc., 1877–1885. Vol. i., part i., containing the longer pilgrim-texts down to Arculf and Bede, is edited by Tobler alone; vol. i., part ii., containing Willibald, Bernard, the tracts, *De Situ Hierusalem, Notitia . . . Patriarchatuum, Descriptio Parrochiæ Hierusalem*, etc., by Tobler and Molinier; vol. ii. containing the minor pilgrim notices, and furnishing a sort of geographical index to the *Acta Sanctorum*, the writings of *Gregory of Tours*, and other Latin Christian records of the first six centuries' travel from the West to the Levant, by Molinier and Kohler. The prolegomena to the first volume, originally printed at the beginning of the second part, are contributed in almost equal portions by Molinier and Tobler, and are mainly concerned with critical questions.

Versions are sometimes mentioned in the notes to text, but we may repeat notice here of:—(1) The Palestine Pilgrims' Text Society, which has furnished translations of all the more important pilgrim texts (Bordeaux Pilg., 1887; Silvia, 1891; Paula, and Paula and Eustoch. to Marcella, 1889; Eucherius and the Breviary, 1890; Theodosius, 1893; Antoninus, 1887; Arculf, 1889; Willibald, 1891; Bernard, 1893, etc.); (2) T. Wright's "Early Travels in Palestine," 1848, which gives Arculf, Willibrand, and Bernard, in an English dress, with an excellent prefatory account of early pilgrims in general; and, among other works, furnishing a more or less complete version of some of the pilgrim-records and other texts of Early Christian Geography, (3) Charton's Voyageurs Anciens et Modernes, 1854–57, vol. ii., for Arculf, Willibald and Cosmas, as well as Fa-Hien. Charton's notes on the Bibliography are especially valuable; (4) Delpit, "Essai sur les Anciens Pèlerinages," 1870, for all the pilgrim-texts down to Arculf, and especially for last-named; (5) Heinrich Hahn, "Reise des Willibald," 1856, for Willibald; (6) F. Tuch and Gildemeister, for Antoninus, 1864 and 1889; (7) Arthur Golding,

for Solinus, 1585 ; (8) Fialon (Étude), for St. Basil, 1861 ; (9) Avezac and
Lelewel, for Æthicus, 1854 and 1857. For the bibliography of the pilgrim-
records, etc., Tobler's "Bibliographia Geographica Palæstinæ," 1875, will
be found especially serviceable (much more so than Rohrricht's work of
same name); and for various points in the early Christian literature of
geography, some use may also be made of collections such as Wright's
"Biographia Britannica Literaria," 1842; Tanner's "Bibliotheca Britannico-
Hibernica," 1748–49; Ceillier's "Histoire des Auteurs Ecclésiastiques,"
1752; "Histoire Littéraire de la France," 1738; Cave's "Scriptores Eccle-
siastici," 1741; Michaud's "Biographie Universelle," and Firmin Didot's
"Nouvelle Biographie Générale;" also of J. A. Fabricius' "Bibliotheca
Mediæ Ætatis" and "Bibliotheca Græca;" as well as of works more frequently
referred to in notes to text, e.g. Assemani's "Bibliotheca Orientalis." Other
works used will be found sufficiently quoted in the special connection
illustrated by them ; for the supplementary chapter (No. vii.), the notes give,
it is hoped, all that will be required in references to literature of subject.

Only one important text of pilgrim-travel has been left unedited by
the Société de L'Orient Latin—*Silvia of Aquitaine*, edited by Gamurrini (who discovered the tract in the Library of Arezzo, under his charge),
Rome, 1885 and 1888. On other works illustrating this tract, see p. 73,
note 4, and add Geyer, "Kritische Bemerkungen zu S. Silvia."

As to separate editions of the various pilgrim-texts, we may notice,
before the work of Tobler, etc. :—

α. Of the Bordeaux Pilgrim : (i.) Pithou's of 1589, from MS. Lat.
4808, at Paris, Bibl. Nat.; (ii.) The Cologne Edition of 1600; (iii.) The
Amsterdam edition of 1619; (iv.) The Amsterdam (Wesseling) edition
of 1735, which only uses the Paris MS.; (v.) The Paris edition of 1811
(Chateaubriand) ; (vi.) Migne (Paris, 1844, tom. viii. in P. L. cc. 783–795,
a reprint of Wesseling) ; (vii.) Paris of 1845, in the "Recueil des Itinéraires
Anciens," p. 171, etc.; (viii.) Berlin of 1848, by Pinder and Parthey, at
end of Antonine Itinerary ; (ix.) Leipsic of 1854 (Berggren), at end of a
Josephus (fragmentary) ; (x.) Paris of 1864, "Révue Archéologique," new
series, x., 99–108, by Barthélemy, from Verona and Paris MSS. Among
the most valuable studies on the Bordeaux Pilgrim is Aurès, "Concordance
des vases Apollinaires et l'Itinéraire de Bordeaux," Nismes, 1868.

β. Of St. Paula's Peregrination ; five editions :—(i.) Roman edition of
1468, among works of St. Jerome (ii. 235); (ii.) Lyons edition, by Erasmus,
of 1528 (i. 195); (iii.) Bollandist of 1613, in A.A.S.S., Jan. ii., 711 ;
(iv.) Paris edition of 1706, among works of St. Eusebius, iv., c. 669, etc. ;
(v.) Verona edition of 1734, among works of Jerome, i., c. 684.

β1. Of Paula and Eustochium, similar editions, but Tobler adds the
Venice edition of 1766 of Jerome, I., part. ii. p. 203, etc., as best.

γ. Of Eucherius, one edition : Ph. Labbé's Paris edition of 1657, from Vatican MSS., 636ᴀ [reprinted by Ugolini(-us) in "Thesaurus Antiquitatum Sacrarum," Venice, 1747].

δ Of the Breviary of Jerusalem, no edition, only Bethmann's notice of 1854, previous to the issue in the Soc. de l'Or. Lat.

ε Of Theodosius, one edition only, before, and one after, Tobler's :— (1) The Einsiedeln edition of 1756 ; (2) The Bonn edition of 1882 ; the most valuable study on Theodosius is in the preface and commentary of Gildemeister's Bonn edition.

ζ. Of Antoninus, four editions :—(i.) The Angers edition of 1640 (anonymous edition using a MS. of Sergius and Bacchus, now lost) ; (ii.) The Bollandist of 1680, May ii., pp. x.–xviii., using a MS. then in Library of St. Martin of Tours, which Tobler believes to be the one now at Brussels ; (iii.) Ugolini's of 1747 ; (iv.) Migne's of 1849, Pat. Lat., lxxii., 898, etc., merely a reprint of the Bollandist. Since Tobler, Gildemeister has edited Antoninus (Berlin, 1889) with a valuable preface and German translation.

η. Of Arculf, five editions :—(i.) Of 1619, Ingolstadt, by Gretser, using MS. now lost ; (ii.) Mabillon's of 1672, in A.A.S.S., sæc. iii. pt. 2, pp. 501–522, from Vatican, 636ᴀ, and Corbey MS. ; (iii.) In Gretser's works of 1734, Ratisbon edition ; (iv.) Migne's of 1850, in P. L. lxxxiii. c. 779, etc., reprint of Mabillon ; (v.) Delpit's of 1870, in his "Essai sur les Anciens Pèlerinages à Jerusalem : " Delpit reprints the text of Mabillon, with some use of the Berne, Paris, and St. Gall MSS.

θ. Of Bede, De Locis Sanctis, six editions :—(i.) The Basle edition of 1563, of all Bede ; (ii.) The Cologne edition of 1612 ; (iii.) Gretser's edition of 1619 (1734), the prototype of which was probably the Basle edition, as may be seen by the tendency, common to both, to confuse Bede's abstract with Arculf's full relation. This tendency the editors of the later edition of 1734 laboured to correct, but inadequately ; (iv.) The Cambridge edition of 1726 (pp. 315–324) [Smith's] a very careless and imperfect issue. (v.) Giles' of 1843 is only a reprint of the Cambridge one of 1726, as Giles himself confesses vol. iv. part vii. In this are many typographical errors ; (vi.) F. Michel's Paris edition of 1839 in vol. iv. (pp. 794, etc.) of the Mémoires de la Société Géographique. Michel only employs the B. Mus. Cotton MS. Faustina B.I. in his edition, with certain points (Var. Lectt.) added from the MS. of Lincoln College.

ι. Of Willibald's Hodœporicon, four editions :—(i.) Canisius of 1603 (Lect. Antiq. iv. 473 ; edit. Basnage ii. 99). This edition employs only the Paris MS. Lat., 9744 ; [Gretser supplies various corrections to Canisius in his work of 1610 ; "Philippi ecclesiæ Eystettensis episcopi, de ejusdem ecclesiæ divis tutelaribus "] ; (ii.) The Acta SS. of Mabillon, 1672, reprints Canisius. sæc. iii. pt. ii. pp. 367–383 (iii) The Bollandist

A.A.S.S. Jul. ii. pp. 500–511; (iv.) The Eichstädt edition of 1857, by Suttuez, canon and afterwards vicar-general of that Church. Of the Itinerarium, three editions :—(i.) Canisius' of 1603 (Lect. Antiq. iv. pp. 705–718; ed. Basnage ii. i. 117–122) ; (ii.) Mabillon's A.A.S.S. of 1672, sæc. iii. pt. ii. pp. 383–392 ; (iii.) Bollandists' A.A.S.S. July ii. pp. 512–517.

κ. Of the "Commemoratorium De Casis Dei " there is only one edition before that of the Soc. de l'Or. Latin ;—De Rossi's (based upon Basle MS.) of 1865, in " Bolletino di Archeologia Christiana " (p. 84, etc.) "not sufficiently accurate," but illustrated by an excellent commentary.

λ Of Bernard (the Wise), three editions :—(i.) Mabillon's of 1672, in A.A.S.S., sæc. iii. pt. ii. p. 523–526, from the now lost Rheims MS. ; (ii.) F. Michel's of 1839, in the "Mémoires de la Société de Géographie," iv. 784-794. " An almost valueless edition," based on Lincoln Coll. MS. (iii.) Migne's reprint of Mabillon in P. L. cxxi. c. 569, etc., 1852.

μ. Of the Descriptio Parrochiæ Hierusalem, one edition :—By Antonius Schelstrate at Rome, 1697, in his De Antiquitatibus Ecclesiæ ii., 744, etc., following the Roman MS. (1) verbatim.

ν. Of the Notitia . . . Patriarchatuum, seven editions :—(i.) The Basle edition of 1549, by Poyssenot, pp. 322–324; (ii.) Edition of Henry Pantaleone, Basle, 1564; (iii.) The Hanover edition of 1611, in "Gesta Dei per Francos " (i. 1044–1046) [Bongars] ; (iv.) Migne's edition of 1855 P. L. ccl. cc. 1065–1067 (and in "Recueil des Historiens des Croisades, Hist. Occident." i. 1135–1137). [v. vi. vii. abridged editions] :—(v.) In the Geographia Sacra " of 1641, pp. 84, 85; (vi.) In the Amsterdam reprint of the above, 1704, pp. 59–61 ; (vii.) In the imperfect edition of 1493 [Rome].

ν1. Of the Qualiter sita est Civitas Hierusalem, there is no earlier edition than that of the Soc. de l'Or. Lat.

Also, of separate works in Geographical Theory during the Patristic period, we may notice the following editions :—

o. Of Solinus ; six chief editions previous to Mommsen's (best and last, 1895) :—(i.) The Roman edition, without name or date, but certainly earlier than 1474 ; (ii.) the Venetian edition of Nicholas Jenson, 1473, which specially relies upon the London MS. Arundel 5; (iii.) Bologna edition of 1500, an amended reprint of the Venice edition of 1473 ; (iv.) the Florentine edition of 1519, following the Roman *Editio Princeps* (reprinted at Vienna in 1520?) ; (v.) the Poictiers edition of 1554; (vi.) Salmasius' Paris edition of 1629 (reprinted at Treves, 1689).

π. Of Cosmas :—(i.) Montfaucon's edition of 1706-7—in "Nova Collectio Patrum," tom. ii., still the standard edition ; (ii.) Bandinius' edition of 1762, Gr. Ecc. Vet. Mon., tom. iii. ; (iii.) Gallandius' edition of 1765, in his Bibl. Vet. Pp. ; (iv.) Migne's edition of 1857, in Pat. Gr. lxxxviii., a reprint of Montfaucon, but with additional prefatory matter from remarks of Fabricius, Gallandius, and Bandinius.

ρ. Of the Ravennese, two chief editions:—(i.) Porcheron's edition of 1688 (Paris); (ii.) Pinder and Parthey, Berlin edition of 1860; [(iii.) Bouquet's edition of " Excerpta ex Cosmographia Ravennatis de Gallia " is, of course, only fragmentary—in the " Recueil des Historiens des Gaules," 1738 (tom. i.).]

ρ1. Of Guido:—Pinder and Parthey's Berlin edition of 1860 is the only one.

ς. Of Dicuil, " De Mensura Orbis terræ " three editions: (i.) Walckenaer's edition of 1807 (Paris); (ii.) Letronne's Paris edition of 1814, best as to commentary; (iii.) Parthey's Berlin edition of 1870, best as to text.

τ. Of Capella, " Nuptials," eight principal editions; among which we need only mention:—(i.) Vicenza edition, by Henricus de St. Urso, 1499; (ii.) Grotius' (possibly with help of Jos. Scaliger) edition of 1599; (iii.) Kopp's Frankfort edition, 1836; (iv.) Eyssenhardt's Leipsic edition (Teubner), 1866.

τ1. Of Macrobius, Commentary on the Dream of Scipio, six chief editions, among which we need only mention:—(i.) Venice edition of 1472, Jenson; (ii.) Liège edition of Gronovius, 1670 (best); (iii.) Leipsic edition of 1774.

υ. Of Orosius (History), twelve chief editions, among which we need only mention:—(i.) The (first) edition of 1471 by Schüssler; (ii.) The Mainz edition of 1615 [B. Mus. copy of this has autograph of Ben Jonson]; (iii.) Havercamp's edition of 1738 [with notes by Fabricius]; (iv.) Gallandius' edition of 1765 in Bibl. Vet. PP. vol. ix.; (v.) Migne's edition of 1844 in P. L. xxxi.; (vi.) Zangemeister's Vienna edition of 1868 (Leipsic : Teubner, 1889).

υ1. Of John Philoponus: On the Creation. The best edition is by Gallandius in Bibl. Vet. Patrum, tom. xii., Venice, 1778. First discovered, published, and translated into Latin (1630) by Balthasar Corderius, S.J., from the oldest MS. at Vienna.

φ. Of Basil, Hexaemeron, three chief editions. (1) At Basel, Froben's Press, for Janus Cornarius, 1551; (2) Best edition by Garnier and Maran, the Benedictines of St. Maur, 1721, etc., the basis of (3) Migne's text, in Pat. Græc., 1857. First edition in Latin by Volaterranus, Rome, 1515.

χ Of Æthicus of Istria best editions in (1) Avezac's " Éthicus " 1852, (2) Wuttke's Cosmog. Æthic., 1854. Of Julius Æthicus in Riese, " Geographi Latini Minores."

ψ. Of Isidore : " Etymologies or Origins," ten chief editions, among which we need only mention:—(i.) (First) Strassburg edition of 1470; (ii.) Migne's edition among coll. works of Isid. Pat. Lat., lxxxi.–iv., 1844.

ω. Of Raban Maur, two editions:—(i.) Cologne edition (of Coll. Works) of 1626-27; (ii.) Migne's edition of 1844 (Coll. Works) P. L. cvii., etc.

For bibliography of chief texts of Arab and Chinese geography in our period, we have already referred readers to notes in chap. vii., but will here collect principal items, viz., on pp. 415, note 1; 427, note 1; 436, note 1; 438, note 1; 439, note 1; 478, notes 1, 2; 487, note 2; 491, note 1; 492, note 5; 503, note 1. Also we may add in this place fuller reference to (1) Goeje's editions of Ibn Khordadbeh in vol. vi. of his Library of Arabic Geographers, Leyden, 1889; (2) Frähn's Ibn Fozlan (Fudlan) in publics. of Imp. Acad. of Sciences, St. Petersburg, 1823; also Rössler's "Ibn Fozlans Reiseberichte," St. Petersburg, 1823; (3) Ouseley's Ibn Haukal, London (1800), at Wilson's Oriental Press; and Anderson's trans. of same in Journ. of Bengal Soc., vol. xx. (1853); (4) the great French edition of Massoudy's "Meadows of Gold," by Barbier de Meynard and Pavet de Courteille, Paris, 1861–1877, in 9 vols. Sprenger in 1841 only turned into English (for Oriental Translation Fund) the first seventeen chapters, about one-sixth part of the whole.

ADDITIONAL NOTE.—III.

It may be useful to refer here to a few points unnoticed or barely noticed in the text. 1. Ammianus Marcellinus (see p. 365) has not only been "credited with earliest mention of Sea of Aral," but also with a reference to the *Wall of China* (xxiii. 6; cf. Ptol. vi. 12). Neither suggestion can be fully accepted. (a) The "Oxian lake" of Ammianus Marcellinus and of Ptolemy is described, not as receiving waters of Jaxartes and Oxus, which flow into Caspian, but apparently as lying somewhere parallel to the course of the two great rivers—? about where the Kara Kul or Denghiz is now found. (β) The words in Amm. Marc. xxiii. 6, "Consertæ celsorum aggerum summitates ambiunt Seres," must surely be understood of mountains and nothing else. Cf. Ptolemy, "Serica girdled round by mountains," etc. (vi. 16), and the context in Amm. Marc. Also see Lassen, Ind. Alt. ii. 536; Reinaud, "Rélations de l'Empire, etc.," p. 192; Yule, "Cathay," xl., xli., clviii., clix.; Bunbury, Anc. Geog., ii. 641, 642.

2. In Annals of the Han (B.C. 202–A.D. 220), the Tsin (A.D. 265–419), and the Thang (A.D. 618–905) various notices of Ta-thsin, or the Roman Orient, occur. Western or "Great China," so called because of likeness of its people to those of the Middle Kingdom, *i.e.* (?) in way of being lords of their quarter of the earth, is also spoken of as the Kingdom of the Western Sea. Distant a voyage of three years from India, it is 2000 miles both in length and breadth; its coinage is gold and silver, in the relation of 10 to 1—a fairly good account of the Byzantine reckoning of twelve miliaresia to one nomisma. The coral fisheries of the Mediterranean (?) are also described; the Western empire is said to have 400 great cities, and abundance of gold and gems—among them some "tablets that shine in the dark" (cf. Benjamin of Tudela, on diamonds in Emperor's crown at Byzantium). Tathsin, "latterly called Fulin," possessed many other wonders, among which the Chinese noticed especially its wonderful jugglers, its pearls formed from the saliva of golden pheasants, its lambs that grew out of the ground to which they remained attached by the

umbilical cord, and its "linen washed with fire" (asbestos?). See Pauthier, "De l'Authenticité de l'Inscription de Singanfu," pp. 34–40, 43, 47, 55, etc.; Klaproth, "Tableaux Historiques de l'Asie," pp. 67, 68, 70, etc.; Yule, Cathay, lv.–lvii.

3. Among notices of attempted intercourse between the Chinese and Mediterranean worlds, is that of the hostile venture of the great Han general Pan-chao, who, reaching the Caspian about A.D. 100, in 102 despatched his lieutenant Kan-yng with orders to make his way to Ta-thsin, and, if possible, to conquer it. He seems to have reached the Indian Ocean, but was deterred from attempting more, by terrifying reports. See Lassen, ii. 352, etc.; Rémusat, in Mem. de l'Acad. Inscr. (new), viii. 116–125; Klaproth, "Tableaux Historiques," p. 67, etc.; Yule, "Cathay," lv.

4. At beginning of Life of Hiouen-Thsang occurs an enumeration of the world-kingdoms which is well worth comparison with that given by Ibn Vahab (see pp. 419, 420) as from the mouth of the "Chinese emperor."

5. Massoudy's detailed comparison of the Habitable Earth to a bird —whose head is at Mecca and Medina, while Africa forms its tail, Irak and India its right wing, and the land of Gog and Magog its left—has been often quoted (as by Desborough Cooley) as if it represented Massoudy's geography. It is merely a poetical illustration. See Marinelli, "Erdkunde," 27.

6. The *Notitia Dignitatum* proved valueless for the purposes of this volume. It gives, as Bunbury says (ii. 699), "no geographical, or even topographical, information, except where we could do without it."

SHORT INDEX OF NAMES

(In Text only, with some few references to Notes).